# ZYGNEMACEAE

# I.C.A.R. MONOGRAPHS ON ALGAE

# ZYGNEMACEAE

BY

## M. S. RANDHAWA, D.Sc., F.N.I., I.C.S.

VICE-PRESIDENT

INDIAN COUNCIL OF AGRICULTURAL RESEARCH
NEW DELHI

PUBLISHED BY

INDIAN COUNCIL OF AGRICULTURAL RESEARCH
NEW DELHI

FIRST PRINTED OCTOBER, 1959

Printed at NATIONAL PRINTING WORKS (THE TIMES OF INDIA PRESS), 10 Daryaganj, DELHI.

# FOREWORD

During the last 40 years, a good deal of research work has been done on algae in India. It was felt that time has now come to digest the research work done so far on this group of plants, and to present it in a connected form in the form of monographs for the benefit of students and research workers, many of whom find difficulty in having access to original papers which lie scattered in numerous journals. Such a stock-taking is necessary even from the point of view of future research. A conference of leading workers on algae was accordingly called by the Indian Council of Agricultural Research in December, 1956, and a comprehensive programme of monographs on 'Algae in India' was drawn. Assignments for compiling the monographs were made in favour of leading research workers who had specialized in the group of plants assigned to them, and had made a significant contribution to the subject.

The present monograph on Zygnemaceae which is the first of the series was assigned to Dr. M.S. Randhawa. Dr. Randhawa is an administrator and not a professional scientist. An official career in the administrative field usually carries with it the extinction of all hopes of engaging in scientific research. But this was not the case with the author of this monograph. Employing such modest means and facilities which he could build up with his private resources, he carried on research on algae enthusiastically, and made some important discoveries particularly in relation to terrestrial algal flora of the Himalayas and the Indo-Gangetic plains. When out on tour in connection with his official work, he used to carry a microscope and a box full of tubes and empty ink bottles. From the lakes of the Punjab and Uttar Pradesh, he collected numerous specimens of fresh-water algae. In the evening he used to examine the collected specimens quickly under the microscope, and preserve such of those which were of interest. On holidays when he was comparatively free from magisterial work, he examined the specimens with great care, made sketches with a camera lucida and photographed the material which was of unusual interest. Thus a hobby which was adopted as a pure pleasure in out of the way places in Uttar Pradesh, ultimately proved to be very productive and useful. As a result of this work, he published 36 original papers in leading journals of Botany in India as well as abroad. His particular

# FOREWORD

interest was in the members of the family Zygnemaceae which forms the subject of this monograph.

This monograph covers a world review of the species of the genera of the Zygnemaceae. Of the 13 recognized genera of the family 580 species have been described. The diagrams of the species have been inset in the description for facility of reference. Maps showing the distribution of the species of various genera have also been provided. Comprehensive bibliography of literature and references provided at the end will be of considerable use to the research workers. This monograph has been compiled with great care and labour. I hope it will be of interest to teachers, students, as well as research workers all over the world, and it will serve as a standard work of reference.

K. R. DAMLE, I.C.S.
Secretary
Ministry of Food and Agriculture
Government of India

New Delhi
April 25,1959

# CONTENTS

# INTRODUCTION

In this introductory note it is proposed to give a short history of the study of Algae with particular reference to the order Zygnemales and the family Zygnemaceae. After describing the contribution made by the European biologists of the late 18th and early 19th centuries in the discovery of the genera and species of the Zygnemaceae, their structure and reproduction, information is given about the work done in the U.S.A., China and India. Greater details are given about the work done on Indian members of this family, followed by an account of the monographs, reviews and summaries on the Zygnemaceae.

September 7, 1674, the date on which Antoni van Leeuwenhoek reported a number of unicellular algae and flagellates is considered as the date of birth of microbiology. Even the crude microscope of the period revealed a new world of life so far hidden from the eyes of man. However, almost a century elapsed before the study of algae was placed on a scientific basis, and even in the last quarter of the eighteenth century, they were mostly designated as *Fucus, Corallina, Ulva,* and *Conferva.* In the closing years of the 18th century the microscope became a workable tool, and algae and Protozoa were studied with zest by the European biologists. From among the fresh-water algae the members of the Zygnemaceae were the earliest to draw their attention. The zygospores in *Spirogyra* were first observed by Muller in 1782, but it was Joseph Gartner who in 1798 observed their formation. Hedwig in the same year saw in their mode of production at least a suggestion of sexuality. It was the Swiss scientist Vaucher (1803) who described reproduction in a number of algae, and thus placed their study on a scientific basis. He called conjugation in *Spirogyra* distinctly a sexual process. However, it was much later following his work on the diatoms that Thwaites (1848) positively stated that conjugation is a sexual process. Emphasizing the importance of Vaucher's work, A.H. Hassall (1845) thus writes in his 'History of the British Fresh-water Algae', "To a right appreciation of the importance of attention to the reproduction of the Confervae it is that the superiority of Vaucher's 'Histoire des Conferves d'Eau Douce', is mainly owing, over other works on the same subject, that close and amiable observer having made—and

9

he was the first, and almost the only one to do so—a knowledge of their reproduction his chief aim and study."

H.F. Link (1820-33) studied the algal flora of Germany and established the genus *Spirogyra* in 1820. C.A. Agardh (1817-24), Professor in Lund University, Sweden, studied the algae of Scandinavia and established in 1824 the genera *Mougeotia* and *Zygnema*. Mentioning Agardh's and Kuetzing's contribution to the study of algae, Prescott observes, " although confused by theories of polymorphism in determination of species the elder Agardh (1824) arranged algae into six well-defined orders : Diatomaceae (including desmids), Nostochineae, Confervoideae, Ulvaceae, Florideae, and Fucoideae and described about twenty genera. Especially significant during these years were the works of Kuetzing, Professor in the Polytechnic School at Nordhausen. He was the author of more genera than any other phycologist, described many species, and reassigned others so that more acceptable generic constitutions took form." Zygnemaceae was recognized as a family of green algae by Meneghini in 1838.

Hassall (1842-45) made some excellent observations on the species of the genera *Zygnema* and *Mougeotia* collected from Great Britain. Discussing the importance of his work, Prescott says, "Hassall made an outstanding contribution in which he described many species. He employed two divisions : *Algae Filiformes* and *Algae Globuliferae*, composed of artificially constructed families which, in some cases, however, included genera grouped nearly the same as they are today. His work is also highly informative on current notions regarding reproduction, function of zoospores, differentiation of plants from animals, etc." Then followed discoveries of sexual process in other genera of green algae in rapid succession. In 1855, Pringsheim discovered the mode of sexual reproduction in *Vaucheria*, and between 1855 and 1860 in *Oedogonium* and *Coleochaete*. Pringsheim watched the spermatozoids of *Oedogonium* push into the receptive tips of the living eggs and saw the formation of the characteristic oospore wall. Such a union of the protoplasmic masses of the two sexual cells was shown to be a characteristic feature of fertilization in a number of algae; thus, De Bary (1858) saw it in *Spirogyra* and Pringsheim (1869) repeatedly observed the gradual fusion of the motile gametes of *Pandorina*. Pringsheim gave detailed descriptions of growth, the formation of sexual organs, the mode of sexual union, and the development of oospores. He also showed in their true connection, the asexual modes of propagation, which are intercalated in the life history of these plants.  As Sachs observes, " these led to the formation of systematic groups, quite different from those founded on the superficial observation of collectors.   It soon appeared in the algae that special investigation must lay new foundations for the system.  From the confused mass of forms not before understood, Pringsheim brought out a series of characteristic groups, which, thoroughly examined and skilfully described in words and by figures, stood out as islands in the chaotic sea of still unexamined forms, and threw light in many ways on all around them.   In like manner the morpholgy of the Conjugatae was thoroughly examined by De Bary before 1860.  Fragments of the history of development in the algae were added by Thuret, who made the zoospores of algae, the subject of detailed examination, while Pringsheim in 1869 established the pairing of the swarm-spores in the Volvocineae.  The algae offer at present a greater variety in the processes of development than any other class of plants ; sexual and asexual propagation and growth work one into the other in a way which opens entirely new glimpses into the nature of the vegetable world." Hertwig in 1876, working on a species of sea urchin, showed for the first time that a significant feature of sexual reproduction was the fusion of the gamete nuclei.  Schmitz (1879) observed a similar fusion of nuclei for the first time in plants in *Spirogyra*.

The genus *Debarya* was established by Wittrock in 1872, *Mougeotiopsis* by Palla in 1894, *Pleurodiscus* by Lagerheim in 1895, and *Temnogametum* by Wests in 1897.  Mobius described members of the Zygnemaceae from Port Elizabeth, Brazil, Australia, and Java from 1888 to 1897.  Pettkoff (1904-35) described a number of forms from Bulgaria. O. Borge (1894-1936) carried out extensive researches on the freshwater algae of Sweden.  He further had the privilege of examining collections of algae sent to him by expeditions and private collectors from Australia, South Patagonia, Argentina, Bolivia, Iceland and China.   In 1913, he edited and compiled a volume on the Zygnemales in Pascher's Süsswasserflora.  Borge and Pascher established the order Zygnemales in 1913.  G. Lagerheim (1883-1902) studied the algal flora of Sweden and also examined collections from Ecuador, Abyssinia and India.  E. Lemmermann (1891-1910) worked on the algae of Germany as well as on the collections received from China and Paraguay.  O. Nordstedt (1873-97) described some new species from Argentina, Patagonia, Cameroons, New Zealand and Australia.

From  among  the  British  workers,  the  studies  of  G.S. West

(1899-1916) and W. West (1889-1909) are classical. The Wests, father and son, not only made an exhaustive study of fresh-water algae discovering a number of new members of the Zygnemaceae but they also examined specimens sent to them by private collectors and leaders of expeditions to countries like Tanganyika, Victoria, Egypt, South-West Africa, Central Africa, Madagascar, West Indies, Ceylon, Burma, Bengal and Madras. G.S. West's "Algae" published under the Cambridge Botanical Handbooks contains a very lucid account of the Zygnemaceae. F.E. Fritsch and F. Rich (1907-37) studied fresh-water algae of South Africa particularly from Natal, Transvaal, Cape Colony and Rhodesia, and described some new species of the genera of the Zygnemaceae.

Germination of zygotes of *Spirogyra* involving two successive nuclear divisions was first reported by Chmielewsky (1890). This phenomenon was studied and confirmed by Karsten (1908) and Tröndle (1907, 1911), and the latter also described details of meiosis. The work of A. Conard (1929-1939) on the cytology and the nucleus of *Spirogyra* and the germination of its zygospores is important. The studies of F.E. Lloyd (1924-29) on the mechanism of conjugation in *Spirogyra* is of historical significance. M.L. Merriman (1906-22) carried on important observations on the nuclear division in *Zygnema* and *Spirogyra*. The recent work on the cytology of *Spirogyra* by Geitler (1930, 1935), Doraiswami (1946), and Godward (1950, 1953) is an outstanding contribution.

From among the European workers of the 20th century the work of V. Czurda (1922-39) on the morphology, physiology, and cytology of the Zygnemaceae is particularly significant. H. Skuja (1924-49) described a number of interesting Zygnemaceae from Latvia, Ceylon and Burma. K.M. Strom (1920-26) described some new forms from Caucasus, Turkey, Norway, and Iceland. Skvortzow (1925-37) described a number of forms from Manchuria and China. Tschernow described some species from the U.S.S.R.

Study of the algae, particularly of the species of the genera of the Zygnemaceae in the U.S.A. has been done on a more systematic basis as compared with other countries. W.J. Hodgetts (1918-25), apart from describing conjugation in *Zygogonium ericetorum*, also described a number of species of *Spirogyra*. E.N. Transeau, C.E. Taft, and L.H.

Tiffany described a number of new species of the genera of the Zygnemaceae from U.S.A.

A number of new species of the Zygnemaceae have been described from China by C.C. Jao, L.C. Li, B.W. Skvortzow, and C.C. Wang. The provinces of China which have been explored are Szechwan, Hupeh, Kiangsu, Shantung, Kiangsi, and Manchuria. The diagrams of spore wall of different species given by Jao are detailed.

Researches on algae in India and the neighbouring countries can be divided broadly into three periods ; firstly, the period of pioneers from 1798 to 1854, secondly, the period of professional botanists mostly Englishmen working in the Botanical Survey of India or in the Universities in England from 1858 to 1907, and thirdly, from 1919 to date, the period of Indian research workers, mostly professors of Botany in Indian Universities, employees of the Botanical Survey of India, or amateurs.

The macroscopic forms like Characeae and sea-weeds were the earliest to attract attention, and description of a new variety of *Chara polyphylla* Braun from Ceylon by Lebeck in 1798 marks the first milestone in the study of algae in India and the neighbouring countries.

In 1860, G.C. Wallich described some desmids from Bengal. In 1865, Grunnow described fresh-water diatoms and desmids from Banka Island near Singapore. In 1863, Hobson described two new species of desmids from Mahabaleshwar in Bombay Presidency. G.V Martens (1871-73) published an account of algae from Bengal and Burma. Zeller (1873) reported from "Kurz's collection from Burma" 15 species of the Zygnemaceae including 3 species of *Zygnema*, 2 of *Mougeotia*, and 10 of *Spirogyra*. Wittrock (1880) described a new species of *Sirogonium* from Ceylon.

W. Joshua enumerated 186 species and varieties of desmids from Burma in 1886. In the same year J. Schaarschmidt described 60 species of algae from Afghanistan. In 1888 G. Lagerheim described 52 species of desmids from Bengal. In 1893 W.B. Turner published an account of "The Fresh Water Algae of East India." This publication added considerably to the existing knowledge of Indian algae, particularly the desmids. But, unfortunately, he described many new species on insufficient grounds. Turner described 22 species of Myxophyceae, 542 species of desmids and 60 species of Chlorophyceae other than desmids. This included record of sterile filaments of *Zygogonium* and *Spirogyra* from Northern India.

In 1897 W. West and G.S. West described 45 species of desmids from Singapore. In 1902, Wests described 7 species of Rhodophyceae, 49 species of diatoms, 33 species of Myxophyceae, 246 species of desmids, and 84 species of Chlorophyceae from Ceylon. In 1907, Wests further recorded 58 species of diatoms, and 148 species of desmids. They also recorded 53 species of other green algae from Burma and Madras, including 2 species of *Spirogyra* and one of *Mougeotia* from Ceylon, and in 1907 one of *Zygnema*, 8 of *Spirogyra* and 3 of *Mougeotia* from Burma, Bengal and Madras.

F.E. Fritsch (1879-1954) studied fresh-water and terrestrial algae of Ceylon in 1903. In 1907, he published a general account of the sub-aerial and fresh-water algae of Ceylon, and suggested extensive scope of studies on the ecology of algae in India.

From 1919 onwards work on algae in India was largely done by Indian workers. M.O.P. Iyengar (1920--58) published a number of papers on Volvocales, Chaetophorales, Zygnemaceae, etc., collected by him from the States of Madras and Mysore. Since 1940, in collaboration with his students, he published a series of papers on a number of new genera and species of green algae. His records of Zygnemaceae include seven new species, including 7 of *Mougeotia*, 2 of *Debarya*, 6 of *Zygnemopsis*, 1 of *Sirogonium*, 1 of *Zygogonium*, 1 of *Spirogyra* and 3 of *Temnogametum* from South India. Considering the volume and quality of his work, he can rightly be called the father of modern algology in India.

R.N. Singh published a series of papers on blue-green algae as well as on Zygnemaceae, Oedogoniaceae and Chaetophorales of Uttar Pradesh. C.B. Rao also published a series of papers on the *Myxophyceae* of Uttar Pradesh from 1935-38. The records of the species of the genera of the Zygnemaceae by them is as follows: R.N. Singh recorded 14 species including a new one of *Zygnema*, 9 of *Spirogyra* including 4 new species, 3 of *Sirogonium* including 1 new species. C.B. Rao (1937-38) recorded 9 species of *Zygnema*, including a new one, and 25 of *Spirogyra* including 3 new species. J.N. Misra (1937) described 5 species of *Zygnema* including 2 new species, and 5 of *Spirogyra*. S.C. Dixit (1937) recorded 2 species *Spirogyra* and 1 of *Sirogonium*.

I published a series of papers from 1933-58, mostly on Zygnemaceae, Oedogoniales, Ulotrichales and Vaucheriaceae collected from the States of

Punjab and Uttar Pradesh. The richest and the most interesting collections were obtained from eastern Uttar Pradesh and Kumaon Himalayas. I recorded 70 species of the genera of the Zygnemaceae including 1 of *Debarya* which is new, 9 of *Mougeotia* including 1 new species, 11 of *Zygnema* including 6 new species, 2 of *Zygogonium*, both new, 30 of *Spirogyra* including 11 new species, and 3 of *Sirogonium* including 2 new species. The discovery of *Z. terrestre*, a terrestrial species of *Zygnema*, in 1938 from Fyzabad district of U.P. is important as it provides a connecting link between the genera *Zygnema* and *Zygogonium*. I described *Ghosella indica* as a new genus and species of the Conjugatae in 1934. A few months earlier in the same year it was named as *Zygnemopsis* by Transeau. In 1937-38, I described 9 new species of *Zygnemopsis* from U.P. and Punjab. Out of these, the discovery of *Zygnemopsis minuta* is important in the sense that it provides a connecting link between Saccoderm desmids and the Zygnemaceae. In 1941, I described *Sirocladium* as a new genus on the basis of a specimen collected from the Kumaon Himalayas and named as *S. kumaoense*. In 1956, it was again collected from Calcutta in West Bengal. In 1957, it was collected from Nainital and Bhowali in Kumaon Himalayas by K.P. Singh. Two more new species of this interesting genus were discovered in 1956—one from Western Ghats in Bombay State, and the other by M.O.P. Iyengar from Vandalur in Madras State.

The above review of the work done in various countries on the algae, particularly the Zygnemaceae reveals that there are large gaps in our knowledge. Still there are vast areas in South America, Africa, U.S.S.R., and South-East Asia which are awaiting exploration and study. A systematic exploration of these areas is likely to reveal many new species. When collection work is more advanced, a study of the geographical distribution of the members of the Zygnemaceae is likely to lead to interesting conclusions, and the species found in South America, South Africa, Madagascar, South India, Indonesia, and Australia which in the Carboniferous period formed one land mass known as Gondwanaland should be compared. Their distribution would undoubtedly throw light on the Wegener's hypothesis and the Gondwanaland problem. The distribution of the seven species of the genus *Temnogametum* is a pointer in this direction. Out of these, three have been reported from South India, one from West Central Africa, one from Trinidad, and two from South America.

As already mentioned, the earliest summary of the Zygnemaceae was given by Borge in 1913 in the volume entitled Zygnemales in Pascher's Süsswasserflora.  Czurda provided another summary in 1932 in Vol. 9 of Pascher's Süsswasserflora, and later on in 1937 in a  volume entitled Conjugatae in Handbuch der Pflanzenanatomie. Kolkwitz and Krieger provided an excellent account of Zygnemales in Rabenhorst's Kryptogamenflora Vol. 13 in 1944.  Apart from containing a general chapter on the occurrence and distribution of the members of the Zygnemaceae, details are given about the vegetative structure, the structure of the protoplasm, chloroplasts, pyrenoids, cytology, and physiology and reproduction in the various genera.  All the species are illustrated by diagrams inserted as close to the text as possible.  The keys to the species are also very helpful. It also contains an exhaustive bibliography.  In fact, all workers on algae are highly indebted to the authors of this monograph for compiling all the available knowledge on the members of the Zygnemaceae in such a methodical form.  In compiling this monograph, I have followed the model provided by Kolkwitz and Krieger.

The most significant contributions to the study of the Zygnemaceae have been made by E.N. Transeau from 1914 to 1951.  His papers on the genera *Debarya*, *Mougeotia*, *Temnogametum*, and *Zygogonium*, and on the new species of Zygnemaceae clarified ideas regarding the delimitation of the genera.  He further had the opportunity of obtaining specimens from Professors Borge, Nordstedt, Farlow, Thaxter, Skuja, E.L. Stephens, C.C. Jao, L.C. Li, G. W. Prescott and myself.  Thus he had the unique advantage of studying the specimens of the genera and species of the Zygnemaceae from the U.S.A., Europe, South Africa, Central and South America, Puerto Rico, Philippine Islands, China, Japan and India.  His most significant contribution to the  systematics of the Zygnemaceae lies in the  recognition of the sculpturing of the spore wall as an important character in the demarcation of species, which has cleared a good deal of confusion. In 1941, he produced  a mimeographed key to the species of the Zygnemaceae, which was of great help to the workers engaged in the study of this group.  The keys for the identification of genera and species which he provided in his recent publication entitled Zygnemataceae in 1951 have greatly helped in the study of this interesting group of algae. I feel greatly indebted to the  author of this work in compiling the  present monograph. G.M. Smith has  provided an excellent summary of the life history and morphology of the genera of the Zygnemaceae in "The Fresh-water Algae of the United States" which I have consulted with profit.  For clarity of text this is undoubtedly an outstanding publication on algae.

Considering the volume of research which has been done on the Zygnemaceae in the last 40 years, and the growing interest in this group in India as well as abroad, it was felt that a monographic treatment of the family was necessary so that the scattered information on the genera and species is brought together. Realising the importance of algae as fish-food as well as the role which they play in soil biology, the Indian Council of Agricultural Research initiated a comprehensive programme of monographs on algae in December, 1956. In this programme assignments for compiling the monographs were made to all prominent workers on algae in India. The present monograph on the Zygnemaceae was assigned to me. Originally it was proposed to deal only with the species which have so far been recorded from India. But as the work progressed, it was felt that a comprehensive treatment of the subject was indicated in the sense that large areas in India are still lying unexplored and a number of species which have been recorded already from other countries may be discovered. In compiling this monograph, I express my indebtedness to the monumental work done by Czurda, Kolkwitz and Krieger and Transeau who have greatly simplified my task by their excellent keys of the species, and by reproduction of diagrams from early publications, some of which are not easily available. I also express my indebtedness to F.E. Fritsch's "The Structure and Reproduction of the Algae" in which facts about the morphology and reproduction of the Zygnemaceae are summarized so succinctly and which reveals great powers of concentration and clarity of thought. The diagrams of the various species have been taken from original papers of the authors concerned, and some new ones, particularly on Indian species have also been provided. Since dimensions are given in descriptions, the figures have not been drawn to a certain scale of magnification. An attempt has been made to place the illustrations of the species described as close to the text as possible. Species which are of morphological significance are described in greater detail.

Kolkwitz and Krieger (1944) in their monograph on Zygnemales described 452 species, 6 of *Debarya*, 91 of *Mougeotia*, 1 of *Mougeotiopsis* 3 of *Temnogametum*, 20 of *Zygnemopsis*, 96 of *Zygnema*, 234 of *Spirogyra* and 1 of *Sirocladium*. Transeau (1951) in his monograph on the Zygnemataceae described 534 species, 1 of *Mougeotiopsis*, 6 of *Debarya*, 99 of *Mougeotia*, 4 of *Temnogametum*, 1 of *Hallasia*, 24 of *Zygnemopsis*, 95 of *Zygnema*, 1 of *Pleurodiscus*, 14 of *Zygogonium*, 1 of *Entransia*, 275 of *Spirogyra*, 12 of *Sirogonium*, and 1 of *Sirocladium*. In the present monograph 580 species have been described including 8 of *Debarya*, 108 of *Mougeotia*, 8 of *Temnogametum*,

31 of *Zygnemopsis*, 100 of *Zygnema*, 289 of *Spirogyra*, 15 of *Sirogonium*, and 3 of *Sirocladium*. The number of species of *Mougeotiopsis*, *Hallasia*, *Pleurodiscus*, *Zygogonium* and *Entransia* is the same as described by Transeau.

So far 174 species of the genera of the Zygnemaceae have been reported from India including 3 of *Debarya*, 18 of *Mougeotia*, 4 of *Temnogametum*, 23 of *Zygnema*, 16 of *Zygnemopsis*, 5 of *Zygogonium*, 94 of *Spirogyra*, 8 of *Sirogonium* and 3 of *Sirocladium*. Most of the species of the genera of the Zygnemaceae have so far been described from the States of Assam, Bengal, Madras, Mysore, Uttar Pradesh, Punjab and Bombay. This shows that a number of States in India still remain unexplored. A systematic survey of the entire country is indicated and this is likely to bring to our notice, besides new records, a large number of new and interesting algae. It is hoped that the publication of monographs under the series, 'Algae of India' will provide guidance to research workers and students in not only acquainting themselves with the species and genera of algae recorded and described in India, but will also provide them with incentive for exploring the States hitherto untouched, and thus extending the frontiers of knowledge in respect of algae.

Before I close I would like to express my appreciation of the devoted assistance provided by Mr. G.S. Venkataraman, Research Officer, Algae Laboratory, Indian Agricultural Research Institute, New Delhi. He has re-drawn some of the diagrams, worked hard in preparing photostat copies of diagrams from original papers, and also assisted me in reading the proofs. Mr. N.S. Bisht, Director of Art Section of the Indian Council of Agricultural Research improved the diagrams and also attended to the preparation of the blocks. Dr. U.N. Chatterji, Editor of the scientific publications of the Indian Council of Agricultural Research also took considerable interest in the complicated task of production of this monograph by maintaining daily contact with the Press. I also record my appreciation of the work done by Messrs. Satya Paul, E. Parthasarathy, L. Rajagopalan, and S. Viswanathan in typing this manuscript which, considering the large number of technical names, was no easy task. I hope this monograph will be of considerable use to students, research workers, as well as teachers who are interested in the study of this important group of algae.

New Delhi
July 15, 1959

M. S. Randhawa

## CHAPTER I

# ORDER ZYGNEMALES

BORGE AND PASCHER 1913

## Classification, Families, Sub-families, and Genera

The members of the Zygnemales are unique among the algae in having amoeboid gametes and in the total absence of free-swimming flagellated gametes. This led Wille (1897) to classify green algae into two groups, Conjugatae and Chlorophyceae. However, the presence of chlorophyll in Conjugatae indicates that they are also green algae, and should be included in the group Chlorophyceae, which includes all green algae. The presence or absence of flagella in the reproductive phase and where they are present, their comparative length and arrangement are important features of fundamental significance in the classification of the green algae. It was on this basis that Blackman and Tansley (1902) divided Chlorophyceae into four classes, viz., Isokontae, Stephanokontae, Akontae (Conjugatae), and Heterokontae. Oltmanns (1904) extended the group Akontae by inclusion of diatoms (Bacillariaceae).

West (1916) recognizes four primary divisions of the Chlorophyceae, Isokontae, Akontae, Stephanokontae, and Heterokontae. Under the division Akontae, he placed the Conjugatae as an order. He defined Akontae as a group of the green algae characterized by the complete absence of ciliated reproductive cells.

Investigations into the nature and composition of pigments, food material synthesized, and the structure of reproductive bodies have provided more specific characters for the classification of the algae. Without going into further details, which are largely of historical interest, I recognize the classification of algae proposed by Fritsch (1948).

Fritsch classifies the algae into 11 classes : Chlorophyceae, Xanthophyceae, Chrysophyceae, Bacillariophyceae, Cryptophyceae, Dinophyceae, Chloromonadineae, Euglenineae, Phaeophyceae, Rhodophyceae, and Myxophyceae. The Chlorophyceae are characterised by the presence of chloroplasts with pigments identical with those found in the higher plants, *i.e.*, Chlorophylls *a* and *b* with small quantities of *a*-Carotene, *b*-Carotene, and Xanthopylls : Lutein, Zeaxanthin, Violaxanthin and Neoxanthin.  Pyrenoids typical with starch sheath are usually present in the chloroplasts and starch is produced as food reserve.  Cellulose is clearly recognisable in the cell-walls.  In the motile phases there are 2 to 4 or many flagella, equal-sized and borne at the anterior end.

The Chlorophyceae are further divided by Fritsch (1935) into nine orders, viz., Volvocales, Chlorococcales, Ulotrichales, Clado-phorales, Chaetophorales, Oedogoniales, Conjugales, Siphonales and Charales.

The Zygnemales are a well-defined group of green algae charac-terised by symmetry of the cell, elaborate chloroplasts and amoeboid gametes.  Free-swimming flagellated gametes are entirely absent. Sexual union takes place through a process known as conjugation in which amoeboid gametes, which are usually undivided protoplasts of ordinary vegetative cells, are brought together through conjugation tubes, which are cylindric projections of mating cells or without conju-gation tubes where the gametangia are geniculate.  There are no conjugation tubes in knee shaped conjugales (geniculation).

The plants consist of unbranched filaments, single cells or loose aggregate of cells within a pectic gel.  The cell walls have an outer pec-tic layer and an inner cellulose layer.  The chromatophores may consist of axial or parietal plates, or spirally wound parietal ribbons, or of two axial stellate bodies often highly diversified among the Desmids.  The spore walls consist of three layers of cellulose.  The median wall may be coloured yellow, brown, black or blue and has chitinous deposits. The zygospores have a dormant period during which there is a fusion of the gametic nuclei followed by a reduction division.  Thus the plant is haploid and zygospore is diploid.  The order includes about 40 genera and 3,000 species which are all fresh-water in habit.

### Classification

The classification of the Zygnemales varies with different authors, and is either based on the characters of chloroplasts, or on the nature of conjugation, or on both.  De Bary (1858) divided the Zygnemales into two families, Mesocarpeae and Zygnemeae which was later supported by Wittrock (1871 and 1878).  Palla (1894), Blackman and Tansley (1902) in their classification considered the structure of the chloroplasts more important than the reproductive characters.

West (1916) based his classification on the structure of the chloro-plasts as well as on the position of zygospores. He divides the Zygne-maceae into three sub-families, Mesocarpeae, Zygnemeae and Spirogyreae. Sub-family Mesocarpeae is based on the presence of zygospores in the conjugation tube, while the other two sub-families are based on the characters of chloroplasts only.

The classification adopted by West is given below:

Order **CONJUGATAE**

Family I. **Zygnemaceae**

Sub-family—MESOCARPEAE

(i) *Debarya*
(ii) *Temnogametum*
(iii) *Mougeotia*
(iv) *Gonatonema*

Sub-family—ZYGNEMEAE

(v) *Zygnema*
(vi) *Zygogonium*
(vii) *Pleurodiscus*
(viii) *Pyxispora*

Sub-family—SPIROGYREAE

(ix) *Spirogyra*
(x) *Sirogonium*

Family 2. **Desmidiaceae**

Sub-family—SACCODERMAE

(xi) *Gonatozygae*
(xii) *Spirotaenieae*

Sub-family—PLACODERMAE

(xiii) *Penieae*
(xiv) *Closterieae*
(xv) *Cosmarieae*

Czurda (1932 b) based his classification of the Zygnemales solely on the character of chloroplasts, and he merged all the genera into three, *Mougeotia*, *Zygnema* and *Spirogyra*. Each of the genera is further sub-divided into groups which are based on the position of the zygospores or the structure of the chloroplasts.   The classification by Czurda is given below :

*Order* **ZYGNEMALES**

*Family* **Zygnemaceae**

**Mougeotia**

| Group | I. | *Mesocarpus* |
|---|---|---|
| ,, | II. | *Oedogonioides* |
| ,, | III. | *Plagiospermum* |
| ,, | IV. | *Staurospermum* |
| ,, | V. | *Gonatonema* |
| ,, | VI. | *Temnogametum* |

**Zygnema**

| Group | I. | *Pectinata* |
|---|---|---|
| ,, | II. | *Leiosperma* |
| ,, | III. | *Collinsiana* |
| ,, | IV. | *Reticulata* |

**Spirogyra**

| Group | I. | *Mirabiles* |
|---|---|---|
| ,, | II. | *Sirogonium* |
| ,, | III. | *Salmacis* |
| ,, | IV. | *Conjugata* |

Smith (1933) divided the order Zygnematales as he calls it into three families, viz. Zygnemataceae, Mesotaeniaceae, and Desmidiaceae. He recognises 9 genera of Zygnemataceae.

*Order* **ZYGNEMATALES**

*Family* 1.   **Zygnemataceae**

(i) *Debarya*
(ii) *Mougeotia*
(iii) *Mougeotiopsis*
(iv) *Zygnema*
(v) *Hallasia*
(vi) *Zygogonium*
(vii) *Pleurodiscus*
(viii) *Spirogyra*
(ix) *Sirogonium*

*Family* 2.   **Mesotaeniaceae**

*Family* 3.   **Desmidiaceae**

Fritsch (1935) divided the Conjugales into two sub-orders, viz. Euconjugatae and Desmidioideae.  Euconjugatae is divided into two groups, viz., the Mesotaenioideae (Saccoderm Desmids)  and the

Zygnemoideae. Fritsch thus recognises the close relationship of the *Saccoderm Desmids* and the Zygnemoideae and regards the *Placoderm Desmids* as a separate order. The classification of the Conjugales by Fritsch is given below :

*Order* **CONJUGALES**

*Sub-order* 1. **Euconjugatae**

a. *Mesotaenioideae (Saccoderm desmids)*

b. *Zygnemoideae*

1. ZYGNEMACEAE

(i) *Debarya*

(ii) *Spirogyra*

(iii) *Zygnema*

2. MOUGEOTIACEAE

(iv) *Mougeotia*

(v) *Sirogonium*

(vi) *Temnogametum*

(vii) *Temnogyra*

(viii) *Zygogonium*

3. GONATOZYGACEAE

(i) *Genicularia*

(ii) *Gonatozygon*

*Sub-order* 2. **Desmidioideae**

Kolkwitz and Krieger (1944) recognise only one family of the Zygnemales which following Meneghini (1838) they called Zygnemaceae comprising 8 genera. The classification by Kolkwitz and Krieger is given below :

*Order* **DESMIDIALES**

*Order* **ZYGNEMALES**

*Family* **Zygnemaceae**

(i) *Mougeotia*

(ii) *Temnogametum*

(iii) *Mougeotiopsis*

(iv) *Debarya*

(v) *Zygnema*

(vi) *Zygnemopsis*

(vii) *Spirogyra*

(viii) *Sirocladium*

Transeau (1951) following Smith divided Zygnematales into 3 families. viz., Zygnemataceae, Mesotaeniaceae and Desmidiaceae.

Transeau has provided a thorough and detailed account of the genera of the Zygnemataceae in his monograph which is the most authoritative and comprehensive publication on the subject. The classification by Transeau is given below :

*Order*   **ZYGNEMATALES**

*Family* 1.   **Zygnemataceae**

(i)   *Zygnema*
(ii)   *Zygnemopsis*
(iii)   *Hallasia*
(iv)   *Zygogonium*
(v)   *Pleurodiscus*
(vi)   *Mougeotiopsis*
(vii)   *Debarya*
(viii)   *Mougeotia*
(ix)   *Temnogametum*
(x)   *Sirocladium*
(xi)   *Entransia*
(xii)   *Spirogyra*
(xiii)   *Sirogonium*

*Family* 2.   **Mesotaeniaceae**
*Family* 3.   **Desmidiaceae**

In this monograph the order Zygnemales as established by Borge and Pascher in 1913 is accepted, and the original name of the family by Meneghini (1838) as Zygnemaceae is maintained. The present author feels that the classification of the Zygnemales is based with greater certainty on the character of the chloroplast, and on this basis the Zygnemaceae can be subdivided into 4 sub-families, viz. Mougeotioideae, Zygnemoideae, Spirogyroideae and Sirocladioideae. The following classification is proposed, and the genera in the sub-families are given in the order of their evolutionary status ; the more highly advanced being lower in the list as compared with the more generalised and primitive ones which are higher up :

*Order*   **ZYGNEMALES**

*Family* **a.**   **Zygnemaceae**

*Sub-family i.*   MOUGEOTIOIDEAE     1.   *Mougeotiopsis*
                                                         2.   *Debarya*
                                                          3.   *Mougeotia*
                                                          4.   *Temnogametum*

*Sub-family ii.*   ZYGNEMOIDEAE      5.   *Hallasia*
                                                          6.   *Zygnemopsis*

7. *Zygnema*
8. *Pleurodiscus*
9. *Zygogonium*
10. *Entransia*

*Sub-family iii.* SPIROGYROIDEAE    11. *Spirogyra*

12. *Sirogonium*

*Sub-family iv.* SIROCLADIOIDEAE    13. *Sirocladium*

*Family* **b. Mesotaeniaceae (Saccoderm Desmids)**
*Family* **c. Desmidiaceae (Placoderm Desmids)**

### The Characters of the Zygnemaceae

The Zygnemaceae are filamentous fresh-water algae, normally unbranched. The cells are cylindrical and cell-walls are without pores. They usually occur as free-floating, though planktonic species of *Mougeotia* with spirally twisted filaments have been recorded. They favour slowly flowing fresh-water streams, or stagnant ponds. Terrestrial forms are also seen among species of three genera, *Zygogonium*, *Sirocladium* and *Zygnema*. The chloroplasts are of four types, axial plate-like or ribbon-like or more or less stellate, or parietal plate-like or ribbon-like bodies spirally twisted. Conjugation of gametes is by means of a tube between the gametangia, or rarely by a mere opening between the gametangia. Zygospores are formed either in the conjugation tube or within one of the gametangia.

### The Sub-families

The shape of the chloroplast and the position of the zygospores have been used as characters to determine the classification of the genera of the Zygnemaceae. While it may be assumed that anisogamy is more advanced as compared with isogamy, even in the same species both isogamy and anisogamy may be seen. Thus it cannot be regarded as a reliable character for the purpose of classification. Hence, the chloroplasts provide the surest basis for classification of the genera of the Zygnemaceae. On this basis the thirteen recognised genera of the Zygnemaceae may be distributed into four sub-families.

### (I) MOUGEOTIOIDEAE

There is a single plate-like chloroplast with or without pyrenoids. *Mougeotiopsis* in which pyrenoids are lacking may be regarded as the most primitive of all the genera. *Debarya* with flat ribbon-like chloroplasts with several pyrenoids and isogamous conjugation comes next. *Mougeotia* with single plate-like chloroplast comes next. *Temnogametum* with similar chloroplast as in *Mougeotia*, but with differentiated gametan-

gia, which are short specialized cells cut off near the ends of long vegetative cells is the most highly developed member of this sub-family.

### (II)  ZYGNEMOIDEAE

The vegetative cells have two axile chloroplasts which are spherical
or undifferentiated with irregular processes, or are stellate.  Each has
a central pyrenoid with nucleus contained in the cytoplasmic  bridge
between the chloroplasts.  The peculiarly elaborate chloroplasts of this
sub-family are possibly evolved from plate-like chloroplasts.  In *Hallasia*
occasionally there are 2-7 chloroplasts arranged in a  row  which can
be regarded as intermediate between the ancestral  plate-like  chloroplast of *Mougeotia* and the stellate chloroplasts of *Zygnema*.  Hence,
*Hallasia* can be regarded as the most primitive member of this sub-family.

*Zygnemopsis*, with its isogamous conjugation, secretion of pectin
and spherical chloroplasts can be considered as a higher form.

*Zygogonium* with ovoid or irregular chloroplasts with or without
irregular processes represents the next stage in evolution of the  chloroplast. During conjugation cytoplasmic residue is left in the gametangia.

*Pleurodiscus* with its pair of disc-shaped chloroplasts is another
specialized form.  *Zygnema* with stellate or globose chloroplasts, each
with a central pyrenoid is the most highly developed member of this sub-
family.  *Entransia* with its two broad parietal chloroplasts, each containing several pyrenoids may be provisionally regarded  as a specialized
member  of Zygnemoideae.

### (III)  SPIROGYROIDEAE

This sub-family includes the most highly developed genera of the
Zygnemaceae, viz., *Spirogyra* and *Sirogonium*.  *Spirogyra* has one to several
parietal spirally arranged chloroplasts, each with many pyrenoids.
Conjugation is lateral or scalariform, and in the latter case always
anisogamous.  In *Sirogonium* there are several chloroplasts which are
only slightly curved, and conjugation takes place directly through an
opening where the gametangia are in contact, without the aid of conjugation tubes.

### (IV)  SIROCLADIOIDEAE

This includes the solitary genus *Sirocladium* with three species which
are all terrestrial and  have two plate-like chloroplasts.   In *Sirocladium
kumaoense* the chloroplasts are plate-like parietal, with numerous scattered pyrenoids.   In *S. vandalurense* the chloroplasts are two laciniate
plates, with scattered pyrenoids, and in *S. maharashtrense* the chloroplasts
are two straight ribbon-like bodies with a row of conspicuous pyrenoids.

CHAPTER 2

# THE ZYGNEMALES

## Evolution and Affinities

The Zygnemales are sharply marked off from other Chlorophyceae by their aplanogametes. Schussnig (1925) suggested a derivation of the Zygnemales from the line of evolution of the Chlorococcales, which also show a tendency to the suppression of motility. This view is, however, based on the concept that the nucleus of the Zygnemales is a compound structure, and presumes that the ancestral forms were multinucleate. According to this theory the conjugating cells are regarded as gametangia which have become uninucleate. There is, however, no adequate evidence in support of this hypothesis.

According to Smith (1938-1954) the occasional occurrence of amoeboid gametes in *Chlamydomonas*, and the presence of a type of conjugation in *Chlamydomonas eugametos* suggests the possibility of a direct derivation from motile, one-celled ancestors belonging to the order Volvocales. The position of the Zygnematales, as he calls the order, and inter-relationship among the various orders of the Chlorophyceae as determined by Smith is given in the diagram below:

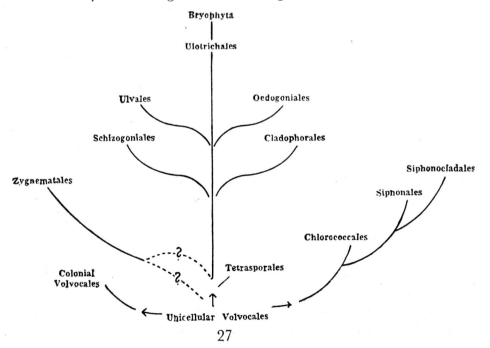

27

According to Fritsch (1938) also the Zygnemales had their origin from among *Chlamydomonas*-like ancestors from among the Volvocales. The conjugation of *Chlamydomonas eugametos* shows resemblance to the process of conjugation in Mesotaeniaceae.

The main difficulty, however, in connecting the Zygnemales with Volvocales arises from the fact that the primitive axile plate shaped chloroplast of the Zygnemales is not seen in the Volvocales. Hence the ancestors of the Zygnemales can only be traced from among the plexus of primitive algae among the Volvocales which may have become extinct. It is likely that the axile chloroplast may in itself have arisen from the more complicated chloroplast of *Chlamydomonas* on account of loss of motility. According to this view the Saccoderm Desmids with their relatively simple chloroplasts, wall structure, and normal production of four individuals from zygote are the most primitive members of the Zygnemales. A form like *Mesotaenium* with single axile chloroplast is undoubtedly primitive, and it is from forms such as these that the genera of the Mesotaeniaceae such as *Cylindrocystis*, *Spirotaenia*, and *Netrium* seem to have evolved by elaboration of chloroplasts.

*Cylindrocystis* with its elaborate stellate chloroplasts provides an ancestral form for the species of *Zygnemopsis*. Species of *Zygnemopsis* such as *Z. desmidioides* and *Z. minuta* can be taken as colonial forms of *Cylindrocystis* which developed the habit of filament forming. The fragmentation of filaments into individual cells which takes place in *Zygnemopsis desmidioides* and *Z. minuta* seems to be a recapitulation of the past. The conjugating cells in *Z. minuta* very much resemble those of *Cylindrocystis*. *Zygnemopsis minuta* in its vegetative characters resembles a colonial form of *Cylindrocystis*. The free-floating cells may meet and fuse in any position, and the zygospores are of various shapes ranging from quadrate-triangular to sickle-shaped. *Zygnemopsis minuta* bridges the gap between the Saccoderm Desmids and filamentous Zygnemaceae even more effectively than *Zygnemopsis desmidioides*.

Similarly *Hallasia reticulata* which produces 2 to 3 sporelings on germination of the aplanospores is also derivable from *Cylindrocystis*. Considering the structure of its chloroplasts, aplanospore formation, and secretion of pectin, *Hallasia reticulata* may in fact be taken as a species *Zygnemopsis*. *Zygnemopsis* considering the comparatively simple nature of its chloroplasts, abundant aplanospore formation in its species, can be regarded as one of the primitive genera of the Zygnemaceae.

*Pleurodiscus* and *Zygnema* seem to have evolved from *Zygnemopsis* by elaboration of chloroplasts. *Zygnema terrestre* provides a connecting link between *Zygnema* and *Zygogonium*. The adoption of terrestrial habit, partial utilisation of the protoplast of the gametangia, and cutting off of the zygospores by walls from the gametangia can be taken as advanced features of *Zygogonium*.

Species of *Spirogyra* with a single chloroplast seem to be derivable from *Spirotaenium* by adoption of the habit of filament forming. Species of *Spirogyra* with many chloroplasts can be regarded as more developed. *Sirogonium* with its numerous band-like chloroplasts is derivable from *Spirogyra*. Adoption of morphological anisogamy, however, marks it off as a much more advanced form.

*Debarya* with its isogamous conjugation seems to have evolved from *Mesotaenium* like ancestors by the adoption of habit of filament forming. *Mougeotia* seems to have arisen from the same stem. *Temnogametum* in which the gametangia are cut off by septa is derivable from the same stock, but can be regarded as higher than *Mougeotia*. *Sirocladium*

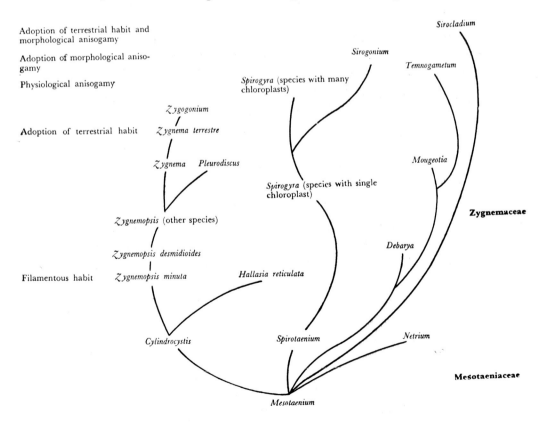

with its two parietal chloroplasts seems to have arisen independently from *Mesotaenium*-like ancestors and has some features in common with *Netrium*. Presence of morphological anisogamy and terrestrial habit mark off this genus as the most highly evolved of the genera of the Zygnemaceae.

The relationship of the genera of the Mesotaeniaceae to the genera of the Zygnemaceae is shown in the diagram on page 29.

Thus the Mesotaeniaceae may be regarded as the most primitive family of the Zygnemales. Close relationship of the Mesotaeniaceae and the Zygnemaceae is indicated by the structure of cell-wall, chloroplasts, and mode of conjugation. Desmidiaceae which comprises the Placoderm Desmids seems to have branched off at an early stage, and may be regarded as on the same level as the Zygnemaceae. The relationship of the families and sub-families of the Zygnemales is shown in the diagram below :

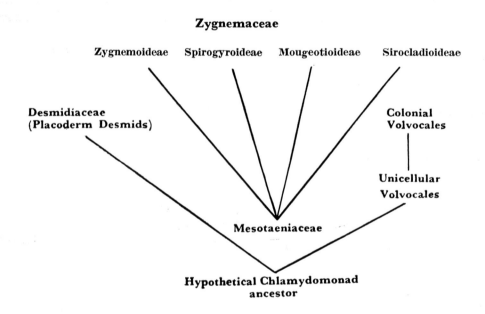

# THE FAMILY ZYGNEMACEAE
## Meneghini 1838

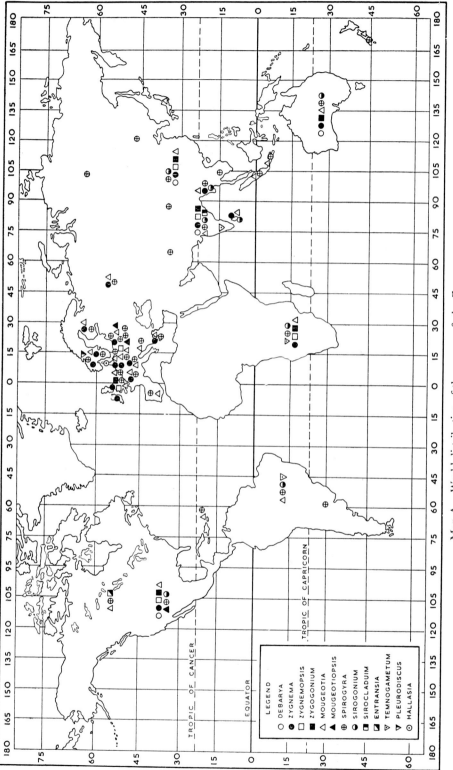

Map A.    World distribution of the genera of the Zygnemaccae

CHAPTER 3

# The Family ZYGNEMACEAE Meneghini 1838

## Occurrence and Distribution

The members of the Zygnemaceae have a wide-spread distribution over the surface of the globe. Intensive work on this family has been done in Europe, the U.S.A., China and India, where most of the known forms have been recorded (Map A). This is likely to give a misleading impression of the distribution of the members of the Zygnemaceae which can only be corrected by more intensive work in countries which remain unexplored from the algal point of view.

According to Transeau there are 13 recognised genera and 536 species. In Table 1 is given the distribution of the species of the 13 genera of the Zygnemaceae in various countries. In temperate countries of the northern hemisphere the Zygnemaceae are specially abundant in spring months, generally occurring as bright green free floating mats. Some of the genera like *Debarya*, *Zygnemopsis*, *Zygogonium*, *Mougeotiopsis Sirocladium*, *Entransia*, *Temnogametum*, *Pleurodiscus* and *Hallasia* have an extremely restricted distribution. Species of *Debarya* have been recorded from India, Australia, China and the United States of America. Species of *Zygnemopsis* have been recorded from India, U.S.A., China, South Africa, and England. Five species of *Zygogonium* have been recorded from India, four from the U.S.A., three from South Africa, and one each from Australia, China and England. The solitary species of *Mougeotiopsis* has been recorded from U.S.A., Czechoslovakia, Austria, and Latvia. All the three species of *Sirocladium* have been recorded from India. The solitary species of *Entransia* has been recorded from Canada. *Temnogametum* has only eight recognised species of which four have been recorded from Brazil, Ecuador, Trinidad, and South Africa and four from India. The solitary species of the genera *Pleurodiscus* and *Hallasia* have been recorded from Puerto Rico and Denmark respectively.

*Mougeotia, Spirogyra* and *Zygnema* have more or less a universal distribution, and have been recorded from most of the countries where collections of algae have been made. Vegetative filaments of these three genera forming green mats have been recorded from Arctic regions also.

33

TABLE 1

The number of species of the genera of the Zygnemaceae recorded from different countries

| Names of Continents and Countries | Debarya | Zyg-nema | Zygne-mopsis | Zygogo-nium | Moug-eotia | Moug-eotiopsis | Spirog-yra | Sirogo-nium | Entran-sia | Temno-gametum | Pleuro-discus | Hallasia | Siro-cladium |
|---|---|---|---|---|---|---|---|---|---|---|---|---|---|
| **AFRICA** | | | | | | | | | | | | | |
| South Africa | | 13 | 5 | 3 | 11 | | 47 | 3 | | 2 | | | |
| **ASIA** | | | | | | | | | | | | | |
| Afghanistan | | | | | | | 2 | | | | | | |
| Burma | | 3 | | | 3 | | 13 | 1 | | 1 | | | |
| Ceylon | | 1 | | | 1 | | 1 | 1 | | | | | |
| China | 1 | 21 | 5 | 1 | 19 | | 99 | 2 | | | | | 3 |
| India | 3 | 23 | 16 | 5 | 16 | | 92 | 8 | | 8 | | | |
| Java | | | | | 1 | | | | | | | | |
| Japan | | | | | 3 | | | | | | | | |
| Siam | | | | | | | 4 | | | | | | |
| Siberia | | | | | | | 1 | | | | | | |
| Sumatra | | | | | 1 | | 1 | | | | | | |
| Tibet | | | | | | | 1 | | | | | | |
| **AUSTRALIA** | | | | | | | | | | | | | |
| Australia | | 3 | | 1 | 4 | | 16 | 1 | | | | | |
| New Zealand | | | | | 1 | | 2 | | | | | | |
| **EUROPE** | | | | | | | | | | | | | |
| Austria | | 3 | | | 4 | 1 | 9 | | | | | | |
| Belgium | | 1 | | | 1 | 1 | | | | | | | |
| Czechoslovakia | | | | | 4 | 1 | 10 | | | | | | |

| | 1 | 2 | 3 | 4 | 5 | 6 | 7 | 8 | 9 | 10 |
|---|---|---|---|---|---|---|---|---|---|---|
| Denmark | 1 | | | | | | | | 2 | |
| England | | | | 4 | | 4 | 1 | 1 | 2 | |
| France | | | | 9 | | 4 | | | 1 | |
| Finland | | | | 12 | | 8 | | | | |
| Germany | | | | 16 | | 10 | | | 6 | |
| Greece | | | | 2 | | 1 | | | 1 | |
| Hungary | | | | 2 | | | | | | |
| Holland | | | | 1 | | 1 | | | | |
| Ireland | | | | | | | | | 1 | |
| Norway | | | | 1 | | | | | 1 | |
| Russia | | | | 7 | | 2 | | | 1 | |
| Rumania | | | | 5 | | | | | | |
| Sweden | | | | 8 | | 10 | | | 4 | |
| Spain | | | | 1 | | 1 | | | | |
| Switzerland | | | | 2 | | 4 | | | | |
| Yugoslavia | | | | 3 | | 1 | | | | |
| **NORTH AMERICA** | | | | | | | | | | |
| Canada | | | | 4 | | 1 | | | | 3 |
| United States of America | | | 5 | 143 | 1 | 52 | 4 | 5 | 47 | |
| **SOUTH AMERICA** | | | | | | | | | | |
| Argentina | | | | 1 | | | | | | |
| Brazil | | 1 | 1 | 13 | | 3 | | | | |
| Puerto Rico | | 1 | | 3 | | 2 | | | | |

(Taylor, 1954). The largest number of species of these three genera has been recorded from the United States of America, China, India, South Africa, and the countries of Europe. When work is done in countries which are unexplored, it is very likely that these genera would be found to be even more widely distributed.

### Distribution in India

The members of the Zygnemaceae are common throughout India in fresh-water ponds, puddles, paddy fields, *jhils* and slowly flowing fresh-water streams. They are fairly abundant in areas of heavy and medium rainfall from 100 inches to 30 inches in the States of Assam, West Bengal, Bihar, Orissa, Uttar Pradesh, Punjab, Andhra, Western Ghats areas of Bombay, Mysore and Kerala as well as Tamil Nad. In the dry areas of the Deccan Plateau, Saurashtra and Gujerat areas of Bombay and in Rajasthan they are rather rare. In the States of Uttar Pradesh, Punjab, West Bengal, Tamil Nad, Mysore and Bombay a fair amount of work has been done on this group of algae. The other States remain more or less unexplored, and hence exact appraisal of their distribution at this stage remains largely a guesswork. They are particularly abundant in slowly flowing fresh-water streams which are the tributaries of rivers. Very few of these algae are found in the major rivers when they are in flood during the monsoons, the current being too fast for the growth of algae, but from November onwards the rivers shrink leaving pools and puddles along their banks in which rich growth of algae, particularly Zygnemaceae takes place. They are also seen growing abundantly in road-side ditches, fresh-water ponds, puddles and paddy fields in villages as well as in large lakes known as *jhils*. Fresh-water streams in Oudh, the eastern part of the Uttar Pradesh are particularly rich in species of Zygnemaceae.

In the Himalayas they are found at the altitudes of 5500 to 10,000 feet. *Sirocladium kumaoense* is found at an altitude of 5,500 feet, *Zygnema himalayense* at 7,750 feet, *Zygnema terrestre* at 6000 to 7500 feet and *Zygogonium kumaoense* at an altitude of 6,500 feet in Kumaon Himalayas. *Zygnemopsis lahaulense* is found at 10,000 feet in Lahaul Valley, Punjab Himalayas, and *Zygnema terrestre* is also found in Kashmir at an altitude of 12,100 feet.

### Climate of India

As already pointed out, the distribution of algae, particularly the members of the Zygnemaceae is closely connected with climate. Hence detailed consideration of the climate of India is necessary.

India is predominantly the land of tropical monsoon climate though half of its area lies north of the Tropic of Cancer. The year may be divided into four seasons, *viz.*, winter (December to February), summer (March to May), monsoon (June to September), and post monsoon period (October to November).

### The Cold Weather: December-January-February

Temperatures below 40°F prevail in the Himalayas, and in the sub-montane area of the north. Night radiation is active, and the low temperatures of the north are due primarily to this. While the maxima and minima in the Punjab are 68.9°F and 40.2°F, at Trivandrum in the south the January means are 84°F and 72.3°F.

### The Hot Weather: March-May

From early in March temperatures rise rapidly and pressures decrease. The mean maximum is already over 100°F in the Deccan in March; by May, the hottest month in most places is over 105°F, with means of 85-95°F in the interior except where modified by altitude. In the Punjab the thermometer rises to over 110°F. The extreme south has a much more equable regime; Trivandrum's mean maxima and minima for April, here the hottest month, are 88.0°F and 77.9°F and the extremes recorded are 93.5°F and 63.0°F.

### Monsoon: June-September

It is the South-west Monsoon which provides the moisture for the growth of crops as well as algae. The S.W. monsoon starts early in June, extends into India in June and July, and finally it retreats southwards in September and October. With the advance of summer, insolation increases rapidly over the higher latitudes so that by the end of May the region of highest air temperature, and the lowest atmospheric pressure lies over north-west India and the adjoining areas of Pakistan, Afghanistan, Persia, and Central Asia. This low pressure system takes control of the air currents over Asia so that the south-east trade winds from the south of the Equator after being diverted into the Arabian Sea and the Bay of Bengal, appear suddenly over the west coasts of India and Burma respectively as the South-west Monsoon. The Arabian Sea branch of the South-west Monsoon, while crossing the Western Ghats, gives copious precipitation over that region, and continues to drift eastwards across the Deccan and Central parts of the country, meeting the Bay branch of the monsoon along the trough of low pressure which extends from Orissa to north-

# ZYGNEMACEAE

## TABLE II

*Normal seasonal rainfall in the 26 rainfall sub-divisions of India*

| Sub-division | Winter: December to February (Inches) | Summer or Pre-monsoon: March to May (Inches) | Monsoon: June to September (Inches) | Post-Monsoon: October to November (Inches) | Full year (Inches) |
|---|---|---|---|---|---|
| (1) | (2) | (3) | (4) | (5) | (6) |
| 1. Assam .. | 2.38 (2.4) | 25.06 (25.7) | 64.26 (65.8) | 5.96 (6.1) | 97.66 |
| 2. Bengal .. | 1.53 (2.0) | 12.42 (16.5) | 56.01 (74.5) | 5.17 (6.9) | 75.13 |
| 3. Orissa .. | 1.82 (3.2) | 5.62 (9.9) | 44.49 (78.2) | 4.98 (8.8) | 56.91 |
| 4. Chota Nagpur .. | 2.57 (5.0) | 3.64 (7.1) | 42.78 (83.4) | 2.26 (4.4) | 51.18 |
| 5. Bihar .. | 1.41 (2.9) | 3.30 (6.8) | 40.96 (85.0) | 2.54 (5.3) | 48.21 |
| 6. U.P. East .. | 1.53 (3.9) | 1.12 (2.9) | 34.44 (88.0) | 2.04 (5.2) | 39.13 |
| 7. U.P. West .. | 2.27 (6.0) | 1.36 (3.6) | 32.98 (87.8) | 0.97 (2.6) | 37.58 |
| 8. Punjab .. | 2.76 (11.9) | 1.89 (8.1) | 18.23 (78.4) | 0.37 (1.6) | 23.25 |
| 9. Kashmir .. | 9.12 (22.1) | 9.09 (22.0) | 22.19 (53.7) | 0.94 (2.3) | 41.34 |
| 10. Rajasthan W. .. | 0.62 (4.8) | 0.56 (4.3) | 11.74 (90.0) | 0.12 (0.9) | 13.04 |
| 11. Rajasthan E. .. | 0.96 (3.8) | 0.78 (3.1) | 22.91 (90.0) | 0.55 (2.2) | 25.20 |
| 12. Gujerat .. | 0.22 (0.7) | 0.24 (0.7) | 31.46 (96.2) | 0.77 (2.4) | 32.69 |
| 13. C. India West .. | 0.85 (2.5) | 0.47 (1.4) | 31.56 (93.8) | 0.75 (2.2) | 33.63 |
| 14. C. India East .. | 1.44 (3.7) | 0.79 (2.0) | 35.05 (90.9) | 1.30 (3.4) | 38.58 |
| 15. Berar .. | 1.01 (3.1) | 0.96 (3.0) | 28.10 (87.4) | 2.07 (6.4) | 32.14 |
| 16. C.P. West .. | 1.47 (3.2) | 1.14 (2.5) | 41.04 (90.4) | 1.76 (3.9) | 45.41 |
| 17. C.P. East .. | 1.58 (3.0) | 2.10 (4.0) | 46.37 (89.1) | 1.99 (3.8) | 52.04 |
| 18. Konkan .. | 0.28 (0.3) | 1.85 (1.7) | 102.45 (93.7) | 4.75 (4.3) | 109.33 |
| 19. Bombay-Deccan .. | 0.51 (1.7) | 2.13 (6.9) | 24.41 (79.1) | 3.82 (12.4) | 30.87 |
| 20. Hyderabad N. .. | 0.67 (1.9) | 1.53 (4.4) | 29.51 (84.5) | 3.20 (9.2) | 34.91 |
| 21. Hyderabad S. .. | 0.57 (1.9) | 2.10 (7.0) | 23.38 (78.1) | 3.88 (13.0) | 29.93 |
| 22. Mysore .. | 0.73 (2.0) | 5.47 (15.2) | 22.27 (61.8) | 7.54 (20.9) | 36.01 |
| 23. Malabar .. | 2.73 (2.6) | 12.61 (12.2) | 71.47 (68.9) | 16.93 (16.3) | 103.74 |
| 24. Madras SE. .. | 4.76 (13.6) | 4.53 (12.9) | 12.01 (34.2) | 13.80 (39.3) | 35.10 |
| 25. Madras Deccan .. | 0.74 (3.0) | 2.42 (9.9) | 15.27 (62.3) | 0.09 (24.8) | 24.52 |
| 26. Madras Coast N. .. | 1.69 (4.2) | 3.44 (8.9) | 25.03 (62.3) | 10.11 (24.9) | 40.16 |

\* In columns (2) to (5) the figures within brackets indicate the seasonal rainfall expressed as percentage of the annual rainfall.

west India. The Bay branch is deflected by the Arakkan Yomas and turned in its course so as to skirt the northern side of the low pressure trough while moving along the submontane tracts to the south of the great Himalayan barrier.

By mid-September the South-west Monsoon rapidly withdraws from the country and is termed the "retreating monsoon". This gradually leads to the north-easterly air currents assuming full sway over the sub-continent and the adjoining seas by January. The North-east Monsoon, as it is called, is associated with rainy weather over the southern parts of peninsular India, particularly over Tamil Nad from November to the end of January.

While the pattern of rainfall already described prevails in the rest of the country, there are three anomalous areas with rainfall in months which are usually dry elsewhere, or rainfall is lacking in the months which are wet in other areas. These are as below:

(*i*) the sub-montane Punjab strip of winter (cyclonic) rain with a feeble extension across the Jamuna. The rainfall in January is 0.5—2 ins.

(*ii*) Assam and Bengal, with 10—20 plus ins. in April-May from the North-Westers.

(*iii*) the S.E. littoral, where the normal rainy months are actually among the driest.

Table II gives the normal rainfall in different seasons of the year and during the year as a whole in the various sub-divisions of India (*cf.* Map B).

**Autumn, the Post-Monsoon Period: October to November**

By the first week of October monsoon normally withdraws and the months of October and November are dry in North India and in November temperature drops by 6° to 10°F.

### Periodicity in Occurrence and Distribution of the Zygnemaceae in Northern India

The normal life of a member of the Zygnemaceae in Northern India is divisible into five periods.

(i) *Period of spore germination*: Though most of the ponds and rivers are full of water from July onwards, very few species appear

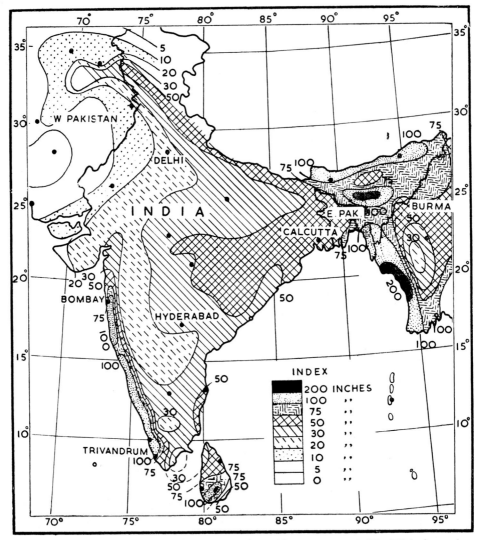

Map B.   Rainfall map of India.  It is in the regions with an average rainfall of 30 inches and over that the members of the *Zygnemaceae* flourish.

even as late as September. There are some species like *Sirogonium ventersicum, Spirogyra daedalea* and *S. oudhensis* in which spores germinate by the end of August, and they become abundant by the end of September. In the majority of the forms, however, the spores germinate in December, there being a long period of dormancy.

(ii) *Period of growth and vegetative development*: Species which germinate by late August show a period of vegetative development for about a month or so. The species which become dominant in January show extensive vegetative development in December and early January when they are rich green in colour.

(iii) *Period of conjugation*: After a period of vegetative development reproduction takes place either in the form of conjugation or aplanospore formation. In early autumn forms, conjugation starts in September or early October, while in late winter and spring forms, conjugation starts in December and January.

(iv) *Period of spore ripening*: In early autumn forms, spores begin to ripen in October and by early November all the spores are ripe. In late winter and spring forms, spores ripen in March and early April. During this period the colour of algae becomes dark brown or dirty blue.

(v) *Period of dormancy*: The spores of all the Zygnemaceae in North India undergo a period of dormancy during the hot months of May and June when the water in the ponds, *jhils* and fresh-water streams dries up. The late winter and spring forms have a longer period of dormancy as compared with the late autumn and early winter annuals.

The seasons in Northern India are fairly sharply defined, and the members of the Zygnemaceae also show a marked periodicity in occurrence and reproduction which is connected with temperature and rainfall. According to their phases of vegetative development, conjugation and period of spore-ripening, the members of the Zygnemaceae in Northern India can be divided into three groups.

## I. Autumn and Early Winter Annuals

The species included in this group become fairly abundant by the last week of September at the close of the rains. They start conjugation and produce ripe spores in September, October and November. The terrestrial members of the order such as *Sirocladium*

*kumaoense, S. maharashtrense, Zygnema terrestre* and *Zygogonium kumaoense*
all come under this group and their spores ripen in September and
October. It is observed that most of the species of *Spirogyra* included
in this group have relatively broad filaments. The common species
are *Debarya costata, Mougeotia tenuis, Zygnema mucigena, Z. cyanosporum,
Spirogyra rhizoides, S. jaoensis, Sirogonium melanosporum* etc.

## II. Late Winter and Spring Annuals

The species included in this group show vegetative activity in
December, conjugate in January and early February, and produce
ripe spores at the end of February or early March. By the middle
of March when wheat is harvested in Uttar Pradesh, these algae have
ripe spores. In the Punjab, further up in the north, conjugation takes
place in March, and ripe spores can be seen in April, a month later
than in Uttar Pradesh. Ponds, *jhils* and small fresh-water streams
which are the habitats of these algae dry up in the months of May and
June when they perennate in the form of zygospores, aplanospores, or
akinetes. In this group are included by far the largest number of
species collected so far. Species of *Zygnemopsis, Mougeotia, Zygnema*
and *Spirogyra* form the largest bulk of the group.

## III. Ephemerals

In this group are included a few species such as *Mougeotia
sphaerocarpa* and *Spirogyra daedalea*, which produce ripe spores in all
the months from September to March.

### Spore Formation in South India

In South India, in the regions which get their maximum amount
of rain during the North East Monsoon rains from October to
December, such as Madras and the remaining Coromandel regions,
the ponds and irrigation tanks get filled up in the months of October
and November, and dry up about the end of March or the beginning
of April. In these areas, the Zygnemaceae begin to reproduce in
November, and continue to do so till February or early March. But
in regions which get their maximum rain fall during the South West
Monsoon such as Mysore and Kerala, and the Western Ghats regions,
the low-lying areas get filled up in June or July. In these areas,
according to Iyengar the Zygnemaceae begin to reproduce in September
or October or even earlier.

CHAPTER 4

# THE ZYGNEMACEAE

## The Structure of the Cell

The members of the Zygnemaceae are generally free-floating, and only a few forms have been reported as growing attached to aquatic substrata by means of haptera or rhizoidal outgrowths. Collections of Zygnemaceae from stagnant ponds with warm water and low oxygen content usually show rounded or distorted cells and rhizoidal outgrowths. Formation of rhizoids is possibly due to contact stimulus, or it may be even a chemical response. In the species of *Spirogyra* growing in flowing water such as *Spirogyra fluviatilis*, the attaching cells are elaborately lobed (Fig. I.i). Iyengar (1923) described some attached forms of *Spirogyra*, *Zygnema* and *Mougeotia* from Madras. In *Zygnema* sp., short knob-like rhizoidal outgrowths are put out from the sides of some of the cells. Iyengar has also recorded a dichotomously branching rhizoid cut off by cross walls in a species of *Zygnema*. He has further reported spirally coiled filaments in *Mougeotia* (Fig. I.iii) and he considers coiling as an arrangement for securing attachment to substrata. Jao (1936) described two species of *Spirogyra* from China, *S. rhizopus* and *S. rhizobrachialis* which have rhizoids. Rhizoids have also been described in *Spirogyra affinis* and *S. dubia*. In the latter they are long pillar-like bodies expanding laterally and frayed at the ends (Fig. I.ii). The chloroplasts in the rhizoids usually get attenuated and may be completely disorganised in some cases.

In terrestrial forms like *Zygnema terrestre*, the rhizoidal cells are very much elongated as compared with the subaerial portion, and the distal part may be expanded. In *Sirocladium kumaoense*, either the terminal cells of the under-ground portion of the filament are drawn out into rhizoidal structures, or intercalary cells give out pillar-like rhizoidal projections (Fig. I.iv). In *Zygogonium kumaoense* the rhizoids are knob-like or elongated bodies (Fig. I.v).

### The Cell Wall

The cell wall in the Zygnemaceae is composed of a single piece, and may be single or many layered. The outer-most layer is composed

43

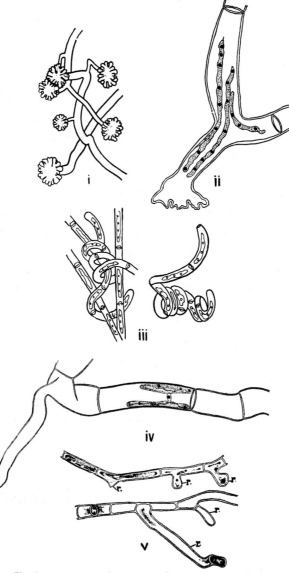

Fig. I. Rhizoids and structures for attachment: i. *Spirogyra fluviatilis* ; ii. *S. dubia* ; iii. *Mougeotia sp* ; iv. *Sirocladium kumaoense* ; v. *Zygogonium kumaoense*, (fig. i. after Czurda, iii. after Iyengar ; ii, iv-v. after Randhawa.)  r, rhizoid.

of pectic substance, while the inner is of cellulose. Sliminess of many members of the Zygnemaceae is due to external pectose mucilage sheath, and this explains their freedom from epiphytes. The species of *Sirogonium*, however, have no pectic sheath, and hence are coarse to touch and are commonly loaded with epiphytes.

## Septa

The filaments are divided into many cells by cross walls which are essentially of five types, viz., plane, replicate, semireplicate, colligate, and unduliseptate (Fig. II). The commonest type is the plane end wall as in *Mougeotia* spp., *Spirogyra* spp. (Fig. II.i-iii). In the replicate type, the middle lamella of the septum expands to form a circular infold over which the apposition layers are gradually deposited (Fig. II. iv-vi). In the semireplicate type, infolds extend only halfway and alternate in position in the adjoining cells (Fig. II.vii). A typical example of the colligate type is afforded by *Spirogyra colligata* where there is a distinct H-shaped piece between the adjoining cells. In the unduliseptate type the septa look like a parallelogram with the middle lamella as a diagonal and the longer sides undulating in a wave-like manner as in *S. undulisepta* (Fig. II.x).

## Cell Division

The growth of the filaments is never localised, and any vegetative cell excepting the attaching cell is capable of division. During cell division, the equatorial plate is formed by the fusion of the spindle fibres at the equatorial region, and this fuses with the annular projection of the cytoplasm. Within this cytoplasmic projection, in the neigh-

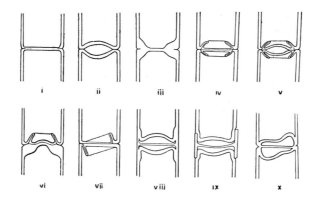

Fig. II. Types of septa. i-iii. Plane ; iv-vi. Replicate ; vii. Semireplicate ; viii-ix. Colligate ; x. Unduliseptate (figs. i-vii. after Jao ; viii after Hodgetts ; x. after Randhawa.)

bourhood of the longitudinal wall, a delicate membrane is suddenly formed, the inner edge of which, covered in by cytoplasm, gradually grows until the cell-cavity is bridged across. The chloroplasts are simply cut into two by this septum (Fig. III). In *Zygnema* and *Mougeotia*, division of the chloroplasts usually precedes that of the protoplast. The daughter cells subsequently deposit secondary thickening layers of cellulose which are proper to the individual cells.

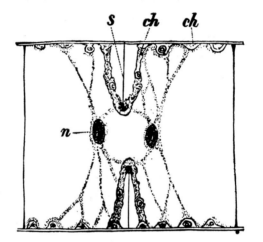

Fig. III. Cell division in *Spirogyra* sp. ch. chloroplast
n, nucleus ; s, septum. (after Strasburger)

### The Cell Sap

The cell-sap is rich in tannins. In *Zygogonium ericetorum* and *Zygnema terrestre* the sap is coloured purple by phycoporphyrin. In shaded situations these algae appear light-green but in exposed situations they appear purple. Streaming movements of the cytoplasm are sometimes seen in *Spirogyra*. Caryoids are small bodies regarded as proteins, but their exact nature and function are not known. They are seen in the cells of some species of *Mougeotia* and *Sirocladium*.

### The Chloroplasts

In the Zygnemaceae the chloroplasts are of four types, viz., an axile plate with or without pyrenoids, two parietal plates with nucleus between them, a pair of stellate bodies with a single large pyrenoid in each, and spirally wound parietal ribbons or more or less straight ribbons with numerous pyrenoids.

1. *Single axile plate-type chloroplasts*: This is probably the most primitive type of chloroplast in the Zygnemaceae. In *Debarya* the

chloroplast is long ribbon-like with a single row of pyrenoids (Fig. IV.i). In *Mougeotia* each cell has one axile flat plate-like chloroplast with the nucleus adpressed to one side of it. Caryoids are found in the chloroplast of species with broad chloroplasts. The pyrenoids are scattered. On exposure to bright light the chloroplast shows a rotation and appears as a linear thread (Fig. IV. iii). In *Temnogametum* also the chloroplast is a single axile plate-like body, and the pyrenoids are arranged in several rows (Fig. IV. vi). In *Mougeotiopsis* each cell has a single quadrate, flat, or dished plate-like axile chloroplast with a thickened and granulated margin which is sometimes inrolled, and pyrenoids are absent (Fig. IV.vii).

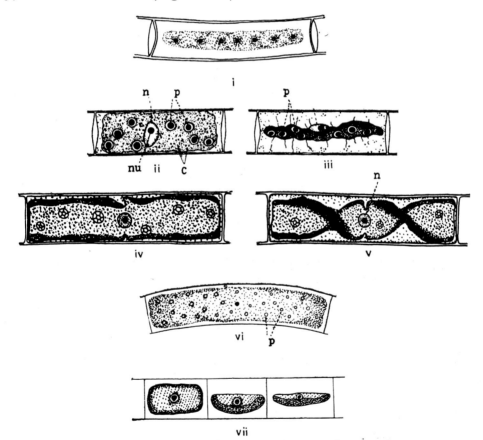

Fig. IV. Plate-like chloroplasts of the genera of *Mougeotioideae*. i. *Debarya costata* ; ii-iii. *Mougeotia sp.*; iv-v. *M. genuflexa* ; vi. *Temnogametum heterosporum* ; vii. *Mougeotiopsis calospora*. (fig. i. after Randhawa ; ii-iii. after West ; iv-v. after Kolkwitz & Krieger ; vi. after West ; vii after Palla.). p, pyrenoid ; n, nucleus ; nu, nucleolus ; c. caryoids.

2. *Two parietal plate-type chloroplasts*: This type of chloroplast is found in the species of *Sirocladium* (Figs. V and VI). In *Sirocladium kumaoense* there are two broad parietal plate-like chloroplasts each bearing

numerous conspicuous pyrenoids.  Nucleus is situated between two plates in a central position, and the margin of the chloroplast is straight (Fig. V.i and ii).  In *Sirocladium vandalurense* the chloroplast consists of two plates with laciniate margin.  Sometimes the plates are bifurcated (Fig. V.v.).  In *Sirocladium maharashtrense* the chloroplasts are two thin, more or less straight ribbons with conspicuous pyrenoids, on both sides of the nucleus (Fig. V.vi).  Caryoids, or refringent granular bodies are also found in the chloroplasts of the species of *Sirocladium*.

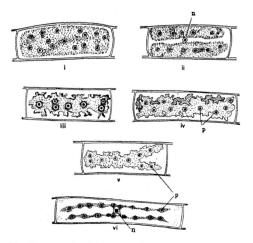

Fig. V.  Two parietal plate-type chloroplasts of *Sirocladioideae*. i-ii. *S. kumaoense*;  iii-v.  *S. vandalurense*;  vi. *S. maharashtrense*; (after Randhawa). n, nucleus; p. pyrenoid.

3.  *Stellate chloroplasts*:  This group comprises genera with chloroplasts which show stages between the plate-like chloroplast of *Mougeotia* and the elaborate stellate chloroplasts of *Zygnema*.  In *Hallasia* though normally the chloroplasts are stellate (Fig.  VII.vi), in the beginning of spore formation there may be an increase in their number from 3 to 7 (Fig. VII.i).  This is possibly a case of reversion to the original type.  In *Zygogonium* also  sometimes the chloroplasts are irregular plate-like bodies with thickenings at the poles (Fig. VII.ii).  In *Zygogonium pectosum* the chloroplasts are two pillow-shaped bodies (Fig. VII.iii).  In *Zygnemopsis orientalis* the chloroplasts are two spherical bodies  (Fig. VII.iv).  In *Zygnema terrestre* the chloroplasts are two spherical bodies each with a conspicuous pyrenoid (Fig. VII.v).  Normally the species of *Zygnema* have two axile chloroplasts in each cell with the nucleus contained in  the cytoplasmic bridge connecting them.  Each chloroplast consists of a rounded body with irregular short branches radiating in all planes and containing a

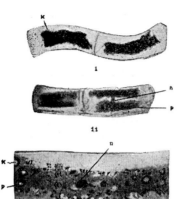
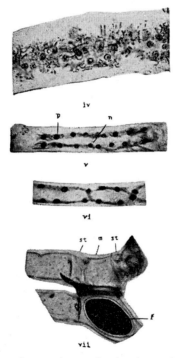

Fig. VI. Chloroplasts and reproduction in species of *Sirocladium*. i. & ii. Chloroplasts in *S. kumaoense*; iii. & iv. Chloroplasts in *S. vandalurense*; v. & vi. Chloroplasts in *S. maharashtrense*; vii. Conjugation in *S. kumaoense*; (after Randhawa). k. caryoids, f. female cell, m. male cell, n. nucleus, p. pyrenoid, st, sterile cell.

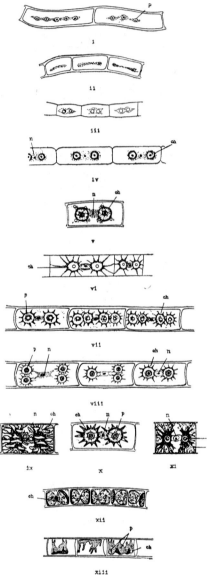

Fig. VII. Stellate chloroplasts of *Zygnemoideae*. i. *Hallasia reticulata*; ii. *Zygogonium kumaoense*; iii. *Z. pectosum*; iv. *Zygnemopsis orientalis*; v. *Zygnema terrestre*; vi. *Hallasia reticulata*; vii-viii. *Zygnema sp.* showing more than two chloroplasts; ix-xi. *Zygnema sp.*; xii. *Pleurodiscus purpurens*; xiii. *Entransia fimbriata*. (figs. ii, v. after Randhawa; i, iv, vi-viii, after Transeau; ix-xi, after Krieger; xii. after West; xiii. after Hughes). n, nucleus; p, pyrenoid; ch, chloroplast.

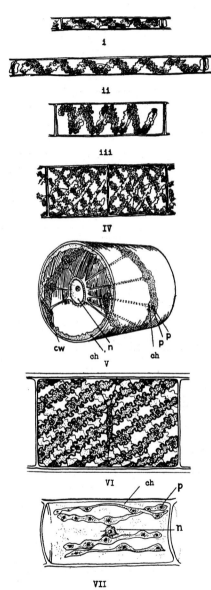

Fig. VIII. Spiral chloroplasts of the genera of *Spirogyroideae*. i-iv. *Spirogyra sp*; v. Section of a *Spirogyra* cell; vi. *S. nitida*; vii. *Sirogonium sticticum*. (figs. i-iv. after Blum; v. after Holmes and Gibbs; vi. after Krieger; vii. after Randhawa). cw, cell-wall; ch, chloroplast; n, nucleus; p, pyrenoid.

conspicuous central pyrenoid (Fig. VII.ix, x and xi). Transeau (1951) has, however, recorded 3 to 4 chloroplasts in each cell in a species of *Zygnema* (Fig. VII.vii and viii). This is possibly a reversion to the original condition, and indicates derivation from the plate-like chloroplast. In *Pleurodiscus* the chloroplasts are smooth-edged disc or saucer-shaped bodies (Fig. VII.xii). *Entransia* has one or two laminate parietal chloroplasts with several irregular finger-like processes extending outward and part way around the cell. Each chloroplast has several scattered pyrenoids. The nucleus is in the bridge between the two chloroplasts (Fig. VII.xiii).

4. *Spiral type chloroplasts*: This type of chloroplast is represented in the species of *Spirogyra* and *Sirogonium*. The chloroplasts of *Spirogyra* are either narrow with a smooth margin or broad with serrated margin. In the former case the pyrenoids occur in an axile series while in the latter they are scattered. The chloroplasts are arranged in a sinistral or left handed or counter-clockwise spiral in the peripheral cytoplasm while the nucleus is suspended in the middle (Fig. VIII.v). The number of spirals may vary from 1 to 16. In most species the number of chloroplasts is uniform while in others it varies within certain limits. Each chloroplast has many disc-shaped pyrenoids spaced at regular intervals. Kolkwitz showed that the chloroplasts of *Spirogyra* elongate both by apical and intercalary growth. In *Sirogonium* the chloroplasts are in the form of bands which run more or less longitudinally with ends only slightly curved (Fig. VIII.vii).

### Pyrenoids

Chloroplasts of the genera of the Zygnemaceae with the exception of *Mougeotiopsis* bear pyrenoids. Cells of small size with small chloroplasts usually have one pyrenoid in a chloroplast. Cells with large chloroplasts have many pyrenoids either irregularly distributed, or in a linear series. In the species of *Mougeotia* with broad chloroplasts there are numerous scattered pyrenoids, while in the species of *Debarya* and the species of *Mougeotia* with narrow chloroplasts there is a single row of pyrenoids. In *Sirocladium kumaoense* and *S. vandalurense* the chloroplasts bear many scattered pyrenoids. In the genera of *Zygnemoideae* there are usually two large chloroplasts, each having a conspicuous pyrenoid. In the species of *Spirogyra* each chloroplast bears numerous pyrenoids.

The pyrenoid consists of a central proteinaceous core sheathed by minute starch plates. According to Czurda (1932 b) the pyrenoid is a

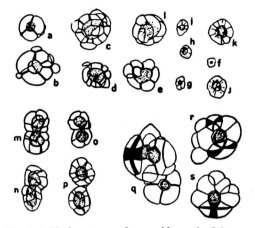

Fig. IX. Various types of pyrenoids. a-b. *Spirogyra tenuis-sima*; c-n. *S. varians*; m-p. *S. weberi*; q-s. *S. setiformis.* (after Czurda).

viscous mass of protein and its interior is structureless (Fig. IX). From their marked constancy in number and position, it is indicated that the pyrenoids are special organs of the cells and they persist even under conditions of starvation. Czurda (1928) has shown a definite relation between the amount of cytoplasm and the total pyrenoid substance in the cell. Pyrenoids often dwindle in size in zygotes, and they multiply when there is a general removal of food reserves, and at the time of active cell division. According to Smith (1950) pure cultures of green algae furnish considerable evidence on the role of the pyrenoid in starch formation. When cells are grown in total darkness but in the presence of glucose or some other carbon source, there is an accumulation of starch around the protein core. This seems to show that the first steps in photosynthesis are carried on by the chlorophyll-containing portion of the chloroplast, and that the last step or steps in formation of starch are performed by the protein core of the pyrenoid.

## The Nucleus

Each cell has a single nucleus situated in the middle of the cell in between the two chloroplasts in the members of Zygnemoideae or apposed to the cell wall in *Mougeotia*. The nucleus in the broader species of *Spirogyra* is lenticular and suspended by cytoplasmic threads within a central vacuole (Fig. X.i). The detailed structure and division of the nucleus of *Spirogyra* have formed the subject of frequent study, and the majority of workers have concluded that the nucleolus contains the bulk of the chromatin. Geitler (1930) showed that at a time when the chromosomes are fully differentiated the nucleolus still

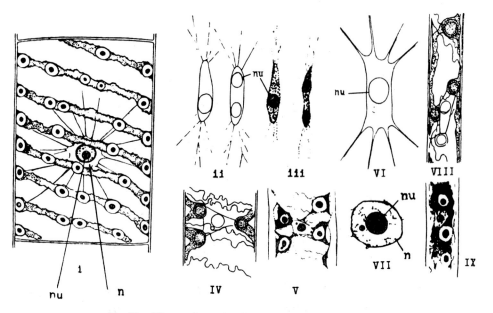

Fig. X. The nucleus. i. *Spirogyra crassa*; ii-iii. *S. majuscula*;
iv-v. *S. varians*; vi-vii. *S. setiformis*; viii-ix. *S. tenuissima*; (fig. i.
after G.S. West. ii-ix. after Czurda) n, nucleus, nu, nucleolus.

persists in an unaltered form. The nucleus of *Zygnema* appears to have
a clear chromatin reticulum.

### Nuclear Division

Nuclear division usually begins about 1 to 2 hours after sunset
and is completed by the early morning. The nuclear division in
*Spirogyra* has been studied by various workers from as early as 1895.
Since then there has been a considerable difference of opinion with
regard to the origin of the chromosomes and the spindle. There are
three prevalent views with regard to the origin of the chromosomes,
*viz.*, chromosomes are nucleolar in origin (Tangl, 1882 ; Mitzkewitsh,
1898) ; they are partly nucleolar and partly reticular in origin
(Flemming, 1882, Wisselingh, 1900, 1902, 1921 ) and they are entirely
reticular in origin (Strasburger, 1888, Geitler, 1930 ; Suematsu, 1936 ;
Doraiswami, 1946.)

Geitler (1930) found in *Spirogyra setiformis* that the outer nucleus
remained unstained while in *S. crassa* a number of darkly staining
granules were found in the outer nucleus. Doraiswami (1946) made
a detailed study of the cytology of the four species of *Spirogyra*, viz. *S.
columbiana* Czurda, *S. fuellebornei* Schmidle, *S. paraguayensis* Borge

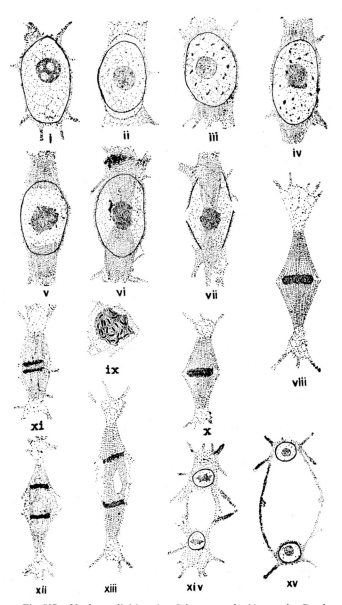

Fig XI. Nuclear division in *Spirogyra columbiana*.  i. Resting
nucleus ; ii. Polar caps at the two poles; iii Chromosomes originating
in the outer nucleus ; iv. Nucleolar membrane breaks ; v. Chromosomes
embedded in the nucleolar mass; vi-vii. Late prophase;  viii-ix. Metaphase ;  ix. Polar view of metaphase, x-xi. Early anaphase; xii-xiii.
Late anaphase : xiv-xv. Telophase.  (All after Doraiswami).

and *S.* sp. During the early prophase in all the species the chromosomes become organised in the outer nucleus while the nucleolus remains intact. The chromosomes are at first scattered in the outer nucleus but at a slightly later stage gather round the nucleolus. The nucleolus later loses its outline, and becomes more or less a mass of granular substance. The chromosomes which had gathered round the nucleolus are seen entering into the granular nucleolar material and finally all the chromosomes are seen completely embedded inside the nucleolar mass (Fig. XI.i-vi). It is clearly seen that the chromosomes do not originate from the nucleolus but are organised in the outer nucleus (Doraiswami, 1946). It is also seen that there is a definite reticulum in the outer nucleus similar to that of the higher plants.

Describing mitosis in *Spirogyra setiformis* Ueda (1956) observes that the granules observed in the prophase and metaphase nuclei are not the chromosomes themselves, or the fragments of the nucleolus, but chromocentres within the chromonemata. According to him the nucleolar substance described by Geitler (1935) is nothing but the chromosomes. Both chromonemata derived from the nucleolus and the 'Auhenkern' or the nuclear part outside of the nucleolus, shift together towards the nuclear plate of the spindle. Thus the nucleolus consists mainly of the 'main chromosome-group.'

Petter (1933) and Yamaha (1935) found that the nucleus of *Spirogyra* was feulgen negative, but Geitler (1935 a,b) found in a number of species that the nucleolus in the resting nucleus remained unstained while some granules (chromocentres) were stained in the outer nucleus. The chromosomes were later developed from these granules. Geitler concluded that the nucleolus did not contain any chromatin material, and the chromosomes were derived from the outer nucleus (reticulum) as in the higher plants.

The resting nucleus is elliptic to spherical in shape (Fig. XI-i). At the beginning of prophase the nucleus slightly enlarges and in the outer nucleus some darkly staining bodies are seen. At this stage the nucleolus becomes slightly irregular in shape and loses its outline and small short rod-like chromosomes are seen scattered in the outer nucleus. Later the nucleolus gets completely disorganised into a granular mass in which the chromosomes are found embedded. At the beginning of prophase a transparent region is seen at each end of the nucleus between the nuclear membrane and cytoplasm. These

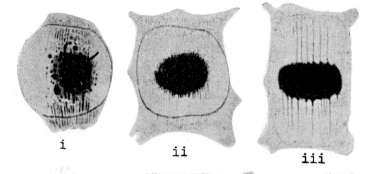

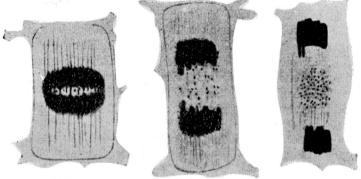

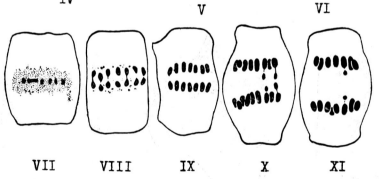

Fig. XII.  Nuclear division in *Spirogyra setiformis*.  i. late prophase;
ii. metakinase ;  iii. metaphase ;  iv. late anaphase ;  v-vi. telophase ;
vii-xi. diagrammatic sketches of the various stages of nuclear division.
(after Geitler).

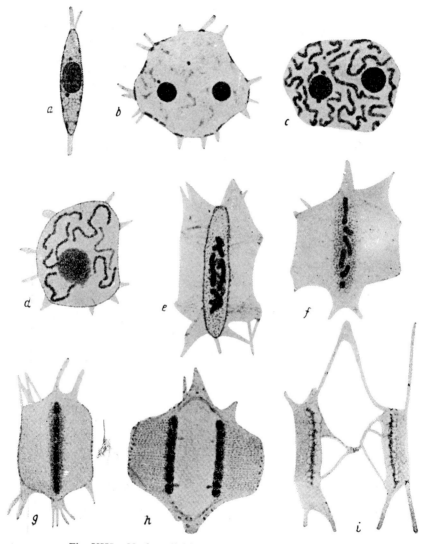

Fig. XIII. Nuclear division in *Spirogyra* sp. (after Geitler).

regions are the polar caps from which parallel striations extend inside the nucleus, and become closely attached to the nucleolar mass. The nuclear membrane breaks down and spindle fibres become well developed (Fig. XI.vi-vii).

During metaphase the nucleolar substance with the chromosomes assumes the form of an equatorial plate, and the chromosomes are arranged closely. The spindle fibres converge towards the pole but end in a more or less round cytoplasmic aggregation (Fig. XI.vii). At the beginning of anaphase the chromosomes divide (Fig. XI.x) and the nuclear plate splits into two transversely. The two plates with a set of daughter chromosomes move towards the poles (Fig. XI.xi). The hyaline space which was seen during the prophase and metaphase around each chromosome (Fig. XI.v-ix) is not seen during anaphase (Fig. XI.x-xi). The disappearance of the hyaline space during anaphase suggests that this area may represent the matrix of the chromosomes, which becomes chromophilic towards the end of metaphase. In the beginning of the telophase the daughter plates become compressed and appear somewhat twisted (Fig. XI.xiii). The nucleolus appears a little later (Fig. XI.xv). The number of chromosomes in various species of the Zygnemaceae is given below:

| | | |
|---|---|---|
| *Spirogyra columbiana* | 24 | Doraiswami (1946) |
| *S.* sp. | 6 | ,, |
| *S. paraguayensis* | 8 | ,, |
| *S. fuellebornei* | 12 | ,, |
| *S. crassa* | 12 | Moll (1893) |
| | | Wisselingh (1898) |
| | | Geitler (1930) |
| *S. dubia* | 5 | Merriman (1916) |
| *S. jugalis* | 14 | Karsten (1908) |
| *S. longata* | 10-12 | Tröndle (1911) |
| *S. neglecta* | 12 | Tröndle (1911) |
| *S. biformis* | 6 | Wisselingh (1900) |
| *Zygnema stellinum* | 12 | Dangeard (1909) |
| *Z. vaucheri* | 14 | Kursanoff (1911) |

## CHAPTER 5

# THE ZYGNEMACEAE

## Reproduction

Reproduction in the Zygnemaceae takes place vegetatively, asexually, or sexually by the union of amoeboid gametes. Vegetative reproduction takes place by fragmentation of filaments into individual cells, or short lengths. Asexual reproduction takes place by akinetes, aplanospores, and parthenospores or azygospores. Sexual reproduction is by a process known as conjugation. Conjugation may be lateral or scalariform. In both the modes of conjugation, whether lateral or scalariform, the union of gametes may be half way in the conjugation canal when it is known as isogamous, the gametes being equally active, or it may be anisogamous, the gametes being sexually differentiated as having plus and minus strain, the more active male gamete moving into the female gametangium where fusion takes place. In some cases as in *Sirogonium*, *Sirocladium*, and *Temnogametum* the differentiation of gametangia from ordinary vegetative cells takes place. The progametangia have dense cell contents and are dark green in colour. In these algae there is a transfer of food material from the vegetative to the reproductive cells before the initiation of conjugation, and that is why the vegetative cells have light-green chloroplasts, and a very transparent cytoplasm. In *Sirogonium* and *Sirocladium* the progametangia are divided into a small and a large cell, the former functioning as the male, and the latter as the female.

### Vegetative Multiplication

Fragmentation of the filaments into short lengths or even into individual cells commonly occurs in *Zygnema*. In *Mougeotia*, the septa split into two circular discs which, according to Lloyd (1926) are separated by a middle lamella of pectic material. The two parts of the septum bulge apart so that it appears biconvex and the intervening mucilage is compressed. When the turgor of the cell diminishes, the septum bulges out, and the dilation of the mucilage increases the curvature. As a result, a sheering strain is exerted on the common longitudinal wall which leads to rupture (Fig. XIV. i-ii).

In the species of *Spirogyra* with replicate end-walls, the septum develops a cylindrical collar-like growth. By the dissolution of the middle lamella, the cells are left connected only by their longitudinal walls. The ingrowth gets evaginated after the cells have broken apart so that the detached cell has a distinct rounded extremity (Fig. XIV.iii-v). Some workers regard replicate septa as special adaptation for fragmentation. Transeau (1951), however, states that plane-walled filaments fragment with as much ease as those with replicate walls. Hence, we may recognise that the function of the replicate septa is not clear.

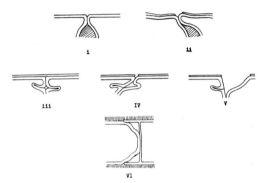

Fig. XIV. Cell disjunction. i-ii. Plane type ; iii-v. Replicate type ; vi. Colligate type. (figs. i-v. after Lloyd ; vi. after Hodgetts.)

In *Spirogyra colligata*, Lloyd (1926 b) observed a method of disjunction by means of H-pieces. The process of disjunction commences with hydrolysis of the longitudinal walls along a circular transverse line coinciding with the ends of a H-piece. The process of solution first leads to a disappearance of the mucilage-layer and then gradually extends into the wall, until the innermost layer investing the protoplast is reached, after which it spreads round the end of the cell, thus setting free the innermost layer from the middle lamella of the septum. As the layer around the protoplast becomes free, it is distended by the turgor of the cell, and ultimately the end rounds off, causing it to slip from the H-piece (Fig. XIV. vi).

The filaments disintegrate readily in *Zygnemopsis desmidioides* where the cross wall regions are deeply constricted, thus facilitating the dissociation of the filaments into individual cells. In *Zygnemopsis minuta*, though there are no such constrictions, dissociation of filaments into cells takes place just as readily.

## Asexual Reproduction

**Akinetes**

Asexual reproduction in the Zygnemaceae takes place by means of akinetes, aplanospores, and parthenospores (azygospores). The simplest and the most primitive method of reproduction in the Zygnemaceae is by akinetes. An akinete is a vegetative cell, the walls of which get thickened by additional layers of cellulose, or cellulose and pectose. *Zygnema sterile* which occurs in the U.S.A., reproduces by akinetes only (Fig. XV.iv). *Zygnema giganteum* which normally has scalariform conjugation also produces a chain of akinetes, which are pitted. *Zygnema terrestre* produces peculiar type of akinetes in high altitudes. Prior to akinete formation, the cell-wall becomes thickened and lamellated. The peculiarity of this form is that akinetes are not formed by the direct conversion of vegetative cells, but the vegetative cells divide into two more or less equal halves by the ingrowth of septa from the side walls which ultimately meet in the middle. Each half contains only one chloroplast surrounded by food reserves like starch. Thus the akinetes are only half as long as an average vegetative cell, and there is greater economy of material in this mode of akinete formation, for double the number of akinetes is formed (Fig. XV.i-iii ). In *Spirogyra farlowii*, the akinetes have thick lamellated walls (Fig. XV.v).

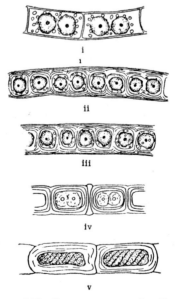

Fig. XV. Akinetes. i-iii. *Zygnema terrestre* ; iv. *Z. sterile* ; v. *Spirogyra farlowii* (i-iii. after Randhawa ; iv-v. after Kolkwitz & Krieger).

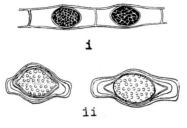

i

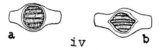

ii

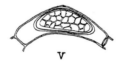

iii

a    iv    b

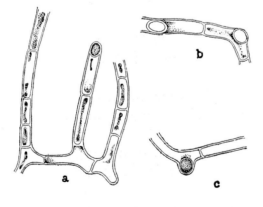

v

a                    c

b

vi

Fig. XVI. Aplanospores. i. *Spirogyra karnalae*; ii. *Zygnemopsis transeauii*; iii. *Z. gracilis*; iv. *Z. iyengarii*; v. *Zygnema terrestre*; vi. a-c. *Zygogonium kumaoense*. (after Randhawa)

According to Fritsch (1948) in *Mougeotia*, akinete formation is specially found in the species that inhabit mountain tarns and lakes with a relatively low temperature. Akinetes are also readily formed in *Zygogonium ericetorum*, and in very dry habitats, the filaments of this species may exist permanently in akinete condition. There is a common notion that akinetes are formed when conditions are un-favourable. According to Transeau (1951), akinetes develop both when conditions seem most favourable and when least favourable. In cultures they appear both in high temperatures and low temperatures. As such, the causes for initiation of akinetes are best stated as unknown.

## Aplanospores

There are 38 species of the Zygnemaceae which reproduce by means of alpanospores. Twelve species of *Zygnema*, 6 of *Zygnem-opsis*, 5 of *Zygogonium*, 7 of *Mougeotia* and 8 of *Spirogyra* reproduce by means of aplanospores. Aplanospores are rounded or ovoid bodies which are produced in the vegetative cells by the contraction of the protoplasts, and in which new walls of cellulose with or without chitinous deposits develop. The spore walls resemble those of zygospores and may be variously coloured, sculptured and ornamented.

Aplanospores were previously regarded as algal errors, and Czurda regarded them as products of lateral conjugation. Sometimes it is indeed difficult to distinguish between zygospores produced by lateral conjugation of the type seen in *Zygnema himalayense* in which the gametes which are isogamous meet in the middle. The entire structure appears superficially like an aplanospore. In *Zygnema terrestre* sometimes it becomes hard to distinguish between aplanospores and laterally produced zygospores. When, however, the length of the cell in which the spore bodies are found is equal to that of a vegetative cell before conjugation, it may be assumed that the spore body is an aplanospore, and if the length is double that of a vegetative cell, it is a zygospore produced by lateral conjugation. *Zygogonium kumaoense* reproduces exclusively by aplanospores which are ovoid bodies formed at the end of cells (Fig. XVI.vi. a) or centrally (Fig. XVI.vi, b and c). Usually they are produced centrally but occasionally they may also be seen in the tips of rhizoids. Various types of aplanospores in species of *Spirogyra*, *Zygnemopsis*, *Zygnema* and *Zygogonium* are shown in Fig. XVI.

## Parthenospores (Azygospores)

Parthenospores are formed when the normal union of gametes fails. Failure of union may take place due to sudden changes in

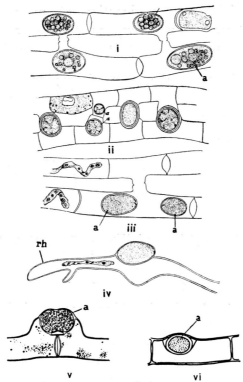

Fig. XVII Azygospores. i, iii. *Spirogyra daedalea* ; ii. *Zygnema collinsianum* ; iv. *Spirogyra rhizoides* ; v. *Mougeotia genuflexa* ; vi. *Zygogonium talguppense* ; (i-iv. after Randhawa ; v. after Kolkwitz & Krieger ; vi. after Iyengar) a, azygospore ; rh, rhizoid.

environmental conditions. Klebs (1896) was able to bring about the formation of parthenospores artificially in *Spirogyra varians*, a species which usually exhibits normal conjugation by placing conjugating filaments in a strong solution of sugar. In *Spirogyra daedalea*, we find that both the gametes have remained in respective positions and have developed independently into parthenospores (Fig. XVII.i). In another specimen of *Spirogyra daedalea*, we find that the male gamete moves into the female gametangium and starts developing independently into a parthenospore instead of fusing with the female gamete (Fig. XVII.iii). In *Zygnema collinsianum*, we notice that both the gametes have moved into the conjugation canal and at that junction they develop into parthenospores (Fig. XVII.ii). In *Mougeotia genuflexa* both the gametes come in contact but they develop independently into azygospores (Fig. XVII.v). In *Zygogonium talguppense* the azygospores are cut off by a wall from the gametangia (Fig. XVII.vi). In *Spirogyra rhizoides* an azygospore was found in a rhizoidal structure

(Fig. XVII-iv). This strange location of an azygospore indicates strong affinity between rhizoids and conjugation canals both of which develop in a similar manner due to contact or chemical stimulus.

Akinetes, aplanospores, and parthenospores have all been seen germinating into new filaments. In Fig. XVIII an azygospore in *Spirogyra mirabilis* is shown germinating and the spore wall is still clinging to the sporeling.

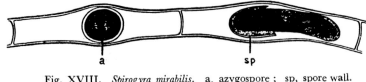

Fig. XVIII. *Spirogyra mirabilis.* a, azygospore ; sp, spore wall. Azygospore on the right is germinating. (after Klebs).

## Sexual Reproduction

Sexual reproduction in the Zygnemaceae is by a process known as conjugation in which amoeboid gametes are involved. There is a marked seasonal periodicity of sexual reproduction, and each species usually fruits at a definite time of the year. Most species fruit between the months of February and June in northern temperate regions. In Northern India, some reproduce in October and November and majority in February to April. Nitrogen deficiency appears to be an important conditional factor. According to Smith, the time of fruiting of *Spirogyra* and *Zygnema* has been shown to be directly correlated with the ratio between the surface and volume of the cell. Czurda (1933) finds that conjugation does not take place until the climax of vegetative activity is passed, when an increase in the $p$H conditions its occurrence. Venkataraman G. S. (unpublished) observed that the members of this group occur under a wide range of $p$H. *Sirogonium sticticum* attains its dominance in Banaras in December, when the amount of dissolved oxygen and $p$H are high (oxygen, 0.9 ppm ; $p$H. 9), but it reproduces only under a range of $p$H 8-8.5 and at still higher $p$H ($p$H 9) it remains purely vegetative. The reproduction of *Zygnema sphaerica* also is conditioned by $p$H, since the zygospores are formed only when the $p$H is 8 and at $p$H 8.5, the alga remains purely vegetative (Venkataraman, unpublished).

Conjugation in the Zygnemaceae is of two types—lateral and scalariform. Out of these, lateral conjugation which involves conjugation between the cells of the same filament may be regarded as more primitive compared with scalariform conjugation in which cells of different filaments are involved.

### Lateral Conjugation

*Isogamous lateral conjugation*: Lateral conjugation is of two types, isogamous and anisogamous. The most primitive type of isogamous lateral conjugation is seen in *Zygnema himalayense*, a species in which both lateral and scalariform conjugations are seen. As a result of swelling of lateral walls, the septum separating the neighbouring cells ruptures and the protoplasts and the chloroplasts move towards each other in a straight line, and fuse in the middle forming zygospore (Fig. XX.i to iv, and Fig. XIX.i). In *Zygogonium indicum*, *Zygogonium sinense*, *Zygnema terrestre*, *Zygnema czurdae*, *Mougeotia jogensis* and *Mougeotia genuflexa*, lateral conjugation is of isogamous type. In *Zygogonium indicum*, the zygospore is cut off by a wall from the mating cells. In *Zygogonium sinense*, the zygospores fill the gametangia, and marked geniculation is also seen. In *Mougeotia jogensis* the zygospores more or less completely fill the gametangia. In *Zygnema czurdae* the zygospores fill the gametangia, which show geniculation (Fig. XX.v). Iyengar has recently made observations on lateral conjugation in *Z. czurdae* which resembles that seen in *Temnogametum indicum*, excepting that no short cells are cut off. Two papillate processes grow from the gametangia, and the contents of the two gametangia fuse through the conjugation canal formed above the cross-well septum. At the same time the outer walls of the fused gametangia bulge out forming a dome-like structure. Later on the walls of the septum open out at the bottom, forming on acute angle, widening into a right angle, and subsequently into an obtuse angle. Ultimately a more or less straight line is formed, and as a result, the filament becomes geniculate. All these stages are shown in Fig. XIX A. The zygospores which are isogamously produced in *Zygogonium sinense* get cut off by a wall from the gametangia (Fig. XIX.v-vi). In *Mougeotia jogensis*, two tube-like protuberances meet, and the zygospore which is produced in the middle gets cut off by a wall from the gametangia (Fig. XIX.viii and ix). In *M. genuflexa* lateral conjugation takes place by means of two tube-like protuberances which meet in the middle producing a zygospore which gets cut off by two walls from the gametangia (Fig. XIX.xi). Isogamous lateral conjugation of a primitive type is also seen in *Mougeotia oedogonioides*. The cross wall dissolves, and a conjugation tube develops between the ends of gametangia. The union of gametes takes place in the middle and the conjugation tube enlarges. The sporangium wall changes into a thick pectic

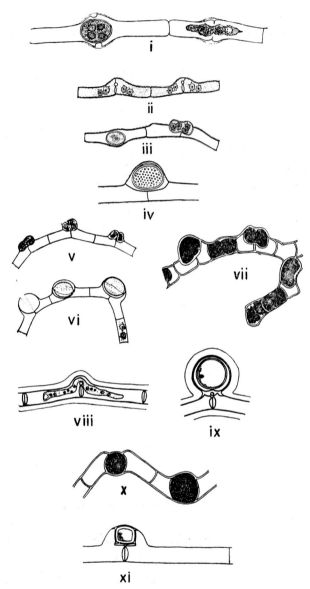

Fig. XIX. Isogamous lateral conjugation in species of *Zygnema*, *Zygogonium* and *Mougeotia*. i. *Zygnema himalayense*; ii-iv. *Zygogonium indicum*; v-vi. *Zygogonium sinense*; vii *Zygnema terrestre* viii-ix. *Mougeotia jogensis*; x *Zygnema czurdae*; xi. *Mougeotia genuflexa*; (figs. i-iv, vii, x, after Randhawa; v-vi. after Jao; viii-ix. after Iyengar; xi. after Wittrock.)

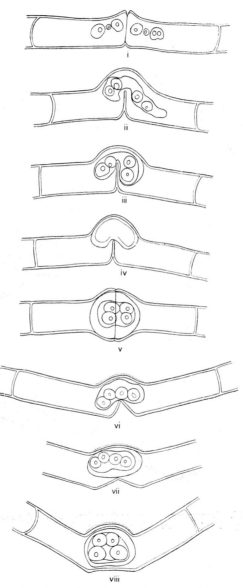

Fig. XIX A.  Stages in isogamous lateral
conjugation in *Zygnema czurdae*. (After Iyengar)

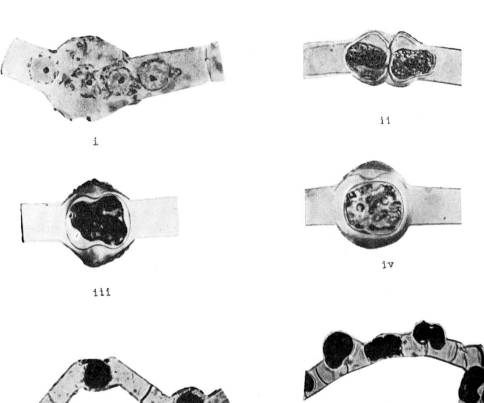

Fig. XX. Isogamous lateral conjugation. i-iv. *Zygnema himalayense*; v. *Z. czurdae*; vi. *Z. terrestre* (after Randhawa).

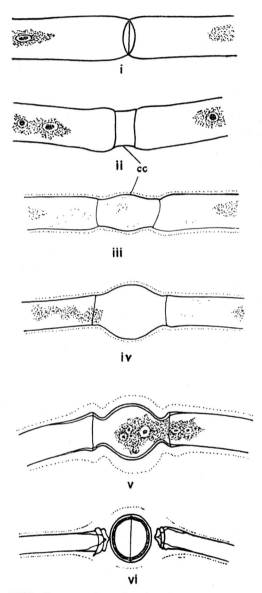

Fig. XXI. Isogamous lateral conjugation in *Mougeotia oedogonioides*. (after Czurda). cc, conjugation tube.

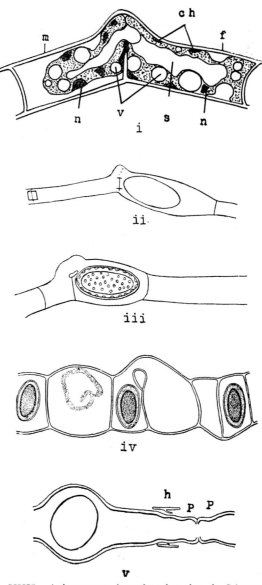

Fig. XXII. Anisogamous lateral conjugation in *Spirogyra*. i. *S. longata*; ii. *S. cylindrica*; iii. *S. ampla*; iv. *S. sahnii*; v. *S. colligata*. (i. after Lloyd; ii. after Czurda; iii. after Jao; iv. after Randhawa v. after Hodgetts). f. female; m. male; n. nucleus; ch. chloroplast; s. central vacuole; v. contractile vacuoles.

layer in which the zygospore seems to float.  The gametangial wall at the point of the union with the sporangium becomes modified, suggesting the ring scars of *Oedogonium* (Fig. XXI.i-vi).

*Anisogamous lateral conjugation*:  Anisogamous type of lateral conjugation is seen in a number of species of *Zygnema* and *Spirogyra*. In *Spirogyra spreeiana*, the male and female cells always occur in pairs, which are separated by a plane wall; after conjugation, therefore, one finds pairs of cells with zygotes separated by pairs of empty cells. Tröndle regards such pairs of male or female cells as sisters, whose sex is determined before the division to form the pair takes place.  A tent-like projection takes place in some species on one side and the male gamete passes through the protuberance either through a pore or otherwise into the female gametangium.  In *Spirogyra ampla* and *S. sahnii* (Fig. XXII iii and iv), tube-like protuberances arise which fuse  resulting in a retort-like structure.  According to Lloyd, the contraction of the gametes is due to the discharge of liquid from a number of large, nearly spherical, contractile vacuoles, which may be sufficiently numerous to produce a frothy appearance and arise sooner in the male than in the female. These vacuoles are stated to receive water, probably containing  some solutes by diffusion from the central vacuole and to discharge it into the space between the protoplast and the cell-wall.  In the male protoplast they appear at the posterior and spread to the anterior  end, while in the female the order of appearance is in the opposite direction (Fig. XXII.i).  Similar vacuoles are also operative  in bringing  about the final contraction of the zygote.

Hodgetts described in *Spirogyra colligata*, a new  and very interesting type of lateral conjugation which he called terminal conjugation.  Here the adjacent ends of the two conjugating cells on either side of the septum grow out in the form of conjugation-tubes and then the  male gamete fuses with  the female gamete by perforating the septum (Fig. XXII. v).

Iyengar (1958) has recently reported *direct* lateral conjugation of anisogamous type in *Spirogyra jogensis*.  In this alga, the filaments are attached to the rocks by the lobed lower end of the  hapteroid basal cell. Lateral conjugation takes place between the two cells situated immediately next to the basal hapteroid cell and the lower cell is always the female.  During the lateral conjugation, the contents of two adjacent cells, which are generally shorter than the vegetative cells, become richer, and then one of these two cells, the female cell, becomes swollen all round, while the other cell, the male cell remains without any change

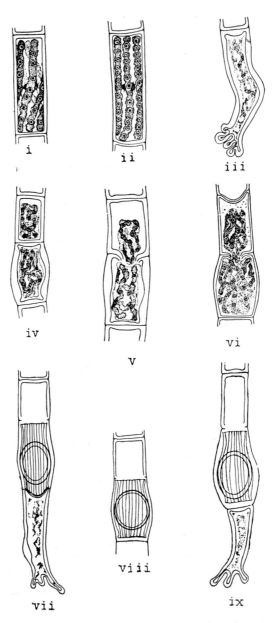

Fig. XXIII. Direct anisogamous lateral conjugation in *Spirogyra jogensis*. (After Iyengar).

(Fig. XXIII). A thick highly refractive mucilaginous layer is secreted by both the male and the female protoplast below the outer wall. This refractive mucilaginous layer is strongly ribbed longitudinally in the female cell, but not in the male cell. The two conjugating cells are generally situated next to the hapteroid basal cell, the lower cell being always the female and the upper the male, though they may also be frequently found higher up in the filament. The protoplast of the male cell becomes somewhat conical on the side next to the female cell and begins to press against the septum while, at the same time, it contracts away from the wall at the opposite end. The conical end of the male gamete then becomes elongated and somewhat rod-shaped and gradually presses more and more against the septum until it finally pierces through it right in the middle (Fig. XXIII.v, vi). The male gamete ultimately passes into the female cell and fuses with the female gamete. According to Iyengar, the perforation of the septum is very probably brought about through the secretion of an enzyme, but a certain amount of physical force also seems to be exerted by the male gamete in effecting its entry through the septum, since the edges of the ruptured transverse wall are bent inwards in the female cell.

## Scalariform Conjugation

Scalariform is the common type of conjugation in the Zygnemaceae. Out of 534 species described in Transeau's Zygnemataceae, 400 show scalariform conjugation only, while 72 show scalariform and lateral conjugation, and 22 show only lateral conjugation. Species in which only scalariform conjugation takes place are dioecious with genotypic sex determination. No doubt species with scalariform conjugation are more advanced as compared with those which show lateral conjugation. Scalariform conjugation is of two types, isogamous and anisogamous. Sometimes, however, isogamous and anisogamous conjugation may be seen in the same species, e.g. *Zygnema collinsianum* (Fig. XXIV. v). Lateral and scalariform conjugation are found in *Zygnema himalayense* and sometimes one finds a conflict between the two tendencies. In Fig. XXIV. vi, we find that though the gametes had mated isogamously in the conjugation canal, a gamete from a neighbouring cell makes an abortive attempt to conjugate laterally. In species of *Mougeotia* and *Debarya* conjugation is isogamous. While in *Debarya* the entire protoplasm is utilised in zygospore formation, remains of protoplasm are found in gametangia of *Mougeotia* (Fig. XXIV. iii). In *Zygnemopsis minuta* the cells dissociate and may conjugate in any position, and where conjugation is isogamous they appear like desmids (Fig. XXIV. ix). In *Temnogametum heterosporum*

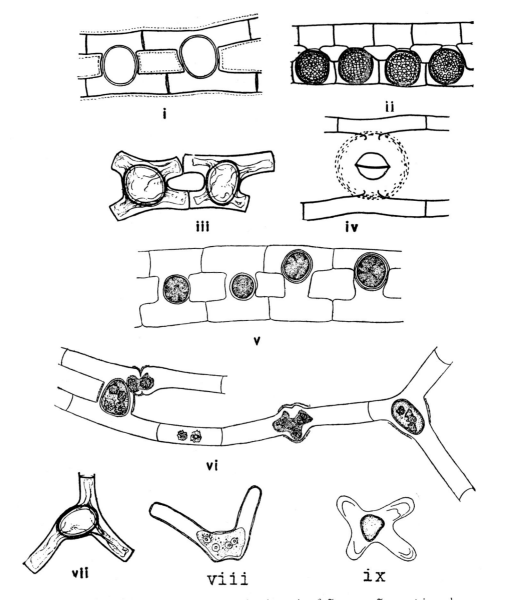

Fig. XXIV. Scalariform conjugation in species of *Zygnema*, *Zygnemopsis*, and *Mougeotia*. i. *Zygnema gangeticum*; ii. *Z. calosporum* ; iii. *Mougeotia sphaerocarpa* ; iv. *M. disjuncta* ; v. *Zygnema collinsianum* ; vi. *Z. himalayense* ; vii. *Mougeotia sphaerocarpa* ; viii-ix. *Zygnemopsis minuta* ; (fig. i, after Rao ; ii, iii & vii. after Jao ; iv. after Transeau ; v, vi, viii and ix. after Randhawa).

the gametes are differentiated from vegetative cells. In *Zygogonium* cytoplasmic residue is found in the gametangia outside the zygospore.

### Conjugation in Spirogyra

A detailed study of the conjugation has been made in the species of *Spirogyra* by a number of workers. Conjugation takes place during the night. It is a recently divided cell that conjugates, such a cell being commonly shorter than a normal vegetative cell. At the commencement of conjugation the filaments become intimately glued to each other by mucilage (Fig. XXV.1). Then papillae arise from one of each pair of opposite cells. According to Saunders (1931) those first formed papillae usually arise on one filament of a pair, but this may be either the male or the female filament ; in few cases the first papillae appear indifferently on the cells of either thread. Subsequently, papillae usually arise from opposite and corresponding points on the other filament, so that the two papillae are in contact from the first moment of their formation and, as they elongate to form the conjugation processes the two threads are gradually pushed apart (Fig. XXV.3). The double wall formed between the conjugation processes is dissolved locally by enzyme action. The two gametes are then in direct contact and the conjugating apparatus is established. Conjugation tubes are usually formed by both the gametangia in 228 species of *Spirogyra* but in 31 species they are outgrowths of male gametangia. The female gametangia usually remain cylindrical or become slightly enlarged, or inflated on one or both sides. The conjugation process produced by the female cell is usually thicker and shorter than that formed by the male. The conjugation processes have been compared to the rhizoids as both probably result from a contact stimulus. Kniep (1928), however, believes that the conjugation process is essentially due to a chemical stimulus.

As soon as conjugation sets in, the cells of the two threads accumulate abundant starch although this subsequently disappears again from those not involved in conjugation ; according to Lloyd (1926 b) mucilage globules also appear. During the early stages of conjugation the osmotic pressure of the sap sinks considerably, more in the male than in the female cells, which is presumably due to a decrease in osmotically active substances, due to the conversion of sugars into starch. The permeability is lowered and, there is an increase in the viscosity of the protoplast, although this is not uniform, but is greatest at the posterior end of the male and least in the region of fusion. At the same time nucleus and nucleolus decrease in size. When the processes have

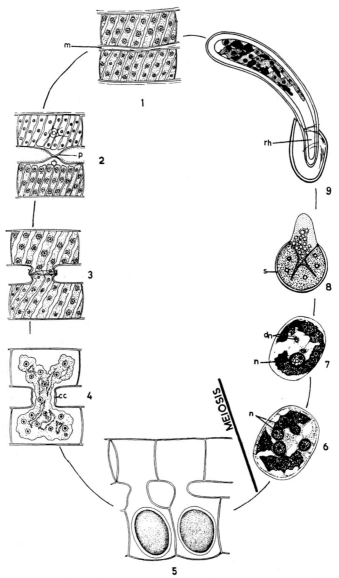

Fig. XXV.  Life-cycle of *Spirogyra*.  1-5.  stages in conjugation ;
6, mature zygospore with four nuclei (n) ; 7, zygospore with three
degenerating nuclei (dn) ; 8-9, stages in the germination of the
zygospore. (figs. 1-4. after Czurda ;  5. after Randhawa ;  6-9.
after Tröndle ). m, mucilage ;  p, papilla; cc, conjugating canal ; n,
nucleus ;  dn, degenerating nuclei ; s, spore wall ; rh, rhizoid.

reached their full length, their end walls are dissolved, so that an open, usually relatively narrow conjugation tube is formed. The prolongations of the two protoplasts that have extended into the processes are thus brought in direct touch.

When the open canal is established the male protoplast without losing contact with the female, contracts away from its wall and the process of fusion commences, surface tension probably gradually pressing the male through the conjugation tube into the female protoplast. It is not until the male has passed entirely over into the female that the latter in its turn contracts away from its membrane. After the amalgamation of the gametes, fusion of nuclei takes place. The fusion nucleus may divide soon after or during the ripening of the zygospore. The zygospore represents the diploid phase while the vegetative plant, the haploid phase in the alternation of the generations in the Zygnemaceae. After the union of the nuclei reduction division occurs and four nuclei result. One of the nuclei enlarges, while the remaining three abort (Fig. XXV.7). The zygospores remain dormant during the unfavourable dry period, and on the onset of rains they germinate. As a preliminary to germination, the fat is converted to starch while the chloroplasts become more distinct. The outer thick layers of the zygospore wall burst at one end (Fig. XXV.8). It may be noted that the chloroplast contributed by the male gamete disintegrates at an early stage. The contents of the zygospore which are surrounded by the inner-most layer grow as a long tube which soon undergoes division into two cells. The lower cell which may be designated the rhizoidal cell is more or less hyaline, contains very little chlorophyll and remains in the zygospore membrane for some time (Fig. XXV.9). The upper cell now proceeds to divide and forms the filament.

### Conjugation in Zygnema

The conjugation in *Zygnema* follows more or less the pattern in *Spirogyra*. Conjugation usually occurs between two or more filaments which lie side by side, and abundant mucilage is secreted. Small dome-shaped protuberances arise from the cells which are lying opposite each other (Fig. XXVI.2). The protuberance from the male cells is longer as compared with the protuberance from the female cell. These outgrowths ultimately come in contact and the wall of each at the point of contact is dissolved and an open conjugation tube is established. The male gamete moves into the female gametangium, and fuses with the female gamete (Fig. XXVI.4). This happens in the case of anisoga-

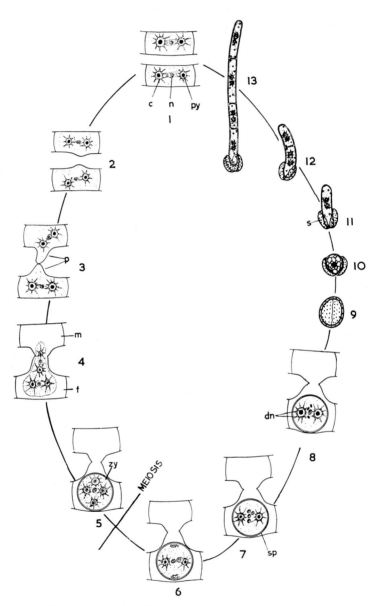

Fig. XXVI. Life cycle of *Zygnema*. 1-5. stages in conjugation;
6-8, nuclear division in the zygospore; 9, mature zygospore;
10-13. germination of the zygospore. (figs. 1-8. after Smith; 9. after
Krieger; 10-13. after Kolkwitz & Krieger.) p, papilla; f, female;
zy, zygospore; sp, spore wall; dn, degenerating nuclei; c, chloroplast; n, nucleus, py, pyrenoid; m, male.

mous species of *Zygnema*. In the case of isogamous species the union of gametes takes place in the conjugation canal. The union of the nuclei may take place immediately in the zygospore, or may be delayed for some time. The zygospore represents the diploid phase. The four chloroplasts which are contributed by the gametes persist for some time, but eventually the chloroplasts contributed by the male gamete degenerate (Fig. XXVI.6). Now the zygospore develops a thick spore wall consisting of an inner thin layer of cellulose, a thick median layer of cellulose which is chitinised and sculptured, and a thin outer layer of cellulose or pectose. The zygospores are eventually liberated by the decay of the gametangial walls. Prior to germination, the reduction division of the nucleus takes place followed by an ordinary division. Four nuclei ultimately result, out of which three degenerate, and only one remains (Fig. XXVI.8). When water is available after the rains the zygospore germinates, the outermost wall ruptures while the protoplast remains surrounded by the innermost walls (Fig. XXVI.10). The contents grow out into a long tube which undergoes division into two cells. Unlike *Spirogyra* there is no distinction into base and apex in *Zygnema* (Fig. XXVI.12). By further cell-division a regular filament is formed to which the outer spore-wall may continue to adhere for some time (Fig. XXVI.13). In *Zygnema terrestre* the normal mode of conjugation is isogamous scalariform type. Usually scalariform conjugation takes place between two separate filaments. K. P. Singh (1958) has reported conjugation between the cells of the same filament, involving the formation of loops as in *Temnogametum tirupatiense*. As the creeping filaments of this terrestrial alga form loops, the opposite cells which are in contact give out conjugation canals which meet, mating of gametes takes place, and the zygospores are formed in the middle (Fig. XXVII.i). A complicated type of looping and conjugation is seen in Fig. XXVII.ii.

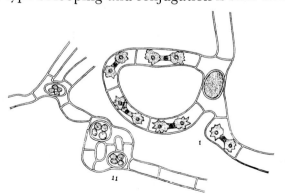

Fig. XXVII. Abnormal conjugation in *Zygnema terrestre*: i. Scalariform conjugation by looping between cells of the same filament; ii. Conjugation by double looping (after K.P. Singh).

Morphological anisogamy has also been recorded in *Zygnema stellinum* and *Spirogyra parvula*. In *Z. stellinum*, according to Steinach, the female cells are longer, broader and have larger chloroplasts and pyrenoids than the male. In *S. parvula* both lateral and scalariform conjugation take place. In laterally conjugating specimens of this species, the female cell becomes very much swollen, granular and vacuolated. In some cases the female cells are swollen on both sides and are flask-shaped in appearance.

### Reproduction in Hallasia

In *Hallasia reticulata* aplanospores are formed. On germination of an aplanospore three sporelings may emerge, each of which may develop into a new filament.

### Conjugation in Zygogonium

In *Zygogonium ericetorum* the gametes are produced only from a part of the cytoplasm of the gametangia. Conjugating papillae are produced by both the gametangia, and they meet in the middle. Before the conjugation canal is fully established, the papillae are still separated by their walls, and the greater part of protoplasts from each of the gametangia passes into the process, and is cut off by a curved wall (Fig. XXVIII. i-ii). A pore is formed between the conjugating processes and it gradually enlarges, and the gametes fuse. The protoplast secretes an independent membrane that gradually enlarges, and forms the outermost layer of the zygote wall. Thus we find that conjugation in *Z. ericetorum* has distinct features, e.g. ,formation of gametes from only a part of the proto-

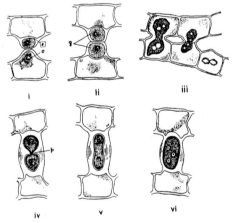

Fig. XXVIII. Conjugation in *Zygogonium ericetorum*. i-iv. successive stages in conjugation; vi, mature zygospore; iii, conjugation without the formation of secondary gametangia. c, chloroplast; g, gametes; p, progametes; s, septum cutting off the gametangium. (figs. i-ii, iv-vi, after Hodgetts; iii, after Transeau).

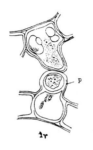

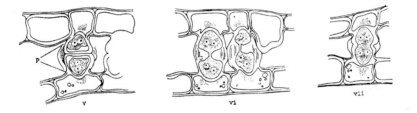

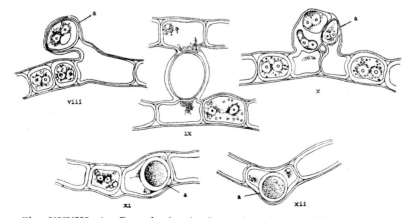

Fig. XXVIII A. Reproduction in *Zygogonium ericetorum*. i-ii. akinetes (note the akinetes with single chloroplasts in fig. ii) i iii-vii, ix. stages in conjugation; viii, x, azygospores (a); xi-xii. aplanospores (a). p. progametangia. (after Randhawa).

plasts, remains of protoplasm in the gametangia, formation of walls which cut off the gametes from the gametangia, and the peculiar method of fusion of the ends of papillae. In his observations on conjugation in *Z. ericetorum*, Transeau has reported instances where conjugation takes place without formation of secondary gametangia. (Fig. XXVIII iii). In samples of *Zygogonium ericetorum* collected from Makoot in Coorg, secondary gametangia are formed and akinetes are also seen (Fig. XXVIIIA.)

### Conjugation in Mougeotia

Out of 103 recorded species of *Mougeotia*, 86 have scalariform conjugation and in only two it is regularly lateral. Almost all the species are isogamous with the exception of three which are anisogamous. Two papillae rise from opposite cells as in *Zygnema*, until they meet and the walls at their contact are dissolved. According to Transeau hormones lead to the movement of the protoplasts of the gametangia into the conjugating tube which enlarges. The union of gametes follows and a series of layers are laid which form the spore wall. The zygospores of *Mougeotia* have only two walls—an outer chitinous wall which is coloured and ornamented, and an inner transparent wall. Cytoplasmic residue is left in the gametangia after the union of gametes in all the species. Some of the published figures of the species of the *Mougeotia* do not show cytoplasmic residue though they are present in all species.

### Reproduction in Temnogametum

*Temnogametum* has long cells, each with a single axile plate-like chloroplast bearing numerous scattered pyrenoids. The gametangia are short specialised cells which are cut off as sections of the vegetative cells. They are gorged with starch and other food material. Conjugation takes place both in scalariform and lateral manner. In scalariform conjugation the gametangia are brought into contact by geniculation, and fusion takes place through a hole which develops within the ring of contact. The zygote fills the whole of the two cells. Thus the walls of the gametangia become the outer walls of the quadrangular sporangium (Fig. XXIX). The protoplasts independently secrete a thin membrane. Thus we find that distinct conjugating tubes are not formed in *Temnogametum*. In lateral conjugation in *T. heterosporum* according to G.S. West (1916), two adjoining gametangia of the same filament enlarge, the intervening septum is dissolved, and the gametes unite. The resultant zygospore is obliquely spindle-shaped (Fig. XXIX. vi).

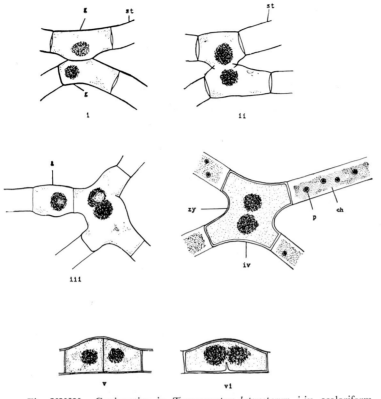

Fig. XXIX. Conjugation in *Temnogametum heterosporum.* i-iv. scalariform
conjugation ; v-vi. lateral conjugation. (after West).

According to Iyengar (1958a) lateral conjugation and zygospore formation in *Temnogametum indicum* takes place a little differently. The
contents of two neighbouring cells move slowly towards each other and become gradually massed against the septum separating the two cells
(Fig. XXX.ii). A short cell is then cut off on either side of the septum so
that each of the two vegetative cells is divided unequally into a short cell
with rich contents, which serves as the gametangium and the long cell with
comparatively poor contents, is the sterile cell (Fig. XXX.iii). The two
new walls which cut off the gametangial cells grow centripetally inwards
and when nearly complete cut through the massed protoplast so that the
major portion of the protoplast goes into the shorter gametangial cell
and the remaining small portion remains in the sterile cell. The adjacent
ends of the two adjoining gametangia then become gradually beaked on
one side into two papillate processes in close contact with each other
(Fig. XXX.v). The two papillae fuse and an open communication
is established between the two gametangia at this region. The septum
between the gametangial cells remains intact. The contents of the two
gametangia then fuse through the conjugation canal formed above the

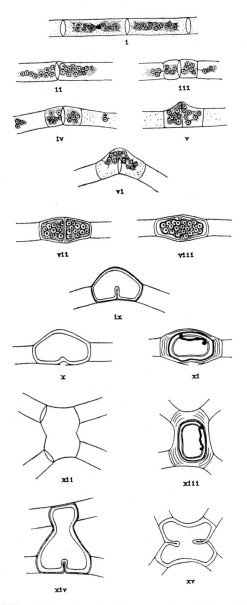

Fig. XXX. Conjugation in *Temnogametum indicum*. i. vegetative cells ; ii.-vi. stages in lateral conjugation ; vii. view of laterally conjugating cells from below ; viii. the same from above ; ix.-xi. zygospores produced by lateral conjugation ; xii. scalariform conjugation ; xiii. zygospore produced by scalariform conjugation ; xiv. zygospore formed by conjugation between 3 gametes ; xv. zygospore produced by conjugation between 4 gametes (after Iyengar).

cross wall septum (Fig. XXX.vi). At the same time the outer walls of the fused gametangia bulge out, and as a result the filament becomes geniculate. The fused protoplast occupies the entire place inside the two cells which now become zygosporangium, but the old cross wall between the cells is not dissolved but persists in the lower part of the zygosporangial cavity. Fig. XXX.viii which is a view of the zygosporangium from the top gives the false impression that the cross wall is dissolved and that the two gametes fuse right through its middle. The view from below (Fig. XXX.vii) indicates that the cross wall between them is quite intact.

After the fusion of the two gametes, protoplast of the zygosporangium secretes a thick refractive mucilaginous layer round itself immediately below the zygosporangial wall. This mucilaginous layer goes even round the old persisting cross-wall which is still projecting inside the zygosporangium. As more and more layers of this refractive mucilaginous material is secreted, it forms a thick lamellate inner layer immediately below the zygosporangial wall. It is broadly rounded on the outer bulged-out side, and on the lower side, where it goes over the persisting old cross-wall, it appears deeply folded inwards (Fig. XXX. ix). About this time the protoplast of the zygosporangium grows somewhat in quantity with the result that the wall of the zygosporangium gradually stretches out. Owing to this pressure from the inside, the infolding of the refractive layer becomes gradually more and more open and finally more or less straight (Fig. XXX.x). As the infolded portion of the refractive layer becomes gradually straightened, the old crosswall projecting inside, owing to the fact that its two sides are closely adhering to this refractive layer, gets gradually separated into its two component layers. These two layers are so closely adhering to the two flanks of the infolding of the refractive layer that it becomes very difficult to distinguish them from the refractive layer. At the same time the old lateral wall of the zygosporangium becomes ruptured at the base of the infolding, and its ruptured end can be seen sticking to the straightened refractive layer on either side of the now open old infolded portion (Fig. XXX.xi).

The protoplast of the zygosporangium then secretes the thick golden brown wall of the zygospore below the refractive mucilaginous layer. The wall of the ripe zygospore consists of a thin hyaline exospore, a thick layered mesospore and a thin hyaline endospore. The outer layer of the mesospore is firm and golden brown in colour and smooth. A peculiar irregularly S-shaped (sigmoid) "riss-linie"(?) is seen on the ripe zygospore wall. This "riss-linie" appears to be imbedded in the thick inner layer of the mesospore. During scalariform conjugation some of the vegetative cells divide unequally to form a large sterile cell and a small fertile one. The fertile cells are brought into contact by geniculation, their separating walls are absorbed and their contents fuse without the formation of a tube (Fig. XXX.xii). The protoplast of the zygote fills the whole of the two cells. As during lateral conjugation, the zygote protoplast secretes gradually a thick, refractive, lamellate, mucilaginous layer round itself and finally the thick golden brown wall of the zygospore below the refractive mucilaginous layer (Fig. XXX.xiii). This wall has the same structure as that of the zygospore formed during lateral conjugation. The sigmoid "riss-linie" is found here also. The ripe zygospore is irregularly quadrangular. Abnormalities in conjugation also take place in this species. Occasionally conjugation takes place between three gametes. The contents of two adjacent gametangia of one filament, after fusing laterally with each other, fuse with the contents of a gametangium of another filament in a scalariform manner (Fig. XXX.xiv). The zygote in this case will be a triploid. Conjugation between four gametes also takes place. The fused contents of two adjacent gametangia of one filament fuse with the fused contents of two adjacent gametangia of another filament (Fig. XXX.xv). The zygote in this case will be a tetraploid. Azygospores which result as a failure of conjugation are also met with.

In *Temnogametum cylindrosporum* reproduction takes place by means of aplanospores which develop in the short cells which serve as gametangia. A single aplanospore is formed in the gametangium. The protoplast of the young gametangium first of all secretes a thick refractive mucilaginous layer round itself immediately below the wall of the gametangium. The gametangial protoplast then secretes the wall of the aplanospore immediately below the refractive mucilaginous layer. The wall of ripe aplanospore is thick and smooth and consists of three layers, a thin hyaline exospore, a thick mesospore and a thin hyaline endospore. The mesospore is smooth and is made up of two layers, a thick greyish lamellated inner layer and a thinner but firm golden brown outer layer. The characteristic S-shaped (sigmoid) "riss-linie" is seen on the mesospore.

In *T. tirupatiense* conjugation takes place between gametangia formed on the same filament, the alga being monoecious. During conjugation the two gametangia are brought into contact with each other by a coiling of the portion of the filament between them (Fig. XXXI.ii). The intermediate coiling portion may consist of only one sterile cell or may consist of one sterile cell and one or more vegetative cells. The coiling may often be very intricate and involve the conjugation of two or more pairs of gametangia (Fig. XXXI.iii).

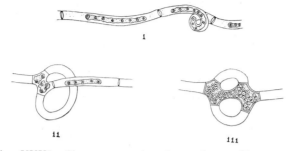

Fig. XXXI. *Temnogametum tirupatiense.* i. a filament showing chloroplasts ; ii. conjugation between cells of the same filament by looping ; iii. conjugation between 2 pairs of gametangia. (after Iyengar)

### Conjugation in Sirogonium

The vegetative cells of *Sirogonium* have plane end-walls, and 2 to 10 chloroplasts which are more or less straight. The external layer of pectin is missing from the cell wall, and as a result the filaments are covered with dust particles and epiphytes.

In the species of *Spirogyra* and *Zygnema* there is only physiological anisogamy, the gametes being more or less similar in appearance though one is more active than the other. In *Sirogonium*, however, we find further advance, and morphological anisogamy is found. The conjugating filaments are coiled together like twisted threads. The male cell arises by the division of an ordinary cell from which two sterile cells are cut off, a small sterile cell and a large sterile cell. From the female cell a small sterile cell is cut off at one end. Thus the female cell is much larger in size as compared with the male cell. The progametangium becomes loaded with starch and other food material. A small protuberance arises from the female cell which comes in contact with the male cell. At the point of contact a pectic ring develops. Thus we see that no conjugation canals are formed in *Sirogonium* (Fig. XXXII.i). The description about the development of the gametangia given above does not hold good in some species of *Sirogonium*, the development of gametangia being highly variable. In some, the progametangia may conjugate without division, and any of the short cells may function as male gametangia. In some cases a terminal short-cell may function as a male cell (Fig. XXXII.ii). The zygospores develop in the female gametangia (Fig. XXXII.v). Cross conjugation has been seen in *Sirogonium sticticum.* The short-cell cut off from the progametangia

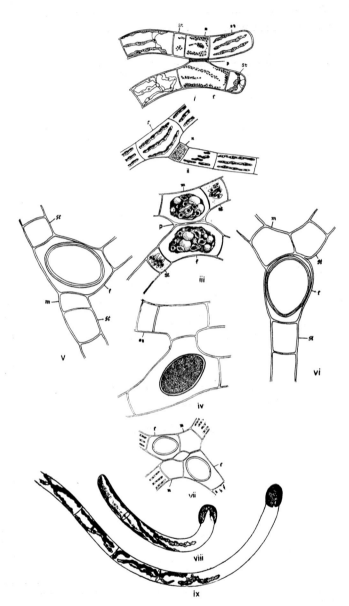

Fig. XXXII. Conjugation in *Sirogonium*. i, *S. sticticum* ; ii, *S. phacosporum*, terminal cell fusion, iii. *S. sticticum*, early stage in conjugation ; iv, *S. melanosporum* ; v, vi, *S. reticulatum*, terminal cell fusion ; vii, *S. sticticum*, cross-conjugation ; viii-ix, *S. sticticum*, germination of the zygospores. f, female cell ; m, male cell ; st, sterile cell ; p, mucilaginous pad. (fig. i, viii-ix, after De Bary ; ii, after Taft ; iii, after Jao ; iv-vii, after Randhawa ).

in each filament behaves as male cell and conjugates with the female cell opposite (XXXII.vii). The zygospores are ellipsoid or ovoid, and are yellow, black, or brown in colour.

### Reproduction in Sirocladium

Conjugation in two species of *Sirocladium*, viz., *S. kumaoense* and *S. maharashtrense* follows the pattern described in *Sirogonium*. During the process of conjugation, the filaments get coiled and this provides points of contact between the cells. Usually only a single sterile cell is cut off from the female cell, while two sterile cells are cut off from the cell which functions as the male. Mucilaginous pads are seen at the point of contact between the mating cells. Conjugation is of a typical geniculate type. The female gametangium is inflated and is loaded with starch and other food materials (Fig. XXXIII).

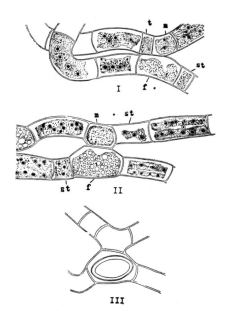

Fig. XXXIII. Conjugation in *Sirocladium kumaoense*. I-II early stage in conjugation; III. mature zygospore. f. female, m. male, st, sterile cell. (after Randhawa)

Monoecism is seen in *S. maharashtrense* and conjugation takes place by coiling of the filaments, the male cell being thus brought in contact with the female cell in the same filament. K.P. Singh (1958) has also reported conjugation between female and male cells in the same filament by the process of coiling in *S. kumaoense* which he collected from Bhowali and Nainital (Fig. XXXIV).

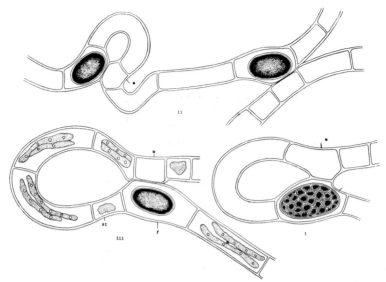

Fig. XXXIV. Conjugation in *Sirocladium* between the cells of the same filament by looping.  i.  *S. maharashtrense*;  ii.-iii.  *S. kumaoense*. m. male cell,  f. female cell, st. sterile cell (i. after Randhawa ; ii-iii, after K.P. Singh).

The zygospores are ellipsoid, yellowish brown in colour. In *S. maharashtrense* they are surrounded by a brownish yellow pectic gel that fills the space between the walls of the female gametangium and the zygospore.

Azygospores have been reported in *S. kumaoense* and *S. vandalurense*.

### Hybridisation

Filaments of diverse species of the Zygnemaceae, particularly *Zygnema*, *Spirogyra*, and *Mougeotia* often occur intermingled with one another. Conjugation between filaments belonging to different species of the above genera occurs, and hybrids result. According to Transeau the filaments that develop from hybrid zygospores are haploid, meiotic, or gametic segregates. In the few instances in which such progeny have been studied, individual filaments inherit the factor for cell diameter, forms of receptive gametangia, zygospore, size, form, and wall marking, independently. They are expressed through cytoplasm of the female gametes. So long as these segregates reproduce by cell division, by akinetes, by aplanospores, and by conjugation between cells of the same haploid filament, the gene complex of the progeny is identical, and the filaments are uniform.

According to Transeau (1951) new species in the Zygnemaceae may also appear by polyploidy and by mutation. However experimental investigation in support of this surmise is lacking at present.

CHAPTER 6

# THE ZYGNEMACEAE

## Characters Used in Identification of Species

The length and breadth of the vegetative cells, the number of chloroplasts and their spirals in the species of *Spirogyra*, the character of the septa, the character of conjugation canals in the species of *Spirogyra*, the shape of fruiting cells, the shape of zygospores, their pigmentation and sculpturing, as well as their dimensions are the characters which are used in identification of the species.

(i) *Vegetative cells*: Although the breadth of the vegetative cells remains the same throughout in most of the filaments, the length varies considerably. The diameter and the length of the vegetative cells are helpful for the identification of the species. The breadth should be taken at the septa.

(ii) *Chloroplasts*: The number of chloroplasts and their spirals are an important feature in the determination of the species of *Spirogyra*. In some species of *Spirogyra* the number of chloroplasts is uniform, and in some it may be slightly variable. In counting the number of chloroplasts in *Spirogyra* counts should be made only in filaments attached to the gametangium. The number of spirals is determined by focussing just below an upper-half turn of the spiral, counting this turn as one, and adding it to the number of optical intersections made by the spirals on the opposite side of the cell. In species with large cells in which the chloroplasts are tightly coiled, the numbers are determined by counting the ends of the spirals near the septa.

(iii) *Septa*: The nature of the septa is an important character in the identification of the species. The septa may be plane, replicate, semireplicate, colligate or unduliseptate (Fig. II).

(iv) *Conjugation canals*: The conjugation canals whether formed by the male cell alone or by both the gametangia is also a systematic character, particularly in species of *Zygnema* and *Spirogyra*.

(v) *The shape of the fruiting cells*: The fruiting cells may be cylindrical, or inflated on one or both sides. These characters are of

93

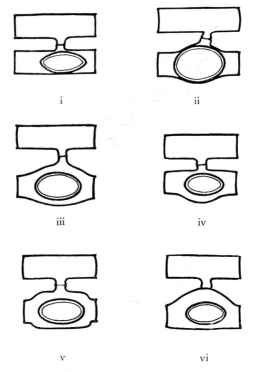

Fig. XXXV. The shape of the fruiting cells.  i. cylindrical ;
ii. enlarged ; iii. inflated on both sides ; iv. inflated on outer side ;
v. cylindrically inflated : ;  vi. inflated on  conjugating  side.
(after Jao)

taxonomic importance. The different shapes of fruiting cells are described below :

(a) *Cylindrical type*: The female gametangium is cylindrical in shape and the zygospore almost touches its sides without compressing (Fig. XXXV.i).

(b) *Inflated type*: The walls of the female gametangium bulge out. This may be divided into two types, viz., compressed-inflated and loose-inflated. In compressed-inflated type the zygospore completely fills the conjugation canal, and presses against the wall causing it to bulge out. In the loose-inflated type the zygospore is smaller and lies loose. The loose inflated type may have further variations, viz., inflated on both sides, the inner wall inflated and the outer wall straight, the outer wall inflated and the inner straight, and cylindrically inflated (Fig. XXXV.ii to vi).

(vi) *The spores, their shape and ornamentation*: The form, size, shape and the ornamentation of the spore wall and their pigmentation

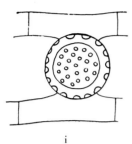
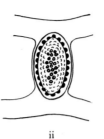
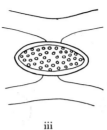

i ii iii iv

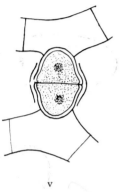
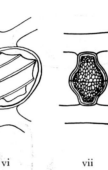
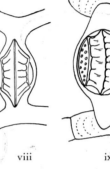
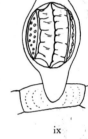

v vi vii viii ix

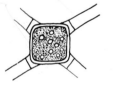
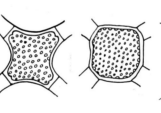

x xi xii xiii xiv

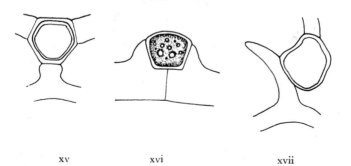

xv xvi xvii

Fig. XXXVI. Shape of Zygospores. i. *Mougeotia pseudocalospora* ; ii. *M. verrucosa* ; iii. *M. depressa* ; iv. *Zygnema carinatum* ; v. *Zygnema mirabilis* ; vi. *Debarya glyptosperma* ; vii. *Mougeotia areolata* ; viii. *Debarya costata* ; ix. *D. smithi* ; x. *Mougeotia elegantula* ; xi. *M. viridis* ; xii. *M. quadrangulata* ; xiii. *M. opelousensis* ; xiv. *M. oblongata* ; xv. *M. poinciana* ; xvi. *M. genuflexa* ; xvii. *M. tubifera.* (fig. i and v. after West ; ii. after Wolle ; iii. after Kütz ; iv. after Taft ; vi-ix, xi-xii, xiv-xv & xvii. after Transeau ; x. after Wittrock ; xiii. after Taft ; xvi. after Krieger.)

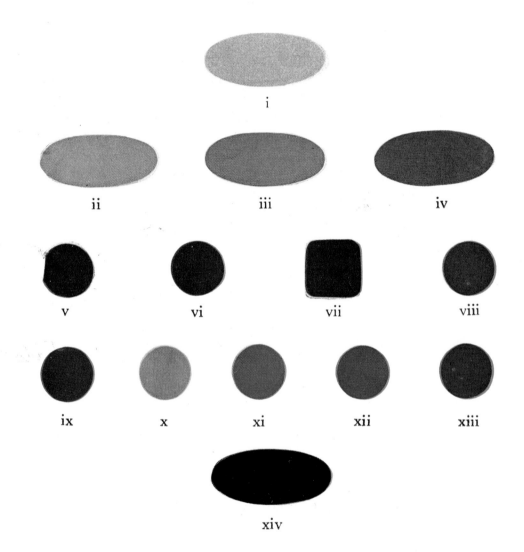

Fig. XXXVII. Colour of the zygospores. i. Pale yellow ; ii. yellow ;
iii. yellowish brown, (golden brown ; brownish yellow); iv. orange; v. reddish
brown ; vi. chocolate brown ; vii. brown ; viii. olive green ; ix. violet ;
x. slate blue ; xi. blue ; xii. dark blue ; xiii. blue black ; xiv. black.

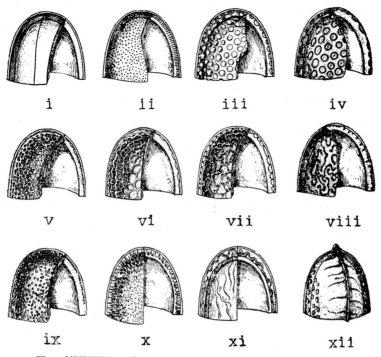

Fig. XXXVIII. Sculpturing of the spore wall. i. Smooth;
ii. Punctate; iii. Scrobiculate; iv. Pitted; v. Reticulate; vi. Foveolate;
vii. Denticulately reticulate; viii. Grooved; ix. Granulate; x. Denticulate;
xi. Outer wrinkled and the inner smooth; xii Ridged. (after Jao).
(Left half showing the surface view and the right half the section of the
zygospore.)

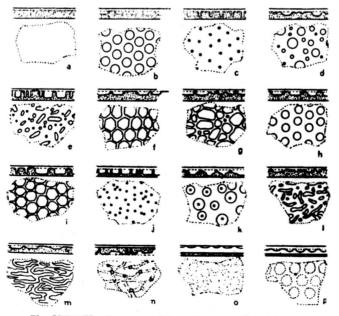

Fig. XXXIX. Structure of the zygospore wall. (after Czurda.)

are all very important characters for the identification of the species and the modern system of classification is based on the characters of the spores.

(a) *Shape of the Spore*: In almost all species with few exceptions the spores are constant in form and shape. They are of essentially three types of shapes with a number of variations.

1. *The globose type*: It is quite common in species of *Mougeotia* and *Zygnema*.

2. *The ellipsoid type*: It is met with in the species of *Spirogyra*.

3. *The quadrangulate type*: It is seen in some species of *Mougeotia*. This type shows a number of variations according to the angle of the corners and the convexity and concavity of the sides.

In *Debarya* the spores are quadrangular, ovoid, compressed-spheroid, or distinctly tricarinate with an equatorial and two lateral keels. The median walls may be further ornamented with pits, ridges and undulations (Fig. XXXVI. vi-viii and ix). Quadrate spores are seen in some species of *Mougeotia* (Fig. XXXVI. x to xvii).

(b) *Ornamentation and Colour of Spore-wall*: For the purpose of identification, ornamentation of the spore-wall of the zygospores or aplanospores and their colour are the main characters. The ornamentation of the spore-wall can be determined only under a high power oil immersion lens. The descriptions which were given by some of the old authors are inaccurate as lenses of the 19th century microscopes did not have the same resolving power as the microscopic lenses of today. It is Transeau and his co-workers and Jao, who have greatly added to our knowledge of the species of the Zygnemaceae by careful examination of the spore-wall of many species. Contraction ridges and irregular folds on the walls should not be mistaken for ornamentation. By applying a dilute solution of potassium hydroxide the contraction ridges disappear, and the real structure of the zygospore wall is made distinct. In studying a dried specimen firstly add a drop of water on the slide, followed by a drop of lactic acid. Heat gently until the acid begins to boil. This treatment removes calcium carbonate and clarifies the wall structure. Even by crushing the zygospores, the sculpturing of the spore-wall as distinct from cell-contents becomes clear.

The principal colours of the zygospores of the species of various genera of the Zygnemaceae are various shades of yellow, brown and blue. In the species of the genera *Mougeotiopsis*, *Debarya*, *Hallasia*, *Temnogametum*, *Spirogyra*, *Sirogonium* and *Sirocladium*, the zygospores are usually light yellow, golden yellow or brownish-yellow. In *Spirogyra*, zygospores of the various shades of brown, such as, yellow-brown, reddish-brown, and chestnut-brown are also seen. In *Sirogonium*, though the majority of the species have yellow or yellow-brown zygospores, some have brown and one species has black zygospores. Zygospores with various shades of blue are found in the species of the genera *Mougeotiopsis*, *Zygogonium*, *Zygnema* and *Zygnemopsis*. In the species of *Zygogonium*, the colours of the zygospores are slate blue, dark blue, greenish blue, brown, yellow and yellow-brown. In the species of *Zygnema*, the colours of the zygospores are blue, light blue, blue-black, dark blue, dark blue-green, yellow, yellow-brown, olive brown and chestnut-brown. In the species of *Zygnemopsis*, the colours of the two species are yellow, yellow-brown, chocolate-brown, chestnut-brown and blue (Fig. XXXVII).

The yellow or chestnut-brown colour of spore-walls represent the chitinous deposits on the cellulose of the median spore-wall, which alone is sculptured and ornamented. In drawing the spore-wall the contents of the zygospores should be omitted, as they are of no taxonomic value. The principal types of ornamentation are *wrinkled*, *granulate*, *verrucose*, *reticulate*, *foveolate*, *denticulate*, *denticulately-reticulate*, *punctate*, *pitted*, *scrobiculate*, *grooved* and *ridged*.

1. *Smooth* : This is a common type in many Indian species of *Spirogyra*, especially the bigger ones.

2. *Punctate* : In this type small dots are seen on the spore-wall.

3. *Scrobiculate* : The spore-wall has small circular pits.

4. *Pitted* : This differs from the scrobiculate type in shallow and more well-defined pits.

5. *Reticulate* : The spore-wall has net-like reticulations.

6. *Foveolate* : This differs from the reticulate type in two features. Firstly the meshes of the network are wider and secondly the islands in the network represent raised parts and not depressed parts.

7. *Granulate* : In this case the spore wall has granular projections on it.

8. *Denticulate* : The spore wall is raised into a number of sharp spines.

In some species, the mesospore possesses a suture which may be straight or wavy.

In most of the species the zygospores are smooth, reticulate, punctate or pitted. The other types which are mentioned are rather uncommon. The various types of sculpturing in zygospores are shown in Figs. XXXVIII and XXXIX.

# REFERENCES

Blackman, F.F. & Tansley, A.G. (1902): A revision of the classification of the green algae. New Phytol, **1.**

Biswas, K. (1949) "Common Fresh and Brackish Water Algal Flora of India and Burma" Rec. Bot. Survey India **15.**

Czurda, V. (1928): Morphologie und Physiologie des Algenstärkekornes. Beih. Bot. Centralbl. **45,** Abt. I.

—(1932): '*Zygnemataceae*' in W. Bosehard, Botanische Ergebnisse der deutschem zentralasion Expedition 1927-28. Fedde, Rep. Spec. nov. **31.**

—(1932b): '*Zygnemales*' in Pascher's Süsswasserflora von Mitteleuropas. **9.**

—(1933): Experimentelle Analyse der Kopulation sauslosenden Bedingungen bei Mikroorganismen. I Untersuchungen an Algen. Beih. Bot. Centralbl. **51,** Abt. A.

—(1937): *Conjugatne*: In K. Liasbauer, Handbuch der Pflanzenanatomie Abt. II, Bd. 6(2): Algen B: Berlin.

De Bary, A. (1858): Untersuchungen über die Familie der Conjugaten. Leipzig.

Doraiswami, S. (1946): Nuclear division in *Spirogyra*. J. Indian Bot. Soc. **25,** (1).

Fleming, W. (1882): Zellsubstanz, Kern und Zellteilung. Leipzig.

Fritsch, F.E. (1935): The structure and reproduction of the Algae. **1.** Camb. Univ. Press.

Geitler, L. (1930): Über die Kernteilung von *Spirogyra*. Arch. f. Protistenk. **71.**

—(1935): Neue Untersuchungen über die Mitose von *Spirogyra*. *Ibid.* **85.**

Hassall, A.H. (1844) "History of the British Fresh-water Algae". London

Hodgetts, W.J. (1918): The Conjugation of *Zygogonium ericetorum* Kütz. New Phytol. **17.**

Iyengar, M.O.P. (1923): Note on some attached forms of *Zygnemaceae*. J. Indian Bot. Soc. **3.**

—(1958a): Three new species of *Temnogametum* from South India. J. Indian Bot. Soc. **37**(2).

—(1958b): A new type of lateral conjugation in *Spirogyra*. J. Indian Bot. Soc. **37**(3).

—(1957): "Algology" Proc. Nat. Inst. Sci. Part **4.**

Jao. C.C. (1936): New *Zygnemataceae* collected in China. Amer. J. Bot. **23.**

Kolkwitz, R. and Krieger, H. (1944): *Zygnemales* in Rabenhorst's Kryptogamenflora, **13,** Abt. **2.**

Klebs, G. (1896): Die Bedingungen der Fortpflanzung bei einigen Algen und Pilzen. Jena.

Kniep. H. (1928): Die Sexualtät der niederen Pflanzen. Jena.

Lanjouw. J. (1952): International code of Botanical Nomenclature. Utrecht-Netherlands.

Lloyd, F.E. (1926a): Studies in *Spirogyra* I. Maturation and conjugation in *Spirogyra longata*. Trans. R. Canad. Inst., *Toronto,* **15.**

—(1926b): Studies on *Spirogyra* II. Additional studies on conjugation, adhesions and geniculations. Trans. R. Soc. Canada, *Toronto,* 2 ser. **20.**

Meneghini, G. (1838): Cenni sulla organografia e fisiologia delle Alghe. Negli Atti della R. Acad. di. Sci. lett. et art. Padova.

Oltmanns, F. (1904): Morphologie und Biologie der Algen. Vol. 1.

Petter, H.F.M. (1933): La reaction nucleare de Feulgen chez quelques vegetaux inferierus. C.R. Acad. Sci. **197.**

Prescott, G.W. (1951): "History of Phycology" in Smith's Manual of Phycology. Chronica Botanica Co. pp. 1-9.

Randhawa, M.S. (1938): "Observation on some Zygnemales from Northern India" Pt. I & II. Proc Indian Acad. Sci. **8.**

—(1941): *Sirocladium,* a new terrestrial member of the Zygnemales. Bot. Gaz. **103**.

—(1958): Further observations on the genus *Sirocladium*. Bot. Gaz. **119**(3).

—(1958): Notes on some new and interesting algae from India. Bot. Gaz. **120**(1).

—(1959): Reproduction in *Zygogonium ericetorum* Kütz. Current Sci., **28.**

—(1958): "Agriculture and Animal Husbandry in India" Pub. ICAR.

Sachs (1906): "History of Botany" Oxford—1890.

Saunders, H. (1931): Conjugation in *Spirogyra*. Ann. Bot. **44.**

Schüssnig. B. (1925a): Die systematische Stellung der Konjugaten. Nouva Not.

Smith, G.M. (1933): The Fresh-water Algae of the United States, New York.

—(1938) :  Cryptogamic Botany, Vol. I., New York, First Ed.

—(1950) :  The Fresh water Algae of the United States, New York.

—(1951) :  "Manual of Phycology" Chronica Botanica Co.

—(1954) :  Cryptogamic Botany. Vol. I , New York, 2nd Ed.

Strasburger, E. (1888) :  Über Kern und Zell teilung im Pflanzenreich.  Jena.

Suematsu, S. (1936) :  Karyological study of *Spirogyra* by means of nuclear reaction.  Sci. Rep. Tokyo Bunrika Daig. Sec. B. **3.**

—(1925b) :  Betrachtungen über das System der niederen Pflanzen. Verh. Zool. Bot. Ges. Wien. **74.**

Singh, K.P. (1958) :  Some observations on conjugation in *Sirocladium kumaoense* Randh.  Current Sci.

—(1959) :  Some peculiarities in conjugation of *Zygnema terrestre* Randh. Sci. & Cult. **24**(7).

Taylor, W.R. (1954) :  Algae : Non—Planktonic. *Bot. Rev.* **20.**

Transeau, E.N. (1951) :  The Zygnemataceae. Ohio State Univ. Press. Columbus.

Tangl, E. (1882) :  Über die Teilung der Kerne im *Spirogyra*-Zellen.  Sitzungsb. d.k. Akad. d. Wiss. Wien. **85.**

Ueda, K. (1956) : Structure of plant cell with special reference to lower plants I.  Mitosis in *Spirogyra setiformis*. Cytologia, **21** (4).

Wittrock, V.B. (1867) :  Algologisk Studien I-II.  Uppsala.

—(1871) :  Beitrag zur Kenntnis der Zygnemaceen und Mesocarpaceen.  Hedwigia **6.**

—(1878) :  On the spore formation of the Mesocarpeae especially of the  new genus *Gonatonema*. Bih. Svensk Vet.—Akad, Handl. **5.**

West, G.S. (1916) :  Algae : **1.** Camb. Univ. Press.

Wille, N. (1897) :  Chlorophyceae in Natürl. Pflanzenfam. **2.**

Wisselingh, C. (1900) :  Über Kernteilung bei *Spirogyra*. Flora, **87.**

—(1902) :  Untersuchungen über *Spirogyra*. Bot. Zeitg. **60.**

—(1921) :  Zehnter Beitrag zur Kenntnis der Karyokinese. Beih. Bot. Centalbl. **38.**

Yamaha, G. (1935) :  Über die Nucleal-Reaction des Pflanzlichen Karyoplasma. Bot. and Zool. **3.**

# KEY TO THE GENERA

1a. Chloroplast single, axile, plate-like (**MOUGEOTIOIDEAE**)

2a. Pyrenoids absent      1. **Mougeotiopsis**

2b. Pyrenoids present

   3a. Special gametangial cells present      4. **Temnogametum**

   3b. Special gametangial cells absent

      4a. Cytoplasmic residue left in the gametangia      3. **Mougeotia**

      4b. Cytoplasmic residue not left in the gametangia; sporangia filled with pectic cellulose-colloid      2. **Debarya**

1b. Chloroplasts usually 2, disc-shaped, globose or stellate (**ZYGNEMOIDEAE**)

   5a. Chloroplasts 2, disc-shaped      8. **Pleurodiscus**

   5b. Chloroplasts a pair of ovoid bodies; zygospores in sporangia of 2 cup-like parts with a suture; cytoplasmic residue left in the gametangia      9. **Zygogonium**

   5c. Chloroplasts 2, stellate; gametangia not filled with pectic cellulose-colloid      7. **Zygnema**

   5d. Chloroplasts 2, globose; gametangia filled with dense pectic cellulose-colloid      6. **Zygnemopsis**

   5e. Chloroplasts 1—2, broad, parietal with laminate margins; reproduction not known      10. **Entransia**

   5f. Chloroplasts 2-7, stellate; aplanospores ellipsoid, on germination 1—3 sporelings develop from each      5. **Hallasia**

1c. Chloroplasts 1—16, more or less spirally arranged, ribbon-like (**SPIROGYROIDEAE**)

   6a. Conjugating tubes present; progametangia absent      11. **Spirogyra**

   6b. Conjugating tubes absent; conjugation directly through an opening where the inflexed gametangia are in contact; pro-gametangia present; chloroplasts more or less straight      12. **Sirogonium**

1d. Chloroplasts 2, flat, straight parallel plates or ribbons (**SIROCLADIOIDEAE**)      13. **Sirocladium**

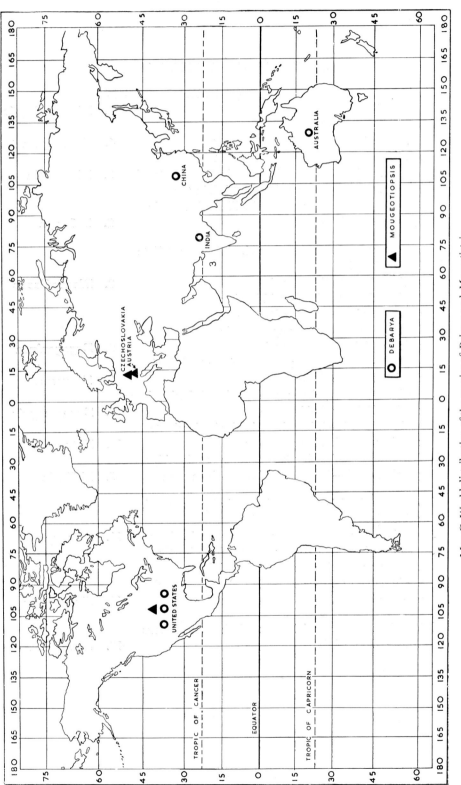

Map C. World distribution of the species of *Debarya* and *Mougeotiopsis*

## CHAPTER 7

# MOUGEOTIOPSIS Palla 1894

This genus was established by Palla in 1894. In 1899 Brand described *Mesogerron* as a new genus from Bavaria. In 1928 Skuja showed that *Mesogerron* is merely a vegetative form of *Mougeotiopsis*. Czurda (1932) included this genus also in *Mougeotia*. In 1950 Transeau recognized it as a distinct genus.

Vegetative cells are cylindrical. Each cell possesses a single quadrate, flat or plate-like axial chloroplast with slightly thickened and granulate margin with nucleus attached laterally near the middle of the cell. *The chloroplast lacks pyrenoids completely.* Oil globules occur on the surface of the chloroplast, and starch granules and oil drops are formed within the chloroplast.

Reproduction is isogamous. Zygospores are ovoid and formed irregularly in the conjugation tube, extending to one or both the gametangia. The zygospores are characterised by thick and highly refractive median wall with sharp-edged pits.

The only species of the genus *Mougeotiopsis calospora* Palla has been described from U.S.A., Austria, Czechoslovakia, Latvia and Southern Bavaria in Europe (Map C).

**Mougeotiopsis calospora**  Palla 1894.  *Berichte Deutsch. Bot. Gesells.* **12,** p.  228. Skuja.
*Acta Horti. Bot. Univ. Latviensis.* **1,** p. 45, Pl. 2, Figs.19-26, 1929.

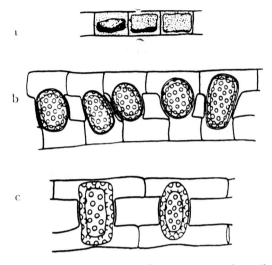

Fig. 1 a-c. *Mougeotiopsis calospora.* a, vegetative cells
showing chloroplasts; b-c, pitted zygospores.
(a. b. after Krieger ; c, after Skuja)

Vegetative cells cylindric, 10-18 × 10-70 $\mu$, end walls plane; chloroplast 1, axial with the nucleus beside it in the centre of the cell; pyrenoids absent; fertile cells similar or somewhat longer.

Conjugation scalariform; zygospores often irregularly placed and irregularly ovoid to quadrate ovoid, 16-23 × 21-38 $\mu$; outer wall thin, transparent; median wall thick, deeply and sharply scrobiculate; pits 1.5-2.5 $\mu$ in diameter, light yellow to brown in colour.

*Distribution* : Austria; Czechoslovakia; Latvia, Southern Bavaria and U.S.A.

## CHAPTER 8

# DEBARYA (Wittrock 1872) emend. Transeau 1934

The genus *Debarya* was established by Wittrock in 1872 and was clearly emended by Transeau in 1934. *Debarya* resembles *Mougeotia* in its vegetative phase but is easily recognizable in its reproductive phase.

Filaments are simple. The vegetative cells possess a single axial plate-like chloroplast with 2-8 pyrenoids. The nucleus is centrally located, and attached to the side of the chloroplast.

Reproduction is by zygospores, aplanospores, parthenospores or akinetes. Conjugation is scalariform. At the beginning of conjugation, the reproductive cells become filled with a shining cellulose colloid deposited in layers. No protoplasmic residue is left in the gametangia outside the spore wall. Zygospores are ovoid, quadrate-ovoid to compressed-spheroid. Mesospore is variously ornamented. In some cases the zygospores are tricarinate with an equatorial and two lateral keels.

Only eight species have been reported from Europe, Asia, North America and New Zealand and they are all very rare (Map C).

## KEY TO THE SPECIES OF DEBARYA

1a. Zygospore median wall quadrangular ovoid       1. **D. hardyi**
1b. Zygospore median wall globose to polyhedric    2. **D. polyedrica**
1c. Zygospore median wall tricarinate
    2a. Polar surfaces with a distinct hub        3. **D. glyptosperma**
    2b. Polar surfaces without a hub
        3a. Vegetative cells less than 18 $\mu$ broad
           4a. Polar surfaces obscurely radially
              striate             4. **D. costata**
           4b. Polar surfaces obscurely pitted   5. **D. ackleyana**
           4c. Polar surfaces smooth       6. **D. jogensis**
        3b. Vegetative cells 18 $\mu$ or more broad   7. **D. smithii**
1d. Zygospore compressed globose to ovoid     8. **D. madrasensis**

**1. Debarya hardyi** G. S. West 1909. *Jour. Linn. Soc. London Bot.* **39**, p. 51, Pl. 2.

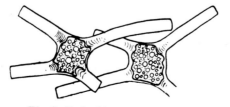

Fig. 2. *D. hardyi.* (after G.S. West)

Vegetative cells 6.5-8 × 57-120 $\mu$ ; chloroplast 1, ribbonlike containing 2 to 4 pyrenoids ;

Conjugation scalariform ; zygospores compressed-quadrangular, 22.5-27 $\mu$ on a side. The spores are quite immature and further details may possibly lend support to its inclusion under the genus *Zygnemopsis*.

*Distribution* : Yan Yean Reservoir; Victoria, Australia.

**2. Debarya polyedrica** Skuja 1937. *"Algae." Symbolae Sinicae.* Pt. 1, p. 84, Pl. 2, Figs. 3-8.

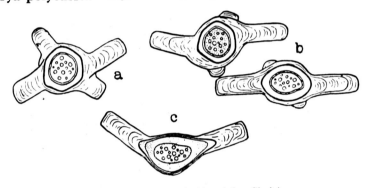

Fig. 3. a-c. *D. polyedrica.* (after Skuja)

Vegetative cells 8-12 × 50-200 $\mu$, with 2 chloroplasts, each containing 2 pyrenoids.

Conjugation scalariform ; fertile cells genuflexed and separating after conjugation ; zygospores globose to polyhedric-ovoid, 26-33 $\mu$ in diameter, completely filling the tubes ; outer spore wall thick lamellate ; median spore wall golden yellow, smooth; inner spore wall moderately thick, hyaline, irregularly scrobiculate within; aplanospores obliquely rotund-fusiform, 24×42-54 $\mu$.

*Distribution* : China, Northwestern Yünnan, on sinter terraces at an altitude of 2,765 meters.

**3. Debarya glyptosperma** (de Bary) Wittrock 1872. *Bih. Kgl. Sensk. Vetensk. Akad. Handl.* **1,** p. 35.

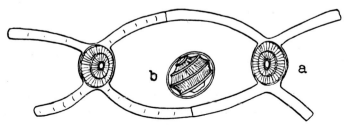

Fig. 4. a-b. *D. glyptosperma.* (after Transeau)

Vegetative cells 10-15 × 40-200 $\mu$ ; chloroplast single, axile, flat, ribbon-like with 8-12 pyrenoids.

Conjugation scalariform, conjugation canal very long, at first slender and increasing in width until spore is mature ; zygospores formed in the tubes, compressed-ellipsoid or broadly ellipsoid, 30-46 × 42-72 $\mu$ ; median spore wall tricarinate, yellow, with an irregular polar ring of protuberances ; radially and distinctly corrugate between the keels and hubs when mature.

*Distribution* : Europe; U.S.A.

**4. Debarya costata** Randhawa 1938. *Proc. Indian Acad. Sci.* **8,** pp. 121-22, Fig. 2.

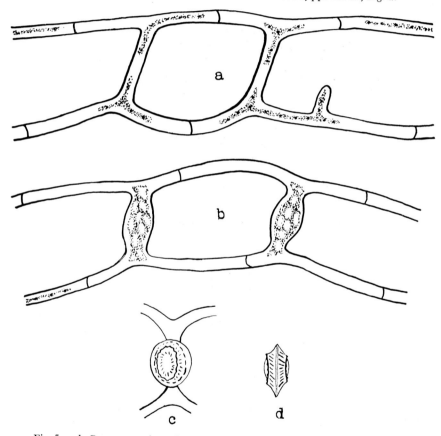

Fig. 5. a-d. *D. costata*. a-b, early stages in conjugation; c-d. mature zygospores; (a-b, after Randhawa; c-d. after Transeau.)

Vegetative cells 6-10 $\mu$ broad and each cell has a single plate-shaped chloroplast bearing 4-9 pyrenoids.

Conjugation only scalariform. The conjugation processes are given out in the shape of long cylindrical phallic bodies, which meet and produce long conjugation canals (fig. a, b). Conjugation between 3 or more filaments is exceedingly common giving it the appearance of a gauze with rectangular or sub-rectangular meshes. Marked geniculation of the cells takes place during the process of conjugation. After the fusion of gametes, the middle part of the conjugation canal swells up, and the contents show a very much vacuolated appearance. The conjugating filaments become glistening white and solid in appearance, and septa of the cells become indistinct due to secretion of mucilage by the protoplasm in a homogeneous mass.

Zygospores are rounded or elliptical and are 22-26 × 32-42 $\mu$ or compressed-globose to ovoid, tricarinate with clearly defined ridges between the keels ; the polar faces of the spores have no "hubs" but are obscurely and radially corrugate toward the margin. The colour is bright yellow, and lateral keels are crinkly (fig. c, d).

*Distribution* :

*India* : Found free-floating mixed with *Spirogyra daedalea* in Bukia jhil near Baskhari, tahsil Tanda, district Fyzabad, U.P., India during the first week of December 1936.

**5. Debarya ackleyana** Transeau 1944, *Ohio Jour. Sci.* **44**, p. 24.

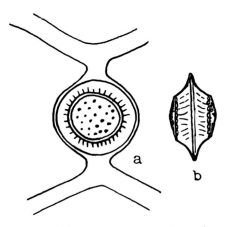

Fig. 6 *D. ackleyana*. zygospores. a, front view;
b, side view (after Transeau)

Vegetative cells 12-15 × 90-140 $\mu$ ; chloroplast single, axile, ribbon-like with 8 pyrenoids.

Conjugation scalariform, tubes long and slender at first, later the median spore wall becomes rounded and the sporangium wall is perfectly distinct ; zygospores golden yellow mostly compressed-globose, sometimes ovoid, 50-54 × 52-65 $\mu$ ; median wall tricarinate, the lateral keels finely ruffled and very distinct, with corresponding corrugations between the keels ; the middle keel is thin, radially striate and up to 10 $\mu$ wide ; polar walls obscurely pitted and without hub.

*Distribution* :  United States of America.

**6. Debarya smithii** Transeau 1944. *Trans Amer. Micros. Soc.* **53,** p. 216.

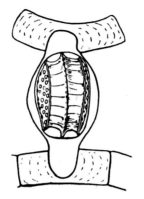

Fig. 7. *D. smithii.* (after Transeau)

Vegetative cells 21-28 × 68-140 *μ* ; chloroplast axile, ribbon-like, containing 2 to 4 pyrenoids.

Conjugation scalariform ; at the time of conjugation, the chloroplasts lengthen as they pass into the sporangium and each may then contain from 10 to 20 pyrenoids ; zygospores compressed-globose or ovoid, 55-72 × 64-80 *μ* ; the median wall strongly tricarinate with projecting ruffled ridges ; the lateral wall between the keels is striate ; the polar faces are distinctly and irregularly pitted, sometimes also finely punctate.

*Distribution* : United States of America.

**7. Debarya jogensis** IYENGAR.

Vegetative cells 7-9 × 90—98 *μ* ; chloroplast single, with 7—10 pyrenoids in a row.

Conjugation scalariform ; tubes very long (up to 70 *μ*) ; at first slender and increasing in width until the spore is mature ; spores formed in the tube ; zygospores golden brown compressed-ellipsoid, 32—39 × 35—43 *μ* ; median spore wall tricarinate ; lateral keels finely ruffled and very distinct ; finely corrugate between the keels ; polar walls without a hub, and neither radially corrugate near the margin nor pitted, but quite smooth.

*Distribution* :

*India* : In rock-pools in the bed of the river Saravathi above Raj Falls, Jog, Mysore State.

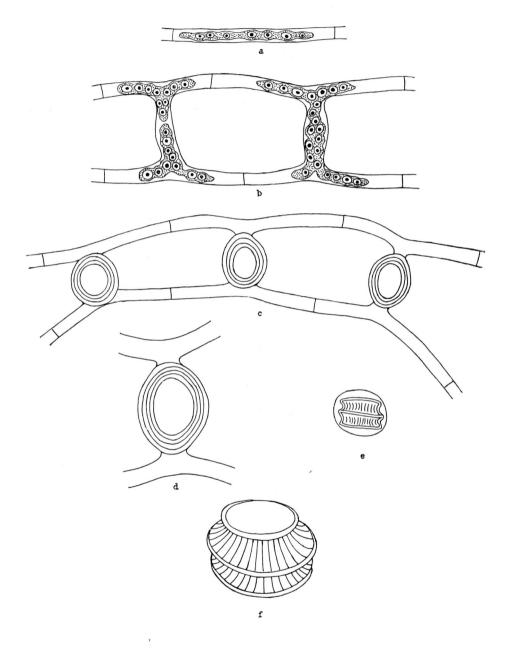

Fig. 7A, a-f. *D. jogensis*. a, vegetative cell with chloroplast; b, conjugation: c-d, final stages of conjugation with ripe zygospore; e-f, zygospores. (after Iyengar).

## 8. Debarya madrasensis IYENGAR.

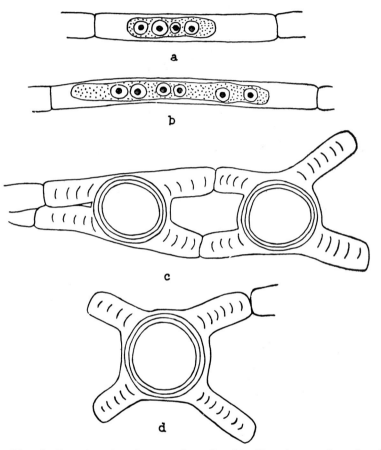

Fig. 7B, a-d. *D. madrasensis*. a-b, vegetative cells with chloroplasts ; c-d, conjugation showing mature zygospores. (after Iyengar).

Vegetative cells 8.5—11 × 30—120 $\mu$ ; vegetative filaments constricted at the joints ; chloroplast single with 2—5 pyrenoids in a row.

Reproduction by zygospores ; conjugation scalariform ; zygospores compressed globose to ovoid, 22—28 × 23—28 $\mu$, median spore-wall golden brown, smooth.

*Distribution* :

*India* : In the roof tank of the Botany Laboratory, Presidency College, Madras.

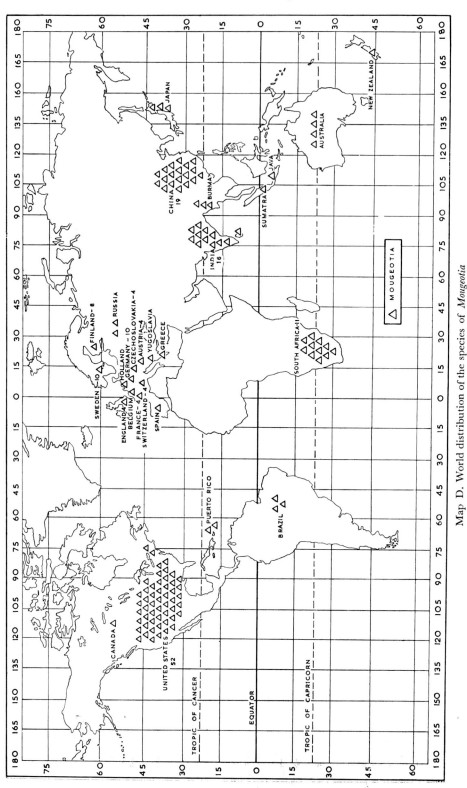

Map D. World distribution of the species of *Mougeotia*

## CHAPTER 9

# MOUGEOTIA C.A. Agardh 1824

Some of the species of *Mougeotia* have been described under the following general names:

*Conjugata* Link (1820) ; *Serpentinaria* Gray (1821) ; *Agardhia* Gray (1821) ; *Mougeotia* Agardh (1824) ; *Genuflexa* Link (1833) ; *Mesocarpus* Hassall (1843) ; *Sphaerocarpus* Hassall (1843) ; *Staurocarpus* Hassall (1843) ; *Staurospermum* Kützing (1843) ; *Pleurocarpus* Braun (1855) ; *Craterospermum* Braun (1855) ; *Plagiospermum* Cleve (1868) ; *Sphaerospermum* Cleve (1868) ; *Gonatonema* Wittrock ( 1878 ) and *Debarya* Wittrock (1897).

Filaments are unbranched consisting of cylindrical cells. The cells are many times longer than broad with plane end walls. The chloroplast is a flat axial plate with the nucleus apposed to the cell wall. Where two chloroplasts occur in each cell as in *M. prona*, the nucleus is situated in between the chloroplasts. The pyrenoids are arranged in one or many rows.

Reproduction in the majority of species is by zygospores, while in some it is by aplanospores. Conjugation is largely scalariform, rarely lateral, and is isogamous in all species excepting three. During conjugation, small papillae are developed by the conjugating cells which unite and fuse to form a conjugation tube. Subsequently, the conjugation canal bulges and the gametangia are cut off by one or two walls. Cytoplasmic residues are left behind in the gametangia and aplanosporangia.

The zygospores are spheroid, compressed-spheroid, ovoid, ellipsoid, dolioform or quadrate-ovoid. The median wall is either colourless and smooth or variously coloured and ornamented. The aplanospores resemble the zygospores in all the essential details.

In all 103 species have been described. (Map D).

## KEY TO THE SPECIES OF MOUGEOTIA

1a. Reproduction by zygospores
  2a. Sporangia between two undivided gametangia

3a.  Sporangia globose to dolioform, longer axis
      parallel with the conjugating tube

    4a.  Mesospore smooth

       5a.  Vegetative cells less than 24 $\mu$ broad

          6a.  Vegetative cells less than 12 $\mu$
              broad

             7a.  Zygospores globose

|     |     |
|-----|-----|
| 8a.  Zygospore colourless | 1.  **M. victoriensis** |
| 8b.  Zygospore blue | 2.  **M. kerguelensis** |
| 8c.  Zygospore brown | |
|    9a.  Zygospores 7-8 $\mu$ broad | 6.  **M. angusta** |
|    9b.  Zygospores 13-14 $\mu$ broad | 5.  **M. parvula** |

             7b.  Zygospores ellipsoid or ovoid

|     |     |
|-----|-----|
| 10a.  Zygospores ovoid | 4.  **M. tenuissima** |
| 10b.  Zygospores asymmetrical ellipsoid or dolioform | 7.  **M. tubifera** |
| 10c.  Zygospores ellipsoid | 8.  **M. ellipsoidea** |

|     |     |
|-----|-----|
| 7c.  Zygospores ellipsoid ovoid variable in position | 3.  **M. calcarea** |
| 7d.  Zygospores spherical, rarely ellipsoidal ; filaments dimorphic | **3a. M. heterogama** |

          6b.  Vegetative cells more than 12 $\mu$
              broad

             11.  Zygospores globose to sub-
                globose

|     |     |
|-----|-----|
| 12a.  Zygospores blue | 9.  **M. maltae** |
| 12b.  Zygospores yellow to brown | |

                13a.  Vegetative cells less
                    than 20 $\mu$ broad

|     |     |
|-----|-----|
| 14a.  Zygospores globose, formed in the conjugating tube | 10.  **M. recurva** |
| 14b.  Zygospores globose, extending into the gametangia | 11.  **M. drouetii** |
| 14c.  Zygospores globose, ovoid or ellipsoid | 13.  **M. adnata** |

14d. Zygospores rhomboid, conjugation is usually lateral 12. **M. reinschii**

13b. Vegetative cells 20-22 $\mu$ broad; zygospores oblong-elliptic to globose, extending only slightly into the gametangia **104. M. bangalorensis**

13c. Vegetative cells more than 20 $\mu$ broad

15a. Zygospores 40—45 $\mu$ broad 14. **M. sphaerocarpa**

15b. Zygospores 47—52 $\mu$ broad 15. **M. jogensis**

5b. Vegetative cells more than 24 $\mu$ broad

16a. Vegetative cells 24—40 $\mu$ broad

17a. Zygospores 30—48 $\mu$ broad

18a. Zygospores 30—40 $\mu$ broad

19a. Conjugation scalariform 21. **M. scalaris**

19b. Conjugation lateral 20. **M. genuflexa**

18b. Zygospores $40 \times 50$—59 $\mu$ 18. **M. ovalispora**

18c. Zygospores 40—50 $\mu$ broad 17. **M. hirnii**

18d. Zygospores 45—55 $\mu$ broad 19. **M. africana**

17b. Zygospores 55—70 $\mu$ broad 16. **M. macrospora**

16b. Vegetative cells more than 40 $\mu$ broad

20a. Zygospores about 50 $\mu$ broad 22. **M. subcrassa**

20b. Zygospores about 65 $\mu$ broad 23. **M. crassa**

4b. Mesospore variously ornamented

21a. Vegetative cells less than 16 $\mu$ broad

22a. Zygospore ovoid, punctate 24. **M. caelestis**

22b. Zygospore compressed-ovoid, rarely subglobose, scrobiculate 26. **M. ovalis**

22c. Zygospore globose to ovoid, scrobiculate 27. **M. nummuloides**

21b. Vegetative cells more than 16 $\mu$ broad

23a. Pyrenoids arranged in a row

24a.   Zygospores globose to subglobose

     25a.   Vegetative cells less than
32 $\mu$ broad

         26a.   Mesospore reticulate 25.   **M. sinensis**

         26b.   Mesospore coarsely
punctate          28.   **M. microspora**

         26c.   Mesospore punctate   29.   **M. ornata**

     25b.   Vegetative cells more
than 32 $\mu$ broad

         27a.   Zygospores 32—38 $\mu$
broad          30.   **M. globulispora**

         27b.   Zygospores40—50 $\mu$
broad          32.   **M. megaspora**

24b.   Zygospores ovoid to ellipsoid

         28a.   Mesospore verru-
cose, outer wall thick   31.   **M. lamellosa**

         28b.   Mesospore verru-
cose, outer wall thin   33.   **M. microverrucosa**

         28c.   Mesospore punctate   36.   **M. pulchella**
         28d.   Mesospore scrobi-
culate          34.   **M. laevis**

         28e.   Mesospore areolate   35.   **M. areolata**

         28f.   Mesospore granulate   39.   **M. verrucosa**

23b.   Pyrenoids scattered

     29a.   Zygospores globose to
subglobose

         30a.   Vegetative cells 17-24 $\mu$
broad

         31a.   Mesospore wrinkled   37.   **M. gotlandica**
         31b.   Mesospore scrobi-
culate          38.   **M. talyschensis**

         31c.   Mesospore pitted      40.   **M. pseudocalo-
spora**

         30b.   Vegetative cells 32-38 $\mu$
broad

         32a.   Mesospore yellow,
punctate          42.   **M. daytonae**

         32b.   Mesospore yellow,
scrobiculate        43.   **M. sanfordiana**

        40b.  Vegetative cells 20-25 $\mu$
              broad                       63.  **M. seminoleana**

      39b.  Zygospores yellow to brown

          41a.  Zygospores 46-57 $\times$ 48-53 $\mu$;
              spore wall smooth       60.  **M. indica**

          41b.  Zygospores 38-47 $\times$ 28-39 $\mu$;
              spore wall smooth       56.  **M. gelatinosa**

          41c.  Zygospores 34-40 $\times$ 25-32 $\mu$;
              spore wall irregularly
              corrugate          57.  **M. oedogonioides**

          41d.  Zygospores 34-40 $\times$ 25-32 $\mu$;
              spore wall scrobiculate   59.  **M. pawhuskae**

          41e.  Zygospores 25-29 $\mu$ board;
              spore wall smooth    108.  **M. baneergat-**
                                    **tense**

    37b.  Sporangia without pectic layer

       42a.  Vegetative cells less than 16 $\mu$
           broad; spore wall punctate   65.  **M. depressa**

       42b.  Vegetative cells 18-21 $\mu$ broad;
           spore wall brown with shallow
           scrobiculations       62.  **M. operculata**

2b.  Sporangia dividing one of the gametangia

  43a.  Zygospores cylindric      66.  **M. varians**

  43b.  Zygospores globose to tri-lobed

    44a.  Vegetative cells less than 14 $\mu$ broad   64.  **M. transeaui**

    44b.  Vegetative cells more than 14 $\mu$ broad

      45a.  Vegetative cells 14-20 $\mu$ broad   67.  **M. floridana**

      45b.  Vegetative cells 21-25 $\mu$ broad   69.  **M. poinciana**

2c.  Sporangia dividing both gametangia

  46a.  Mesospore smooth

    47a.  Vegetative cells less than 14 $\mu$ broad

      48a.  Zygospores compressed-globose ; vege-
          tative cells 4-5 $\mu$ broad ; spore wall
          smooth and colourless    68.  **M. caimani**

      48b.  Zygospores globose; vegetative cells 7-9 $\mu$
          broad ; spore wall smooth, yellow to
          yellow-brown        70.  **M. cherokeana**

      48c.  Zygospores globose; vegetative cells
          12-13 $\mu$ broad; spore wall smooth or
          with reticulate wrinkles   102.  **M. kwangsiensis**

      48d.  Zygospores quadrate-ovoid

        49a.  Zygospores with rounded, undulate
           or truncate ends

          50a.  Vegetative cells 3.5-4.5 $\mu$
              broad            71.  **M. elegantula**

50b.  Vegetative cells more than
    7 $\mu$ broad
    51a.  Vegetative cells 8-9 $\mu$
        broad                          72.  **M. virescens**
    51b.  Vegetative cells 11-14 $\mu$
        broad                          73.  **M. paludosa**
    51c.  Vegetative cells 9-11 $\mu$
        broad                          75.  **M. subpaludosa**
49b.  Zygospores with retuse ends
    52a.  Vegetative cells 3-5 $\mu$ broad  74.  **M. delicata**
    52b.  Vegetative cells 6-8 $\mu$ broad  76.  **M. viridis**
49c.  Zygospores with produced ends
    53a.  Zygospore angles rounded
        54a.  Spores regularly quad-
            rate                       77.  **M. corniculata**
        54b.  Spores irregularly quad-
            rate                       78.  **M. uberosperma**
    53b.  Zygospore angles retuse or
        truncate
        55a.  Spores with truncate
            processes                  79.  **M. americana**
        55b.  Spores with retuse pro-
            cesses                     80.  **M. craterophora**
47b.  Vegetative cells more than 14 $\mu$ broad
    56a.  Zygospores less than 30 $\mu$ broad   103.  **M. fragilis**
    56b.  Zygospores more than 35 $\mu$ broad    81.  **M. granulosa**
    56c.  Zygospores more than 50 $\mu$ broad    83.  **M. capucina**
46b.  Mesospore ornamented
    57a.  Zygospores concave-quadrate, spore wall
        verrucose                      82.  **M. gracillima**
    57b.  Zygospores quadrate, wall minutely to
        coarsely punctate
        58a.  Vegetative cells less than 13 $\mu$ broad
            59a.  Vegetative cells less than 8 $\mu$
                broad
                60a.  Vegetative cells 4-5 $\mu$ broad  84.  **M. boodlei**
                60b.  Vegetative cells 5-8(9) $\mu$
                    broad
                    61a.  Angles of zygospores
                        rounded          85.  **M. austriaca**
                    61b.  Angles of zygospores
                        produced
                        62a.  Zygospores quadr-
                            angular; spore wall
                            colourless, punctate;
                            angles  truncate    87.  **M. producta**

62b.　Zygospores quadr-
angular; spore wall
yellow to yellow-
brown, scrobiculate,
angles truncate　　88.　**M. thylospora**

62c.　Zygospores rounded
quadrate; spore wall
golden brown; angles
apiculate　　106.　**M. tambaramensis**

62d.　Zygospores trapae-
zoid spore wall
yellowish brown,
smooth; angles
apiculate　　107.　**M. trapaeze-
formis**

61c.　Angles of zygospores
retuse　　86.　**M. tumidula**

59b.　Vegetative cells 8-13 $\mu$ broad
63a.　Angles of spores truncate　　89.　**M. quadrangulata**

63b.　Angles of spores retuse　　92.　**M. punctata**
63c.　Angles of spores irregularly
quadrate-ovoid　　90.　**M. regellii**
63d.　Angles of spores quadrate
to globose-quadrate　　91.　**M. quadrata**
63e.　Angles of spores tumid-
quadrangular　　93.　**M. rotundangulata**

58b.　Vegetative cells more than 13 $\mu$
broad
64a.　Zygospores ovoid-globose　　101.　**M. aspera**
64b.　Zygospores irregular quadrate　　94.　**M. irregularis**
64c.　Zygospores quadrangular ovoid　　81.　**M. granulosa**

1b.　Reproduction by aplanospores
65a.　Vegetative cells less than 8 $\mu$ broad
66a.　Aplanospores 18-20 $\mu$ broad　　95.　**M. miamiana**
66b.　Aplanospores 27-30 $\mu$ broad　　96.　**M. tropica**
66c.　Aplanospores ellipsoid
67a.　Vegetative cell 4-5 $\mu$ broad　　97.　**M. tenerrima**
67b.　Vegetative cell 6-9 $\mu$ broad　　100.　**M. ventricosa**

65b.　Vegetative cells 8-15 $\mu$ broad
68a.　Spore wall smooth ; vegetative cells 8-12 $\mu$
broad　　55.　**M. rava**
68b.　Spore wall punctate
69a.　Vegetative cells 8-12 $\mu$ broad　　99.　**M. prona**
69b.　Vegetative cells 13-15 $\mu$ broad　　98.　**M. mayori**

**1. Mougeotia victoriensis** G.S. West 1909, *Jour. Linn. Soc. London, Bot.* **39**, p. 51.

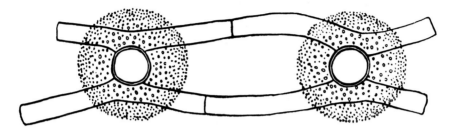

Fig. 8. *M. victoriensis.* (after West)

Vegetative cells 11-12 $\mu$ × 100-160 $\mu$ : chloroplasts 2-7 (usually 5-6), pyrenoids in a single, more or less irregular row.

Conjugation scalariform ; zygospores formed wholly in the conjugating tube, globose, 21-24 $\mu$ in diameter ; spore wall smooth. Surrounding the sporangium a layer of pectic material develops which extends even beyond the outer sides of the gametangia, 60-63 $\mu$ in diameter.

*Distribution*: Victoria, Australia.

**2. Mougeotia kerguelensis** Kolkwitz & Krieger 1944. Rabenhorst's *Kryptogamenflora.* **13** (2), p. 134.

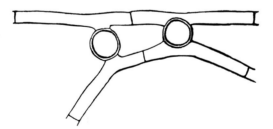

Fig. 9. *M. kerguelensis.* (after Kolkwitz & Krieger)

Vegetative cells about 12 $\mu$ × 48-96 $\mu$ ; chloroplasts with several pyrenoids in a single row.

Conjugation scalariform ; zygospores in the conjugating tubes, sometimes extending slightly into the gametangia, about 27$\mu$ in diameter ; spore wall smooth, dark blue.

*Distribution*: Kerguelen Islands, South Indian Ocean.

**3. Mougeotia calcarea** (Cleve) Wittrock 1872. *Bih. Kgl. Svensk. Vetensk. Akad. Handl.* **1**, p. 40. pl. 2.

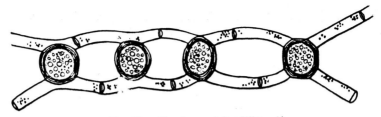

Fig. 10.  *M. calcarea.* (after Wittrock)

Vegetative cells 8-14$\mu$ × 40-280 $\mu$; chloroplasts with 4-8 pyrenoids in a single row ; cells elongating, becoming geniculate before spore formation.

Conjugation scalariform ; zygospores formed wholly in the conjugating tube or extending into one or both gametangia, globose 25-30 $\mu$ in diameter, or angular-globose, 22-28 $\mu$ × 30-50 $\mu$ ; spore wall smooth, colourless, or pale yellow; aplanospores globose, lateral to the sporogenous cell, 17-21 $\mu$ in diameter, or rarely trapezoid-ovoid, dividing the sporogenous cell, 15-20$\mu$ × 20-28$\mu$ .

*Distribution: India:* In puddles, U.P.

*Other countries*:  North America ;  Brazil;  Europe ;  North Africa ; Southern Asia

### 3A.  Mougeotia heterogama Geitler 1958. *Ost. Bot. Z.* **105** 301-322.

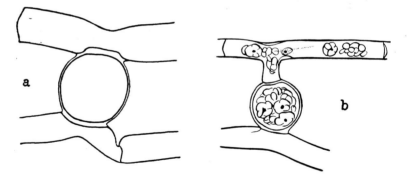

Fig. 10A.  a-b. *M. heterogama.* a, zygospore, b. azygospore. (after Geitler)

Filaments dimorphic, vegetative and sexual ; Male cells (7.5—) 8-9 × 50—140 $\mu$ ; female cells (11.5—) 12-13 × 80-325 $\mu$ ; cell walls variously thickened ; nucleus, chloroplast and pyrenoids variously big ; pyrenoids in a single row, in the male cells mostly 2, in the female cells mostly 3-5, rarely upto 8.

Conjugation scalariform, isogamous, very rarely the gametangia are divided ; conjugating cells more or less geniculate, bent or straight ; zygotes mostly spherical, rarely ellipsoidal with two polar caps ; 23-29 × 24-36 $\mu$ ; exospore thin, smooth and colourless ; mesospore thick, smooth and brown ; azygospores common, mostly formed in the conjugation papillae, mostly irregularly formed ; 15-25 × 18-25 $\mu$.

*Distribution :*  Germany.

**4. Mougeotia tenuissima** (de Bary) Czurda 1932. *Süsswasserflora Mitteleuro-pa,* **9**, p. 66.

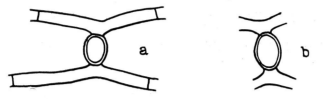

Fig. 11. a-b.   *M. tenuissima.* (after De Bary)

Vegetative cells $5 \times 6$ $\mu$ in diameter.

Conjugation scalariform ; zygospores formed wholly in the conjugation tube, ovoid, $11\text{-}15 \times 12\text{-}14$ $\mu$ ; spore wall brown, thick, smooth.

*Distribution*:   Germany; France.

**5. Mougeotia parvula** Hassall 1843.   *Ann. and Mag. Nat. Hist.* **11**, p. 434.

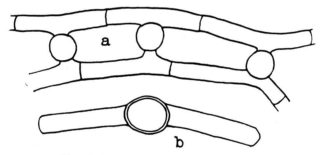

Fig. 12. a-b.   *M. parvula.* (after Kolkwitz)

Vegetative cells $8\text{-}13 \times 30\text{-}140$ $\mu$ ;   chloroplast usually occupying two-thirds of the cell, with 4-8 pyrenoids.

Conjugation scalariform ; zygospores formed wholly in the conjugating tube, globose, 13-25 $\mu$ in diameter ; spore wall brown, thick, smooth ; aplanospores obliquely ovoid, 16-20 $\mu \times 20\text{-}24$ $\mu$ .

*Distribution*:   Africa ; Brazil ; China ; Europe ; Japan ; U.S.A.

**6. Mougeotia angusta** (Hassall) Kirchner 1878. *Kryptogamenflora Schlesien,* p. 128.

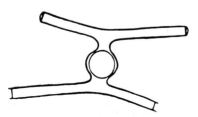

Fig. 13.   *M. angusta.* (after Hassall)

Vegetative cells 5-6 × 30-95μ ; chloroplast with 4 pyrenoids in a row.

Conjugation scalariform ; zygospores formed wholly in the conjugating tube, globose, about 7-8 μ in diameter ; spore wall brown, smooth.

*Distribution*: U.S.A. ; British Isles ; Germany ; Austria ; Belgium ; Bulgaria ; Czechoslovakia ; North Africa ; Netherland Indies.

**7. Mougeotia tubifera** Tiffany 1934.　*Trans. Amer. Micros. Soc.* **53,** p. 218.

Fig. 14.　*M. tubifera.* (after Transeau )

Vegetative cells 9-10 × 90-400 μ ; chloroplast with 4-12 pyrenoids in a single, more or less irregular row.

Conjugation tubes usually greatly elongated (10-65 μ), often spirally twisted and nearly as large as the filaments (7-9μ in diameter).　Conjugation occurs through the lateral wall of the papillae as well as through the end.　Zygospores asymmetrically ovoid, usually showing a great bulge on one side than on the other, 27-30 × 33-45 μ, not including the outer sporangial pectic layer which is 6-12 μ in thickness; sporangium wall smooth, hyaline ; spore wall colourless, thicker, smooth.

*Distribution*: U.S.A.

**8. Mougeotia ellipsoidea** (W. & G.S. West) Czurda 1932. *Süsswasserflora Mitteleuropa.* **9,** p. 66.

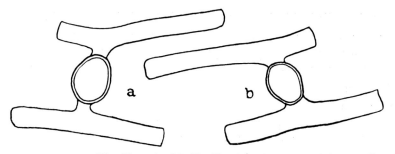

Fig. 15. a-b. *M. ellipsoidea.* (after West)

Vegetative cells 9.5-11.5 $\mu$ in diameter.

Conjugation scalariform ; zygospores formed wholly in the conjugating tube, ellipsoid, 16-26 × 22-28 $\mu$ ; spore wall smooth, brown at maturity.

*Distribution:* Australia, Burma.

**9. Mougeotia maltae** Skuja 1926. *Acta Horti. Bot. Univ. Latviensis.* **1**, p.109. Fig. 1.

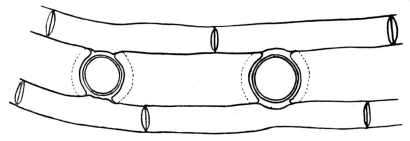

Fig. 16. *M. maltae.* (after Skuja)

Vegetative cells 17-22 × 60-120 (-200) $\mu$ ; chloroplast nearly as long as the cell, with 4-8 pyrenoids in a single row.

Conjugation scalariform; zygospores formed wholly in the conjugating tube, globose (30-) 32-35 (-40) $\mu$ in diameter; spore wall blue, smooth, surrounded by a gelatinous layer 4-6 $\mu$ in diameter.

*Distribution:* Latvia, Usma Lake.

**10. Mougeotia recurva** (Hassall) de Toni 1889. *Sylloge Algarum,* **1,** p. 714.

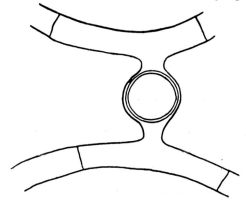

Fig. 17. *M. recurva.* (after Transeau)

Vegetative cells 12-18 × 50-180 $\mu$; chloroplast with 4-8 pyrenoids.

Conjugation scalariform ; zygospores formed wholly in the conjugating tube, globose 22-33 $\mu$ in diameter; spore wall brown, smooth; aplanospores globose, 24-30 $\mu$ in diameter ; at the bends in genicluate cells, or cylindric ovoid, 14-18 × 28-34 $\mu$, in straight cells.

*Distribution:*

> *India* : Rain water pools, M.P; Gorakhpur, U.P.
> *Other Countries* : U.S.A. ; Canada ; British Isles ; Germany ;

Australia; Puerto Rico ; South America.

**11. Mougeotia drouetii** Transeau 1938. *Amer. Jour. Bot.* **25,** p. 524, Fig. 1.

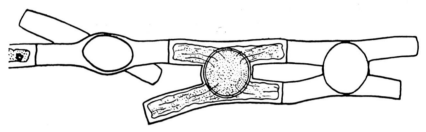

Fig. 18. *M. drouetii.* (after Transeau)

Vegetative cells 14-18 × 72-180 $\mu$, chloroplast with 4 to 8 pyrenoids in a single row.

Conjugation scalariform ; zygospores globose in the enormously enlarged tube and extending into the gametangia, 32-37 × 33-42 $\mu$; spore wall smooth, yellow-brown obscured by the granular membranous residue left after conjugation.

*Distribution:* South America ; Brazil.

**12. Mougeotia reinschii** Transeau 1934. *Trans. Amer. Micros. Soc.* **53,** p. 224.

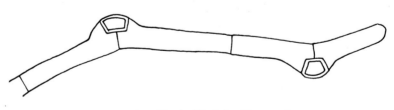

Fig. 19. *M. reinschii.* (after Transeau)

Vegetative cells 15-24 $\mu$ in diameter ; chloroplast with 4-8 pyrenoids in a single row.

Conjugation lateral, very rarely scalariform ; zygospores quadrately ovoid, 24-30 × 26-32 $\mu$; spore wall brown, smooth.

*Distribution:* U.S.A. ; Germany ; Poland; Czechoslovakia ; Java.

**13.  Mougeotia adnata** Iyengar 1932.   *Rev. Algolog.*  **6,** p. 270, Fig. 3.

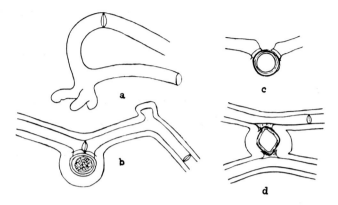

Fig. 20.   a-d.  *M. adnata.* (after Iyengar)

Vegetative cells 15-17 × 180-240 $\mu$, enveloped by a sheath 6-8 $\mu$ thick; chloroplast plate-like, with 4-10 pyrenoids in a row.

Conjugation lateral and scalariform; zygospores formed in the enlarged conjugating tube, which also develops an outer pectic layer ; in lateral conjugation ellipsoid or rarely reniform, 26-32 × 30-38 $\mu$; in scalariform conjugation globose or dolioform, 31-33 × 35-37 $\mu$; spore wall brown, smooth.

*Distribution:*

*India* :   Periyar, on wet rock slopes, South India.

**14.  Mougeotia sphaerocarpa** Wolle 1887. *Freshwater Algae of the United States,* p. 227, Pl.146, Figs. 1-2.  (=*M. sphaerocarpa forma* Rao).

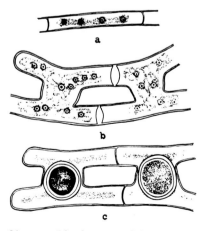

Fig. 21.   a-c.  *M. sphaerocarpa.* (after Randhawa)

Vegetative cells 19-24 × 60-120 (—240) $\mu$; chloroplast plate-like, with 4-16 pyrenoids in an irregular row.

Conjugation scalariform; zygospores formed in the greatly enlarged conjugating tubes and extending somewhat into both gametangia, ovoid to subglobose, 36-40 × 40-55 $\mu$; spore wall brown, smooth; aplanospores ovoid to obliquely ovoid, 24-30 × 35-50 $\mu$.

*Distribution:*

India :    Free-floating in *jhils*, ponds and streams, Fyzabad., U.P.
*Other countries* :   China ; U.S.A.

**15. Mougeotia jogensis** Iyengar 1932.   *Rev. Algolog.* **6,** p. 268, Fig. 2.

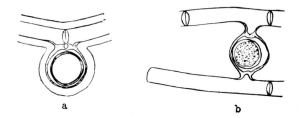

Fig. 22. a-b. *M. jogensis.* (after Iyengar)

Vegetative cells 22-26 × 100-200 $\mu$, with a pectic sheath 6-7 $\mu$ in thickness ; chloroplast plate-like with 4-8 pyrenoids in a single row.

Conjugation scalariform and lateral ; zygospores formed in the greatly enlarged conjugating tubes and finally cut off from the adjoining gametangia by lamellate thickenings of the sporagium wall; zygospores globose to ellipsoid, 47-52 $\mu$ in diameter ; spore wall brown, smooth.

*Distribution:*

India :   Mysore.

**16. Mougeotia macrospora** (Wolle) de Toni 1889.   *Sylloge Algarum.* **1,** p. 716.

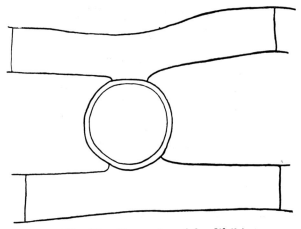

Fig. 23.  *M. macrospora.* (after Wolle)

Vegetative cells $30 \times 180\text{-}300 \; \mu$.

Conjugation scalariform ; zygospores formed in the conjugating tubes, globose, 55-70 $\mu$ in diameter; spore wall smooth.

*Distribution:* U.S.A.

**17. Mougeotia hirnii** Transeau 1934. *Trans. Amer. Micros. Soc.* **53,** p. 218.

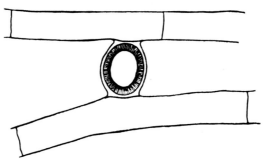

Fig. 24. *M. hirnii.* (after Hirn)

Vegetative cells $25\text{-}28 \times 60\text{-}140 \; \mu$; chloroplast with 4-8 pyrenoids in a row.

Conjugation scalariform; zygospores formed wholly in the conjugating tube, ovoid, $50\text{-}48 \times 43\text{-}50 \; \mu$; spore wall yellow-brown, smooth.

*Distribution:* China ; Finland ; U.S.A.

**18. Mougeotia ovalispora** Kolkwitz & Krieger 1944. Rabenhorst's *Kryptogamenflora.* **13** (2), p. 134.

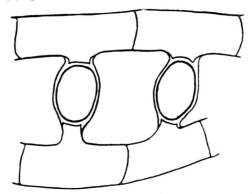

Fig. 25. *M. ovalispora.* (after Kolkwitz & Krieger)

Vegetative cells $37\text{-}40 \times 80\text{-}120 \; \mu$; chloroplast with 8 to 10 scattered pyrenoids.

Conjugation scalariform ; zygospores in the conjugating tubes, ovoid to ellipsoid, $39\text{-}41 \times 51\text{-}59 \; \mu$; spore wall thick, smooth, yellow-brown.

*Distribution:* Brandenburg, Grünrade, Germany.

**19. Mougeotia africana** (G.S. West) Transeau 1944. *Ohio Jour. Sci.* **44,** p. 244.

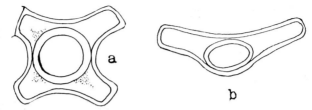

Fig. 26.  *M. africana.* a, zygospore; b, aplanospore. (after Transeau)

Vegetative cells 24-28 × 44-200μ; chloroplast with 4-16 pyrenoids in a single row.

Conjugation scalariform ; zygospores in the greatly enlarged conjugating tubes and extending nearly or quite across the gametangia, globose to ovoid, 35-44 × 44-60μ; spore wall brown, smooth; walls of gametangia usually thickened by an apparent change to pectic compound, and superficially suggesting a *Debarya*, readily distinguished from the latter, however, by the absence of completely filled gametangia ; aplanospores and parthenospores ovoid, 20-25 × 22-30μ ; formed near the middle of the sporogenous cells.

*Distribution* :  Phillippine Islands ; Africa.

**20. Mougeotia genuflexa** (Dillwyn) C.A. Agardh 1824. *Systema Algarum,* p. 83.

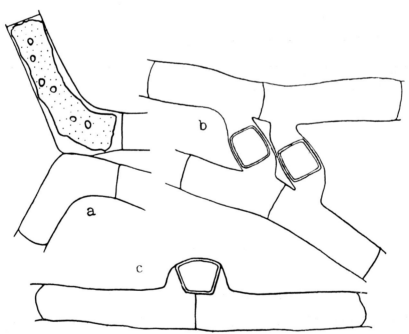

Fig. 27.  a-c. *M. genuflexa.* a-b, scalariform conjugation; c, lateral conjugation. (after Wittrock)

Vegetative cells 25-38 × 50-225μ, often geniculate and attached to other similar cells, forming extensive nets, sometimes with rhizoidal branches.

Conjugation lateral, less frequently scalariform ; zygospores quadrately ovoid to globose, 30-40μ in diameter ; spore wall smooth, brown.

*Distribution*:   Manchuria; Kiangsi, China; U.S.A. ; Europe ; Morocco, Africa.

**21.  Mougeotia scalaris** Hassall 1842.   *Ann. and Mag. Nat. Hist.* **10**, p.45.

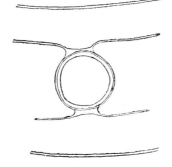

Fig. 28.   *M. scalaris.* (after Randhawa)

Vegetative cells 20-34 × 40-180 $\mu$ ; chloroplast with 4-10 pyrenoids in a single row ; fertile cells straight or slightly curved.

Conjugation scalariform ; zygospores formed wholly in the conjugating tube, ovoid to globose, 30-38 (-40) $\mu$ in diameter ; spore wall yellow-brown, smooth.

*Distribution*:

        *India*:   Fresh-water stream, V. Mubarakpur, Fyzabad Dist., U.P.

        *Other countries*:   China ; U.S.A. ; Southern Ontario ; Japan ; New Caledonia ; Queensland.

**22.  Mougeotia subcrassa** G.S. West 1909.   *Jour. Linn. Soc. London, Bot.* **39**, p. 50.

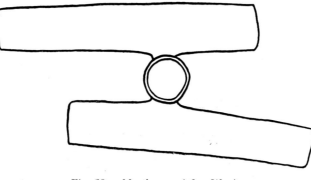

Fig. 29.   *M. subcrassa.* (after West)

Vegetative cells 41.5-43 × 240-280 $\mu$ ; chloroplast with 15-24 pyrenoids arranged irregularly ; gametangia straight or slightly curved.

Conjugation scalariform ; zygospores formed in the conjugating tube, globose, 40-41$\mu$ in diameter ; spore wall smooth and indistinctly lamellate ; sporangial wall thicker at the ends of the tube.

*Distribution* :   Victoria, Australia.

**23.   Mougeotia crassa** (Wolle) de Toni 1889.   *Sylloge Algarum.*   **1,** p. 716.

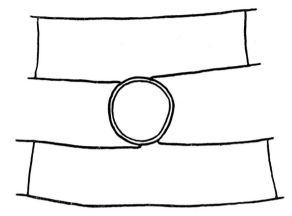

Fig. 30.   *M. crassa.* (after West)

Vegetative  cells  $50 \times 200\text{-}500\ \mu$.

Conjugation scalariform ; zygospores in the greatly enlarged conjugating tube, globose, about $65\mu$ in diameter ; spore wall smooth.

*Distribution* :   U.S.A.

**24.   Mougeotia caelestis** Transeau 1934.   *Trans. Amer. Micros. Soc.*   **53,** p. 218.

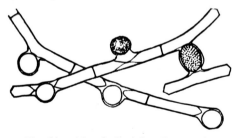

Fig. 31.   *M. caelestis.* (after Transeau)

Vegetative cells $7\text{-}9 \times 50\text{-}75\ \mu$ ; chloroplast with 2-6 pyrenoids, usually 4.

Conjugation scalariform ; zygospores in the conjugating tube, rarely extending slightly into the gametangia, ovoid to subglobose, $18\text{-}20 \times 21\text{-}25\ \mu$; spore wall light yellow, punctate, reproduction usually by aplanospores ; aplanospores globose to sub-globose, usually near the middle of the cell, either dividing it or wholly external, rarely terminal, $16\text{-}18\ \mu$ in diameter ; spore wall punctate.

*Distribution* :   U.S.A.

**25.   Mougeotia sinensis** Li 1933.   *Ohio Jour. Sci.* **33,** p.152.

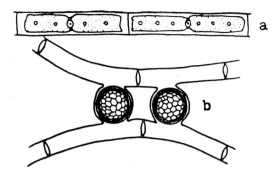

Fig. 32.  a-b.  *M. sinensis.* a, vegetative cells with chloroplasts;
b, gametangia with ripe zygospores. (after Li)

Vegetative cells 15-22 × 100-132 $\mu$ ; chloroplasts with 4-6 pyrenoids in a single row ; conjugating cells slightly geniculate.

Conjugation scalariform ; zygospores in the conjugating tube, ovoid to globose, 25-31 × 25-31$\mu$ ; spore wall yellow-brown, angularly reticulate.

*Distribution*:   Tinghai, China.

**26.  Mougeotia ovalis** (Hassall) Nordstedt 1886.  *Bot. Notiser.*  p. 136.

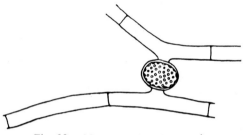

Fig. 33.  *M. ovalis.* (after Transeau)

Vegetative cells 11-14 × 110-140 $\mu$.

Conjugation scalariform ; zygospores in the conjugating tubes, compressed-ovoid to subglobose, 29-38 × 26-36 $\mu$ ; spore wall finely scrobiculate, brown.

*Distribution*:   British Isles ; Germany ; Italy and Switzerland.

**27.  Mougeotia nummuloides** (Hassall) de Toni 1889.  *Sylloge Algarum.*  **1,** Pt. 2, p. 713.

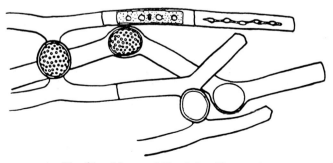

Fig. 34.  *M. nummuloides.* (after Transeau)

Vegetative cells 8-16 × 32-160 $\mu$ ; chloroplasts with 2-6 pyrenoids in a row.

Conjugation scalariform ; zygospores in the conjugating tubes, globose to ovoid (17-) 22-23 (-37)$\mu$ in diameter ; spore wall brown, scrobiculate ; aplanospores ovoid, within the angled sporogenous cell.

*Distribution*:   U.S.A. ; British Isles ; Finland and Bulgaria.

**28.   Mougeotia microspora** Taft 1934.   *Trans. Amer. Micros. Soc.*   **53,** p.218. Fig. 62.

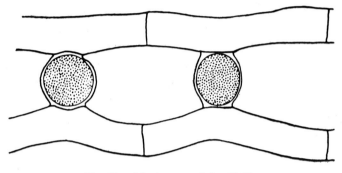

Fig. 35.   *M. microspora*. (after Taft)

Vegetative cells 18-23 × 60-160 $\mu$ ; chloroplast with 4-6 pyrenoids in a row.

Conjugation scalariform ; zygospores in the conjugating tube, globose to ovoid, or rarely slightly compressed-ovoid, 26-36 × 36-30$\mu$ ; outer sporangium wall a pectic layer 5-12 $\mu$ in thickness ; spore wall brown, distinctly punctate ; pores 0.5-1$\mu$ in diameter.

*Distribution*:   U.S.A.

**29.   Mougeotia ornata** Jao 1935.   *Sinensia.*   **6,** p. 577, Figs. 34-35.

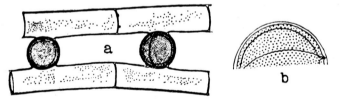

Fig. 36.   a-b.   *M. ornata*. (after Jao)

Vegetative cells 16-22 × 76-176 $\mu$; chloroplast with 4-10 usually  6, pyrenoids in a single row ; gametangia straight.

Conjugation scalariform ; zygospores in the conjugating tubes, globose to sub-globose, 28-35$\mu$ in diameter ; spore wall thick, more or less regularly and distinctly punctate, with a prominent, ridged suture ; margin of ridge finely undulate; yellowish-brown at maturity.

*Distribution*:—Szechwan, China.

**30.   Mougeotia globulispora** Jao 1935.   *Sinensia*, **6,** p. 578.

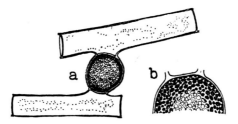

Fig. 37. a-b. *M. globulispora.* (after Jao)

Vegetative cells 19-32 × 96-228 $\mu$ ; chloroplast with 10-12 pyrenoids in a single row.

Conjugation scalariform ; zygospores in the conjugating tubes, globose to subglobose, 32-38.4 × 32-35 $\mu$ ; spore wall yellow-brown at maturity, finely and closely scrobiculate.

*Distribution* : China and Puerto Rico.

**31. Mougeotia lamellosa** Jao 1935. *Sinensia,* **6,** p. 577, Pl. III. Figs. 36-39.

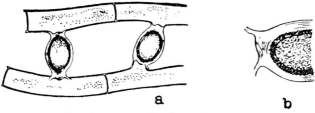

Fig. 38. a-b *M. lamellosa.* (after Jao)

Vegetative cells 19-30 × 60-186 $\mu$ ; chloroplast plate-like with 4-9 pyrenoids in a single row.

Gametangia straight ; sporangia adjoined by two cells, zygospores situated in the conjugation tubes, transversely ellipsoid, 28-45 × 24-32 $\mu$ ; exospore thick, lamellose mesospore verrucose, yellow in colour.

*Distribution* : Chungking, China.

**32. Mougeotia megaspora** Wittrock 1872. *Bih. Kgl. Svensk Vetensk. Akad. Handl.* **1**(1).

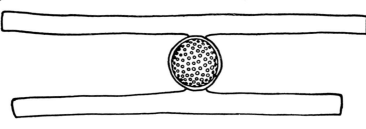

Fig. 39. *M. megaspora.* (after Wittrock)

Vegetative cells 17-21 × 170-380 $\mu$.

Conjugation scalariform ; zygospores in the conjugating tubes, globose, 40-50 $\mu$, or ovoid, 41-44 × 45-48 $\mu$; spore wall brown, irregularly scrobiculate.

*Distribution* :　U.S.A. ; Sweden.

**33. Mougeotia microverrucosa** Kolkwitz. & Krieger 1944. Rabenhors't *Kryptogamenflora.* **13** (2), p. 155.

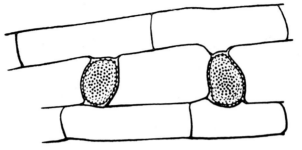

Fig. 40.　*M. microverrucosa.* (after Kolkwitz & Krieger)

Vegetative cells about $27 \times 70\text{-}108\mu$ ; chloroplast with several pyrenoids in a single row.

Conjugation scalariform ; zygospores filling the conjugating tubes, ovoid, $33\text{-}36 \times 44\text{-}49\,\mu$ ; spore wall irregularly verrucose ; elevations about $1\mu$ in a diameter.

*Distribution* :　Brandenburg, Trebnitz, Germany.

**34. Mougeotia laevis** (Kützing) Archer 1866. *Quart. Jour. Micros. Soc.* **6,** p. 272, and **7,** pl. 8, Figs. 1-3. Kützing. *Species Algarum,* p. 447. 1849.

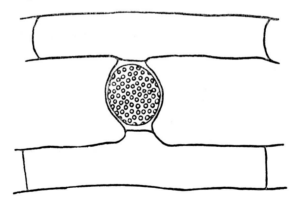

Fig. 41.　*M. laevis.* (after Kolkwitz & Krieger)

Vegetative cells $20\text{-}36 \times 20\text{-}100\,\mu$ ; chloroplast with 2 to 4 pyrenoids in a row.

Conjugation scalariform ; zygospores ellipsoid to ovoid, $20\text{-}36 \times 35\text{-}50\,\mu$ ; wall scrobiculate ; pits about $3\mu$ in diameter, $2\text{-}3\mu$ apart.

*Distribution* :　England ; Finland ; Poland ; North Africa ; United States of America and Yugoslavia.

**35. Mougeotia areolata** Transeau 1934. *Trans. Amer. Micros. Soc.* **53,** p. 219, Figs. 47-49.

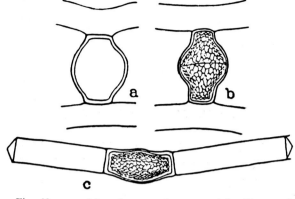

Fig. 42. a-c. *M. areolata.* c, aplanospore. (after Transeau)

Vegetative cells 17-26 × 90-400 $\mu$ ; cross walls more refractive than lateral walls and slightly colligate ; chloroplast with 1-10 pyrenoids in a row, occupying two-third to one-fourth the cell length.

Conjugation scalariform ; zygospores in the conjugating tubes, dolioform, with the ends short or extended, 43-50 × 50-70 $\mu$ ; wall frequently in 3 layers, the outer thin, yellow, minutely punctate, the second heavy, yellow areolate with a prominent equatorial ridge and suture, the innermost wall thin and hyaline ; aplanospores asymmetricaly ovoid, 27-33 $\mu$ × 55-56 $\mu$; markings similar to those of the zygospores.

*Distribution :* U.S.A.

### 36. **Mougeotia pulchella** Wittrock 1871. *Hedwigia* **10**, p.88.

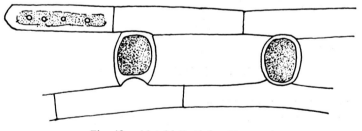

Fig. 43. *M. pulchella.* (after Transeau)

Vegetative cells 24-29 × 48-150 $\mu$ ; chloroplast with 4-8 pyrenoids in a row.

Conjugation scalariform ; zygospores in the conjugating tubes, ovoid, to ellipsoid, with ends more or less flattened, 28-35 × 40-50 $\mu$ ; spore wall yellow-brown, punctate.

*Distribution :* China ; Finland ; Germany ; Latvia ; Sweden and United States of America.

### 37. **Mougeotia gotlandica** (Cleve) Wittrock 1872. *Bih.Kgl. Svensk. Vetensk. Akad. Handl.* **1** (1).

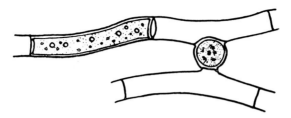

Fig. 44. *M. gotlandica*. (after Cleve)

Vegetative cells about 17-24 × 75-150 $\mu$ ; chloroplast with scattered pyrenoids. Conjugation scalariform ; zygospores in the conjugating tubes, globose, about 30-34 $\mu$ in diameter ; spore wall yellow-brown, wrinkled.

*Distribution :*

        *India* : Free-floating in Tons nadi, Akbarpur, Fyzabad Dist., U.P.

        *Other countries* : China ; Sweden ; Latvia ; Estonia ; Luxemburg.

Var. *crassa* Randh (*Proc. Ind. A cad Sci.* 1938, **8** : 125) differs in having a single row of pyrenoids and larger zygospores.

**38. Mougeotia talyschensis** (Woronichin) Czurda 1932. *Süsswasserflora Mitteleuropa.* **9,** p. 73.

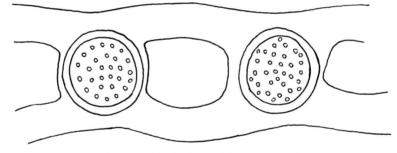

Fig. 45. *M. talyschensis*. (after Skvortzow)

Vegetative cells 18-21 × 80-100 $\mu$.

Conjugation scalariform ; zygospores formed in the broad conjugating tube, globose, 42-50 $\mu$ in diameter ; spore wall yellow-brown, punctate.

*Distribution :* Baku ; Russia, Manchuria, China.

**39. Mougeotia verrucosa** Wolle 1887. Kolkwitz & Krieger 1944. Rabenhorsts *Kryptogamenflora,* **13,** (2), p. 153. Fig. 65.

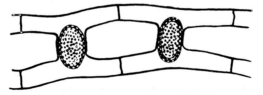

Fig. 46. *M. verrucosa*. (after Wolle)

Vegetative cells 13-14 $\mu$ broad.

Conjugation scalariform. Zygospores formed in the conjugating canals and sometimes extend into the gametangia. Zygospores ellipsoid, 20-25 × 40 $\mu$. Mesospore dark brown and granulate.

*Distribution :* North America.

**40. Mougeotia pseudocalospora** Czurda 1932 B. *Süsswasserflora Mitteleuropa* **9,** p. 71, Fig. 50 (=*Debarya calospora* W. & G.S. West).

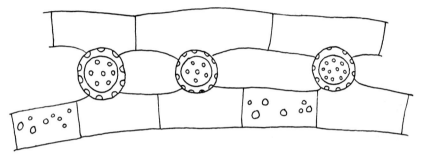

Fig. 47. *M. pseudocalospora.* (after West)

Vegetative cells 11-13 $\mu$ broad. Chloroplast plate-like with many pyrenoids.

Conjugation scalariform. Zygospores globose, 20 $\mu$ in diameter, exospore thin ; colourless. Mesospore thick, brown, pitted.

*Distribution :* England.

**41. Mougeotia handelii** Skuja 1937. *Symbolae Sinicae.* **1,** P. 83, Fig. 11.

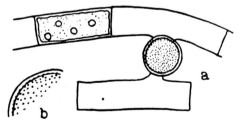

Fig. 48. a-b *M. handelii.* (after Skuja)

Vegetative cells about 35 × 70-175 $\mu$ ; chloroplast plate-like, with 8-14 scattered pyrenoids.

Conjugation scalariform ; zygospores globose, 40-42 $\mu$ in diameter ; spore wall olive-brown, scrobiculate on the inner side.

*Distribution :* China.

**42. Mougeotia daytonae** Transeau 1934. *Trans. Amer. Micros. Soc.* **53,** p. 219 Fig. 55.

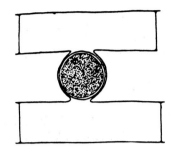

Fig. 49. *M. daytonae.* (after Transeau)

Vegetative cells 32-36 × 100-250 $\mu$ ; chloroplast with numerous scattered pyrenoids.

Conjugation scalariform ; zygospores in the conjugating tubes, globose, 40-50 $\mu$ in diameter, or subglobose, 39-42 × 45-50 $\mu$ ; spore wall yellow, coarsely and irregularly punctate ; pits about 1.5 $\mu$ in diameter and about the same distance apart ; the wall is also irregularly contracted and reticulate-wrinkled.

*Distribution :* United States of America.

**43. Mougeotia sanfordiana** Tiffany 1934.     *Trans. Amer. Micros. Soc.* **53,** p. 219, Fig. 58.

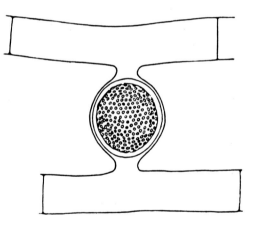

Fig. 50. *M. sanfordiana.* (after Transeau)

Vegetative cells 33-38 × 100-250 $\mu$ ; chloroplast with numerous scattered pyredoids.

Conjugation scalariform ; zygospores in the conjugating tube, globose, 63-68 $\mu$ in diameter, or subglobose, 54-65 × 65-72 $\mu$ ; spore wall yellow, scrobiculate ; pits 2-3 $\mu$ in diameter.

*Distribution :* United States of America.

**44. Mougeotia robusta** (de Bary) Wittrock 1885. Wittrock and Nordstedt, *Algae Exsiccatae,* No. 651.

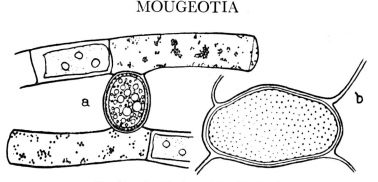

Fig. 51. a-b. *M.robusta*. (after De Bary)

Vegetative cells 25-33 × 75-260 $\mu$ ; chloroplast with 10-20 scattered pyrenoids.

Conjugation scalariform ; zygospores in conjugating tubes, ovoid, to subglobose, 35-41 × 47-58 $\mu$ ; spore wall brown, scrobiculate ; pits 1-1.6 $\mu$ in diameter, scattered.

*Distribution :* Ceylon ; Finland ; France ; Japan ; Germany ; North Africa ; Latvia ; Sweden and United States of America.

**45. Mougeotia sumatrana** Schmidle 1895. *Hedwigia*. **34**, p. 297.

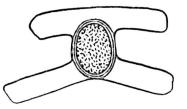

Fig. 52. *M. sumatrana*. (after Schmidle)

Vegetative cells 20-24 × 80-220 $\mu$ ; chloroplast with scattered pyrenoids ; gametangia somewhat shorter and thicker walled than the vegetative cells.

Conjugation scalariform ; zygospores formed in the enlarged conjugating tube and extending into the gametangia, ovoid, about 42 × 52 $\mu$ ; spore wall brown, granulate.

*Distribution :* Sumatra.

**46. Mougeotia angolensis** W. & G.S. West 1897, *Jour. Bot.* **35**, p. 39.

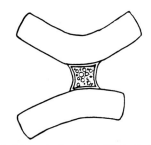

Fig. 53. *M.angolensis*. (after W. & G. S. West)

Vegetative cells 25-29 × 100-145 $\mu$ ; chloroplast with 4-6 very small pyrenoids, irregularly disposed.

Conjugation scalariform ; zygospores in the conjugating tubes, short-cylindric with concave sides, 19-21 $\mu$ in diameter ; wall smooth ; gametangia slightly curved.

*Distribution :* Africa.

**47. Mougeotia oblongata** Transeau 1934.   *Trans. Amer. Micros. Soc.* **53**, p.219, Fig.38.

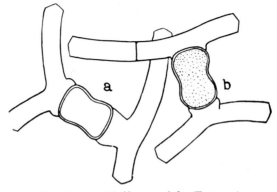

Fig. 54. a-b. *M.oblongata.* (after Transeau)

Vegetative cells 14-22 × 80-200 $\mu$ ; chloroplast with 6-12 (-16) pyrenoids in a single row.

Conjugation scalariform, often connecting several filaments ; zygospores in the conjugating tubes, usually bilobate-ovoid, sometimes more cylindric with concave sides. 28-36 × 47-58 $\mu$ ; spore wall yellow, sometimes finally punctate.

*Distribution :* United States of America.

**48. Mougeotia opelousensis** Taft 1944.   *Ohio Jour. Sci.* **44**, p. 238.

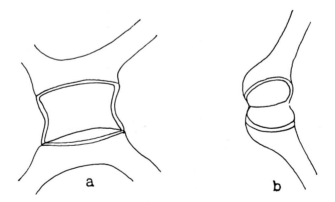

Fig 55. a-b. *M.opelousensis.* Zygospores at different angles. (after Taft.)

Vegetative cells 25-28 × 150-340 $\mu$ ;   chloroplast with 6-12 pyrenoids in a single row.

Conjugation scalariform ; zygospores short-cylindric, with concave ends and sides, formed in the tubes, 55-64 × 30-34 $\mu$ ; spore wall yellow punctate ; punctations about 0.8 $\mu$ in diameter and evenly spaced over the entire wall.

*Distribution :* United States of America.

**49. Mougeotia laetevirens** (Braun) Wittrock 1877.   Wittrock and Nordstedt *Algae Exsiccatae*, No. 58. *Bot. Notiser* 1877, p. 23.

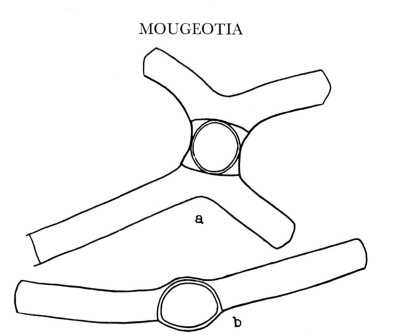

Fig. 56 a-b. *M.laetevirens.* a, gametangia with zygospore ; b, aplanospore. (after Transeau)

Vegetative cells 35-40 × 65-350 $\mu$ ; chloroplast with numerous scattered pyrenoids ; conjugating cells geniculate.

Conjugation scalariform ; zygospores in the conjugating tubes ; outer wall shortcylindric, 36-47 $\mu$ × 45-72 $\mu$, with concave sides ; spore wall yellow-brown, smooth ; aplanospores ovoid or obliquely ovoid. Spores quite variable in form.

*Distribution :*

*India :* Rain water pools, Bombay.

*Other countries :* Australia ; China ; Europe ; South America ; southern Siberia and United States of America.

**50. Mougeotia acadiana** Transeau 1934. *Trans. Amer. Micros. Soc.* **53,** p. 224.

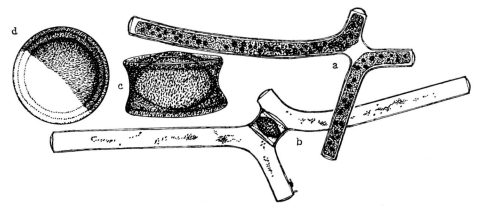

Fig. 57. a-d. *M.acadiana.* a-b, conjugating filaments ; c-d, zygospores in different views. (after Skuja)

Vegetative cells 43-54 × 100-400 $\mu$ ; chloroplast with many scattered pyrenoids conjugating cells geniculate.

Conjugation scalariform ; zygospores in the greatly enlarged conjugating tubes, cylindric-ovoid, usually with concave sides, ends convex 51-70 × 57-78 $\mu$ ; spore wall yellow, thick, smooth.   Similar to *M. laetevirens* but larger in all dimensions.

*Distribution :*   Czechoslovakia ; Latvia and United States of America.

**51.  Mougeotia pectosa** Transeau 1934.   *Trans. Amer. Micros. Soc.* **53**, p. 220, Figs. 53-54.

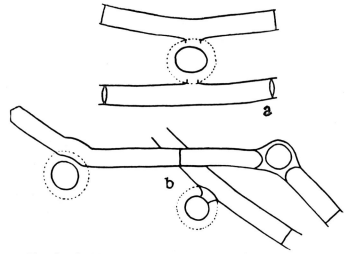

Fig. 58. a-b. *M.pectosa.* a, gametangia with zygospore ; b, spores
and aplanospores. (after Transeau)

Vegetative cells 14.5-19 × 120-190 $\mu$ ;   chloroplast with 4-8 pyrenoids in a single row.

Conjugation scalariform, but reproduction frequently by aplanospores ; zygospores in the conjugating tubes enclosed in a 5-10 $\mu$ thick pectic sporangium wall, compressed-globose, 26-29 × 20-22 $\mu$ ;   spore wall colourless, smooth ; aplanospores globose to compressed-globose, formed partly within or largely outside the mother cells, 18-21 $\mu$ in diameter, when formed outside the mother cell covered with a pectic layer.

*Distribution :*   United States of America.

**52.  Mougeotia cyanea** Transeau 1926.   *Ohio Jour. Sci.* **26**, p. 321.

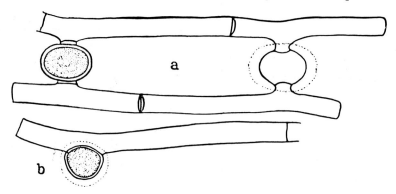

Fig. 59. a-b. *M. cyanea.* b, aplanospore. (after Transeau)

Vegetative cells (14-)16-18(-20) × 160-200 $\mu$ ; chloroplast occupying one-third to one-half of the cell, with 4-10 pyrenoids in a row.

Conjugation scalariform ; zygospores in the conjugating tubes, compressed-spherical, 38-48 × 30-40 $\mu$ ; with the long axis parallel to the filaments ; spore wall blue, finely punctate ; aplanospores spheroidal, laterally placed in the sporogenous cell, 30-32 $\mu$ in diameter ; both kinds of spores surrounded at maturity with a transparent pectic layer, 4-8 $\mu$ thick.

*Distribution*: United States of America.

**53. Mougeotia atubulosa** Kolkwitz & Krieger 1944. *Rabenhorst's Krypto-gamenflora.* **13**(2), p. 168.

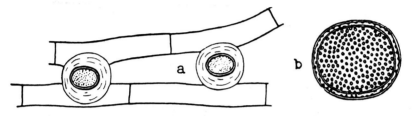

Fig. 60. a-b. *M. atubulosa.* (after Kolkwitz & Krieger)

Vegetative cells 19-21 × 100-140 $\mu$ ; chloroplast with several pyrenoids in a row.

Conjugation scalariform ; zygospores compressed-ovoid, 25-27 × 20-21 $\mu$ , with the longer axis parallel with the filaments, wholly within the conjugating tubes ; at maturity the tube wall becomes a pectic wall 8-10 $\mu$ in thickness ; spore wall blue, coarsely punctate ; pits about 0.5 $\mu$ in diameter, 1-1.5 $\mu$ apart.

*Distribution*: Java.

**54. Mougeotia cotopaxiensis** Prescott 1947. *Ohio Jour. Sci.* **47**, p. 132.

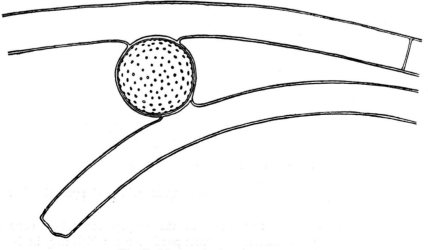

Fig. 61. *M. cotopaxiensis.* (after Prescott)

Vegetative cells 10-16 × 80-250 $\mu$ ; chloroplast with 2-4 pyrenoids in a row.

Conjugation scalariform ; zygospores globose or compressed at right angles to the short conjugating tubes, 30-32 $\mu$ in diameter ; spore wall steel-blue, scrobiculate with pits about 1 $\mu$ in diameter, 4-5 $\mu$ apart ; sporangium wall thin, smooth.

*Distribution* : Ecuador, South America.

**55. Mougeotia rava** Transeau 1944. *Ohio Jour. Sci.* **44,** p. 244.

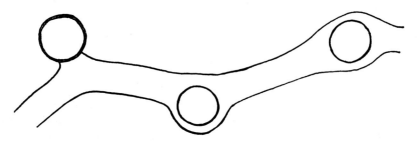

Fig. 62. *M. rava.* aplanospores variously placed. (after Transeau)

Vegetative cells 8-12 $\mu$ ; chloroplast with 4-8 pyrenoids in a row.

Reproducing by aplanospores ; spores formed mostly outside the recurved sporiferous cells ; aplanospores globose, 16-20 $\mu$ in diameter ; wall grey-brown and smooth.

*Distribution* : United States of America.

**56. Mougeotia gelatinosa** Wittrock 1889. Wittrock and Nordstedt, *Algae Exsiccatae*, No. 957.

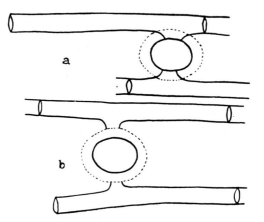

Fig. 63. a-b. *M. gelatinosa.* (after Wittrock)

Vegetative cells 12-18 × 120-180 $\mu$ ; chloroplast with 3-6 pyrenoids in a single row.

Conjugation scalariform ; zygospores in the conjugating tubes, compressed-ovoid, 38-47 × 28-39 $\mu$ , not including the outer pectic layer, which may be 7-10 $\mu$ in thickness ; spore wall brown, smooth.

*Distribution*: British Isles ; Finland ; Latvia, Spain and Sweden.

**57.  Mougeotia pawhuskae** Taft 1934. *Trans. Amer. Micros. Soc.* **53**, p. 220.

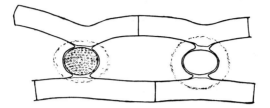

Fig. 64.  *M. pawhuskae.* (after Taft)

Vegetative cells $18\text{-}22 \times 90\text{-}170 \, \mu$ ; chloroplasts with 6-8 pyrenoids in a row.

Conjugation scalariform ; zygospores in the conjugating tubes, compressed-globose, $34\text{-}40 \times 25\text{-}32 \, \mu$, with the longer axis at right angles to the tubes, surrounded by a pectic layer $4\text{-}16 \, \mu$ in thickness ; spore wall yellow to yellow-brown, scrobiculate, with a distinct equatorial suture.

*Distribution*: United States of America.

**58.  Mougeotia chlamydata** Prescott 1947. *Ohio Jour. Sci.* **47**, p. 130.

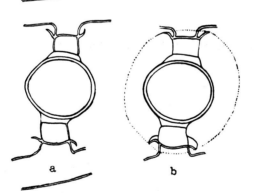

Fig. 65. a-b.  *M. chlamydata.* (after Prescott)

Vegetative cells $12\text{-}16 \times 200\text{-}240 \, \mu$ ; chloroplast with 4-6 pyrenoids in a row.

Conjugation scalariform ; zygospores compressed-globose, $26\text{-}28 \times (30\text{-}) \, 32\text{-}38 \, \mu$; sporangium wall bluish (by refraction), spore wall thick, metallic green, and smooth. The sporangium wall is quite unique in that after conjugation it has an inner and outer layer of cellulose separated by a thick pectic layer. The outer layer disintegrates equatorially as the spore reaches maturity and the pectic layer dissolves leaving a collar around the base of each half of the conjugating tube.

*Distribution*: Ecuador.

**59.  Mougeotia oedogonioides** Czurda 1931. *Beih. Bot. Centralbl.* **48**, p. 286.

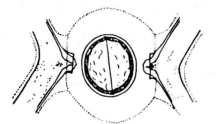

Fig. 66. *M.oedogonioides.* (after Czurda)

Vegetative cells 16-18 $\mu$ in diameter, with 1-2 plate-like chloroplasts, each with 2-3 pyrenoids.

Conjugation scalariform between geniculate cells ; lateral by the solution of the cross wall and the development of a conjugating tube between the ends of the gametangia ; subsequently, in both cases, following the union of the gametes, the sporangium wall changes to a thick pectic layer, 8-20 $\mu$ in width ; the gametangial wall at the point of union with the sporangium becomes modified, suggesting the ring scars of *Oedogonium* cells ; zygospores globose or compressed-globose, 41-50 $\times$ 40-41 $\mu$ ; outer wall thick, colourless, smooth ; spore wall yellow, thick, and irregularly corrugate, with a distinct equatorial suture.

*Distribution* :   Tibet, Asia.

**60.   Mougeotia indica** Randhawa 1958.   *Bot. Gaz.* **119**, p. 26-27.

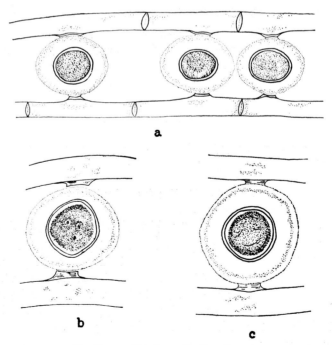

a

b

c

Fig. 67. a-c. *M.indica.* (after Randhawa)

Vegetative cells 12-18 $\times$ 36-72 $\mu$, with a single plate-like chloroplast.

Conjugation scalariform. Zygospores formed in the conjugating tubes enclosed in a colourless pectic layer 15 $\mu$ thick. Zygospores compressed-ovoid, 46-57 × 48-53 $\mu$. Mesopore thick, dark brown and smooth.

*Distribution* :

*India* :   Free-floating in a fresh-water lake near Baskhari, Fyzabad, U.P.

**61.  Mougeotia disjuncta** Transeau 1934. *Trans. Amer. Micros. Soc.*  **53,** p. 222, Figs. 50-51.

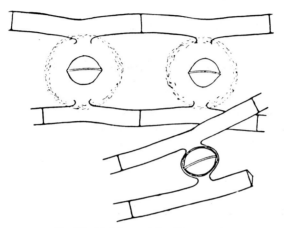

Fig. 68. *M.disjuncta.* (after Transeau)

Vegetative cells 14-18 × 50-200 $\mu$ ; chloroplast with 2-8 pyrenoids in a line.

Conjugation scalariform ; zygospores in the conjugating tubes, compressed-globose, 24-32 × 21-28 $\mu$ ; sporangium wall changing during maturity to pectic substance and becoming as much as 25 $\mu$ thick and pushing the 2 gametangia apart, but supporting the zygospore within ; spore wall chestnut brown, punctate, suture prominent.

*Distribution* :   China and United States of America.

**62.  Mougeotia operculata** Transeau 1934. *Trans. Amer. Micros. Soc.*  **53,** p. 220, Fig. 52.

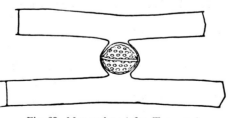

Fig. 69. *M.operculata.* (after Transeau)

Vegetative cells 18-21 × 60-285 $\mu$ ; chloroplast with 4-8 pyrenoids, usually 4.

Conjugation scalariform ; zygospores in the conjugating tubes, compressed-spheroid, 27-30 × 21-27 $\mu$, with a prominent equatorial ridge and suture on the wall ; spore wall pale yellow, shallow-scrobiculate.

*Distribution* : United States of America.

**63. Mougeotia seminoleana** Tiffany 1934. *Trans. Amer. Micros. Soc.* **53**, p. 220, Fig. 40.

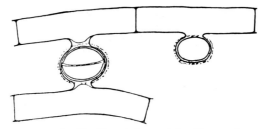

Fig. 70. *M.seminoleana.* (after Transeau)

Vegetative cells 20-25 × 70-200 $\mu$ ; chloroplast with 4-12 pyrenoids in a row.

Conjugation scalariform ; zygospores in the conjugating tubes, compressed-globose, 32-47 × 25-36 $\mu$ ; outer sporangium wall a pectic layer 2-4 $\mu$ thick, absent from most of the mature spores ; spore wall brown to dark chestnut brown, coarsely punctate, suture sometimes prominent, sometimes scarcely visible ; aplanospores smaller, 20-22 × 25-29 $\mu$, usually outside the mother cell, otherwise similar to the zygospores.

*Distribution* : United States of America.

**64. Mougeotia transeaui** Collins 1912. *Tufts College Studies.* Sci. Ser. **3**, p. 77. Wittrock. *Bih. Kgl. Svensk Vetensk. Akad. Handl.* **1**, p. 39. 1872 (as *M. tenuis*).

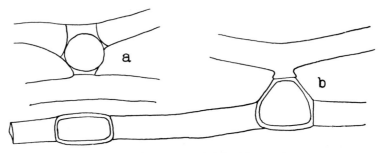

Fig. 71. a-b. *M.transeaui.* (after Transeau)

Vegetative cells 9-13 × 50-150 $\mu$ ; chloroplast with 4-8 pyrenoids in a single row.

Conjugation scalariform ; zygospores globose to triangular-ovoid, 20-30 × 26-36 $\mu$, occupying the middle portion of the receptive gametangium and the tube, spore wall yellow, smooth ; aplanospores obliquely ovoid, 12-20 × 20-32 $\mu$ formed at the middle of a straight or slightly angled cell which may be as long as the gametangium or longer.

*Distribution* : England ; Sweden and United States of America.

**65. Mougeotia depressa** (Hassall) Wittrock 1880. *Skandinaviens Vaxter.* **4**, p. 23.

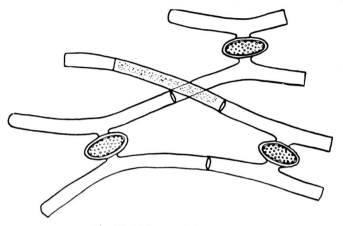

Fig. 72. *M.depressa*. (after Kütz)

Vegetative cells 7-12 × 35-144 $\mu$.

Conjugation scalariform and lateral ; zygospores in the conjugating tubes, compressed-ellipsoid with the longer axis parallel to the filaments, 28-32 × 12-14 $\mu$ ; spore wall brown, punctate.

*Distribution*:  British Isles ; Luxemburg, Germany ; Sweden ; Switzerland and United States of America.

**66.  Mougeotia varians** (Wittrock) Czurda 1932.  *Süsswasserflora Mitteleuropa.* **9,** p. 79.

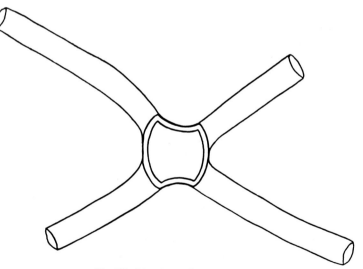

Fig. 73. *M.varians* (after Wittrock)

Vegetative cells 25-27 $\mu$ ; chloroplasts with numerous scattered pyrenoids.

Conjugation scalariform ; zygospores in the conjugating tubes, extending into or across the gametangia, cylindric-ovoid, usually with concave sides, ends convex,

48-60 × 64-78 $\mu$ ; spore wall yellow-brown, smooth ; sporangia adjoined by 2, 3, or 4 cell remnants.

*Distribution* :   Czechoslovakia, Finland, Holland, Sweden and United States.

**67.   Mougeotia floridana** Transeau 1934.   *Trans. Amer. Micros. Soc.* **53,** p. 224.   (=*M. abnormis* Kissel).

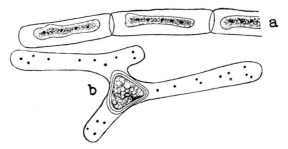

Fig. 74. a-b. *M. floridana.* (after Randhawa)

Vegetative cells 14-20 × 60-200 $\mu$ ; chloroplast with 6-8 pyrenoids in a single row.

Conjugation scalariform ; zygospores occupying the middle of the  receptive gametangia and the tubes, globose to triangular-ovoid, 30-40 × 36-48 $\mu$ ; spore wall yellow, smooth ; aplanospores obliquely ovoid, 18-24 × 30-45 $\mu$, occupying the middle part of the cell ; spore wall yellow, smooth.

*Distribution* :

*India* :   Free-floating along with *Zygnemopsis lamellata* in a jhil near Tanda, Fyzabad, U.P.

*Other countries* :   United States of America.

**68.   Mougeotia caimani** Transeau 1938.   *Amer. Jour. Bot.* **25,** p. 525, Fig. 2.

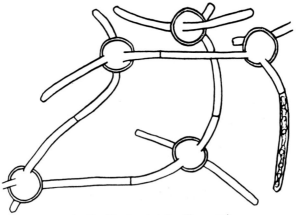

Fig. 75. *M.caimani.* (after Transeau)

Vegetative cells 4-5 × 60-100 $\mu$ ; chloroplast with 2-8 pyrenoids in a single row.

Conjugation scalariform ; zygospores dividing both gametangia, subglobose,

20-25 $\mu$ in diameter, surrounded by a thin pectic layer. Zygospores were smooth and colourless, probably immature.

*Distribution*: Haiti, Trou Caiman.

**69. Mougeotia poinciana** Transeau 1934. *Trans. Amer. Micros. Soc.* **53,** p. 224, Figs. 45-46.

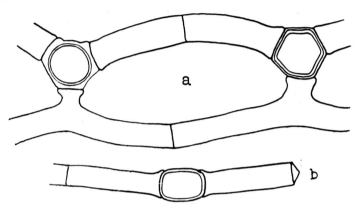

Fig. 76. a-b, *M. poinciana*. b, aplanospore. (after Transeau)

Vegetative cells 21-25 × 100-200 $\mu$; chloroplast with 6-10 pyrenoids in a single row.

Conjugation scalariform; zygospores occupying the middle portion of the receptive gametangia and the tubes; triangular-ovoid to globose, 36-44 × 35-51 $\mu$; spore wall yellow, smooth; aplanospores occupying the middle part of the cell; obliquely ovoid, 24-30 × 32-48 $\mu$.

*Distribution*: United States of America.

**70. Mougeotia cherokeana** Taft 1934. *Trans. Amer. Micros. Soc.* **53,** p. 222, Fig. 39.

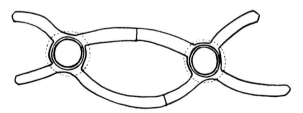

Fig. 77. *M. cherokeana*. (after Transeau)

Vegetative cells 7-9 × 90-120 $\mu$; chloroplast with 2-6 pyrenoids in a single row.

Conjugation scalariform; zygospores filling the tube and dividing both gametangia, globose, rarely subglobose, 21-25 $\mu$ in diameter, surrounded by an outer pectic layer 4-6 $\mu$ in thickness; spore wall yellow to brownish-yellow, smooth.

*Distribution* : United States of America.

**71. Mougeotia elegantula** Wittrock 1872. *Om Gotland och Oelands Söt. Alg.*, p. 40.

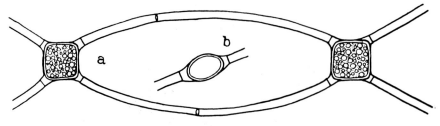

Fig. 78. a-b. *M.elegantula.* (after Wittrock)

Vegetative cells 3·5 -5 × 50-135 $\mu$ ; chloroplast with 4-8 pyrenoids in a row.

Conjugating cells geniculate ; conjugation scalariform ; sporangium dividing both gametangia ; zygospores cruciate-quadrate, 18-24 × 18-24 $\mu$, with rounded corners ; spore wall hyaline, smooth ; aplanospores ellipsoid, 6-9 × 20-24 $\mu$, otherwise similar to the zygospores.

*Distribution* : China ; Europe ; United States of America and West Indies.

**72. Mougeotia virescens** (Hassall) Borge 1913. *Süsswasserflora Deutschland.* **9,** p. 43.

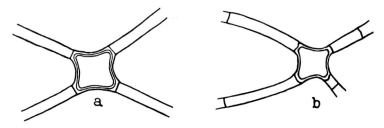

Fig. 79. a-b. *M.virescens.* a. (after Hassal); b, (after Kolkwitz & Krieger.)

Vegetative cells 8-9 × 50-220 $\mu$.

Conjugation scalariform ; sporangia dividing both gametangia ; zygospores quadrangular, with concave sides, 29-35 × 29-35 $\mu$ ; wall colourless, smooth, with rounded corners.

*Distribution* : China ; Canada, England ; Germany ; France ; Yugoslavia and United States of America.

**73. Mougeotia paludosa** G.S. West 1899. *Jour. Bot.* **37,** p. 108, Pl. 395, Figs. 4-6.

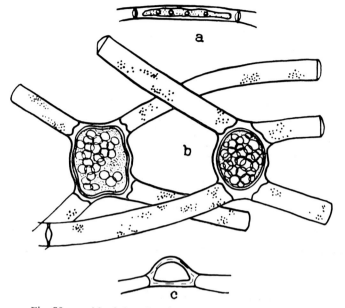

Fig. 80. a-c. *M.paludosa*. (b, after G.S. West, a and c, after
Kolkwitz and Krieger)

Vegetative cells 11·5 -13·5 × 70-185 $\mu$ ; chloroplast short, occupying about
one-third the length of the cell, with 4-6 pyrenoids in a single row ; fertile cells
recurved.

Conjugation scalariform ; sporangia dividing both gametangia ; zygospores
ovoid to quadrangular-ovoid, angles undulate truncate, 32-38 × 44-49 $\mu$ ; outer wall
of zygospores thick, smooth ; inner wall smooth, thin.

*Distribution* : England.

**74. Mougeotia delicata** Beck 1926. *Archiv f. Protistenk.* **55,** p. 179, Fig. 17.

Fig. 81. *M.delicata*. (after Beck)

Vegetative cells about 3·5 $\mu$ in diameter.

Conjugation scalariform ; sporangia dividing both gametangia ; zygospores
cruciate-quadrate, with concave sides, angles with hornlike processes ; spores about
28 $\mu$ on a side.

*Distribution* : Austria.

**75. Mougeotia subpaludosa** Ley 1944. *Sinensia.* **15,** p. 97.

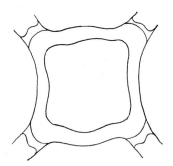

Fig. 82. *M. subpaludosa.* (after Ley)

Vegetative cells 9-11 × 30-152 $\mu$ ; pyrenoids 2.

Conjugation scalariform ; sporangia dividing both gametangia ; zygospores quadrangular-ovoid, sometimes much rounded, 25-29 × 21-29 $\mu$, 20-27 $\mu$ thick ; spore wall very thick, smooth, deep yellow at maturity.

*Distribution* :   China.

**76.  Mougeotia viridis** (Kützing) Wittrock 1872.  *Bih. Kgl. Svensk Vetensk, Akad. Handl.* **1,** p. 39.

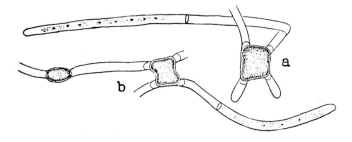

Fig. 83. a-b. *M. viridis.* (after Randhawa)

Vegetative cells 6-9 × 40-160 $\mu$ ; chloroplast occupying most of the cell with 2-6 pyrenoids in a single row.

Conjugation scalariform ; sporangia dividing both gametangia ; zygospores quadrate with concave sides and retuse angles,  20-32 × 20-32 $\mu$; spore wall smooth, colourless ; aplanospores oblique-ellipsoid, 14-16 × 30-36 $\mu$.

*Distribution* :

*India* :   In a freshwater jhil, Tahlisahib, Hoshiarpore, Punjab.

*Other countries* :   China ; Europe ; North Africa and United States of America.

**77.  Mougeotia corniculata** Hansgirg 1886.  *Oesterr. Bot. Zeitschr.* No.  10.

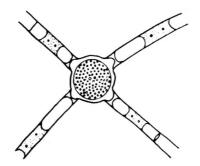

Fig. 84. *M.corniculata.* (after Hansgirg)

Vegetative cells 5-7 × 30-180 $\mu$.

Conjugation scalariform ; sporangia dividing both gametangia ; zygospores quadrately ovoid, 22-26 × 22-26 $\mu$ ; spore wall yellow-brown, smooth, thickened, forming rounded processes at the angles.

*Distribution :* France ; Czechoslovakia and North Africa.

**78. Mougeotia uberosperma** W. & G.S. West 1897. *Jour. Bot.* **35**, p. 37.

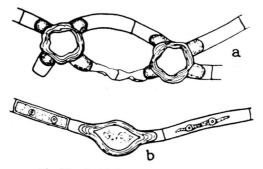

Fig. 85. a-b. *M.uberosperma.* (after West)

Vegetative cells 6-8 × 24-64 $\mu$.

Conjugation scalariform ; zygosporangium dividing both gametangia ; zygospores angular-globose (4-6 angles), wall very thick and lamellate, smooth and colourless, with corners extended into 4 solid, unequal processes which project into the gametangia ; zygospores 21-27 $\mu$ in diameter, processes 3-18 $\mu$ long ; aplanospores 20-30 $\mu$ with 2 processes.

*Distribution :* Africa.

**79. Mougeotia americana** Transeau 1918. *Tech. Pub.*, No. 9. New York State College of Forestry, p. 237.

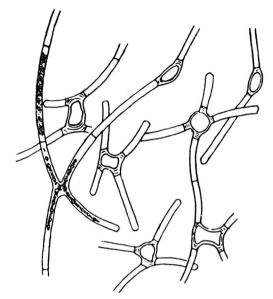

Fig. 86. *M.americana.* (after Transeau)

Vegetative cells 4-5 × 40-120 $\mu$ ; chloroplast with 4-10 pyrenoids in a single row.

Conjugating cells slightly or strongly geniculate ; zygospores dividing both gametangia, irregularly quadrate with concave or convex sides ; angles produced and truncate, the space between the zygospore and the sporangium walls being filled with pectic material ; spores 13-24 × 18-32 $\mu$ ; wall colourless, smooth, transparent ; aplanospores obliquely elliptical, ends truncate at the middle of very long genuflexed vegetative cells, 10-14 × 20-26 $\mu$.

*Distribution :* United States of America.

**80. Mougeotia craterophora** Bohlin 1901. *Bih. Kgl. Svensk Vetensk. Akad. Handl.* **27,** p. 50.

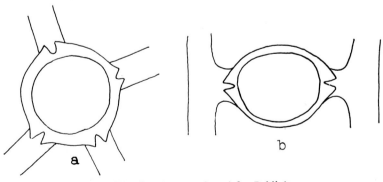

Fig. 87. a-b. *M. craterophora.* (after Bohlin)

Vegetative cells 7-9 $\mu$ in diameter, 8-14 times as long.

Conjugation scalariform ; zygospores in the conjugating tubes, or dividing **one,** or both, gametangia ; zygospores globose to ovoid, 18-22 × 24-28 $\mu$, with 2 to 4 crateriform or retuse processes ; spore wall brown, smooth.

*Distribution :* Azores.

**81. Mougeotia granulosa** Transeau 1938. *Amer. Jour. Bot.* **25**, p. 525.

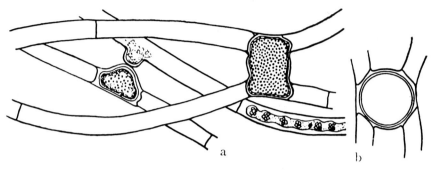

Fig. 88. a-b. *M. granulosa.* (after Transeau)

Vegetative cells 14.4-18 $\mu$ × 140-180 (-320) $\mu$, chloroplast with 4 to 8 pyrenoids in a row.

Conjugation scalariform ; sporangium wall thick, transparent, dividing both gametangia, varying from broadly ovoid to quadrangular-ovoid ; spores 36-47 × 42-52 $\mu$ ; walls yellow to brown, rarely smooth, mostly granulose when mature, either apparently single or distinctly double; both layers granulose when separated.

*Distribution :* South Africa.

**82. Mougeotia gracillima** (Hassall) Wittrock 1872. *Bih. Kgl. Svenk, Vetensk. Akad. Handl.* **1,** p. 40.

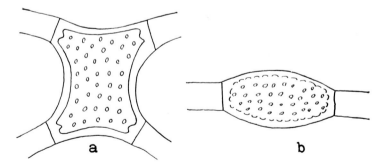

Fig. 89. a-b. *M.gracillima.* a, zygospore, b, aplanospore (after Transeau)

Vegetative cells 5-7 × 55-140 $\mu$.

Conjugation scalariform ; sporangia dividing both gametangia ; zygospores quadrate, with deeply concave sides, 20-25 × 20-28 $\mu$, angles retuse ; spore wall minutely verrucose ; aplanospores spindle-shaped.

*Distribution :* Europe and United States of America.

**83. Mougeotia capucina** (Bory) Agardh 1824. *Systema Algarum*, p. 84.

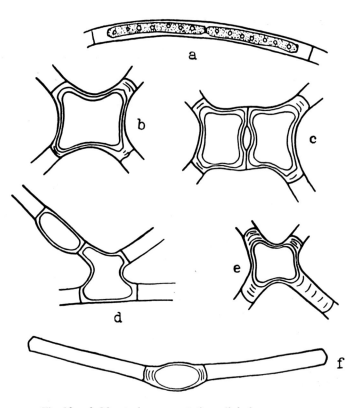

Fig. 90. a-f. *M. capucina.* a, vegetative cell, b,d,e, zygospores,
c, parthenospore, d, f, aplanospore. (after Transeau)

Vegetative cells 14-21 × 70-280 (-340) $\mu$, usually violet coloured ; 1 or 2 chloroplasts either rod-shaped occupying one-third to one-fourth of the cell with 4-8 pyrenoids, or ribbon-like occupying three-fourths of the length of the cell with 12-16 pyrenoids in a single row.

Conjugation scalariform ; the first sporangium walls are formed at a distance (5-52 $\mu$) from the zygospores, the intervening space filled with pectic compounds ; sporangium divides both gametangia ; zygospores irregularly quadrangular with concave sides, 50-70 × 60-100 $\mu$ ; spore wall violet to brown, thick especially at the angles, smooth ; aplanospores not uncommon, 20-36 × 45-70 (-80) $\mu$, with more or less produced ends.

*Distribution :* Europe ; Central Africa ; northern South America ; Hawaii ; New Zealand and United States of America.

**84. Mougeotia boodlei** (W. & G.S. West) Collins 1912. *Tufts College Studies.* **3**(2), p. 76.

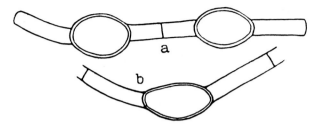

Fig. 91. a-b. *M.boodlei*. aplanospores. (after W & G.S. West)

Vegetative cells 4-5-5 × 25-225 $\mu$ ; chloroplast 0.5-0.8 of the length of the cell, with 4-6 pyrenoids in a single row.

Reproduction usually by aplanospores, very rarely by zygospores ; conjugation scalariform ; zygospores quadrangular, 15-18 × 15-23 $\mu$, corners somewhat rounded ; aplanospores ellipsoid, 12-15 × 23-25 $\mu$, projecting slightly on the convex side of the slightly curved sporangia ; spore wall yellow to brown, punctate.

*Distribution :* British Isles and United States of America.

**85. Mougeotia austriaca** Czurda 1932. *Süsswasserflora Mitteleuropa*, **9**, p. 90, Fig. 82.

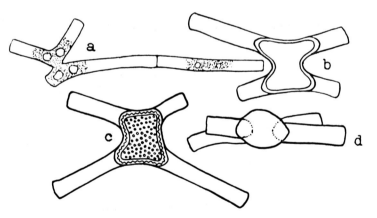

Fig. 92. a-d. *M. austriaca*. (after Czurda.)

Vegetative cells 7-9 × 50-140 $\mu$ ; chloroplast with 2 pyrenoids.

Conjugation scalariform ; zygospores quadrangular, with concave sides and rounded corners bulging into the gametangia, 20-25 × 27-30 $\mu$ ; spore wall golden-brown, thick, scrobiculate ; pits about 1 $\mu$ in diameter.

*Distribution :* Austria and United States of America.

**86. Mougeotia tumidula** Transeau 1914. *Amer. Jour. Bot.* **1**, p. 297.

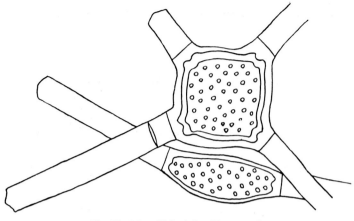

Fig. 93. *M.tumidula.* (after Transeau.)

Vegetative cells 6-8.5 × 70-120 $\mu$ ; chloroplast with 4-8 pyrenoids.

Conjugation scalariform ; sporangia dividing both gametangia ; zygospores quadrangular, with convex walls, 22-26 × 26-30 $\mu$, angles retuse ; spore wall colourless, distinctly punctate ; aplanospores obliquely ellipsoid, 12-14 × 28-32 $\mu$, with retuse ends and coarsely punctate.

*Distribution :*  Puerto Rico and United States of America.

**87. Mougeotia producta** G.S. West 1907. *Ann. Roy. Bot. Gard., Calcutta.* **6,** Part 2.

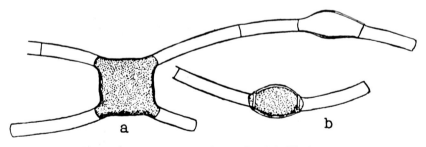

Fig. 94 a-b. *M.producta.* (after G.S. West)

Vegetative cells 7-8 × 84-160 $\mu$.

Conjugation scalariform ; sporangia dividing both gametangia ; zygospores quadrangular, with concave or slightly convex sides, angles produced and truncate, 29-37 $\mu$ on a side ; spore wall colourless, punctate ; aplanspores obliquely ellipsoid with ends produced, 14-18 × 30-40 $\mu$, otherwise similar to the zygospores.

*Distribution :*

*India :*  Assam ; In a ditch at the side of salt works, Vizagapatam, Andhra State.

*Other countries :*  Burma.

**88. Mougeotia thylespora** Skuja 1929. *Acta Horti Bot. Univ. Latviensis.* **4,** p. 48.

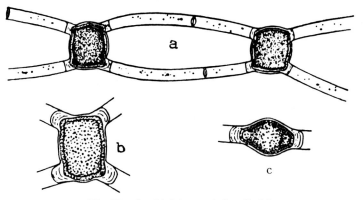

Fig. 95. a-b. *M.thylespora.* (after Skuja)

Vegetative cells 5-8 × 25-80 μ ; chloroplast with 4-8 pyrenoids in a single row.

Conjugating cells geniculate ; conjugation scalariform ; sporangia dividing both gametangia ; zygospores quadrangular with angles produced and truncate, 16-22 × 20-32 μ ; spore wall yellow-brown, scrobiculate, with tumid sides and rounded projecting corners ; aplanospores oblique-ellipsoid, 18-25 × 28.8-39.6 μ.

*Distribution :* Estonia and United States of America.

**89. Mougeotia quadrangulata** Hassall 1843. *Ann. and Mag. Nat. Hist·* **11,** p. 434.

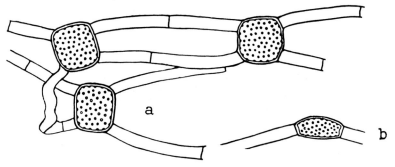

Fig. 96. a-b. *M.quadrangulata.* a, (after Transeau); b, (after Jao).

Vegetative cells 8-13 × 50-140 μ ; chloroplast with 8-16 pyrenoids in a single row.

Conjugating cells geniculate ; conjugation scalariform; sporangia dividing both gametangia ; zygospores quadrangular with straight sides and truncate corners or rarely with angles retuse, 28-40 × 28-40 μ; spore wall colourless, punctate ; aplanospores obliquely ovoid, 20-21 × 36-44 μ.

*Distribution :* China ; England ; Russia ; South and North Africa ; Madagascar ; South America ; Chile and United States of America.

**90. Mougeotia regellii** Skuja 1937. *Hedwigia.* **77,** p. 53, Pl. 2, Figs. 1-3.

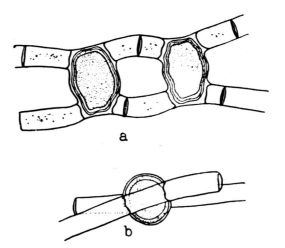

Fig. 97. a-b. *M.regellii.* (after Transeau)

Vegetative cells 7-9 × 50-160 $\mu$ ; chloroplast sometimes constricted in the middle, with 2-4 pyrenoids in a row.

Conjugation scalariform ; conjugating cells slightly geniculate ; zygospores dividing both gametangia, hexagonal-ovoid, 22-25 × 29-30 $\mu$; spore wall thin, yellow-brown, smooth ; inner wall colourless to pale yellow, densely and finely punctate.

*Distribution :* Greece.

**91. Mougeotia quadrata** Randhawa 1938. *Proc. Ind. Acad. Sci.* **8,** p. 126, Fig. 9.

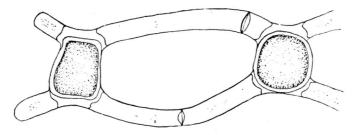

Fig. 98. *M.quadrata.* (after Randhawa)

Vegetative cells are 10-12 $\mu$ broad, 80-120 $\mu$ long, each with a plate-like chloroplast bearing 3-6 pyrenoids.

Conjugation is scalariform, with the zygospores extending into both the gametangia. Zygospores are quadrate to globose-quadrate 22-23 $\mu$ broad and 27-30 $\mu$ long, with an average size of 27 $\mu$, are yellowish in colour, and have pads of white mucilage at the angles. Spore-wall is smooth.

*Distribution :*

*India* :  Found free-floating in a fresh-water stream near Mubarakpur, district Fyzabad, U.P.

**92.  Mougeotia punctata** Wittrock 1867. *Algologiska Studier.* **I.** Uppsala.

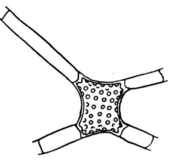

Fig. 99. *M punctata.* (after Kolkwitz and Krieger.)

Vegetative cells 8-10 × 50-120 $\mu$ ; chloroplast with 4 pyrenoids in a row.

Conjugation scalariform ; sporangia dividing both gametangia ; zygospores quadrangular with concave sides and obtuse or retuse angles, 30-38 × 30-38 $\mu$, 18-20 $\mu$ thick ; outer wall finely scrobiculate, inner nearly smooth.

*Distribution :*  Brazil ; Sweden and United States of America.

**93.  Mougeotia rotundangulata** Jao 1935. *Sinensia.* **6,** p. 579, Pl. 2, Figs. 45-46.

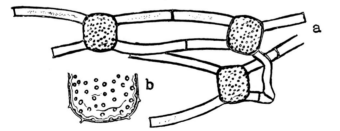

Fig. 100. a-b. *M. rotundangulata.* (after Jao.)

Vegetative cells 8-10 × 160-420 $\mu$ ; chloroplast with 8-14 pyrenoids in a single row.

Conjugation scalariform ; sporangia dividing both gametangia ; zygospores quadrangular, somewhat tumid, 32-35 × 32-35 $\mu$, with rounded angles ; wall scrobiculate with scattered pits, 1-2 $\mu$ in diameter, colourless at maturity.

*Distribution :*  China.

**94.  Mougeotia irregularis** W. & G.S. West 1897. *Jour. Bot.* **35,** p. 38.

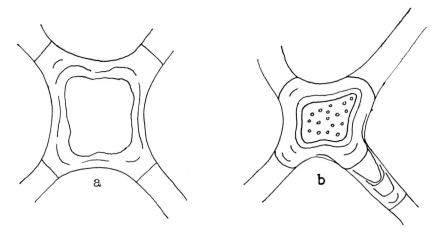

Fig. 101. a-b. *M.irregularis*. (after West.)

Vegetative cells 13.5-15 × 70-90 μ.

Conjugation scalariform ; conjugating cells more or less recurved ; sporangium dividing both gametangia; zygospores irregularly quadrate to trapezoid with concave sides and thick walls, 38-63 × 42-48 μ including the processes, angles with hornlike processes of varying length with rounded ends; spore wall thick, yellow to yellow-brown, punctate.

*Distribution :* Africa.

**95. Mougeotia miamiana** Transeau 1934. *Trans. Amer. Micros. Soc.* **53,** p. 222, Pl. 19, Figs. 41-42.

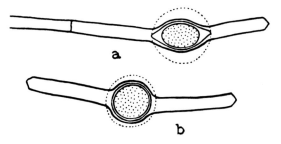

Fig. 102. a-b. *M. miamiana.* aplanospores. (after Transeau )

Vegetative cells 6-7.2 × 60-130 μ; chloroplast with 2-6 pyrenoids.

Zygospores unknown ; aplanospores formed in the middle of straight or slightly angled cells ; outer sporangium wall covered at all stages by a pectic layer; aplanospores globose to ovoid to ellipsoid with projections at either end; globose spores 18-20 μ in diameter, ellipsoid spores 16-18 × 25-32 μ ; spore wall yellow, punctate.

*Distribution :* United States of America.

**96. Mougeotia tropica** (W. & G.S. West) Transeau 1926. *Ohio Jour. Sci.* **26,** p. 325, Pl. 7, Fig. 112.

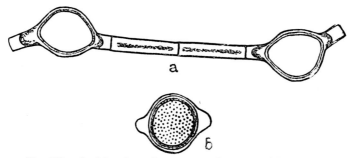

Fig. 103. a-b. *M.tropica*. aplanospores. (after W. and G.S. West.)

Vegetative cells 6-7 × 36-56 $\mu$ ; chloroplast with 2 pyrenoids.

Zygospores unknown ; aplanospores obliquely globose with projecting mammilate solid processes, wall yellow-brown, scrobiculate, 27-28 × 27-29 $\mu$, with the processes 42-46 $\mu$ in length.

*Distribution :* Africa.

**97. Mougeotia tenerrima** G.S. West 1914. *Mem. Soc. Neuchateloise Sci. Nat.* **5,** p. 1028.

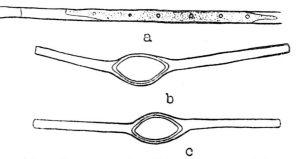

Fig. 104. a-c. *M. tenerrima*. a, vegetative cell, b-c, aplanospores (after G.S. West.)

Vegetative cells 4-5 × 110-135 $\mu$; chloroplast with 6 pyrenoids in a single row.

Zygospores unknown ; aplanospores oblique-ellipsoid, 12-13 × 24-25 $\mu$, ends slightly mammilate, wall smooth.

*Distribution :* South America.

**98. Mougeotia mayori** (G.S. West) Transeau 1926. *Ohio Jour. Sci.* **26,** p. 327. G.S. West. *Mem. Soc. Neuchateloise Sci. Nat.* **5,** p. 1027.

Fig. 105. *M. mayori*. aplanospore. (after G.S. West.)

Vegetative cells 13-15 × 235-315 $\mu$ ; chloroplast with 11-14 pyrenoids in an irregular row.

Zygospores unknown ; aplanospores obliquely ellipsoid with truncate ends, 24-26 × 34-38 $\mu$ ; spore wall yellow, punctate.

*Distribution :* South America.

**99. Mougeotia prona** Transeau 1926. *Ohio Jour. Sci.* **26,** p. 326, Pl. 7, Figs. 109-11.

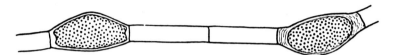

Fig. 106. *M.prona.* aplanospores. (after Transeau)

Vegetative cells 8-12 × 60-140 (-280) $\mu$ ; chloroplast 2 with the nucleus between, pyrenoids 4-6 in each ;

Zygospores unknown ; aplanospores obliquely ellipsoid with ends prcduced and truncate, 20-24 × 50-52 (-60) $\mu$ ; spore wall faintly yellow, punctate, with rounded or retuse ends.

*Distribution :* United States of America.

**100. Mougeotia ventricosa** (Wittrock) Collins 1912. *Tufts College Studies.* **3,** p. 76.

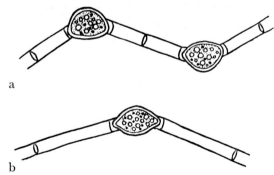

a

b

Fig. 107. a-b. *M.ventricosa* aplanospores. (after Wittrock)

Vegetative cells 6-9 × 100-140 $\mu$ ; chloroplast with about 4 pyrenoids in a single row.

Zygospores unknown ; aplanospores obliquely ellipsoid to subglobose, 12-24 × 16-29 $\mu$ ; spore wall smooth, yellow-brown.

*Distribution:* United States of America, Sweden and Latvia.

**101. Mougeotia aspera** Woronichin 1923. *Notulae Syst. Inst. Crypt. Hort. Bot. Petrop.* **2,** p. 192.

Vegetative cells 13-16.5 × 78-112 $\mu$.

Conjugation scalariform ; sporangia dividing both gametangia ; zygospores globose, 36-46 $\mu$ in diameter, rarely ovoid, 46 × 66 $\mu$ ; spore wall pale brown, punctate.

*Distribution*: Asia Minor, Finland.

**102. Mougeotia kwangsiensis** Jao 1947. *Bot. Bull. Acad. Sinica.* **1,** p. 100.

Vegetative cells 12-13 × 115-313 $\mu$ ; chloroplast with 4 to 6 pyrenoids in a single row.

Gametangia geniculate ; zygosporangia dividing both gametangia, compressed-globose ; zygospores, 35-42 × 33-35 $\mu$ ; outer spore wall thick, lamellose, and hyaline ; spore wall yellow, either smooth, or with thin reticulate wrinkles.

*Distribution*: China.

**103. Mougeotia fragilis** (Zeller) de Toni 1889. *Sylloge Algarum.* **1**(2), p. 721.

Vegetative cells 17-22 × 85-200 $\mu$.

Conjugation scalariform ; zygospores quadrangular, 22-28 × 22-28 $\mu$ ; spore wall smooth.

*Distribution*: Burma.

**104. Mougeotia bangalorensis** IYENGAR.

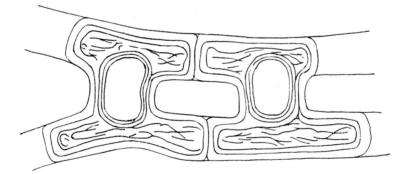

a

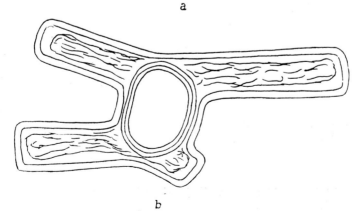

b

Fig. 107A, a-b. *M. bangalorensis* Conjugation with mature zygospores.
(after Iyengar)

Vegetative cells 20—22 $\mu$ broad ; chloroplast single with 5—8 pyrenoids in a row.

Conjugation scalariform ; conjugating cells straight or slightly geniculate ; zygospore oblong-elliptic to globose in the enlarged conjugating tube and extending slightly into one of the gametangia, 25—26 $\mu$ high and 36—38 $\mu$ broad when oblong-elliptic and 32 × 35 $\mu$ when globose ; spore-wall yellow brown, smooth and obscured by the granular membranous residue left after conjugation.

*Distribution* :

*India* :   In a pool in Bangalore, Mysore State.

### 105.   **Mougeotia mysorense** Iyengar.

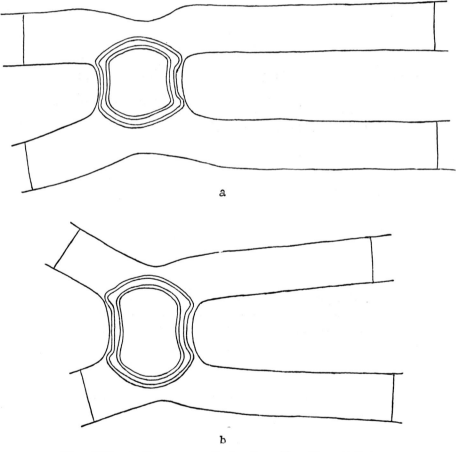

a

b

Fig.   107B, a-b *M. mysorense*,   Conjugation with  mature zygospores.
(after Iyengar).

Vegetative cells 26 $\mu$ broad.

Conjugation scalariform ; conjugating cells slightly geniculate ; zygospore in the conjugation tube and very slightly extending into the gametangia, but not reaching completely across the gametangia ; zygospore cask-shaped with the lateral  walls strongly convex ; upper and lower wall slightly concave with the corners thickened into strong knobs ; median spore layer thick, golden-brown and smooth ; zygospore 46—55 $\mu$ broad and 42—43 $\mu$ high at the corners.

*Distribution* :

*India* :   In a pool at Banneergatta in Bangalore, Mysore State.

### 106.  **Mougeotia tambaramensis** IYENGAR.

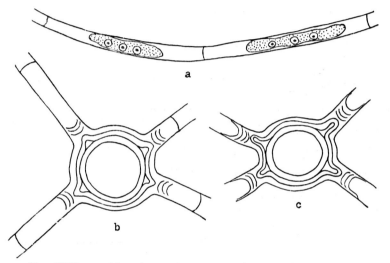

Fig. 107C, a-c. *M. tambaramensis*, a, vegetatative cells with chloroplasts;
b-c, conjugation with mature zygospores. (after Iyengar).

Vegetative cells 4—4.5 $\times$ 60—65 $\mu$ ; chloroplast with 3—8 pyrenoids in  a row.

Conjugation scalariform ; conjugating cells geniculate ; zygospores dividing both gametangia ; zygospores rounded quadrate, with the corners  produced into shorter or longer apiculate ends ; 16.5—18 $\times$ 18—23 $\mu$ ; median spore-wall golden brown, smooth.

*Distribution* :

*India* :   In a tiny channel in a scrub jungle at Nemmangalam near Tambaram, Madras State.

### 107.  **Mougeotia trapaeziformis** IYENGAR.

Vegetative cells 4—4.5 $\mu$ broad ; chloroplast single with 3—5 pyrenoids in a row.

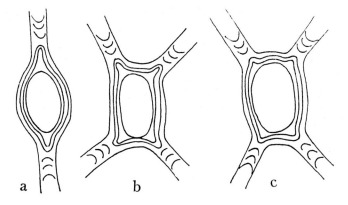

Fig. 107D, a-c, *M. trapaeziformis*. a, azygospore, b-c, conjugation with mature zygospore, (after Iyengar)

Conjugation scalariform ; conjugating gametangia geniculate ; sporangia dividing both gametangia ; zygospores trapaezoid to nearly oblong with the angles produced into apiculate ends ; corner spines 2-4.5 $\mu$ long ; zygospores 12-13 $\times$ 18-21 $\mu$ ; spore wall yellowish brown, smooth ; azygospores elliptic with the ends produced into short conical end, 13-15 $\times$ 24-27 $\mu$.

*Distribution* :

*India* : In a quarry pool in Bangalore, Mysore State.

### 108. Mougeotia banneergattense IYENGAR.

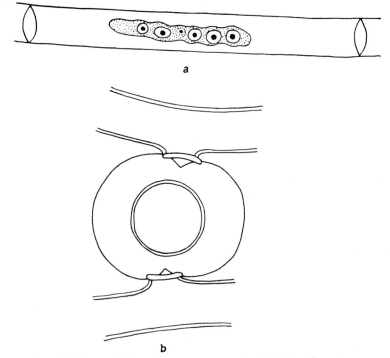

Fig. 107E, a-b, *M. banneergattense*, a, vegetative cell with chloroplast,
b, conjugation. (after Iyengar)

Vegetative cells 11.5-12.8 × 110-240 $\mu$ ; chloroplast single, with 5-8 pyrenoids in a row.

Conjugation scalariform ; gametangia not geniculate ; sporangia wall, after union of gametes changing to a thick pectic layer upto 16 $\mu$ wide ; gametangial wall at the point of union with sporangium becoming modified into ring-scars suggesting those of Oedogonium cells ; ring-scars, with a thickened rim and a raised central portion ; zygospores globose or compressed globose ; 25-29 $\mu$ broad ; median spore layer yellowish-brown, smooth and without an equatorial suture.

*Distribution* :

*India* : In a pool at Banneergatta, about 12 miles from Bangalore, Mysore State.

CHAPTER 10

# TEMNOGAMETUM W. & G.S. West 1897

The genus *Temnogametum* was established by Wests W. and G.S. in 1897 on the type species *T. heterosporum* from West Central Africa. It resembles *Mougeotia* in its vegetative cells and filaments. Vegetative cells are cylindrical, 2-25 times as long as broad. Each cell has a single axial plate-like chloroplast with many pyrenoids in one or many rows. The cell sap is purple in three species.

Reproduction is by isogamous conjugation, scalariform or lateral. The gametangia are small cells, which are cut off from the ends of the vegetative cells; are quite distinct from the other cells, and are gorged with starch and other food material. In scalariform conjugation a hole develops within the ring of contact on the sides of two gametangia. In lateral conjugation the adjoining gametangia of the same filament enlarge and conjugate.

Zygospores are ovoid to cruciate with truncate or rounded ends.

In all eight species have been described from tropical and subtropical areas, one each from Brazil, Ecuador, Trinidad and West Central Africa, and four from South India (Map E).

## KEY TO THE SPECIES OF TEMNOGAMETUM

1a.  Chloroplast with pyrenoids in one row

    2a.  Filaments coiling during conjugation       7.  **T. tirupatiense**

    2b.  Filaments not coiling during conjugation

        3a.  Reproduction by azygospores       6.  **T. cylindrospermum**

        3b.  Reproduction by zygospores

            4a.  Cells 10-12 $\mu$ broad, zygospores
                20-40 × 40-60 $\mu$       2.  **T. uleanum**

            4b.  Cells 14-17 $\mu$ broad, zygospores
                20-26 × 61-67 $\mu$       4.  **T. heterosporum**

            4c.  Cells 14-20 $\mu$ broad, zygospores
                35-42 × 80-100 $\mu$       3.  **T. transeaui**

1b.  Chloroplast with scattered pyrenoids

    5a.  Cells 19-23 $\mu$ broad, zygospores
        52-56 × 35-45 $\mu$       5.  **T. indicum**

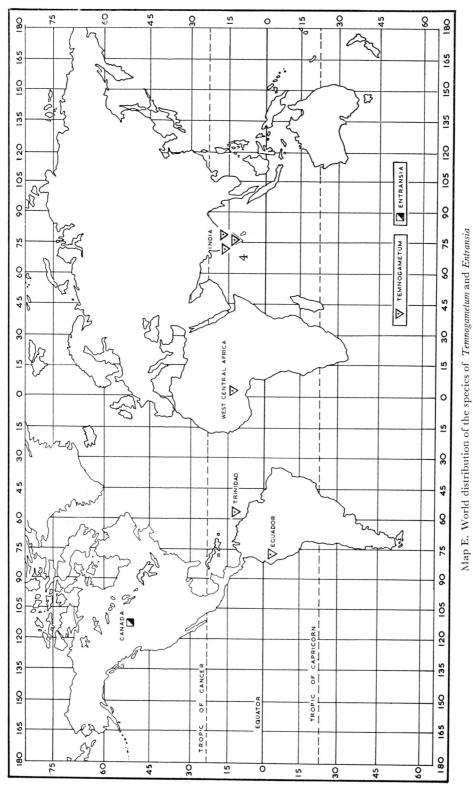

Map E. World distribution of the species of *Temnogametum* and *Entransia*

5b.  Cells 32-48 $\mu$ broad. zygospores
     32-48×64-84 $\mu$

8.  **T. mayyanadense**

5c.  Cells 39-45 $\mu$ broad, zygospores
     60-75×90-120 $\mu$

1.  **T. thaxteri**

**1.  Temnogametum thaxteri** Transeau 1932.  *Ohio Jour. Sci.* **32,** p. 489, Pl. 1, Figs. 14-20.

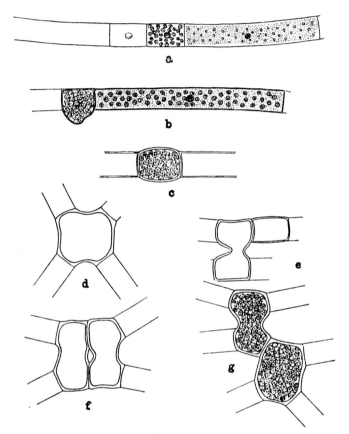

Fig. 108. a-g. *T. thaxteri.* (after Transeau)

Vegetative cells 39-45 × 220-360 $\mu$ ; chloroplast broad with 30-120 pyrenoids scattered throughout.

Conjugation scalariform ; gametangia 36-90 $\mu$ long ; zygospores quadrangular-ovoid, 60-75 × 90-120 $\mu$, occasionally in pairs which are somewhat longer and narrower ; lateral walls concave ; aplanospores tumid, about 60 × 75 $\mu$.

*Distribution* :  Trinidad, Australia.

**2.  Temnogametum uleanum** (Möbius) Wille 1909. *Pflanzenfamilien, Nachtragezum* 1 *Teil,* 2 abt., p. 13, Fig. 3.

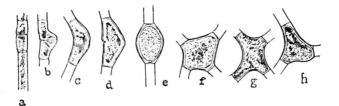

Fig. 109. a-h. *T. uleanum.* (after Möbius)

Vegetative cells 10-12 × 60-126 $\mu$ ; chloroplast axile with 4 pyrenoids, cell sap purple ; cells elongating to 20-25 diameters at the time of conjugation.

Conjugation usually lateral, sometimes scalariform ; gametangia 20-30 $\mu$ long ; zygospores formed by lateral conjugation obliquely ovoid, 20-40 x 40-60 $\mu$ ; zygospores formed by scalariform conjugation quadrangular with truncate angles, 25-40 × 30-50 $\mu$ ; spore walls transparent and smooth. Aplanospores also seen.

*Distribution* : Brazil.

**3. Temnogametum transeaui** Prescott 1947. *Ohio Jcur. Sci.* **47,** p. 132.

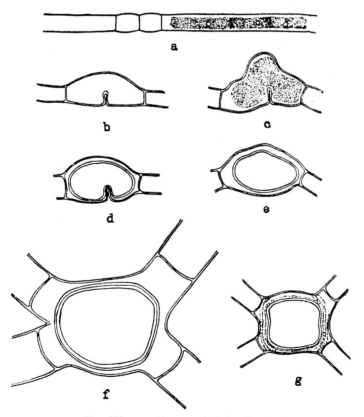

Fig. 110. a-g. *T. transeaui.* (after Prescott)

Vegetative cells 14-20 × 100-400 $\mu$, with a narrow axial chloroplast with 2-4 pyrenoids in a row.

Conjugation scalariform and lateral ; gametangia 20-22 × 20-30 $\mu$ at the ends of vegetative cells ; zygospores by lateral conjugation obliquely ovoid, 35-42 × 80-100 $\mu$ ; zygospores by scalariform conjugation, 40-45 × 45-60 $\mu$ ; median wall smooth, orange brown at maturity.

*Distribution*:　Ecuador, volcano Cotopaxi, hanging bog at 14,000 feet.

**4. Temnogametum heterosporum** W. & G. S. West 1897. *Jour. Bot.* **35,** p. 37. Pl. 370, Figs. 5-9.

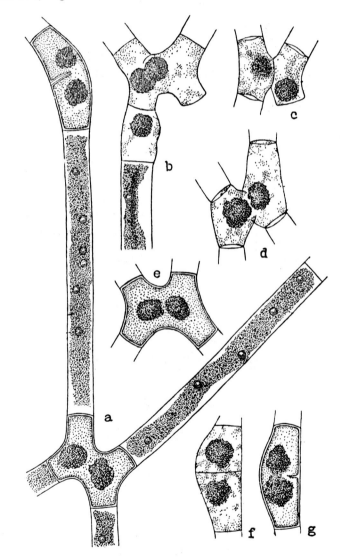

Fig. 111. a-g. *T. heterosporum.* (after West and West)

Vegetative cells 14-17 × 90-200 $\mu$ ; chloroplasts with 2-6 pyrenoids, colour of the cell sap unknown.

Conjugation scalariform and lateral ; gametangia 22-40 $\mu$ in length ; zygospores by scalariform conjugation quadrangular with concave sides, 39-50 × 48-59 $\mu$ ; zygospores by lateral conjugation, obliquely ovoid, 20-26 × 61-67 $\mu$ spore wall smooth, transparent.

*Distribution*:   Africa.

**5.  Temnogametum indicum** Iyengar 1958.   *Jour. Indian. Bot. Soc.* **37,** *p. 203 Figs. 1-32.*

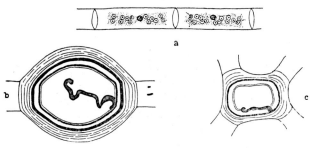

Fig. 112. *T. indicum.* (after Iyengar)

Vegetative cells 19-23 $\mu$ broad and 3-12 times as long as broad; chloroplast plate-shaped with 8-32 pyrenoids in a row ; cell-sap in living specimens purple in colour.

Conjugation, both lateral and scalariform, the former more common ; gametangia 19-23 × 20-25 $\mu$ ; zygospores by lateral conjugation elliptic ovoid to barrel-shaped with rounded or truncate ends often planoconvex or slightly reniform ; zygospores 42-50 $\mu$ broad and 60-65 $\mu$ long ; zygospores by scalariform conjugation irregularly quadrangular and 52-56 $\mu$ broad and 35-45 $\mu$ high ; zygospore-wall three layered ; mesospore thick, smooth and orange golden brown in colour ; riss-linie in zygospore-wall sigmoid.

*Distribution*:   In a small channel in the scrub jungle near Tambaram, South of Madras, India.

**6.  Temnogametum cylindrosporum** Iyengar 1958.   *Jour. Indian Bot. Soc.* **37,** *p. 210, Figs. 33-9.*

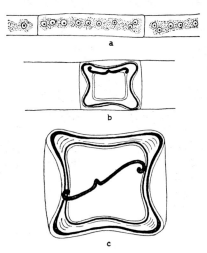

Fig. 113. *T. cylindrosporum.* (after Iyengar)

Vegetative cells 43-48 $\mu$, 4-8 times as long as broad ; chloroplast plate-like with about 10-18 pyrenoids in a row.

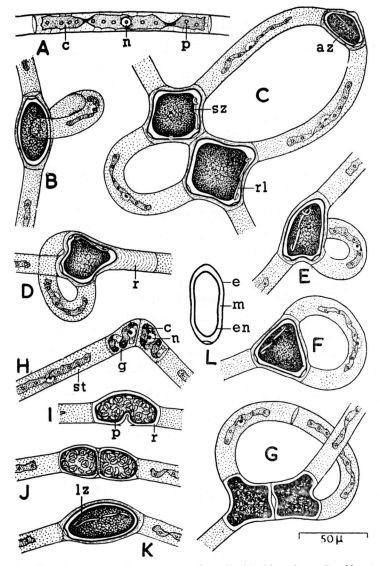

Fig. 114A. *Temnogametum tirupatiense*. A, vegetative cell with chloroplasts ; B, self conjugation with a mature zygospore in side view; C, two zygospores formed by self conjugation and an azygospore; D—G; zygospores in different views, formed by self conjugation ; H, early stage in lateral conjugation ; I, side view of the zygospore formed by the lateral conjugation ; J, view of the same from below ; K, mature zygospore showing the "riss-linie" ; L, mature zygospore showing the spore walls. az, azygospore ; c, chloroplast ; e, exospore ; en, endospore ; g, gametangium, lz, zygospore formed by lateral conjugation ; m, mesospore ; n, nucleus ; p, pyrenoid ; r, refractive pectic cellulose ; rl, riss-linie; st, sterile cell ; sz, zygospore formed by self-conjugation. (after Erady and Rajappan)

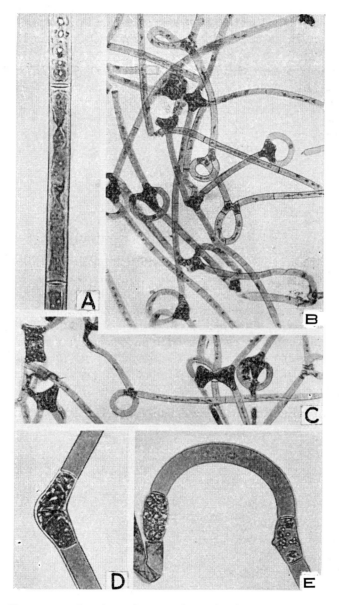

Fig. 114B. *Temnogametum tirupatiense.* A, vegetative cells with chloroplasts ; B, C, irregularly coiled filments showing self, lateral and scalariform conjugation ; D, early stage in conjugation ; E, azygospores. (after Erady and Rajappan)

Conjugation absent ; only azygospores formed in short gametangia cut off from vegetative cells; gametangia 43-49 × 50-66 $\mu$ ; azygospores quadrate-cylindrical to oblong-cylindrical in shape with the terminal ends depressed and deeply concave ; azygospore-wall three layered ; mesospore, thick, smooth and orange golden brown in colour ; azygospores 43-49 $\mu$ broad and 50-65 $\mu$ long ; riss-linie in zygospore-wall sigmoid.

*Distribution:* In a stream in Western Ghats, Coimbatore District, Madras State, India.

**7. Temnogametum tirupatiense** Iyengar 1958, *Jour. Indian Bot. Soc.*, **37**, *p. 212, Figs. 40-42.*

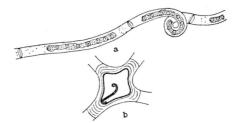

Fig. 114. *T. tirupatiense.* (after Iyengar)

Vegetative cells 11-13 $\mu$ broad and 12-16 times as long as broad ; chloroplast narrow plate-shaped with 10-15 pyrenoids in a row.

Filaments monoecious, conjugation unique in being brought about between gametangia situated apart from each other in the same filament, through the coiling of the intervening portion of the filament ; gametangia 11-13 $\mu$ × 12-15 $\mu$ ; zygospores about 40-45 $\mu$ in diameter ; zygospore-wall three-layered ; mesospore thick orange golden brown ; riss-linie in zygospore-wall sigmoid.

*Distribution :* In a hill stream at Tirupati, Madras State, and Trivandrum, Kerala State, India.

**8. Temnogametum mayyanadense** Erady and Rajappan 1959.

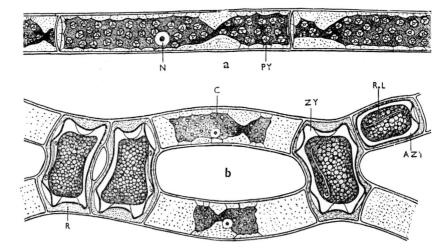

Fig. 1I4C. a-b- *T. mayyanadense.* a, Vegetative cells with chloroplast, b, Scalariform conjugation showing two zygospores formed side by side and one separate with an adjoining azygospore, N, nucleus, PY, pyrenoid with the surrounding starch plates, C, chloroplast, ZY, zygospore, R.L. riss-linie, AZY, azygospore, R, refractive pectic cellulose. (after Erady & Rajappan.)

Vegetative cells 30-38 $\mu$ broad and 80-602 $\mu$ long; chloroplast axial, plate-shaped and with about 30-84 scattered pyrenoids; cell-sap purple in colour.

Conjugation only scalariform; gametangia 30-38 $\mu$ broad and 20-78 $\mu$ long, zygospores 32-48 $\mu$ broad and 64-84 $\mu$ high, irregularly quadrangular, corners truncate and shallowly concave, end walls depressed, zygospore wall light golden brown in colour, smooth, three layered, mesospore thick, riss-linie sigmoid, azygospores 28-36 $\mu$ broad and 32-76 $\mu$ long, quadrate cylindrical to imperfectly oblong cylindrical in shape, terminal ends depressed and shallowly concave, wall structure similar to that of the zygospore.

*Distribution*: In shallow water in paddy fields at Mayyanad, Kerala State, South India along with species of *Desmidium* and *Spirogyra*.

CHAPTER 11

# HALLASIA Rosenvinge 1924

The genus Hallasia was proposed by Rosenvinge in 1924. It resembles *Zygnemopsis* in its vegetative features and in the deposition of pectic material in the cells at the time of aplanospore formation. Sometimes at the beginning of the spore formation the number of choloroplasts increases upto seven. It differs from *Zygnemopsis* and *Zygnema* in the production of 1-3 sporelings on the germination of aplanospores. Species of *Zygnema* are known with 2-4 chloroplasts, and the life history of the species of *Zygnemopsis* has not been worked out. It is very likely that some species of *Zygnemopsis* may be producing 1-3 sporelings on the germination of the aplanospores. Perhaps, it may be advisable to include the solitary species of this genus in *Zygnemopsis*.

The only species recorded is *Hallasia reticulata* from Copenhagen, Denmark (Map F.)

**Hallasia reticulata** Rosenvinge 1924. *Rev. Algolog.* **1,** pp. 209-12. Hallas. *Bot. Tidsskrift.* **20,** pp. 1-16. 1895 (as *Zygnema reticulatum*).

Vegetative cells 18-20 × 35-100 $\mu$ with 2 to 7 stellate chloroplasts in each cell.

Reproduction by aplanospores only ; aplanospores ellipsoid up to 35 $\mu$ in diameter, 60 $\mu$ long ; median spore wall yellow, scrobiculate or irregularly reticulate; sporogenous cells lengthen up to 240 $\mu$. On germination the contents of the spores may become divided into 2 or 3 parts from each of which a new filament develops. Sometimes only a single plant develops from a spore.

*Distribution:* Denmark.

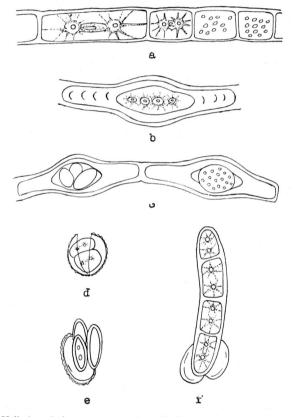

Fig. 115. a-f. *Hallasia reticulata*. a, vegetative cell; b,c. aplanospores (note the secondary spores inside the aplanospores); d,e, liberation of the secondary spores; f, four celled germling. (after Hallas)

## CHAPTER 12

# ZYGNEMOPSIS (Skuja) Transeau 1934

In 1930 Skuja described *Zygnemopsis* as a section of *Debarya*. In 1934 Randhawa described *Ghosella* as a separate genus of the *Zygnemaceae*. Species which have now been grouped in this genus have been variously described under *Debarya*, *Mougeotia* and *Zygnema*. Transeau gave a clear definition of this genus in 1934. Species of *Zygnemopsis* are not easily distinguishable from *Zygnema* during the vegetative phase, but at the beginning of the reproductive phase, the cell contents are partially replaced by refractive pectic material, which may be smooth or lamellated.

Vegetative cells are 2-5 ( – 10) times as long as broad with two slightly stellate, or polster-form stellate chloroplasts with a single large pyrenoid in each.

Reproduction is by zygospores, parthenospores and aplanospores. All the known species of the genus have isogamous conjugation. During reproduction the vegetative cells slightly swell, and get filled with a shining pectic colloid. Zygospores are compressed-spheroid or quadrate with round, truncate, or retuse angles filling the conjugation canal and extending into the gametangia. At maturity the zygospores have four lamellate solid appendages attached to them. Aplanospores are common, and are ovoid to ellipsoid in shape. Mesospore is smooth, punctate, scrobiculate, or verrucose.

So far 25 species have been described, of which ten are from India, five from North America, five from Africa, four from China and one from Europe (Map F).

## KEY TO THE SPECIES OF ZYGNEMOPSIS

1a. Reproduction by zygospores
    2a. Vegetative cells less than 8 $\mu$ broad
        3a. Spore wall punctate                     1. **Z. sikangensis**
        3b. Spore wall smooth                        2. **Z. orientalis**
        3c. Spore wall scrobiculate; ovoid to quadrate ovoid  3. **Z. floridana**
        3d. Spore wall scrobiculate; spores round      27. **Z. tambara-mensis**

    2b. Vegetative cells 8-16 $\mu$ broad
        4a. Zygospores less than 32 $\mu$ broad
            5a. Vegetative cells less than 12 $\mu$ broad

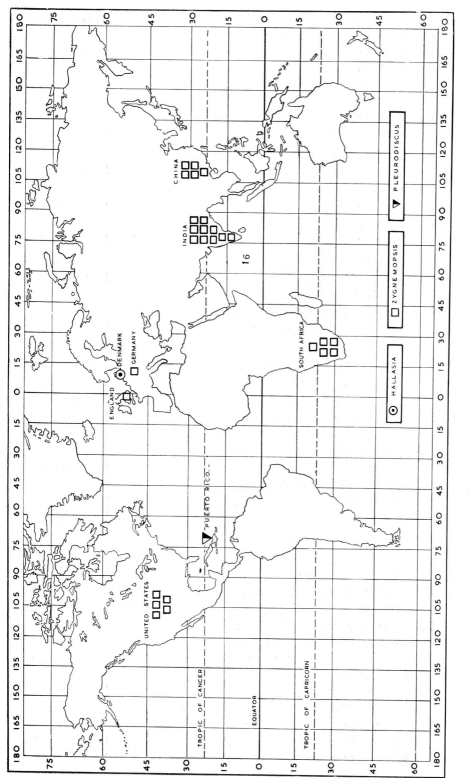

Map F. World distribution of the species of *Hallasia*, *Zygnemopsis* and *Pleurodiscus*.

| 6a. | Spore wall smooth, chocolate brown | 4. | **Z. minuta** |
| 6b. | Spore wall punctate, yellow brown | 5. | **Z. desmidioides** |
| 6c. | Spore wall punctate, chestnut brown | 6. | **Z. columbiana** |
| 6d. | Spore wall punctate, yellow | 7. | **Z. tiffaniana** |
| 6e. | Spore wall scrobiculate, yellow | 8. | **Z. sinensis** |
| 6f. | Spore wall finely scrobiculate, yellow | 9. | **Z. americana** |
| 6g. | Spore wall scrobiculate, yellow brown; angles produced into four horns | 29. | **Z. kilpaukensis** |

5b. Vegetative cells more than 12 μ broad

7.   Spore wall scrobiculate, granulose       11. **Z. splendens**

4b. Zygospores more than 32 μ broad

8a. Spore wall punctate       13. **Z. sphaerospora**

8b. Spore wall punctate or undulate, granulose       12. **Z. iyengarii**

8c. Spore wall scrobiculate

    9a. Zygospores 32-36 μ broad       10. **Z. stephensiae**

    9b. Zygospores more than 36 μ broad

        10a. Spore wall smooth or undulate, granulose       14. **Z. indica**

        10b. Spore wall with deeply scrobiculate, angular pits       15. **Z. wuchangensis**

        10c. Spore wall with scrobiculate, rounded pits       16. **Z. quadrata**

    8d. Median spore wall tricarinate       30. **Z. hazaragattense**

2c. Vegetative cells more than 16 μ broad

      11a. Zygospores 24-30 μ broad       17. **Z. decussata**

      11b. Zygospores 45-49 μ broad       31. **Z. jogensis**

      11b. Zygospores 28-36 μ broad       18. **Z. spiralis**

      11c. Zygospores 36-52 μ broad       19. **Z. lamellata**

1b. Reproduction by aplanospores

    12a. Vegetative cells less than 8 μ broad; spore wall punctate       20. **Z. gracilis**

    12b. Vegetative cells 9-10 μ broad; spore wall smooth       28. **Z. mysorensis**

    12c. Vegetative cells 14-22 μ broad

        13a. Azygospores globose to subglobose with wavy corrugations       21. **Z. lahaulense**

        13b. Azygospores spindle-shaped, spore wall scrobiculate       22. **Z. transeauiana**

        13c. Azygospores compressed-ovoid, tricarinate 24. **Z. fertilis**

    12d. Vegetative cells 30-50 μ broad

        14a. Azygospores 40-55 μ broad       23. **Z. hodgettsii**

        14b. Azygospores 70-94 μ broad       25. **Z. pectinata**

lc.   Reproduction by aplanospores, less frequently by
    zygospores; aplanospores spindle-shaped; spore wall
    scrobiculate                           26.  **Z. saravatiensis**

    **1.  Zygnemopsis sikangensis** Li 1939.  *Bull. Fan. Mem. Inst. Biol., Botany.* **9,**
p. 225.

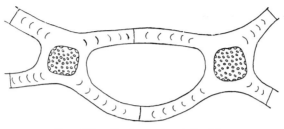

Fig. 116.  *Z. sikangensis.*  (after Li.)

Vegetative cells 4-6 × 38-68 $\mu$ each with 2, sometimes 4, chloroplasts.

Conjugation scalariform; zygospores quadrangular-ovoid, 18-22 × 18-22, $\mu$ filling
the tube and extending into the gametangia; median spore wall yellow and punctate.

*Distribution* :   China.

    **2.  Zygnemopsis orientalis** (Carter) Transeau 1944.  *Ohio Jour. Sci.* **44,**
p. 244.  *Records Bot. Surv. India.* **9,** p. 281.  1926 (as *Debarya desmidioides* var. *orientalis*
Carter).

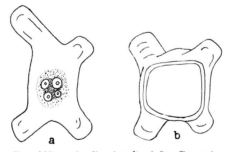

Fig. 117.  a-b. *Z. orientalis.* (after Carter.)

Vegetative cells 6-7 × 30-67 $\mu$.

Conjugation scalariform; zygospores quadrangular,  pillow-form, 20-25 $\mu$ on
a side, filling the broad tubes and dividing the gametangia; median spore wall golden-
brown, (whether smooth or punctate not stated).

*Distribution* :

*India* :   Matiana, Himachal Pradesh, the Simla Tibet road at an altitude 8,500 feet.

    **3.  Zygnemopsis floridana** Transeau 1934.  *Trans. Amer. Micros. Soc.* **53,**
p. 215, Pl. 18, Fig. 20.

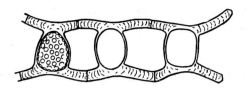

FIG. 118 *Z. floridana*. (after Transeau.)

Vegetative cells 7-8×30-40〗(—50) *μ*; chloroplasts 2, pillow-form, each with a pyrenoid.

Conjugation scalariform ; zygospores formed in the greatly enlarged conjugating tubes and extending but little into the gametangia which lengthen during conjugation to 50-90 *μ*; spores ovoid to quadrate-ovoid, 18-25×28-30 *μ*; median spore wall bright yellow, scrobiculate; pits 2-3 *μ* in diameter and about the same distance apart.

*Distribution*:   United States of America.

**4. Zygnemopsis minuta** Randhawa 1937.   *Proc. Indian Acad. Sci.* **5**, p. 312, Fig. 8.

Vegetative cells 8-10 *μ* broad and 36-46 *μ* long. Each cell contains two irregularly rounded chloroplasts.   The septa are plane, and the cells have a tendency to dissociate from each other.

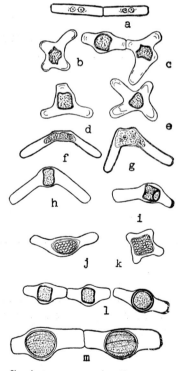

FIG. 119.   a-m. *Z. minuta*. a, vegetative filament; b-c, e, four-horned zygospores; d, three-horned zygospore; f-j, end to end conjugation of free-floating cells; k, a ripe zygospore; l-m, aplanospores. (after Randhawa.)

Conjugation in this form takes place between free-floating cells which may meet in any position and produce zygospores. Conjugation is isogamous, and H-shaped pairs of conjugating cells may be seen free-floating in water. The protoplasm secretes a shining white pectic cellulose substance in a homogeneous mass. Zygospores are squarish, retain the stumpy arm-like remains of gametangia, are 22-24 $\mu$ broad excluding the mucilaginous coat and inclusive of it may be as broad as 30 $\mu$ and are dark chocolate-brown in colour. The spore-wall bears small reticulations on surface and is composed of two layers, a thin and hyaline exospore and a thick dark brown mesospore. Three-horned zygospore is also seen (Fig. 119 d). Cudgel-shaped bodies described as aplanospores were found to be zygospores produced by end to end conjugation of cells (Fig. 119 f-j). These are 18-20 $\mu$ broad and 18-30 $\mu$ long.

*Distribution*:

*India*: Free-floating in Tons nadi, Akbarpur, district Fyzabad, U.P., mixed with *Zygnemopsis lamellata* and *Zygnema oudhense* in February, March and April 1937 and 1938.

**5. Zygnemopsis desmidioides** (W. & G.S. West) Transeau 1934.  *Trans. Amer. Micros. Soc.* **53,** p. 215, Fig. 25.

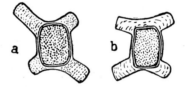

FIG. 120.  a-b. *Z. desmidioides*. (after Transeau.)

Vegetative cells 8-11 $\times$ 19-56, $\mu$ constricted at the ends; chloroplast an axial plate with 2 pyrenoids; filaments fragment readily.

Conjugation scalariform between free cells; zygospores formed in the broad conjugating tubes and extending somewhat into both gametangia; spores quadrangular with straight concave, or slightly convex sides and rounded angles, 14-18 $\times$ 18-24 $\mu$; median spore wall golden-brown, thick, finely punctate.

*Distribution*: England and United States of America.

**6. Zygnemopsis columbiana** TRANSEAU 1934.  *Trans. Amer. Micros. Soc.* **53,** p. 215 Figs. 27-29.

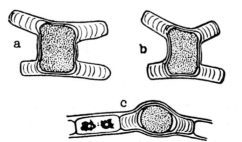

FIG. 121.  a-c. *Z. columbiana*. c, aplanospore. (after Transeau.)

Vegetative cells (8-)9.5-11.5 × 40-100 $\mu$ with 2 pillow-shaped chloroplasts each with a central pyrenoid.

Conjugation scalariform; zygospores formed in the wide conjugating tubes and extending far into each gametangium; spores quadrate-ovoid, 23-32 × 23-34 $\mu$, with angles rounded, produced, or retuse; median spore wall with a prominent suture, finely punctate, chestnut brown; aplanospores ellipsoid to ovoid, 18-20 × 25-30 $\mu$, otherwise similar.

*Distribution*: Canada.

**7. Zygnemopsis tiffaniana** TRANSEAU 1944. *Ohio Jour. Sci.* **44,** p. 244. (*Debarya cruciata* and $Z$. *cruciata* Price, 1911).

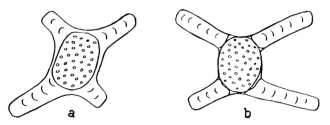

Fig. 122. a-b. $Z$. *tiffaniana*. (after Transeau.)

Vegetative cells 10-12 × 30-60$\mu$; chloroplast with 2 pyrenoids.

Conjugation scalariform; zygospores formed in the broad conjugating tubes and extending into both gametangia; spores quadrangular with concave or rarely straight sides, angles produced or slightly concave, 20-24 × 28-32 $\mu$; median spore wall yellow, punctate.

*Distribution*: Canada and United States of America.

**8. Zygnemopsis sinensis** TRANSEAU 1934. *Trans. Amer. Micros. Soc.* **53,** p. 215, Fig. 22.

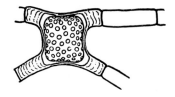

Fig. 123. $Z$. *sinensis*. (after Transeau.)

Vegetative cells 10-13 × 29-72 $\mu$, with 2 more or less elongate, stellate chloroplasts.

Conjugation scalariform; zygospores formed in the broad conjugating tubes and extending far into both gametangia; spores quadrate-ovoid, 29-32 × 29-36 $\mu$; median spore wall yellow, scrobiculate; pits 2-2.5 $\mu$ in diameter, 2.5-3 $\mu$ apart.

*Distribution*: China.

**9.  Zygnemopsis americana** TRANSEAU 1934.  *Trans. Amer. Micros. Soc.* **53,** p. 215.

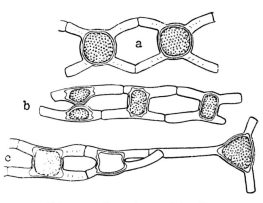

Fig. 124. a-c.  *Z. americana.* (after Transeau.)

Vegetative cells 9-12 × 27-100 $\mu$; 2 compressed-ovoid chloroplasts.

Conjugation scalariform; zygospores formed in the broad conjugating tubes and extending far into both gametangia; spores ovoid to quadrate-ovoid, 20-40 × 30-40 $\mu$; parthenospores 15-20 × 20-30 $\mu$, unilaterally ellipsoid with retuse ends; median spore wall minutely scrobiculate, usually hidden by layer of yellow-brown granules between the outer and median walls.

*Distribution*:  Canada and United States of America.

**10.  Zygnemopsis stephensiae** TRANSEAU 1934.  *Trans. Amer. Micros. Soc.* **53,** p. 215, Fig. 21.

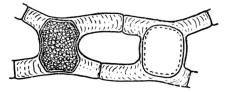

Fig. 125.  *Z. stephensiae.* (after Transeau.)

Vegetative cells 12-15 × 36-60 $\mu$, with 2 more or less stellate chloroplasts.

Conjugation scalariform; zygospores formed in the greatly enlarged conjugating tubes and extending into both gametangia, which are otherwise filled with pectic-cellulose material; spores quadrately ovoid, 32-36 × 36-42 $\mu$; with angles rounded or truncate, and sides straight or concave; median spore wall yellow, irregularly scrobiculate, pits about 2-4 $\mu$ in size.

*Distribution*:  South Africa.

**11. Zygnemopsis splendens** Randhawa 1937. *Proc. Indian Acad. Sci.* **5,** p. 297. Fig. 2.

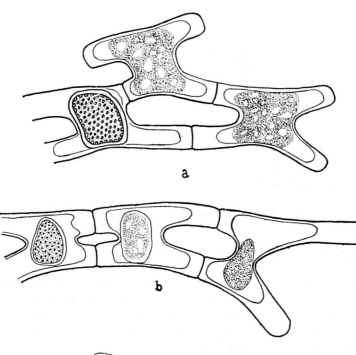

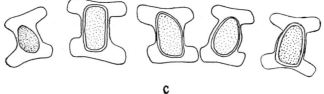

Fig. 126. a-c. *Z. splendens.* a-b, stages in conjugation; c, ripe zygospores. (after Randhawa.)

Vegetative cells 12-14 $\mu$ broad, 30-40 $\mu$ long each containing two irregularly rounded chloroplasts, each with a central pyrenoid. Septa plane.

Conjugation scalariform, isogamous. The protoplasm secretes a shining white pectic cellulose substance in a homogeneous mass. Zygospores quadrately ovoid or conical, 26-30 $\mu$ broad and 40-50 $\mu$ long. Exospore thin, smooth light blue, separated by a wide space filled with yellowish matter from the brownish sinuous mesospore. In fully mature zygospores the spore-wall is scrobiculate with pits 1 $\mu$ in diameter (Fig. 126 b-c).

*Distribution*:

*India*: In ponds and paddy fields in villages Mhow Jadubanspur, Rampur and Rasoolpur, district Fyzabad, U.P., in January, February and in early March 1937.

**12. Zygnemopsis iyengarii** RANDHAWA. 1937.  *Proc. Indian Acad. Sci.* **5,** pp. 306-8, Figs. 5-6.

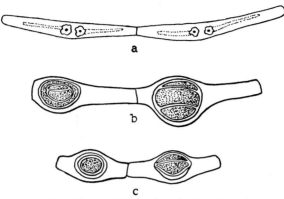

Fig. 127. a-c. *Z. iyengarii.* (after Randhawa)

Vegetative cells 12-16 $\mu$ broad, 60-100 $\mu$ long.

Zygospores globose, 44-54 $\mu$ in diameter, with a thick bluish green exospore separated by a space filled with light yellowish-brown matter from the yellowish-brown mesospore.  Spore-wall with ridges on surface.  Asexual reproduction by barrel-like, or spindle-like aplanospores bearing a number of parallel ridges on surface, 24-28 $\mu$ in diameter (Fig. 127 b-c).

*Distribution* :

*India* :  Free-floating in Pikia nadi, near Rajeh Sultanpur, district Fyzabad, U.P., on 15th January 1937.

**13. Zygnemopsis sphaerospora** RANDHAWA. 1938. *Proc. Indian Acad. Sci.* **8,** p. 131, Fig. 16.

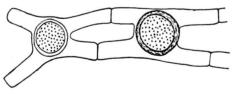

Fig. 128.   *Z. sphaerospora.* (after Randhawa)

Vegetative cells are 14-16 $\mu$ broad and 45-50 $\mu$ long.

Reproduction takes place by means of zygospores.   Immature zygospores resemble those of *Z. splendens* in shape.  Mucilage is secreted in the form of a homogeneous mass.  Zygospores are globose, chocolate-brown in colour, and 34-38 $\mu$ in diameter.   Spore wall is punctate with pits about 0.5 $\mu$ in diameter.

*Distribution* :

*India* :  Mixed with *Zygnema* sp. and *Oedogonium* sp. in Thirua nadi near V. Paikolia, tehsil Tanda, district Fyzabad, U.P., in a greenish mass on 10th May 1938.

**14. Zygnemopsis indica** RANDHAWA. 1937. *Proc. Indian Acad. Sci.* **5,** p. 297, Fig. 1.

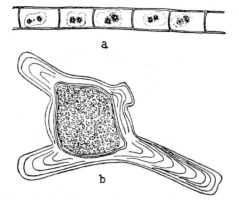

Fig. 129. a-b. *Z. indica.* a, vegetative cells with chloroplasts ;
b, mature zygospore. (after Randhawa)

Vegetative cells 10-15 $\mu$ broad, 4-5 times as long, each with two semi-stellate chloroplasts with one pyrenoid in each.

Reproduction by means of zygospores and aplanospores. Conjugation canals wide, deposition of shining white pectic cellulose in lamellae takes place in gametangia. Zygospores globose or quadrately ovoid 36-46 $\mu$ broad excluding the coats of mucilage. Zygospore wall composed of three layers, a thin, smooth, light blue exospore, thick chocolate brown mesospore, and yellowish brown endospore. Spore wall is verrucose (Fig. 129b). Triangular zygospores common. Aplanospores spindle-shaped.

*Distribution* :

*India* : Found free-floating in a yellowish mass in a pond near Hamira, district Jullundur, and V. Shahpur, district Hoshiarpur, Punjab, in the months of February, March and April 1930.

**15. Zygnemopsis wuchangensis** Li 1937. *Bull. Fan. Mem. Inst. Biol., Botany.* **8,** p. 18.

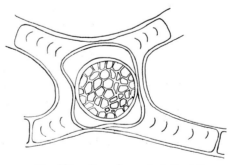

Fig. 130. *Z. wuchangensis.* (after Li)

Vegetative cells 12-15 × 32-84 $\mu$, each with 2 stellate chloroplasts.

Conjugation scalariform ; Zygospores quadrangular-ovoid, 36-56 × 42-64 × 28-35 $\mu$ in thickness ; median spore wall yellow, angularly scrobiculate, with very deep distinct pits, 2-4 $\mu$ in diameter, and with a distinct suture.

*Distribution* : China.

**16. Zygnemopsis quadrata** Jao 1935. *Sinensia.* **6,** p. 573, Pl. 2, Figs. 26-30.

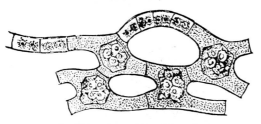

Fig. 131. *Z. quadrata.* (after Jao)

Vegetative cells 13-16 × 29-71 $\mu$ ; 2 (rarely 3 or 4) chloroplasts.

Conjugation scalariform ; fertile cells slightly geniculate ; zygospores in the conjugating tubes often extending into the gametangia ; zygospores compressed-ovoid to quadrangular-ovoid, 38-48 × 45-60 × 29-32 $\mu$ ; outer wall smooth, transparent, usually remote from the median layer ; median layer golden yellow, scrobiculate ; pits about 3 $\mu$ in diameter, 1.5-2.5 $\mu$ apart, suture prominent.

*Distribution* : China.

**17. Zygnemopsis decussata** TRANSEAU 1934. *Trans. Amer. Micros. Soc.* **53,** p. 214. (Includes *Zygnema pseudodecussatum* Czurda 1932).

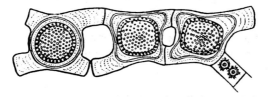

Fig. 132. *Z. decussata.* (after Transeau)

Vegetative cells 16-20 × 24-50 $\mu$; chloroplast as in *Zygnema*, each with ! pyrenoid.

Conjugation scalariform ; zygospores extending far into each gametangium, ovoid to quadrate-ovoid, and irregular, 24-30 × 30-48 $\mu$, the angles rounded, retuse, or produced ; aplanospores unilaterally ovoid, the plane of the convex side changing in successive cells, 17-25 × 20-40 $\mu$ ; parthenospores 15-20 × 20-30 $\mu$ ; median wall in all the spores scrobiculate ; akinetes with smooth, heavy walls, 18-20 × 20-36 $\mu$.

*Distribution* : Bohemia, China, Canada, Europe, United States of America.

**18. Zygnemopsis spiralis** (FRITSCH) TRANSEAU 1934. *Trans. Amer. Micros. Soc.* **53,** p. 214.

Fig. 133. *Z. spiralis.* (after Skuja)

Vegetative cells 18-25 × 26-60 $\mu$, with 2 stellate chloroplasts.

Conjugation scalariform ; gametangia sometimes elongating to 130 $\mu$ ; zygospores quadrately ovoid, 28-36 × 48-56 $\mu$ ; outer wall thin or thick, transparent, usually separated from the median wall and sometimes covered internally with granules ; median wall punctate or finely scrobiculate.

*Distribution* : Latvia, South Africa and United States of America.

**19. Zygnemopsis lamellata** RANDHAWA 1937. *Proc. Indian Acad. Sci.* **5,** p. 302, Figs. 3-4.

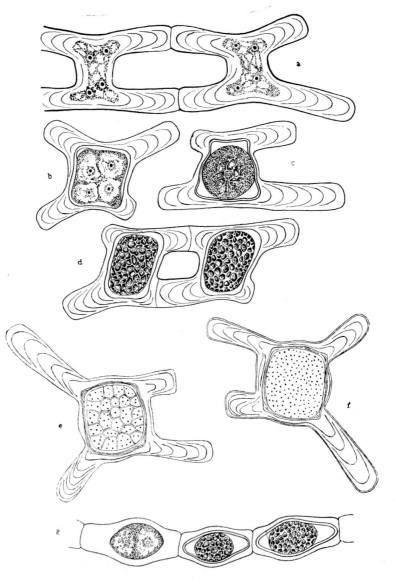

Fig. 134. a-g. *Z. lamellata*. a-d, different stages in the scalariform conjugation ; d-f, mature zygospores ; g, aplanospores. (after Randhawa)

Vegetative cells 15-18 $\mu$ broad and 32-42 $\mu$ long, each containing two rounded chloroplasts.

Zygospores globose, quadrangular, spindle-shaped or irregular in shape, dark bluish green in colour, 44-52 $\mu$ broad. The spore-wall bears broad reticulations and is also punctate with pits 1 $\mu$ in diameter, and 3-4 $\mu$ apart. Triangular zygospores also seen.

*Distribution* :

*India* : Found free-floating in a darkish purple mass in Tons nadi near tehsil buildings, Akbarpur, district Fyzabad, U.P., in February, March and April 1937 and also in February, March and April 1938.

**20. Zygnemopsis gracilis** RANDHAWA. 1938. *Proc. Indian Acad. Sci.* **8**, p. 133, Fig. 18.

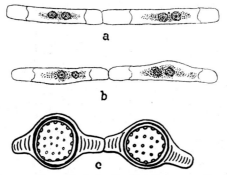

Fig. 135. a-c. *Z. gracilis.* (a-b after Randhawa; c, after Mehra)

Vegetative cells are 6-7 $\mu$ broad and 40-70 $\mu$ long. Each contains two small more or less rounded chloroplasts surrounded by granular matter.

No conjugation has been noticed in this species. The only mode of reproduction is by means of aplanospores. In early stages the vegetative cells begin to swell up on one side and the protoplasm becomes granular (Fig. 135c). The ultimate result is the formation of globose or ovoid aplanospores with granular contents ; about 20 $\mu$ in diameter ; spore wall punctate. The retreating protoplasm secretes mucilaginous lamellae of shining pectic cellulose.

*Distribution* :

*India* : Found free-floating mixed with *Mougeotia sphaerocarpa* and *Zygnema oudhensis* in a purely vegetative condition on 20th February 1938, and producing aplanospores on 12th March 1938 in Achhnaiya nadi near V. Makrahi, tehsil Tanda, district Fyzabad, U.P. ; also reported from Kolwada, Bombay, October, 1955.

**21. Zygnemopsis lahaulense** RANDHAWA. 1958. *Bot. Gaz.* **119**, 27, figs. 11-14.

Fig. 136, *Z. lahaulense.* (after Randhawa)

Vegetative cells 15 × 60-70 $\mu$ with two stellate chloroplasts.

Reproduction is entirely by aplanospores. The aplanosporangia get swollen and filled with shining pectic-cellulose. Spores are globose to subglobose, 30.4-38 $\mu$ in diameter ; blue in colour with wavy corrugations or ribs on the surface.

*Distribution* :

*India* : Free floating in a lake at Sissoo in the bed of Chandra river, Lahaul, Punjab Himalayas along with *Sphaeroplea annulina* at an altitude of 10,000 feet above sea-level.

**22. Zygnemopsis transeauiana** RANDHAWA. 1938. *Proc. Indian Acad. Sci.* **8,** p. 132, Fig. 17.

a

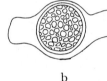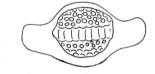

b                    c

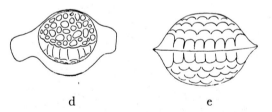

d                    e

Fig. 137. a-e.  *Z. transeauiana.* (after Randhawa)

Vegetative cells are 16-18 $\mu$ broad and 30-60 $\mu$ long. However the average size is 16 × 35 $\mu$.

Reproduction takes place exclusively by means of aplanospores. In some cases the retreating protoplasm secretes mucilage in a homogeneous mass and in others in the form of lamellae. Aplanospores are oval (Fig. 137.b-c) or depressed-globose with an equatorial ridge ; 16-25 × 23-50 $\mu$. Spore-wall is scrobiculate with pits about 2 $\mu$ in diameter.

*Distribution* :

*India* : Found in shallow water of a tributary of Tons nadi near Goshaingunj, district Fyzabad, U.P., in February, March and April 1937 and 1938; Kerala 1958.

**23. Zygnemopsis hodgettsii** Transeau 1934. *Trans. Amer. Micros. Soc.* **53**, p. 216. Hodgetts. *Trans. Roy. Soc. S. Africa.* **13**, p. 67. 1925.

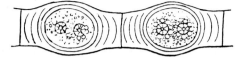

Fig. 138. *Z. hodgettsii.* (after Hodgetts)

Vegetative cells 35-50 × 20-75 *μ* in diameter, with 2 stellate chloroplasts .

Zygospores unknown ; aplanospores ovoid, 40-55 × 65-80 *μ*, immature.

*Distribution* : South Africa.

**24. Zygnemopsis fertilis** (Fritsch & Rich) Transeau 1934. *Trans. Amer. Micros. Soc.* **53**, p. 216.

Fig. 139. *Z. fertilis.* (after Fritsch & Rich)

Vegetative cells 20-22 *μ* in diameter ; slight constrictions between the cells ; chloroplasts 2, stellate.

Zygospores unknown ; sporogenous cells distended in the centre ; aplanospores compressed-ovoid, 31-32 *μ* × 41-49 *μ* ; median spore wall with 3 (or more) longitudinal ridges ; spores immature.

*Distribution* : South Africa.

**25. Zygnemopsis pectinata** (Fritsch) Transeau 1934. *Trans. Amer. Micros. Soc.* **53**, p. 216. *Ohio Jour. Sci.* **25**, p. 198, Figs. 28-44. 1925.

Fig. 140. a-b. *Z. pectinata.* a, vegetative filament ; b, aplanospore. (after Fritsch & Rich)

Vegetative cells 36-42 × 83-200 *μ* ; chloroplasts 2, stellate or elongated stellate, each with a pyrenoid or rarely 2 or 3 pyrenoids.

Zygospores unknown ; akinetes swollen towards the middle to 80 *μ*, with walls 6-8 *μ* thick, sometimes obliquely ventricose, alternating in successive cells ; aplanospores ellipsoid, or with polar thickenings, 70-94 × 100-128 *μ* ; outer spore wall 4-8 *μ* thick, smooth ; median spore wall irregularly granulose.

*Distribution* : South Africa.

### 26. Zygnemopsis saravatiensis IYENGAR.

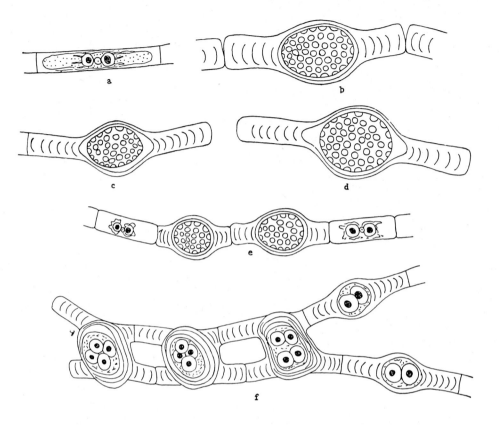

Fig. 140A, a-f. *Z. saravatiensis.* a, vegetative cell with chloroplast ; b, portion of a filament with mature azygospore; c-e, mature azygospores; f, conjugation with immature azygospores (note the two immature azygospores also). (after Iyengar)

Vegetative cells $9.6\text{-}12.8 \times 40\text{-}100 \; \mu$ ; chloroplasts two.

Reproduction usually by azygospores, less frequently by zygospores ; ripe azygospores broadly spindle shaped to ellipsoid, $21\text{-}25 \times 30\text{-}37 \; \mu$ ; median spore-wall brown, scrobiculate, with round pits about $2 \; \mu$ in diameter ; mature zygospores not observed.

*Distribution :*

*India :* In rock pools, in the bed of the river Saravati, immediately above the Jog Falls, Mysore State.

### 27. Zygnemopsis tambaramensis IYENGAR.

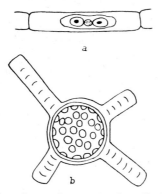

Fig. 140B, a-b. *Z. tambaramensis*. a, vegetative cell with chloroplasts ;
b, conjugation with mature zygospore. (after Iyengar)

Vegetative cells 6-7 × 30-40 $\mu$ ; chloroplasts 2, cushion-shaped, each with a pyrenoid.

Conjugation scalariform ; gametangia geniculate ; zygospores perfectly round, extending fully into the gametangia ; zygospores 20—25 $\mu$ broad ; median spore-wall dark violet brown and scrobiculate with rounded pits about 2—3 $\mu$ in diameter and about the same distance apart.

*Distribution* :

*India* :  In a tiny channel in a scrub jungle at Nemmangalam, near Tambaram, 18 miles South of Madras.

### 28. Zygnemopsis mysorensis IYENGAR.

a

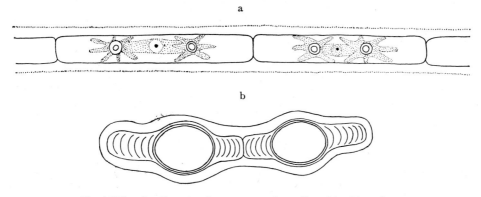

b

Fig. 140C, a-b. *Z. mysorensis*. a, vegetative cells with chloroplasts and the mucilage envelope; b, two azygospores. (after Iyengar)

Vegetative cells 9-10 × 67-77 $\mu$ ; filaments constricted at the joints and surrounded by a mucilage sheath, about 3-4 $\mu$ wide ; chloroplasts 2, star-shaped.

Reproduction by azygospores ; azygospores ovoid, 16-18 × 22-24 $\mu$ ; median spore-wall golden brown and smooth.

*Distribution* :

*India* : In an artificial fountain in the Lalbagh, Bangalore, Mysore State.

**29. Zygnemopsis kilpaukensis** IYENGAR.

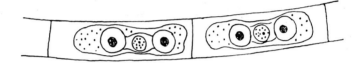

a

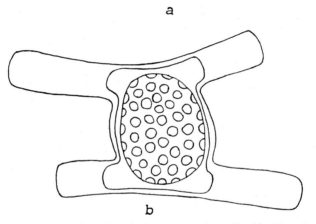

b

Fig. 140D, a-b. *Z. kilpaukensis*. a, vcgetative cells with chloroplasts; b, conjugation with mature zygospore. (after Iyengar)

Vegetative cells 10-12 × 26-60 $\mu$ ; chloroplasts 2, each with one pyrenoid.

Conjugation scalariform ; zygospores in the greatly distended conjugation canal and extending completely across both the gametangia ; irregularly quadrate with the corners produced into four shorter or longer rounded horns ; zygospores often with less number of horns or without any horns whatever ; 30-32 × 24-30 $\mu$ ; median spore-wall yellow brown and scrobiculate ; pits 2.5-3 $\mu$ in diameter.

*Distribution* :

*India* : In an experimental tank at the Corporation Water Works, Kilpauk, Madras.

**30.   Zygnemopsis hesaragattense** IYENGAR.

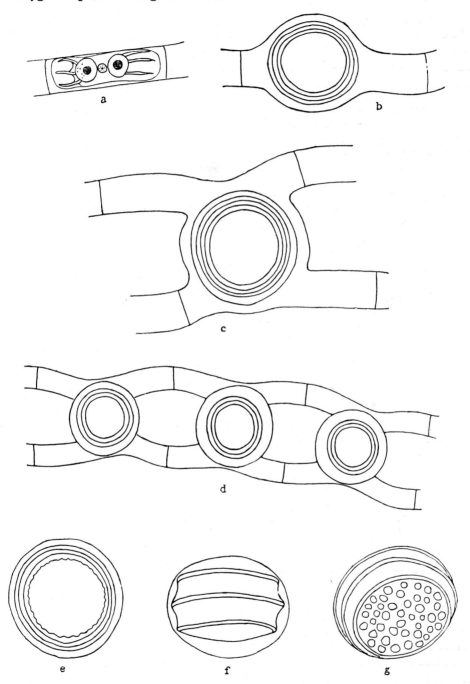

Fig. 140E, a-g. *Z. hesaragattense.* a, vegetative cell with chloroplast; b, azygospore formation ;
c-d, conjugation with mature zygospores ; e, zygospore in surface view ; f, zygospore in side
view, showing the tricarinate spore wall; g , zygospore in oblique view showing the granular
polar wall.   (after Iyengar)

Vegetative cells 10-12.8 $\mu$ broad and upto 64 $\mu$ long ; chloroplasts two.

Conjugation scalariform ; zygospore formed in the very much distended conjugation canal and extending completely across both the gametangia, zygospore globose to round ; median spore-wall tricarinate ; polar wall granular ; golden-brown ; zygospores 36-42 × 39-48 $\mu$ ; azygospores occasionally present, 24-28 × 26-33 $\mu$.

*Distribution* :

    *India* :   Among aquatic plants in the benthic region, in Hesaragatta reservoir, near Bangalore, Mysore State.

**31.  Zygnemopsis jogensis** Iyengar.

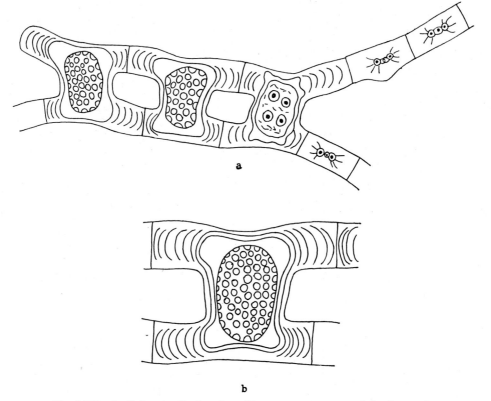

Fig. 140F, a-b. *Z. jogensis.* Conjugation with mature zygospores.  (after Iyengar)

Vegetative cells 17-19 × 25-27 $\mu$ ; chloroplasts two, with one pyrenoid in each.

Conjugation scalariform ; zygospores lying in the widened conjugation canal and extending far into each gametangium ; zygospores irregularly cushion-shaped with three to four more or less rounded horns, 45-49 × 48-99 $\mu$ ; exospore fairly thick and hyaline ; mesopore formed after the contraction of the protoplast ; ellipsoid ; mesopore thick, golden brown and scrobiculate with round pits about 3 $\mu$ wide.

*Distribution* :

    *India* :   Rock-pools in the bed of the river Sarathi, Jog Falls, Mysore State.

## CHAPTER 13

# ZYGNEMA Agardh 1824

The species of Zygnema have been classified previously in the genera : *Globulina* Link (1820) ; *Tendaridea* Bory (1822-31) ; *Stellulina* Link (1833) ; *Thwaitesia* Montagne (1838) ; *Tyndaridea* Hassall (1841) ; *Zygogonium* Kützing (1843) ; *Leda* Bory z. T. Grunow (1868) ; and *Pyxispora* West, W. & G.S. (1897).

The filaments are unbranched with short cylindric cells. Vegetative cells are 1-9 times as long as broad with two stellate chloroplasts with a prominent central pyrenoid, one on either side of a centrally situated nucleus. Sometimes the chloroplasts may appear as two rounded globose bodies due to the accumulation of food material.

Reproduction is by zygospores and akinetes. Conjugation canal is scalariform and, or lateral. Zygosopores are formed either wholly in the conjugation canal or in one of the gametangia. Their shapes vary from compressed-globose to ovoid. The outer wall is thin, colourless ; median wall chitinous varying in colour from pale yellow to chestnut brown or bright blue to blue-black. Mesospore is smooth or variously ornamented. Parthenospores and akinetes resemble zygospores in the structure of spore-wall.

The species of *Zygnema* are widely distributed and range from the sea-level to the Alpine zone. In all 100 species have been described (Map G.). Almost all the species are aquatic with the exception of *Z. terrestre* Randh.

## KEY TO SPECIES OF ZYGNEMA

1a. Reproduction by aplanospores (Zygospores infrequent or absent)

  2a. Aplanospores blue

    3a. Spore wall punctate with irregular elongate pits            76. **Z. borzae**

    3b. Spore wall scrobiculate ; vegetative cells 21-23 $\mu$ broad            77. **Z. frigidum**

    3c. Spore wall scrobiculate ; vegetative cells 33 $\mu$ broad            78. **Z. hypnosporum**

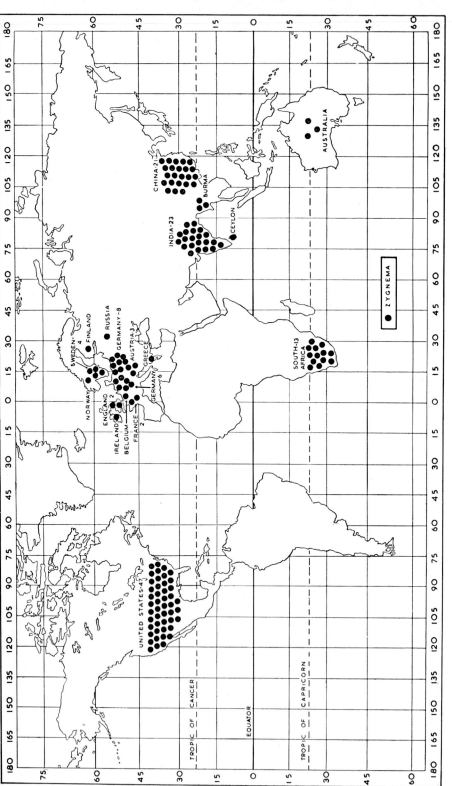

Map G. World distribution of the species of *Zygnema*

     3d.   Spore wall smooth          79.  **Z. quadrangulatum**

2b.   Aplanospores or akinetes yellow to brown
    4a.   Vegetative cells less than 35 $\mu$ broad
        5a.   Zygospores dolioform ; vegetative cells
            15-18 $\mu$ broad          80.  **Z. mirificum**
        5b.   Zygospores ovoid ; vegetative cells 16-21 $\mu$
            broad          81.  **Z. spontaneum**
        5c.   Zygospores cylindric ; vegetative cells
            17-20 $\mu$ broad          82.  **Z. schwabei**
        5d.   Zygospores ellipsoid ; vegetative cells
            20-22 $\mu$ broad          83.  **Z. ellipsoideum**
    4b.   Vegetative cells 26-36 $\mu$ broad
        6a.   Spore wall scrobiculate          84.  **Z. cylindricum**
        6b.   Spore wall granulose          85.  **Z. subcylindricum**
        6c.   Spore wall pitted          86.  **Z. khannae**
    4c.   Vegetative cells more than 36 $\mu$ broad
        7a.   Vegetative cells 40-42 $\mu$ broad          87.  **Z. irregulare**
        7b.   Vegetative cells 44-54 $\mu$ broad          88.  **Z. sterile**

1b.   Reproduction by zygospores (sometimes by aplanospores
    also)
    8a.   Zygospores formed in the conjugation tube
        9a.   Median spore wall colourless, yellow or brown
            when mature
            10a.   Zygospores globose to ovoid
                11a.   Vegetative cells less than 20 $\mu$ broad
                    12a.   Vegetative cells 8-12 $\mu$ broad    1.  **Z. oveidanum**
                    12b.   Vegetative cells 16-20 $\mu$ broad   2.  **Z. gangeticum**
                    12c.   Vegetative cells 12-16 $\mu$ broad
                        13a.   Spore wall scrobiculate    97.  **Z. carterae**
                        13b.   Spore wall smooth    3.  **Z. laevisporum**
                11b.   Vegetative cells 20-30 $\mu$ broad
             14a.   Median spore wall single
                15a.   Spore wall smooth    4.  **Z. czurdae**
                15b.   Spore wall scrobiculate,
                    pits less than 4 $\mu$
                    16a.   Lateral conjugation through
                        end walls    6.  **Z. himalayense**
                    16b.   Conjugating tubes of usual form
                    17a.   Zygospores less than 40 $\mu$
                      broad
                      18a.   Spores 24-33 $\mu$,
                        scrobiculate, pits less
                        than 2 $\mu$ broad    7.  **Z. conspicuum**
                    18b.   Spores 33-40 $\mu$,
                        scrobiculate, pits 3-4 $\mu$
                        broad    8.  **Z. lawtonianum**

18c.   Spores 38-42 $\mu$,
punctate and ridged        9.  **Z. chungii**
18d.   Spores 36-45 $\mu$,
scrobiculate, pits 2 $\mu$
broad                     10.  **Z. adpectinatum**
17b.   Zygospores more than 40 $\mu$
broad                     96.  **Z. skujae**
15c.   Spore wall scrobiculate, pits more
than 4 $\mu$ broad
19a.   Pits 4 $\mu$ broad        12.  **Z. globosum**
19b.   Pits 5-8 $\mu$ broad      11.  **Z. sinense**
15d.   Spore wall reticulate      5.  **Z. pseudopectinatum**

14b.   Median spore wall double
20a.   Outer layer wrinkled, inner
verrucose              13.  **Z. verrucosum**
20b.   Outer layer scrobiculate,
inner verrucose        95.  **Z. laetevirens**
20c.   Outer layer pitted, inner
verrucose              14.  **Z. areolatum**
11c.   Vegetative cells 30-40 $\mu$ broad
21a.   Median spore wall single
19a.   Pits 2-3 $\mu$ broad     15.  **Z. pectinatum**
19b.   Pits 3-4 $\mu$ broad     16.  **Z. excrassum**
21b.   Median spore wall double, inner
verrucose              13.  **Z. verrucosum**
11d.   Vegetative cells more than 40 $\mu$ broad
22a.   Median spore wall single    17.  **Z. neopectinatum**
22b.   Median spore wall double    21.  **Z. giganteum**
10b.   Zygospores compressed, at right angles to the
tubes
23a.   Zygospores blue, carinate and punctate    20.  **Z. carinatum**
23b.   Zygospores yellow brown
24a.   Vegetative cells 14-20 $\mu$ broad
25a.   Spore wall smooth, zygospores
15-25 $\times$ 25-35 $\mu$     29.  **Z. ralfsii**
25b.   Spore wall punctate, zygospores
28-32 $\times$ 36-40 $\mu$     30.  **Z. micropunctatum**

24b.   Vegetative cells more than 20 $\mu$
broad
26a.   Mesospore smooth, brown     89.  **Z. momoniense**
26b.   Mesospore pitted, yellow-brown  31.  **Z. circumcarinatum**

26c.   Median spore wall double, outer
smooth, inner verrucose    32.  **Z. pawhuskae**

9b. Median spore wall blue when mature
  27a. Vegatative cells less than 17 $\mu$ broad      18. **Z. gedeanum**
  27b. Vegetative cells 17-27 $\mu$ broad
    28a. Mesospore smooth
      29a. Spore wall dark blue ; zygospores 30-40 $\mu$
         broad      19. **Z. cyanosporum**
      29b. Spore wall light blue ; zygospores 30-40 $\mu$
         broad      4. **Z. czurdae**
    28b. Mesospore not smooth
      30a. Vegetative cells 16-18 $\mu$ broad, spore
         compressed      20. **Z. carinatum**
      30b. Vegetative cells 17-24 $\mu$ broad      22. **Z. synadelphum**
      30c. Vegetative cells 24-26 $\mu$ broad ;
         spores 32-35 $\mu$ broad      23. **Z. coeruleum**
      30d. Vegetative cells 23-27 $\mu$ ; Spores
         36-42 $\mu$ broad      24. **Z. gorakhpor-**
                                         **ense**
      30e. Vegetative cells 18-24 $\mu$ ; forming
         mats on soil      25. **Z. terrestre**
  27c. Vegetative cells more than 27 $\mu$ broad
      31a. Vegetative cells 27-30 $\mu$ broad      26. **Z. majus**
      31b. Vegetative cells 32-38 $\mu$ broad      27. **Z. kiangsiense**
      31c. Vegetative cells 36-41 $\mu$ broad      28. **Z. indicum**
8b. Zygospores formed in one of the gametangia
  32a. Mesospore colourless, yellow or brown
    33a. Vegetative cells less than 20 $\mu$ broad
      34a. Vegetative cells 9-12 $\mu$ broad ; spore
         wall punctate      33. **Z. stagnale**
      34b. Vegetative cells 14-20 $\mu$ broad ;
         spore wall punctate      100. **Z. subtile**
      34c. Vegetative cells 15-18 $\mu$ broad ;
         spore wall punctate      34. **Z. cylindrosper-**
                                           **mum**
      34d. Vegetative cells 16-18 $\mu$ broad ;
         pits 3-4·5 $\mu$ broad      90. **Z. yunnanense**
    33b. Vegetative cells 20-30 $\mu$ broad
      35a. Spore wall smooth
        36a. Vegetative cells 20-24 $\mu$ broad      35. **Z. leiospermum**
        36b. Vegetative cells 26-30 $\mu$ broad      36. **Z. insigne**
        36c. Vegetative cells 43-50 $\mu$ broad      37. **Z. kashmirense**
      35b. Spore wall punctate to scrobiculate
        37a. Pits 2 $\mu$ or less broad
          38a. Vegetative cells 22-29 $\mu$
             broad ; pits widely spaced      38. **Z. luteosporum**
          38b. Vegetative cells 23-26 $\mu$
             broad ; pits closely spaced      39. **Z. calosporum**
          38c. Vegetative cells 24-30 $\mu$
             broad ; pits 2 $\mu$ apart      40. **Z. subcruciatum**

37b.　Pits more than 2 $\mu$ broad
　　39a.　Pits 2-4 $\mu$ broad
　　　　40a.　Gametangia cylindric　　　　41.　**Z. vaucherii**
　　　　40b.　Gametangia swollen　　　　 42.　**Z. substellinum**
　　　　40c.　Gametangia swollen on the
　　　　　　 conjugating side
　　　　　　41a.　Vegetative cells 18-24 $\mu$
　　　　　　　　 broad　　　　　　　　　 43.　**Z. tenue**
　　　　　　41b.　Vegetative cells 24-28 $\mu$
　　　　　　　　 broad　　　　　　　　　 44.　**Z. normani**
　　　　　　41c.　Vegetative cells 28-38 $\mu$
　　　　　　　　 broad　　　　　　　　　 45.　**Z. stellinum**

　　39b.　Pits more than 4 $\mu$ broad
　　　　42a.　Vegetative cells less
　　　　　　 than 24 $\mu$ broad
　　　　　　39a.　Pits 4·5-6 $\mu$ broad　46.　**Z. extenue**
　　　　　　39b.　Pits 7-9 $\mu$ broad　　47.　**Z. hausmannii**
　　　　42b.　Vegetative cells more
　　　　　　 than 24 $\mu$ broad
　　　　　　43a.　Gametangia swollen
　　　　　　　　 on the inner side.　99　**Z. insignisporum**
　　　　　　43b.　Gametangia globo-
　　　　　　　　 sely inflated　　　　48.　**Z. germanicum**
　　　　　　43c.　Gametangia nearly
　　　　　　　　 cylindric　　　　　　49.　**Z. fanicum**
　　　　　　43d.　Gametangia en-
　　　　　　　　 larged　　　　　　　50.　**Z. subfanicum**

35c.　Spore wall verrucose
　　　　44a.　Spore wall verrucose　51.　**Z. vaginatum**
　　　　44b.　Spore wall with raised
　　　　　　 prominences　　　　　　52.　**Z. tholosporum**
　　　　44c.　Spore wall double ;
　　　　　　 inner layer verrucose　53.　**Z. flavum**

33c.　Vegetative cells verrucose, more than
　　 30 $\mu$ broad
　　45a.　Vegetative cells 30-40 $\mu$ broad
　　　　46a.　Median spore wall scrobi-
　　　　　　 culate or pitted
　　　　　　47a.　Spores globose ; pits 3-4 $\mu$
　　　　　　　　 broad　　　　　　　　45.　**Z. stellinum**
　　　　　　48b.　Spores globose; pits
　　　　　　　　 1-2 $\mu$ broad　　　　57.　**Z. cruciatum**
　　　　　　48c.　Spores cylindric-ovoid ;
　　　　　　　　 pits 1-2 $\mu$ broad　　58.　**Z. cylindrosporum**
　　　　47b.　Pits more than 4 $\mu$ broad
　　　　　　49a.　Pits 2-6·5 $\mu$ broad　61.　**Z. kwangtungense**
　　　　　　49b.　Pits 4-5 $\mu$ broad　　60.　**Z. inconspicuum**

49c.  Pits 7-12 $\mu$ broad    92.  **Z. transeauianum**

46b.  Median spore wall verrucose    55.  **Z. bohemicum**
and wavy

46c.  Median spore wall 2 layered ;
inner reticulate, verrucose, outer
smooth and thick    56.  **Z. mirandum**

45b.  Vegetative cells 40-50 $\mu$
broad    91.  **Z. neocruciatum**

45c.  Vegetative cells 50-60 $\mu$
broad    54.  **Z. crassiusculum**

32b.  Mesospore blue

50a.  Gametangia cylindric or
slightly enlarged

51a.  Vegetative cells less than 27 $\mu$
broad

52a.  Spore wall with scatter-
ed punctations    59.  **Z. mucigenum**

52b.  Spore wall smooth    62.  **Z. chalybeospermum**

52c.  Spore wall punctate    63.  **Z. melanosporum**

52d.  Spore wall scrobiculate
and carinate    64.  **Z. excompressum**

51b.  Vegetative cells more than
27 $\mu$ broad

53a.  Vegetative cells 30-40 $\mu$
broad ; mesospore
smooth    65.  **Z. cyaneum**

53b.  Vegetative cells 36-40 $\mu$
broad ; mesospore
smooth    98.  **Z. srinagarense**

53c.  Vegetative cells 26-33 $\mu$
broad ; mesospore
smooth    66.  **Z. sphaericum**

53d.  Vegetative cells 26-29 $\mu$
broad mesospore
punctate    67.  **Z. azureum**

53e.  Vegetative cells 27-32 $\mu$
broad ; mesospore
pitted    68.  **Z. ornatum**

53f.  Vegetative cells 30-37 $\mu$
broad ; mesospore
scrobiculate    94.  **Z. catenatum**

50b.  Gametangia swollen

54a.  Vegetative cells less than
20 $\mu$ broad

55a.  Vegetative cells 14-17 $\mu$
broad    93.  **Z. atrocoeruleum**

55b.  Vegetative cells 18-24 $\mu$
broad    69.  **Z. collinsianum**

55c.  Vegetative cells 30-40 $\mu$ broad.       70.  **Z. misrae**

54b.  Vegetative cells 20-30 $\mu$ broad

    56a.  Spore wall with broad reticulations and punctate, punctae 0·5 $\mu$ broad    71.  **Z. oudhense**

    56b.  Spore wall with pits 1-2 $\mu$ broad    72.  **Z. peliosporum**

    56c.  Spore wall with pits 3-4 $\mu$ broad    73.  **Z. carinthiacum**

    56d.  Spore wall with pits 4-5 $\mu$ broad    69.  **Z. collinsianum**

    56e.  Spore wall with pits 7-11 $\mu$ broad    74.  **Z. pawneanum**

54c.  Vegetative cells more than 30 $\mu$ broad

    57a.  Pits 6 $\mu$ broad    68.  **Z. ornatum**

    57b.  Pits 3 $\mu$ broad    75.  **Z. excommune**

**1.  Zygnema oveidanum** TRANSEAU 1934. *Trans. Amer. Micros. Soc.* **53**, p. 208, Pl. 16, Fig. 1.

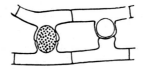

Fig. 141.  *Z. oveidanum.*  (after Transeau)

Vegetative cells 8-12 × (32-) 35-40(-68) $\mu$.

Conjugation scalariform ; zygospores formed in the conjugating tubes, ovoid to globose, 12-15 × 15-30 $\mu$; median spore wall colourless to yellow, punctate, pits about 1 $\mu$ in diameter.

*Distribution* :  U.S.A.

**2.  Zygnema gangeticum** RAO 1937.  *J. Indian. Bot. Soc.* **16**, p. 270.

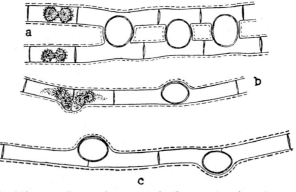

Fig. 142. a-c.  *Z. gangeticum.*  a, scalariform conjugation ; b, early stage in lateral conjugation (note the aplanospore) ; c, later stage in lateral conjugation. (after Rao)

Vegetative cells 16-20 × 40-60 $\mu$.

Conjugation scalariform and lateral, zygospores formed in the conjugating tubes and extending into the gametangia ; zygospores globose to ovoid, 30-36 × 30-45 $\mu$ ; median spore wall yellow-brown and smooth.

*Distribution :*

   *India :* Banaras, U.P.

Zygospores are immature and as such this species is doubtful.

**3. Zygnema laevisporum** JAO 1935. *Trans. Amer. Micros. Soc.* **54**, p. 56. Pl. 1, Figs. 7-8.

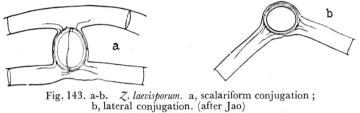

Fig. 143. a-b. *Z. laevisporum.* a, scalariform conjugation ; b, lateral conjugation. (after Jao)

Vegetative cells 13-16 × (48-) 64-128 $\mu$ ; chloroplasts usually 2, sometimes 3 or 4, occupying the middle of the cell.

Conjugation usually lateral, rarely scalariform ; zygospores compressed-globose, formed in the conjugating tubes, 35-42 × 32-35 $\mu$ ; median spore wall smooth and yellow-brown at maturity.

*Distribution :* United States of America.

**4. Zygnema czurdae** RANDHAWA 1936. *Proc. Indian Acad. Sci.* **4**, p. 239.

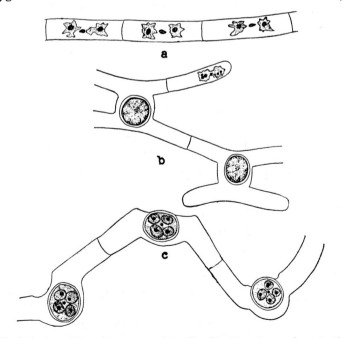

Fig. 144. a-c. *Z. czurdae.* a, vegetative cells with chloroplasts ; b, scalariform conjugation ; c, lateral conjugation. (after Randhawa)

Vegetative cells are 20-27 $\mu$ broad, and 1½ to 4 times as long. Two more or less rounded chloroplasts with a conspicuous pyrenoid in each, are seen in each cell (Fig. 144 a).

Conjugation both lateral and scalariform.

*Lateral conjugation*: Lateral conjugation is the commonest mode of reproduction in this alga. The zygospore fills the whole of the conjugation canal area, as well as the lower part of the conjugating cells. The zygospores are 30-40 $\mu$ in diameter, and are oval in shape in early stages but later on become rounded. The exospore and mesospore are smooth, while the endospore is slightly sinuous. Distinct geniculation is noticeable in later stages, and the flattened basal part ruptures. (Fig. 144 c).

Venkataraman (1959) reports an abnormal type of lateral conjugation in which conjugation canals are formed. He further records azygospores also in this form.

*Scalariform conjugation*: Some of the filaments also show the normal type of scalariform conjugation, with globose zygospores in the conjugation canal. Geniculation is noticeable (Fig. 144 b).

*Distrubution :*

*India*: Found free-floating in a bluish green mass, mixed with a species of *Spirogyra* during the third week of February 1931, in a fresh-water spring at Tahli Sahib, tehsil Dasuya, district Hoshiarpur, Punjab. Also collected from Pennar river, district Anantpur, Andhra Pradesh, August, 1958.

**5. Zygnema pseudopectinatum** CZURDA 1932. *Süsswasserflora Mitteleuropa* **9**, p. 115, Fig. 117. Fritsch and Stephens. *Trans. Roy. Soc. S. Africa.* **9**, p. 53, 1921.

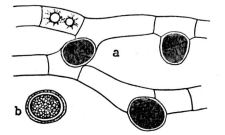

Fig. 145. a-b. *Z. pseudopectinatum.* (after Fritsch)

Vegetative cells 27-30 × 50-74 $\mu$.

Conjugation scalariform and lateral ; zygospores formed in the conjugating tubes, globose to ovoid, 33-36 × 40 $\mu$; median spore wall brown, thick, reticulate.

*Distribution :* South Africa, Transkei.

**6. Zygnema himalayense** RANDHAWA 1940. *Proc. Indian Acad. Sci.* **12**, p. 129.

The vegetative cells are on the average 21 $\mu$ broad and 3-6 times as long. Usually each cell contains two stellate chloroplasts, but in some cases cells containing four chloroplasts were also found.

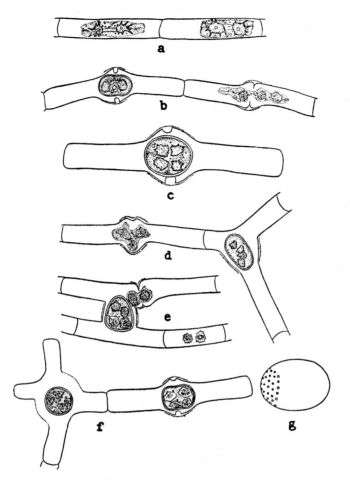

Fig. 146. a-g. *Z. himalayense*. a, vegetative cells with chloroplasts ;
b-c, lateral conjugation ; d, showing lateral conjugation
and scalariform conjugation by the union of terminal
cell ; e, scalariform conjugation (note the entry of the
male gamete after the formation of a zygospore) ;
f, showing scalariform and lateral conjugation ; g,
zygospore showing the spore wall structure. (after
Randhawa)

Lateral conjugation is the predominant mode of conjugation in this species of
*Zygnema*, though scalariform conjugation is also seen in some filaments. In some cases
neighbouring cells may be found conjugating in a ladder-like and lateral fashion.
Between these two modes of conjugation, we find a number of intermixed stages
showing a conflict between two different sexual tendencies of this alga. In one case
it was seen that though a zygospore had formed by the fusion of protoplasm from two
opposite cells in the conjugation canal, still the chloroplasts and protoplasm from a
neighbouring cell had invaded a portion of one of the cells in an abortive attempt to
conjugate laterally (Fig. 146 e). An opposite case also was noticed where two neighbouring cells had conjugated laterally and produced an immature zygospore, and a
contiguous cell of a neighbouring filament gave out a broad conjugation canal which
could be seen attached to it.

In one instance it was seen that the terminal cell of a filament had fused with the middle part of another resulting in the formation of a zygospore surrounded by three arms of the gametangia (Fig. 146 d). This resembles the three-horned zygospores described by the present author in various species of *Zygnemopsis*.

*Lateral Conjugation*: However it is in its peculiar mode of lateral conjugation that this alga differs from other species of *Zygnema* as well as other members of the order Zygnemales. In most of the laterally conjugating species of *Zygnema* and *Spirogyra* tent-like conjugation processes arise from adjacent ends of neighbouring cells, as a result of a gradual protrusion of the longitudinal wall on either side of the septum. In the region of the protrusion the septum breaks down, and the male protoplast passes over to the female cell, where it fuses with the female protoplast. From among Indian forms such a mode of lateral conjugation is seen in *Zygnema mucigena* Randhawa. This is an isogamous mode of lateral conjugation with the zygospore lodged in the female gametangium and is the commonest type prevalent.

Mature zygospores are globose or sub-globose, are bluish-green in colour, 36-40 $\mu$ broad, and 45-72 $\mu$ long. The spore-wall is scrobiculate with pits 1-1$\frac{1}{2}$ $\mu$ in diameter and 3-4 apart (Fig. 146 g).

*Distribution :*

*India*: Fresh-water stream, Loharkhet, 5750 feet above sea-level, Almora, September 15, 1939.

**7. Zygnema conspicuum** (HASSALL) TRANSEAU 1943. *Trans. Amer. Micros. Soc.* **53**, p. 208, Pl. 17, Fig. 2.

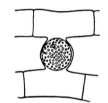

Fig. 147. *Z. conspicuum.* (after Transeau)

Vegetative cells 22-27 × 50-90. $\mu$

Conjugation scalariform; zygospores formed in the conjugating tubes, globose to ovoid, 24-32×26-33 $\mu$; median spore wall brown, scrobiculate; pits about 1.5-2.0 $\mu$ in diameter and the same distance apart.

*Distribution :* Austria; Belgium; Bulgaria; England; Germany; Russia; U.S.A.

**8. Zygnema lawtonianum** TAFT 1934. *Trans. Amer. Micros. Soc.* **53**, p. 209, Pl. 17, Fig. 5.

Fig. 148. *Z. lawtonianum.* (after Taft)

Vegetative cells 23-27 × 23-99 μ.

Conjugation scalariform ; zygospores formed in the conjugating tubes, globose, to ovoid, globose with a distinct equatorial suture, 22-40 × 33-46 μ ; outer spore wall united with the tube wall ; median spore wall brown, coarsely scrobiculate ; pits 3-4μ in diameter and about the same distance apart. Spores are cut off from the gametangia by a distinct cross wall.

*Distribution :* Burma, U.S.A.

**9. Zygnema chungii** Li 1934. *Trans. Amer. Micros. Soc.* **53**, p. 213, Pl. 18, Fig. 15.

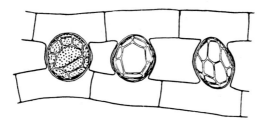

Fig. 149. *Z. chungii.* (after Taft)

Vegetative cells 24-28 × 58-72 μ.

Conjugation scalariform, zygospores formed in the conjugating tubes, globose to ovoid, 38-42 × 38-47μ; outer wall colourless, smooth ; median spore wall yellow-brown, thick, punctate, and marked by an irregular network of ridges ; pits about 1 μ in diameter, 3-6 apart.

*Distribution :* Hupeh, Wuchang, China.

**10. Zygnema adpectinatum** Transeau 1934. *Trans. Amer. Micros. Soc.* **53**, p. 209, Pl 17, Fig. 6.

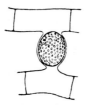

Fig. 150. *Z. adpectinatum.* (after Transeau)

Vegetative cells 25-30 × 30-100 μ.

Conjugation scalariform ; zygospores formed in the conjugating tubes, ovoid to globose, 36-40—40-50 μ ; median spore wall yellow-brown, scrobiculate ; pits 2 μ in diameter.

*Distribution :* U.S.A.

**11. Zygnema sinense** Jao 1935. *Sinensia.* **6**, p. 567, Pl. 1, Fig. 5.

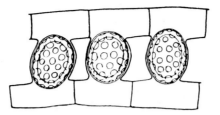

Fig. 15ʃ. *Z. sinense.* (after Jao)

Vegetative cells 25-27 × 26-48 μ .

Conjugation scalariform ; spores formed in the enlarged tubes, extending slightly into the gametangia ; zygospores subglobose to ovoid, not compressed 35-42 × 40-48 μ ; median spore wall brown, pitted ; pits 5-8 μ in diameter, 3-9 μ apart.

*Distribution :*  Szechwan, China.

**12.** **Zygnema globosum** Czurda 1932.  *Süsswasserflora Mitteleuropa.*  **9** p. 109, Fig. 110 (*Zygnema globosum* forma Singh; *Z. globosum* forma Rao).

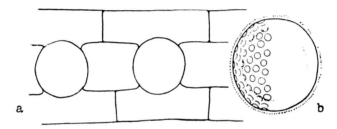

Fig. 152. a-b.  *Z. globosum* (after Czurda)

Vegetative cells 26-28  × 70-95 μ.

Conjugation scalariform ; zygospores formd in the conjugating tubes, globose or ovoid, 45-50 × 50-65 μ ; median spore wall brown, thick, pitted, pits about 3 μ in diameter.

*Distribution :*

*India :*  In a stagnant pond, Jubbulpore ; Gorakhpur, U.P.

*Other countries :*—Bohemia.

**13.** **Zygnema verrucosum** Jao 1935.  *Sinensia.* **6**, p. 566, P. 1, Figs. 3-4.

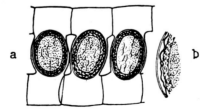

Fig. 153. a-b. *Z. verrucosum.* (after Jao)

Conjugation scalariform; zygospores formed in the conjugating tubes, subglobose
to ovoid, 32-37 × 38-55 μ ; outer spore wall smooth, hyaline; median wall of 2 layers,
of which the outer is yellow and irregularly wrinkled, the inner, yellow-brown and
densely granulate to verrucose.

*Distribution :*   Szechwan, China.

**14. Zygnema areolatum** Taft & Transeau 1934.   *Trans. Amer. Micros. Soc.*
**53**. p. 210, Pl. 17, Fig. 8.

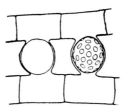

Fig. 154. *Z. areolatum.* (after Taft)

Vegetative cells 27-30 × 46-66 μ.

Conjugation scalariform ; zygospores formed in the conjugating tubes, globose
to ovoid, 32-46 × 33-50 μ ; median spore wall brown, of 2 layers, of which the outer is
pitted ; pits 5-6 μ in diameter 1.5-3 μ apart, the inner layer densely and minutely verrucose.

*Distribution :*   U.S.A.

**15. Zygnema pectinatum** (Vaucher) Agardh 1817. *Synopsis Algarum,* p. 102.

Fig. 155. *Z. pectinatum.* (after Czurda)

Vegetative cells 30-36 × 25-120 μ.

Conjugation scalariform, rarely lateral ; zygospores formed in the conjugating
tubes, globose to ovoid, 35-44 × 40-45 μ ; median spore wall brown, scrobiculate ;
pits about 2-3 μ in diameter ; aplanospores ovoid or cylindric, 30-38 × 30-60 μ ; walls
similar.

*Distribution :*   U.S.A. ; Europe ; Asia ; Africa and South America.

**16. Zygnema excrassum** Transeau 1934.   *Trans. Amer. Micros. Soc.* **53**,
p. 209, Pl. 17, Fig. 14.

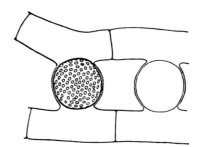

Fig. 156. *Z. excrassum.* (after Transeau)

Vegetative cells 32-36 × 32-80 μ.

Conjugation scalariform ; zygospores formed in the conjugating tubes, usually ovoid, rarely globose (40—) 50-60 × 50-70 (—80) μ; median spore wall brown, scrobiculate ; pits 3-4 in diameter and about the same distance apart ; aplanospores cylindric ovoid, nearly filling the sporogenous cells.

*Distribution :* U.S.A.

**17. Zygnema neopectinatum** Transeau 1934. *Trans. Amer. Micros. Soc.* **53**, p. 209, Pl 17, Fig. 7.

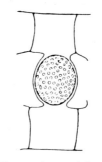

Fig. 157. *Z. neopectinatum.* (after Transeau)

Vegetative cells 40-45 × 40-85 μ.

Conjugation scalariform ; zygospores formed in the conjugating tubes, ovoid to globose, 45-54 × 55-60 μ ; median spore wall brown, scrobiculate ; pits about 3 μ in diameter.

*Distribution :* U.S.A.

**18. Zygnema gedeanum** Czurda 1932. *Süsswasserflora Mitteleuropa.* **9**, p. 115, Fig. 118.

Fig. 158. *Z. gedeanum.* (after Czurda)

Vegetative cells 13-15 × 32-34 μ.

Conjugation lateral ; zygospores formed in the conjugating tubes, ovoid,

22-24 × 30-32 μ; median spore wall blue to blue-black, thick, pitted ; pits about 1μ in diameter.

*Distribution* : Java.

**19. Zygnema cyanosporum** CLEVE 1868. *Nova. Acta Reg. Soc. Sci. Upsali.* **6**, p. 28, Pl. 8, Figs. 6—8 ; Transeau, 1951, p. 27.

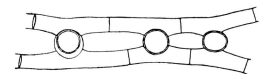

Fig. 159. *Z. cyanosporum.* (after Cleve)

Vegetative cells are 20-22 μ broad and 3-4 times as long. Chloroplasts two, rounded in each cell with the nucleus in the middle.

Conjugation is scalariform with the zygospore in the conjugation canal. Zygospores rounded in shape. Zygospore wall is composed of two layers only, a thick, hyaline exospore, and a bluish and smooth mesospore. Zygospores are 26-30 μ in diameter. Conjugation between three or more filaments is quite commonly seen.

*Distribution* :

*India* : Found free-floating in a yellowish green mass in a fresh-water stream near Makrahi, district Fyzabad, U.P. ; In ponds, Bombay.

*Other Countries* : Finland ; Greenland ; Sweden ; South Africa.

**20. Zygnema carinatum** TAFT 1934. *Trans. Amer. Micros. Soc.* **53**, p. 210, Pl. 17, Fig. 9.

Fig. 160. *Z. carinatum.* (after Taft)

Vegetative cells 16-18 × 32-36 μ.

Conjugation scalariform ; zygospores formed in the conjugating tubes, compressed globose, with the longer axis at right angles to the conjugating tube, 23-26 × 29-33 μ ; median spore wall blue, punctate, and encircled by a prominent suture. During development the sporangium wall is enclosed in a pectic layer 3-6 μ in thickness.

*Distribution* : U.S.A.

**21. Zygnema giganteum** RANDHAWA 1936. *Proc. Indian. Acad. Sci.* **4**, p. 241.

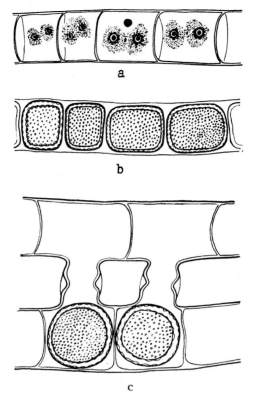

Fig. 161. a-c. *Z. giganteum.* (after Randhawa)

Vegetative cells are 38-48 $\mu$ broad and $1\frac{1}{2}$-$2\frac{1}{2}$ times as long. In thinner filaments, the chloroplasts show a typically stellate structure each with a conspicuous pyrenoid (Fig. 161, a). In bigger filaments the chloroplasts are loaded with starch granules, and the stellate structure of the chloroplasts is obscured, and they appear to be more or less rounded in appearance. Cell wall is fairly thick as compared with other species of *Zygnema.*

Reproduction both sexual and asexual.

*Asexual Reproduction*: Asexual reproduction takes place by means of brick-shaped aplanospores which develop brownish thick walls, and are 36-45 $\mu$ broad and 34-96 $\mu$ in length. These may be seen singly, in rows of twos or threes, and in later stages in long chains of many. (Fig. 161, b). The outer wall is undulate pitted and the inner is granulate.

*Sexual Reproduction*: In some filaments zygospores are found in the conjugation canals, and in others in the conjugating cells, the conjugation being isogamous and anisogamous in the same alga.

*Anisogamous Conjugation*: This type of reproduction is quite common in most filaments. The male filaments sometimes show an alternation of cells which produce male gametes, and vegetative cells, in which the chloroplasts are surrounded by a shining mucilaginous material and thick walls.

The zygospores are 42-46 $\mu$ broad and 50-58 $\mu$ long, and are oval in shape. The zygospore wall is composed of two layers only. The outer wall is undulate pitted and the inner is granulate. The ripe zygospores are brown like the parthenospores.

*Isogamous Conjugation*: This is the commoner mode of reproduction in this alga. Zygospores are typically oval in appearance, and project partly into the gametangia, completely filling the conjugation canals at the same time. Zygospores produced by isogamous conjugation are longer than those produced by anisogamous conjugation, being 70-75 $\mu$ long. Azygospores also may be seen.

*Distribution*:

*India*: Free-floating along with *Zygnema coeruleum* in Siah Baeen, a perennial fresh-water stream in Kapurthala State, Punjab, during the second week of March 1931.

**22. Zygnema synadelphum** SKUJA 1926. *Acta Horti Bot. Univ. Latviensis.* **1**, p. 110, Pl. 1, Fig. 2.

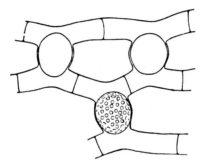

Fig. 162. *Z. synadelphum*. (after Skuja)

Vegetative cells 17-21 × 34-120 $\mu$.

Conjugation scalariform ; zygospores formed in the conjugating tubes, ovoid to spheroid, 27-36 × 34-44 $\mu$ ; median spore wall blue, of 3 layers of which the outer is irregularly punctate ; pits about 1-2 $\mu$ in diameter ; suture sometimes prominent, usually not. Aplanospores cylindric-ovoid, filling the vegetative cells, otherwise similar to the zygospores.

*Distribution*: Africa; Burma; China; Latvia; U.S.A.

**23. Zygnema coeruleum** CZURDA 1932. *Susswasserflora Mitteleuropa.* **9**, p. 107, Fig. 107.

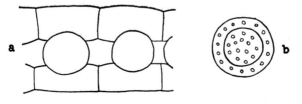

Fig. 163. a-b. *Z. coeruleum*. (after Czurda)

Vegetative cells 20-24 $\mu$ broad and 3-4 times as long. Chloroplasts rounded with conspicuous pyrenoids.

Conjugation scalariform, Zygospores in the conjugation canal, completely filling the canal. Zygospores rounded, or ellipsoid in shape, 26-36 $\mu$ in diameter. Exospore hyaline, mesospore thick, scrobiculate. Some of the zygospores have mucilaginous coating.

*Distribution* :

*India* : Free-floating in a fresh-water stream near Beas during the second week of March 1931, along with *Zygnema giganteum* Randhawa and species of *Spirogyra*.

*Other countries* : Bohemia, South Africa.

**24. Zygnema gorakhporense** SINGH 1938. *Jour. Indian Bot. Soc.* **17**, p. 370.

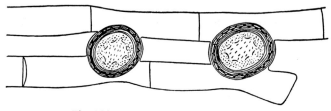

Fig. 164. *Z. gorakhporense.* (after Singh)

Vegetative cells 23-27 × 66-83 $\mu$.

Conjugation scalariform ; zygospores formed in the tubes and extending into the gametangia, zygospores ovoid to globose, 30-36 × 36-43 $\mu$ ; median wall blue, scrobiculate ; pits about 4 $\mu$ in diameter and 1-3 $\mu$ apart.

*Distribution* :

*India* : Gorakhpur, U.P.

**25. Zygnema terrestre** RANDHAWA 1938. *Proc. Indian Acad. Sci.* **8**, p. 147. Fig. 29.

The filaments are usually intricately intertwined, and consist of two parts, which are rather sharply defined. Of these the subaerial part consists of short cells usually 18-24 $\mu$ broad and 36-60 $\mu$ long, each with two spherical chloroplasts each of which bears a massive pyrenoid and with a nucleus in the middle (Fig. 165, b). In some cases the outline of chloroplasts is obscured due to abundance of starch granules and other food material. The lower cells of the subaerial part contain smaller chloroplasts more irregular in outline and fewer granules. The cells of the underground part are very much elongated and in some cases may be as long as 250 $\mu$. Their chloroplasts are very much attenuated, and the distal part of the lowermost cell is usually expanded. No branching of cells was seen in the underground part. Apparently the function of the subterranean cells is that of fixation like rhizoids. The subterranean part rarely consists of 4-5 cells, but what is lacking in number is made up in length of cells.

Reproduction by means of conjugation, aplanospores and akinetes.

*Akinetes* : Prior to akinete formation cell-wall becomes thickened and lamellated.

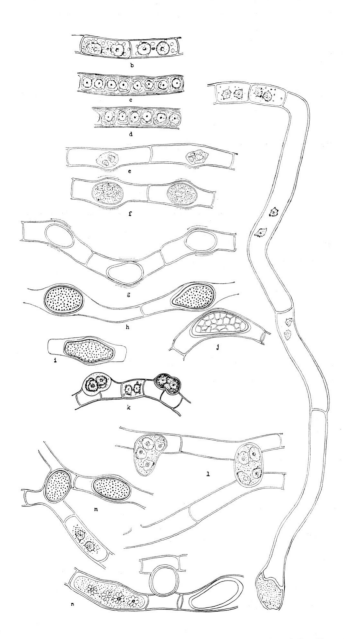

Fig. 165. a-n. *Z. terrestre*. a, lower part of a filament showing two subaerial cells and underground rhizoidal cells ; b, vegetative cells with chloroplasts ; c, d, akinetes ; e-j, stages in aplanospore formation ; k, lateral conjugation ; l-n, scalariform conjugation. (after Randhawa)

In mature akinetes cell-wall is about 6 $\mu$ thick, while in ordinary vegetative cells, it is only about 2 $\mu$ thick. The peculiarity of this form lies in the fact that akinetes are not formed by the direct conversion of vegetative cells into akinetes, as in *Zygnema giganteum* Randh, or other forms, but the vegetative cells divide into two more or less equal halves by the ingrowth of septa from the side walls, which ultimately meet in the middle. So each half contains one chloroplast only surrounded by food-reserves, like starch and oil. The akinetes are 24-27 $\mu$ broad and 18-21 $\mu$ long, i.e., half as long as an average vegetative cell. Akinete formation is a mode of perennation in this alga in the high altitudes.

*Aplanospore formation* : In early stages of aplanospore formation, cells show a slight swelling on one side. Later on the cells swell up on both sides, and a gelatinous mucilaginous cover is seen surrounding the swollen part. In some filaments geniculation of cells, giving the filaments a zig-zag appearance is also seen. The mature aplanospores are of dark greenish blue colour, and are of diverse shapes. Some are pyramidal, some are barrellshaped, but oval shape with slight modification preponderates. Spore-wall consists of three layers, of which the mesospore is the thickest and is dark greenish-blue in colour, while the exospore and endospore are thinner and are light slate-blue in colour. The aplanospores are 30-34 $\mu$ broad and 36-65 $\mu$ long, but the average size is 36 $\times$ 46 $\mu$. The spore-wall is punctate with pits 0.5$\mu$ in diameter and 3.5-5 $\mu$ apart. Reticulations are also seen on the spore-wall.

*Conjugation* : Isogamous scalariform conjugation seems to be the predominant mode of conjugation in this alga. However, possibilities of lateral conjugation are not altogether excluded. In one case a swollen cell was seen with four pyrenoids, each of which was surrounded by a ring of starch granules. This could only result from a lateral fusion of gametes. So it is quite possible that some spores which appear like aplanospores, may have resulted in some cases from lateral conjugation. The occurrence of some spores in very long cells also shows the possibility of such a lateral fusion. No remains of protoplasm were seen in the gametangia and the zygospores are not cut off by any walls from the gametangia. The zygospores are oval in shape, 28-38 $\mu$ broad and 36-54 $\mu$ long. In structure they resemble the alplanospores in all details.

*It is remarkable that this alga in the plains and at an altitude of 5,000-6,000 feet shows scalariform conjugation, between 7,000-8,000 feet shows lateral conjugation exclusively and higher up shows akinetes only.*

*Distribution* :

*India* : Found growing in moist fields lying fallow on the sides of a fresh-water stream near V. Mamrezpur, district Fyzabad, U.P., in late September, October and early November 1937 ; Material reproducing by akinetes were collected from near Dhakuri in Almora District at an altitude of about 9,000 feet above sea-level. Nainital, U.P.

**26. Zygnema majus** CZURDA 1932. *Süsswasserflora Mitteleuropa.* **9,** p. 106. Fritseh & Rich. *Trans. Roy. Soc. S. Africa,* **9,** p. 56. 1921.

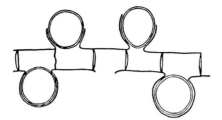

Fig. 166. *Z. majus.* (after Fritsch)

Vegetative cells 27-30 × 27-90 $\mu$.

Conjugation scalariform ; zygospores formed in the conjugating tubes, globose to ovoid, 33-48 × 42-50 $\mu$ ; median spore wall blue, smooth.

*Distribution* :   Transkei Territory, Africa.

**27. Zygnema kiangsiense** LI 1938. *Bull. Fan Mem. Inst. Biol.* **8,** p. 94.

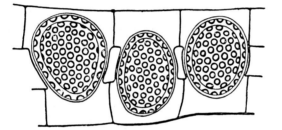

Fig. 167. *Z.kiangsiense.* (after Li.)

Vegetative cells 32-38 × 36-50 $\mu$.

Conjugation scalariform ; zygospores formed in the conjugating tubes, ovoid to subglobose, 36-46 × 44-58 $\mu$ ; median spore wall blue, coarsely scrobiculate ; pits 3-5 $\mu$ in diameter, 4-7 $\mu$ apart.

*Distribution* :   Kiangsi, China.

**28. Zygnema indicum** MISRA 1937. *Proc. Indian Acad. Sci.* **5,** p. 110. Fig. 1 A.

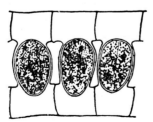

Fig. 168. *Z.indicum,* (after Misra.)

Vegetative cells 36-41 × 56-66 $\mu$.

Conjugation only scalariform ; zygospores formed in the conjugation canal which is bulged. Zygospores ellipsoidal with long axis at right angles to the conjugating cells ; exospore thin and smooth ; mesospore slightly thick, smooth and blue.

*Distribution* :

*India* :   Found in a road-side pond, Srinagar, Kashmir.

Zygospores immature and as such this species is doubtful.

**29.  Zygnema ralfsii** (HASSALL) DE BARY 1858. *Untersuchungen uber die Familie der Conjugation*, p. 77.

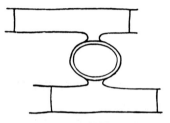

Fig. 169. *Z.ralfsii.* (after G.S. West.)

Vegetative cells 14-20 × 38-80 $\mu$.

Conjugation scalariform ; zygospores formed in the conjugating tubes, 15-25 × 25-35 $\mu$ ; median spore wall brown, smooth.

*Distribution* :   U.S.A., British Isles and continental Europe.

**30.  Zygnema micropunctatum** TRANSEAU 1934.   *Trans. Amer. Micros. Soc.* **53,** p. 210, Pl. 17, Fig. 13.

Flg. 170. *Z.micropunctatum.* (after Transeau.)

Vegetative cells 14-16 × 24-52 $\mu$.

Conjugation scalariform ; zygospores formed in the greatly enlarged conjugating tubes, compressed-globose, with the longer diameter at right angles to the conjugating tube, 28-32 × 36-40 $\mu$ ; median spore wall yellow-brown, minutely and densely punctate.

*Distribution* :   U.S.A.

**31.  Zygnema circumcarinatum** CZURDA 1930.   *Beih. Bot. Centralbl.* **47,** p. 53, Fig. 15.

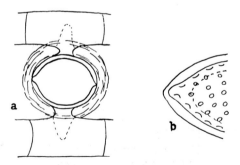

Fig. 171. a-b. *Z.circumcarinatum.* b, part of the zygospore showing the ornamentation of the spore wall. (after Czurda.)

Vegetative cells 20-22 $\mu$ in diameter.

Conjugation scalariform ; zygospores formed in the conjugating tubes, globose or compressed-globose, 24 to 29 $\mu$ in diameter ; median spore wall golden-brown, thick, scrobiculate, with pits 2-2.5 $\mu$ in diameter and 1-2 $\mu$ apart ; spore wall more or less carinate. As the spores mature the tube walls change to pectic compounds and form persistent colloidal walls as thick as the spores themselves. This often results in separation of the spores from their subtending gametangia. Aplanospores similar but smaller, often maturing outside the sporogenous cell.

*Distribution* :   Bohemia ; U.S.A.

**32.   Zygnema pawhuskae** TAFT 1934.   *Trans. Amer. Micros. Soc.* **53**, p. 209, Pl. 21, Fig. 61.

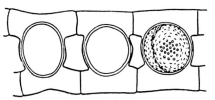

Fig. 172. *Z.pawhuskae.* (after Taft)

Vegetative cells 21-24 × 40-60 $\mu$.

Conjugation scalariform ; zygospores formed in the conjugating tubes, ovoid to compressed-globose, extending into the gametangia, 34-48 x 46-65 $\mu$ ; median spore wall seal-brown, of 2 layers, the outer smooth with a distinct equatorial suture, the inner densely and minutely verrucose, sometimes reticulate-verrucose. During the early stages of conjugation the outer sporangium wall is a   pectic   layer   3-6   $\mu$ in thickness.

*Distribution* :   U.S.A.

**33.   Zygnema stagnale** (HASSALL) Kützing 1849.   *Species Algarum*, p. 444

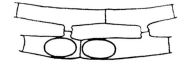

Fig. 173. *Z. stagnale.* (after G. S. West)

Vegetative cells 9-12 × 20-50 $\mu$.

Conjugation scalariform ; zygospores in one of the   gametangia ;   receptive gametangia enlarged on the inner side ; zygospores globose to subglobose, 14-18 × 14-20 $\mu$ ; median spore wall brown, punctate.

*Distribution* :   U.S.A., England.

**34.   Zygnema cylindrospermum** (W. & G.S. WEST)   KRIEGER   1941.

*Rabenhorst's Kryptogamenflora.* **13**, p. 260.   (=*Zygnema cylindrospermum*   var *crassa* Rao).

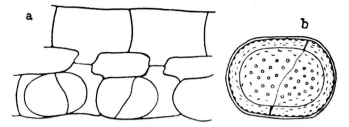

Fig. 174. a-b. *Z. cylindrospermum.* (after Czurda.)

Vegetative cells 15-18 $\mu$ in diameter.

Conjugation scalariform ; zygospores formed in one of the gametangia ; receptive gametangia cylindric or slightly enlarged ; zygospores ovoid, 15-19 $\times$ 23-54 $\mu$ ; median spore wall brown, punctate.

*Distribution*:

*India*: In a rain-water pool, U.P.

*Other countries*: Shetlands ; Wales ; Cape Colony.

**35. Zygnema leiospermum** DE BARY 1858. *Untersuchungen uber die Familie der Conjugaten*, p. 77, Pl. Figs. 7-14.

Fig. 175. *Z. leiospermum.* (after De Bary.)

Vegetative cells 20-24 $\times$ 20-40 $\mu$.

Conjugation scalariform ; zygospores in one of the greatly enlarged or inflated gametangia ; zygospores globose to ovoid, 23-30 $\times$ 23-32 $\mu$ ; median spore wall brown, smooth ; aplanospores similar, but smaller in diameter.

*Distribution*: U.S.A., Greenland, Iceland, British Isles, Europe.

**36. Zygnema insigne** (Hassall) Kützing 1849. *Species Algarum*, p. 444.

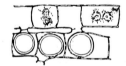

Fig. 176. *Z. insigne.* (after Jao.)

Vegetative cells 26-32 $\times$ 26-60 $\mu$.

Conjugation scalariform or lateral ; zygospores in one of the gametangia ; receptive gametangia cylindric or enlarged ; zygospores globose or subglobose, 27-33

×27-35 μ ; median spore wall yellow-brown, smooth ; aplanospores 28-33 μ, ovoid to cylindric-ovoid, otherwise similar.

*Distribution* :   China ; U.S.A. ; Europe, Australia and South America ; Sikkim, (7000 ft.)

**37. Zygnema kashmirense** MISRA 1937. *Proc. Indian Acad. Sci.* **5,** p. 112, Fig. 1, D.

Fig. 177. *Z kashmirense.* (after Misra.)

Vegetative cells 43-50 × 43-56 μ.

Conjugation scalariform ; zygospores formed in the gametangia, fructifying cells unswollen ; zygospores almost spherical ; exospore thin and smooth ; mesopore thin, smooth and brown ; zygospores 52-53 μ in diameter.

*Distribution* :

India :   Found in a road-side pond, Srinagar, Kashmir.

Zygospores are immature and as such this species is doubtful.

**38. Zygnema luteosporum** CZURDA 1932. *Süsswasserflora Mitteleuropa.* **9,** p. 122, Fig. 225.

Fig. 178. *Z. luteosporum.* (after Czurda.)

Vegetative cells 22-24 × 45-80 μ.

Conjugation scalariform ; zygospores in one of the   gametangia ;   receptive gametangia cylindric or slightly enlarged ; zygospores ovoid,   26 × 38 μ ; median spore wall yellow, thick, scrobiculate, with pits widely spaced.

*Distribution* :   Bohemia.

**39. Zygnema calosporum** JAO 1935.   *Sinensia.* **6,** p. 568, Pl. 1, Fig. 7.

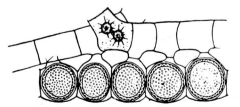

Fig. 179. *Z. calosporum.* (after Jao.)

Vegetative cells 23-26 × 16-48 $\mu$.

Conjugation scalariform ; receptive gametangia shortened and greatly enlarged ; zygospores globose to sub-globose, 29-35 × 32-35 $\mu$ ; median spore wall densely scrobiculate ; pits 1.5-2.5 $\mu$ in diameter, 1-1.5 $\mu$ apart, yellowish-brown at maturity.

*Distribution* :   Szechwan, China.

**40.  Zygnema subcruciatum** Transeau 1934. *Trans. Amer. Micros. Soc.* **53,** p. 212.

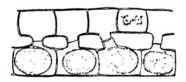

Fig. 180 *Z. subcruciatum*. (after Jao.)

Vegetative cells 24-30 × 26-60 $\mu$.

Conjugation scalariform ; zygospores in one of the gametangia ; receptive gametangia cylindric or enlarged, mostly on the inner side ; zygospores globose to ovoid, 25-32 × 28-40 $\mu$ ; median spore wall brown, finely scrobiculate.

*Distribution* :   China ; Sweden ; Norway ; France and U.S.A.

**41.  Zygnema vaucherii** Agardh 1824. *Systema Algarum*, p. 77.

Fig. 181. *Z. vaucherii*. (after Tiffany)

Vegetative cells 24-28 × 50-180 $\mu$.

Conjugation scalariform ; zygospores in one of the gametangia ; receptive gametangia gradually or abruptly inflated toward the middle ; zygospores ovoid, 24-36 × 26-45 $\mu$ ; median spore wall brown, scrobiculate ; pits 2-3 $\mu$ in diameter.

*Distribution* :    U.S.A.  and  Europe.

**42.  Zygnema substellinum** Taft 1934. *Trans. Amer. Micros. Soc.* **53,** p. 212, Pl. 17, Fig. 10.

Fig. 182. *Z. substellinum*. (after Traft.)

Vegetative cells 22-24 × 50-70 $\mu$.

Conjugation scalariform ; zygospores in one of the gametangia ; receptive gametangia greatly enlarged, becoming nearly globose ; zygospores globose, filling

or nearly filling the gametangia, 42-46 $\mu$ in diameter; median spore wall yellow-brown, scrobiculate ; pits 3 $\mu$ in diameter.

*Distribution* : U.S.A.

**43. Zygnema tenue** KUTZING 1849. *Species Algarum*, p. 445.

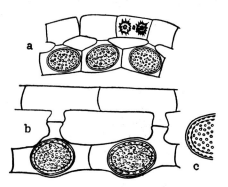

Fig. 183. a—c *Z. tenue*. (a, after Jao ; b—c after Kolkwitz & Krieger)

Vegetative cells 18-24 × 20-70 $\mu$.

Conjugation scalariform ; zygospores in one of the gametangia ; receptive gametangia greatly enlarged or inflated toward the middle ; zygospores globose to ovoid, often somewhat compressed, 25-30 × 25-40 $\mu$ ; median spore wall brown, scrobiculate ; pits 2-3 $\mu$ in diameter, 3-4 $\mu$ apart.

*Distribution* : China ; U.S.A. ; Europe ; North and South Africa ; Ceylon.

**44. Zygnema normani** TAFT 1934. *Trans. Amer. Micros. Soc.* **53,** p. 213, Pl. 17, Fig. 12. (=*Z. normani* forma Singh).

Fig. 184. *Z. normani*. (after Jao.)

Vegetative cells 24-28 × 30-73 $\mu$.

Conjugation scalariform ; zygcspores in one of the gametangia ; receptive gametangia greatly inflated on the conjugating side ; zygospores globose or subglobose, 36-46 × 35-45 $\mu$ ; median spore wall yellow-brown, scrobiculate ; pits 3-4 $\mu$ in diameter, 2.5-4 $\mu$ apart.

*Distribution* :

   *India* : Free floating, Banaras, U.P.

   *Other countries* : U.S.A.

**45. Zygnema stellinum** (VAUCHER) AGARDH 1824. *Systema Algarum*, p. 77.

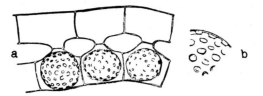

Fig. 185. a—b, *Z. stellinum.* (after Jao)

Vegetative cells 28-38 × 27-100 $\mu$.

Conjugation scalariform, rarely lateral between occasional pairs of cells ; zygospores in one of the gametangia ; receptive gametangia inflated especially on the conjugating side ; zygospores ovoid, 30-42 × 35-48 (—57) $\mu$ ; median spore wall yellow-brown, thick, scrobiculate ; pits 3-4 $\mu$ in diameter, 3-4 $\mu$ apart ; aplanospores common, usually cylindric, very rarely globose, the former filling the sporongenous cells, the latter occupying the middle of the cells ; spore walls similar to those of the zygospores.

*Distribution* :

    *India* :   Bombay, Poona, Nasik.

    *Other countries* :   U.S.A. ; Canada ; Greenland ; Europe ; Asia ; South America and North Africa.

**46. Zygnema extenue** JAO 1935.  *Sinensia.*  **6,** p. 568, Pl. 1, Fig. 8.

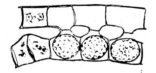

Fig. 186. *Z. extenue.* (after Jao.)

Vegetative cells 19-25 × 32-48 $\mu$.

Conjugation scalariform and sometimes lateral ; receptive gametangia more or less enlarged ; zygospores subglobose to ovoid, 23-32 × 26-39 $\mu$ ; median spore wall scrobiculate ; pits 4.5-6.5 $\mu$ in diameter and 2-3 $\mu$ apart, yellow-brown at maturity.

*Distribution* :  Szechwan, China.

**47. Zygnema hausmannii** (DE NOTARIS) CZURDA 1932.  *Süsswasserflora Mitteleuropa.*  **9,** p. 121, Fig. 125.

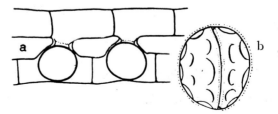

Fig. 187. a—b. *Z. hausmannii.* (after Czurda)

Vegetative cells 21-23 × 34-72 $\mu$.

Conjugation scalariform ; zygospores in one of the gametangia ; receptive gametangia enlarged mostly on the inner side ; zygospores globose or slightly compressed, 32-34 × 28-34 $\mu$ ; median spore wall yellow-brown, pitted ; pits 7-9 $\mu$ in diameter ; equatorial suture distinct.

*Distribution*:   Austria ; Northern Italy ; Southern Australia.

**48. Zygnema germanicum** CZURDA 1932. *Süsswasserflora Mitteleuropa.* **9,** p. 125, Fig. 129.

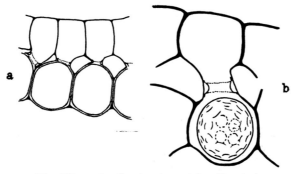

Fig. 188. a—b. *Z. germanicum.* (after Czurda.)

Vegetative cells 26-28 × 30-36 $\mu$.

Conjugation scalariform ; zygospores in one of the gametangia ; receptive gametangia greatly enlarged or inflated ; zygospores globose or compressed-globose, 36-38 × 36-45 $\mu$ ; median spore wall brown, thick, pitted ; 6-7 $\mu$ in diameter.

*Distribution*:   Germany ; Czechoslovakia.

**49. Zygnema fanicum** LI 1934. *Trans. Amer. Micros. Soc.* **53,** p. 212, Figs. 17-19.

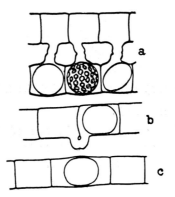

Fig. 189. a—c. *Z. fanicum.* a. scalariform   conjugation ;
b, lateral c, aplanospore. (after Li.)

Vegetative cells 28-33 × 28-80 $\mu$.

Conjugation usually scalariform, sometimes lateral ; zygospores in one of the gametangia ; receptive gametangia cylindric or enlarged ; zygospores globose to ovoid, 30-36 × 34-42 $\mu$ ; median spore wall yellow, sharply pitted ; pits 4-7 $\mu$ in diameter, 2-3 $\mu$ apart, each with a distinct, raised margin ; aplanospores similar to zygospores.

*Distribution* : Hupeh, Kiangsi, Anhwei, Szechwan, Shantung, China.

**50. Zygnema subfanicum** Jao 1940. *Sinensia*. **11**, p. 295, Pl. 4, Fig. 1.

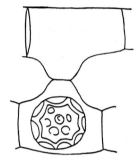

Fig. 190. *Z. subfanicum*. (after Jao.)

Vegetative cells 24-26 × 30-65 $\mu$, with 2 stellate chloroplasts.

Conjugation scalariform ; spores formed in one of the gametangia ; receptive gametangia enlarged on the conjugating side ; zygospores globose to subglobose, 29-35$\mu$ in diameter ; median wall pitted ; pits 7-8 $\mu$ in diameter, 1.8-2.7 $\mu$ apart, yellow-brown in clolour.

*Distribution* : Hunan, China.

**51. Zygnema vaginatum** Klebs 1886. *Untersuch. Bot. Inst. Tubingen*. **2**, p. 135, Pl. 3, Fig. 13. *Notarisia*. **1**, pp. 340-41. 1886. (=*Z. vaginatum* forma Parukutty).

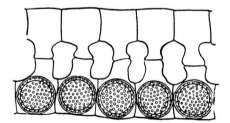

Fig. 191. *Z. vaginatum*. (after Kolkwitz & Krieger)

Vegetative cells 25-27 × 37-75 $\mu$.

Conjugation scalariform ; zygospores in one of the gametangia ; receptive gametangia slightly enlarged ; zygospores globose to ovoid, diameter about 28 $\mu$ ; median spore wall brown, verrucose-tuberculate.

*Distribution* :

    *India* : Assam.

    *Other countries* : Austria, Germany.

**52. Zygnema tholosporum** Magnus & Wille 1884. *Sydamerica Algflora*, p. 33, Pl. 1, Figs. 49-52.

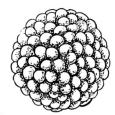

Fig. 192. *Z. tholosporum.* (after Magnus & Wille)

Vegetative cells 20 × 20-40 $\mu$.

Conjugation scalariform ; zygospores in one of the gametangia ; receptive gametangia inflated ; zygospores globose, 36 $\mu$ in diameter ; median spore wall brown, with numerous circular prominences (umbonate).

*Distribution*:   Uruguay, Montevideo.

**53.  Zygnema flavum** TAFT 1946.   *Trans. Amer. Micros. Soc.* **65,** p. 24.

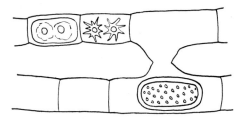

Fig. 193. *Z. flavum.* (after Taft)

Vegetative cells 22-27 × 48-68 $\mu$.

Conjugation scalariform ; zygospores formed in one of the gametangia ; receptive gametangia cylindric or slightly enlarged ; zygospores cylindric-ovoid to ovoid, 24-29 × 35-51 $\mu$ ; outer spore wall thin and smooth ; median spore wall of 2 layers, the outer thick and smooth, the inner irregularly verrucose ; both layers light yellow ; innermost spore wall thin, smooth.

*Distribution*:   U.S.A.

**54.  Zygnema crassiusculum** TRANSEAU 1938.   *Amer. Jour. Bot.* **25,** p. 542, Fig. 3.

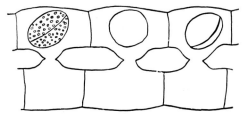

Fig. 194. *Z. crassiusculum.* (after Transeau.)

Vegetative cells 52-58 × 52-144 $\mu$.

Conjugation scalariform ; zygospores formed in one of the gametangia, compressed-globose to compressed-ovoid,  54-58 × 54-65 × 47-55 $\mu$ ; median spore wall brown, of 2 layers, of which the outer is scrobiculate ; pits about 2 $\mu$ in diameter, the inner finely and irregularly verrucose.

*Distribution*: Cape Town, Africa.

**55. Zygnema bohemicum** CZURDA 1932. *Süsswasserflora Mitteleuropa.* **9,** p. 124, Fig. 128.

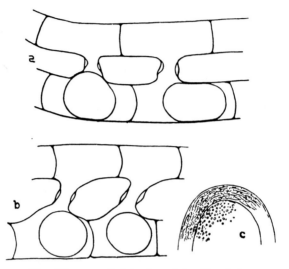

Fig. 195. a—c. *Z. bohemicum.* (after Czurda.)

Vegetative cells 31-33 × 45-95 $\mu$.

Conjugation scalariform ; zygospores in one of the gemetangia ; receptive gametangia cylindric or enlarged on the conjugating side ; zygospores ovoid to cylindric-ovoid, 32-36 × 42-60 $\mu$ ; median spore wall yellow-brown, thick, outwardly shallow, pitted and densely and finely verrucose.

*Distribution*: Czechoslovakia.

**56. Zygnema mirandum** TAFT 1946. *Trans. Amer. Micros. Soc.* **65,** p. 24.

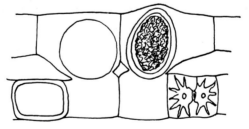

Fig. 196. *Z. mirandum.* (after Taft.)

Vegetative cells 28-35 × 32-64 $\mu$.

Conjugation scalariform ; zygospores formed in one of the gametangia ; receptive gametangia greatly enlarged on the conjugating side ; zygospores compressed-globose to ovoid ; median wall carinate ; spore wall thin and smooth ; median spore wall

yellow-brown, of 2 layers, the outer thick and smooth, the inner reticulate, with the thin ridge, crests irregularly broken ; innermost spore wall smooth.

*Distribution* : U.S.A.

**57. Zygnema cruciatum** (VAUCHER) AGARDH 1817. *Synopsis Algarum,* p. 102.

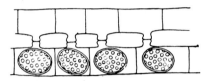

Fig. 197. *Z. cruciatum.* (after Skvortzow.)

Vegetative cells 30-36 × 30-60 $\mu$.

Conjugation scalariform ; zygospores in one of the gametangia ; receptive gametangia cylindric or enlarged ; zygospores globose to ovoid, 30-38 × 32-40 $\mu$ ; median spore wall brown, scrobiculate ; pits 1.5-2 $\mu$ in diameter, 3-5 $\mu$ apart ; aplanospores short, cylindric-ovoid, 30-35 × 30-60 $\mu$, filling the vegetative cells, otherwise similar to the zygospores.

*Distribution* : U.S.A. (Reported from all the continents).

**58. Zygnema cylindrosporum** CZURDA 1932. *Süsswasserflora Mitteleuropa.* 9, p. 22.

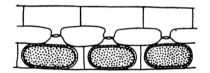

Fig. 198. *Z. cylindrosporum.* (after W. & G. S. West.)

Vegetative cells 31-36 × 60-80 $\mu$.

Conjugation scalariform ; zygospores in one of the gametangia ; receptive gametangia cylindric or enlarged ; zygospores short cylindric-ovoid to globose, 36-42 × 42-60 $\mu$ ; median spore wall yellow-brown, scrobiculate ; pits about 1.5-2 $\mu$ in diameter, 3-5 $\mu$ apart ; suture obliquely encircling the smaller circumference of the spore.

*Distribution* :

> *India* : In a rain-water pool, U.P.
>
> *Other countries* : Macedonia, South Africa.

Var. *crassa* Rao differs in having always spherical or sub-spherical zygospores and numerous small, widely set, sharp scrobiculations.

**59. Zygnema mucigenum** RANDHAWA 1938. *Proc. Indian Acad. Sci.* **8,** p. 141, Fig. 25.

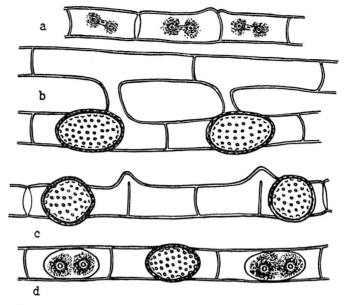

Fig. 199. a—d. *Z. mucigenum*. a, vegetative cells ; b, scalariform conjugation ;
c, lateral conjugation ; d, aplanospores. (after Randhawa)

Vegetative cells 12-14 $\mu$ broad, 50-100 $\mu$ long, each with two more or less globose chloroplasts.

Conjugation both lateral and scalariform, but the former mode of conjugation ls very common. In filaments reproducing by means of scalariform conjugation, the conjugation canals are very much elongated, and zygospores are found in one of the gametangia (Fig. 199, b).

The zygospores are dark bluish green in colour, oval in shape, 20-22 $\mu$ broad, and 30-36 $\mu$ long. Mesospore is thick, greenish bluish and prominently pitted. There are 5-6 rows of pits, which are about 1-1$\frac{1}{2}$ $\mu$ in diameter, 3-4 $\mu$ apart (Fig. 199, b, c).

*Distribution* :

*India* : Found free-floating in a light blue mucilaginous mass in Rampur jhil tehsil Akbarpur, district Fyzabad, on 15th December 1937.

**60. Zygnema inconspicuum** CZURDA 1932. *Süsswasserflora Mitteleuropa.* **9,** p. 122, Fig. 127.

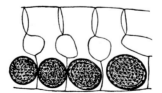

Fig. 200. *Z. inconspicuum*. (after Randhawa)

Vegetative cells 30-36 $\mu$ broad, and 40-50 $\mu$ long, each with two massive stellate chloroplasts.

Conjugation anisogamous. Zygospores globose to oval in shape 30-48 $\mu$ in diameter. Zygospore wall composed of two layers, a thin smooth and brown exospore, and a thick chocolate brown scrobiculate mesospore. Pits about 2 $\mu$ in diameter. Fruiting cell not swollen.

*Distribution* :

    *India* :    Found in a slowly flowing nadi near Tanda, district Fyzabad, U.P., on 10th January 1937.

    *Other countries* :    Finland; Manchuria.

**61. Zygnema kwangtungense** Ley 1944.   *Sinensia.*   **15,** p. 97.

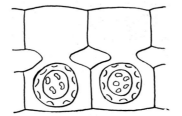

Fig. 201. *Z. kwangtungense.* (after Ley.)

Vegetative cells 38-42 × 25-75 $\mu$.

Conjugation scalariform ; receptive gametangia slightly inflated ; zygospores globose or subglobose, slightly compressed, 44-61 × 39-72 $\mu$ ; outer spore wall smooth, transparent ; median wall 7-11 $\mu$ thick, lamellate and foveolate ; pits very irregular in form and diameter, 1.8—6.5 $\mu$, 1.8-7.2 $\mu$ apart, brown at maturity.

*Distribution* :    Rice fields, China Tong-Kau, North Kwangtung,

**62. Zygnema chalybeospermum** Hansg. 1888 *Hedwigia.* **27,** p. 253. (=*Zygnema chalybeospermum* forma *inflata* Singh).

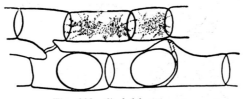

Fig. 202. *Z. chalybeospermum.*

Vegetative eells 20-27 $\mu$ thick, 1-3 times as long. Chloroplasts typically stellate, each with one pyrenoid.

Conjugation scalariform. Zygospores lodged in the gametangia more or less rounded in shape 28-30 $\mu$ broad and 30-32 $\mu$ long.

*Distribution* :

    *India* :    Free-floating in a pond at V. Jhingran, district Hoshiarpore,

Punjab, during the middle of March 1930.     Also collected near Hamira from a pond, about the middle of April, 1930 ; Gorakhpur, U.P.

*Other countries* :    Europe, North Africa, United States.

**63.**   **Zygnema melanosporum** Lagerheim 1884.   *Bot. Zentralbl.* **18,** p. 279.

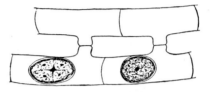

Fig. 203 *Z. melanosporum.* (after Misra.)

Vegetative cells 22-27 $\times$ 36-100 $\mu$.

Conjugation scalariform ; zygospores in one of the gametangia ; receptive gametangia cylindric or slightly enlarged ; zygospores ovoid to cylindric-ovoid, 23-30 $\times$ 28-36 $\mu$ ; median spore wall dark blue, finely punctate.

*Distribution* :

*India* :    Dal Lake, Srinagar, Kashmir.

*Other countries* :    U.S.A. ; Sweden ; North Africa.

**64.**   **Zygnema excompressum** Transeau 134. *Trans. Amer. Micros. Soc.* **53,** p. 213.

Fig. 204. a—b. *Z. excompressum.* (after Czurda.)

Vegetative cells 23-26 $\times$ 32-80 $\mu$.

Conjugation scalariform ; zygospores in one of the gametangia ; receptive gametangia cylindric or enlarged ; zygospores globose to subglobose, more or less compressed in the plane of the conjugating tube, 28 $\times$ 28-36 $\mu$ ; median spore wall blue, carinate, scrobiculate ; pits 2.5-3 $\mu$ in diameter and about the same distance apart.

*Distribution* :   U.S.A., Bohemia.

**65.**   **Zygnema cyaneum** Czurda 1932. *Süsswasserflora Mitteleuropa.* **9,** p. 127, Fig. 132. (=*Z. melanosporum* forma *dalense* Misra).

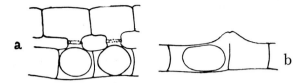

Fig. 205. a-b. *Z. cyaneum.* (after Czurda.)

Vegetative cells 30-32 × 45-60 $\mu$.

Conjugation scalariform or lateral ; zygospores in one of the gametangia ; receptive gametangia cylindric or slightly enlarged ; zygospores globose to cylindric-ovoid, 30-34 × 38-45 $\mu$ median spore wall blue, thick, smooth.

*Distribution* :

    *India* : Widely distributed.

    *Other countries* : Bohemia.

**66. Zygnema sphaericum** Misra 1937. *Proc. Indian Acad. Sci.* **5**, p. 111, (=*Z. sphaerica* f. *longearticulata* Misra ; *Z. sphaerica* f. *megaspora* Rao ; *Z. sphaerica* forma Rao)

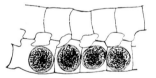

Fig. 206. *Z. sphaericum.* (after Misra.)

Vegetative cells 26-33 × 53-59 $\mu$.

Conjugation scalariform. Zygospores formed in the gametangia ; fructifying cells not swollen. Zygospores spherical. Exospore thin and smooth; mesopore thin. smooth and blue. Zygospores 28-32 × 29-33 $\mu$.

*Distribution* :

    *India* : Found in a side-way pond, Shalimar Bagh, Srinagar, Kashmir ; Banaras, U.P.

Zygospores are immature and as such this species is doubtful.

**67. Zygnema azureum** Taft 1934. *Trans. Amer. Micros. Soc.* **53**, p. 214, Pl. 17, Fig. 2.

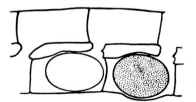

Fig. 207. *Z. azureum.* (after Taft.)

Vegetative cells 26-29 × 46-66 $\mu$.

Conjugation scalariform ; zygospores in one of the gametangia ; receptive gametangia enlarged on the inner side, or cylindric ; zygospores globose, sub-globose to ovoid, gametangia slightly to greatly enlarged ; zygospores ovoid to cylindric-ovoid, 27-33 × 33-50 $\mu$ ; median spore wall blue, finely punctate.

*Distribution* : U.S.A.

**68. Zygnema ornatum** (Li) Transeau 1934. *Oiho Jour. Sci.* **34**, p. 420; Li *Ohio Jour. Sci.* **33**, p. 153, Pl. 1, Figs. 9-10, 1933.

Fig. 208. *Z. ornatum.* (after Li.)

Vegetative cells 27-32 × 34-96 $\mu$.

Conjugation scalariform ; zygospores in one of the gametangia; receptive gametangia 28-38 × 32-38 $\mu$; median spore wall blue, pitted; pits about 6 $\mu$ in diameter and about 2 $\mu$ apart.

*Distribution* : Nanking, China, U.S.A.

**69. Zygnema collinsianum** Transeau 1914 *Amer. Jour. Bot.* **1**, p. 2891, Pl. 25, Figs. 1-3.

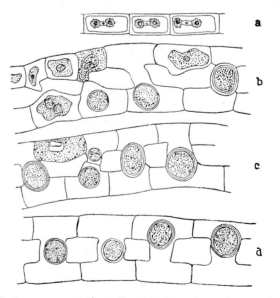

Fig. 209. a-d. *Z. collinsianum.* a, vegetative cells with chloroplasts ; b-c., scalariform conjugation (note the azygospores); d, zygospores in various positions. (after Randhawa)

Vegetative cells 18-24 $\mu$ broad, and $2\frac{1}{2}$ $3\frac{1}{2}$ times as long.   Chloroplasts two in each cell, rounded, each with a conspicuous pyrenoid.

This remarkable species of *Zygnema* shows a peculiar mode of conjugation which hovers between isogamy and anisogamy as in *Z. giganteum*.   In the same filament we see isogamously produced zygospores lodged in the conjugation canal, or anisogamously produced zygospores lying in one of the cells.

The sexuality of this alga is very much unsettled, cells of the same filament producing isogamous gametes, passive female gametes, and more active male gametes.

Zygospores are rounded in shape and are 24-36 $\mu$ in diameter.   Only immature spores were observed.

*Azygospores*:   Azygospores may also be seen in some of the cells.   In some filaments the contents of one of the cells of filament have rounded off and developed a thick wall, before the establishment of a continuous conjugation canal.

*Distribution* :

*India* :   Found free-floating mixed with a species of *Oedogonium* in a fresh-water lake near Baskhari, tehsil Tanda, district Fyzabad, U.P., in the first week of December 1936.

*Other countries* :   United States of America.

**70.   Zygnema misrae** KOLKWITZ & KRIEGER 1944.   *Rabenhorst's Kryptogamenflora.*   **13**, p. 242, Fig. 280.   (=*Z.* atrocoeruleum var. *craassa* Misra).

Fig. 210. *Z. misrae.* (after Misra)

Vegetative cells 30-40 $\mu$ broad.

Conjugation scalariform ; zygotes formed in the gametangia ; fertile cells clearly swollen on all sides.   Zygospores spherical to ellipsoidal, 40-50 × 53-60 $\mu$.   Exospore thin, smooth and colourless.   Mesospore thin, smooth and blue.

*Distribution* :

*India* :   Srinagar, Kashmir.

**71.   Zygnema oudhense** RANDHAWA 1938.   *Proc. Indian Acad. Sci.* **8**, p. 146, Fig. 28.

Vegetative cells are 22-34 $\mu$ broad and 52-70 $\mu$ long, and each cell contains two stellate  chloroplasts (Fig. 211, a).

Reproduction is by means of both isogamous and anisogamous conjugation. While some filaments may be conjugating exclusively in an isogamous fashion, others may show exclusive anisogamy, while still others hover between isogamy and anisogamy.   Zygospores are globose to conical in shape, are 34-46 $\mu$. in diameter, and are dark greenish blue in colour. The spore-wall bears broad reticulations on its surface and is also punctate with pits 0.5 $\mu$ in diameter (Figs. 211 d-e).

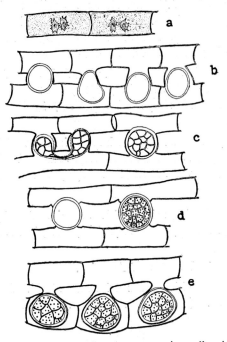

Fig. 211. a-e *Z. oudhense*. a, vegetative cells with chloroplasts ; b-e, scalariform conjugation. (after Randhawa.)

In one peculiar case two cells were seen conjugating with the same cell. The spores resulting from this peculiar union were much smaller in size compared with normal spores, and were joined together by an isthmus (Fig. 211, c).

*Distribution* :

*India* : This is the commonest species of *Zygnema* in Oudh, and was collected from January to March in 1937 and 1938 in Fyzabad, Azamgarh, and Gonda district, U.P.

**72. Zygnema peliosporum** WITTROCK 1868. *Bot. Notiser*, p. 190.

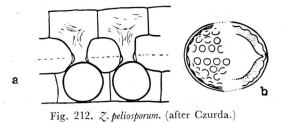

Fig. 212. *Z. peliosporum*. (after Czurda.)

Vegetative cells 23-30 × 24-80 $\mu$.

Conjugation scalariform, zygospores in one of the gametangia ; receptive gametangia enlarged, or inflated on the conjugating side ; zygospores globose to ovoid, slightly compressed, 28-36 × 28-46 $\mu$ ; median spore wall blue, finely scrobiculate or punctate, with pits 1-2 $\mu$ in diameter, spaced 2-3 $\mu$ apart ; equatorial suture usually distinct, sometimes prominent ; aplanospores cylindric-ovoid, smaller and with similar markings.

*Distribution* : China ; U.S.A. ; Sweden ; Hungary ; Spain ; France, Norway ; and Finland.

**73. Zygnema carinthiacum** Beck 1929. *Archiv f. Protistenk.* **66**, p. 1.

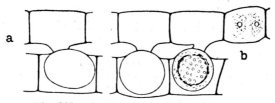

Fig. 213. a-b. *Z. carinthiacum.* (after Beck.)

Vegetative cells 25-30 × 25-100 $\mu$.

Conjugation scalariform ; zygospores in one of the gametangia ; receptive gametangia much enlarged ; zygospores globose to ovoid, 32-35 × 36-52 $\mu$ ; median spore wall blue, scrobiculate ; pits 3-4 $\mu$ in diameter, 3-5 $\mu$ apart.

*Distribution* : Austria ; China ; U.S.A.

**74. Zygnema pawneanum** TAFT 1934. *Trans. Amer. Micros. Soc.* **53**, p. 214, Pl. 18, Fig. 16.

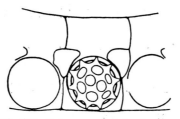

Fig. 214. *Z. pawneanum.* (after Taft.)

Vegetative cells 26-28 × 33-88 $\mu$.

Conjugation scalariform ; zygospores in one of the gametangia ; receptive gametangia greatly enlarged on the inner side ; zygospores globose, subglobose, or rarely ovoid, 36-46 × 36-48 $\mu$ ; median spore wall blue when mature, pitted ; pits 7-11 $\mu$ in diameter, 2-3 $\mu$ apart.

*Distribution* : U.S.A.

**75. Zygnema excommune** TRANSEAU 1934. *Trans. Amer. Micros. Soc.* **53**, p. 213, Czurda. *Süsswasserflora Mitteleuropa.* **9**. p. 119 (as *Z. commune*).

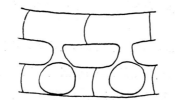

Fig. 215. *Z. excommune.* (after Czurda.)

Vegetative cells 30-32 × 55-90 $\mu$.

Conjugation scalariform ; zygospores formed in one of the gametangia ; receptive gametangia greatly enlarged on the conjugating side ; zygospores globose to ovoid, 40 × 50 $\mu$ ; median spore wall blue, thick, scrobiculate ; pits about 2.5 $\mu$ in diameter, about 4 $\mu$ apart.

*Distribution* :   Bohemia.

**76.  Zygnema borzae** KRIEGER 1941.   *Rabenhorst's   Kryptagamenflora.* **13.** p. 264.

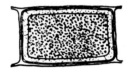

Fig. 216. *Z. borzae.* (after Krieger)

Vegetative cells 24-26 × 18-55 $\mu$.

Reproduction by aplanospores only ; aplanospores cylindric filling the  sporangium wall, 14-27 × 18-54 $\mu$ ; median wall thick, blue, punctate with irregular elongate and variously curved pits 0.5 × 1.2 $\mu$ in size.

*Distribution* :   Rumania, Transylvanian Alps at 6,000 feet.

**77.  Zygnema frigidum** TAFT 1934.   *Trans. Amer. Micros. Soc.* **53**, p. 214, Pl. 17, Fig. 11.

Fig. 217. *Z. frigidum.* (after Taft.)

Vegetative cells 21-23 × 29-83 $\mu$.

Conjugation unknown ; reproduction by aplanospores, cylindric to tumid-cylindric with rounded ends, 22-24 × 24-44 $\mu$ ; median spore wall blue, scrobiculate ; pits 1.5-2 $\mu$ in diameter, 3-4 $\mu$ apart.

*Distribution* :   U.S.A.

**78.  Zygnema hypnosporum** RICH 1935.   *Trans. Roy. Soc. S. Africa.* **23**, p. 125.

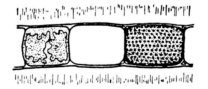

Fig. 218. *Z. hypnosporum.* (after Rich.)

Vegetative cells about 33 $\mu$ in diameter, with 2 large stellate chloroplats.

Reproduction by aplanospores only; aplanospores cylindric ovoid, 34 × 34-70 $\mu$; median wall scrobiculate, blue.

*Distribution* :  Africa, South Rhodesia.

**79.  Zygnema quadrangulatum** JAO 1940.  *Sinensia*, **11**, p. 294, Pl. 4, Fig. 3.

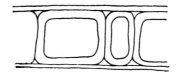

Fig. 219. *Z. quadrangulatum.* (after Jao.)

Vegetative cells 24-27 × 25-100 $\mu$, with 2 stellate chloroplasts.

Reproduction by aplanospores only ; aplanospores cylindric ovoid, 25-29 × 20-28 $\mu$ ; median spore wall dark blue, smooth, lamellate.

*Distribution* :  Hunan, China.

**80.  Zygnema mirificum** JAO 1947.  *Bot. Bull. Acad. Sinica.* **1**, p. 97.

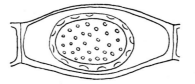

Fig. 220. *Z. mirificum.* (after Jao.)

Vegetative cells 15—18 × 25—63 $\mu$.

Conjugation unknown; outer aplanospore wall similar in shape and just inside the dolioform sporangium, 22-30 × 38-60 $\mu$, the median wall varies from ellipsoid to ovoid in the bulge of the outer wall, 20-30 × 25-30 $\mu$. The space between the 2 walls is filled with yellowish colloidal material.  The median wall is irregularly and minutely scrobiculate, yellow-brown in colour.

*Distribution* :  Kwangsi, Suijen, China.

**81.  Zygnema spontaneum** NORDSTEDT 1878.  *De Algis et Characeis Sandwicensibus*, p. 17, Pl. 1, Figs. 23-24.

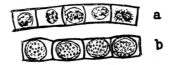

Fig. 221. a-b. *Z. spontaneum.* (after Jao.)

Vegetative cells 16-22 × 28-90 $\mu$.

Reproduction by aplanospores only ; aplanospores ovoid to cylindric-ovoid, 18-22 × 22-32 $\mu$ ; median spore wall brown, scrobiculate ; pits about 2 $\mu$ in diameter, 3-5 $\mu$ apart.

*Distribution* :  China; Java; South Africa; India; Hawaii.

**82. Zygnema schwabei** KRIEGER 1941. *Rabenhorst's Kryptogamenflora.* **13,** p. 261.

Fig. 222. *Z. schwabei.* (after Kolkwitz and Krieger.)

Vegetative cells 17-20 × 36-71 $\mu$.

Reproduction by aplanospores only ; spores cylindric filling the cells, 19-21 × 37-70 $\mu$ ; median spore wall thick, yellow-brown, scrobiculate ; pits 1-3 $\mu$ in diameter and 2-6 $\mu$ apart, with several irregular sutures.

*Distribution* : South America, Southern Chile.

**83. Zygnema ellipsoideum** JAO 1947. *Bot. Bull. Acad. Sinica.* **1,** p. 97.

Fig. 223. *Z. ellipsoideum.* (after Jao.)

Vegetative cells 20-22 × 25-40 $\mu$.

Conjugation unknown ; aplanospores ellipsoid, with somewhat pointed ends, 15-20 × 22-25 (—30) $\mu$ ; median spore wall yellow-brown, scrobiculate ; sporiferous cells cylindric, or somewhat inflated on one side.

*Distribution* : Kwangsi, Suijen, China.

**84. Zygnema cylindricum** TRANSEAU 1915. *Ohio. Jour. Sci.* **16,** p. 22.

Fig. 224. *Z. cylindricum.* (after Kolkwitz & Krieger)

Vegetative cells 28-33 × 28-66 $\mu$.

Conjugation unknown ; reproduction by akinetes and aplanospores ; aplanospores cylindric to tumid-cylindric, filling the cell, 30-33 × 24-54 $\mu$ ; median spore wall brown, scrobiculate ; pits about 3 $\mu$ in diameter, suture irregular.

*Distribution* : U.S.A., South America, South Chile.

**85. Zygnema subcylindricum** KRIEGER 1941. *Rabenhorst's Kryptogamen-flora,* **13,** p. 262.

a        b

Fig. 225. a-b. *Z. subcylindricum.* (a, after Kolkwitz ; b, after Czurda.)

Vegetative cells 28-35 × 54-71 $\mu$.

Reproduction by aplanospores only ; spores cylindric filling the cells, 29-33 × 55-70 $\mu$ ; median wall brown, granulose and with shallow pits, and 1-2 $\mu$ irregular sutures.

*Distribution* : Germany ; Bohemia.

**86. Zygnema khannae** SKUJA 1949 *Nova. Acta Soc. Sci. Upsali, Ser.* **4**, 14, p. 99, Pl. 22, Figs. 6-7.

Fig. 226. *Z. khannae.* (after Skuja.)

Vegetative cells 24-28 × 30-70 $\mu$.

Conjugation unknown ; reproduction by aplanospores, the outer wall of which is cylindric, just inside the sporangium wall, densely punctate ; the median wall, formed after contraction, varies from ellipsoid to ovoid, 22-25 × 25-46 $\mu$, yellow-brown with shallow irregular pits 1.5-5 $\mu$ in diameter.

*Distribution* : Burma.

**87. Zygnema irregulare** KRIEGER 1941. *Rabenhorst's Kryptogamenflora.* **13**, p. 263.

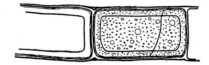

Fig. 227. *Z. irregulare.* (after Kolkwitz & Krieger.)

Vegetative cells 40-42 × 68-82 $\mu$.

Reproduction by aplanospores only; spores cylindric-ovoid with very heavy walls ; median wall brown, outwardly finely verrucose, with irregularly and widely separated pits 3-6 $\mu$ in diameter and 4-6 $\mu$ apart.

*Distribution* : Germany.

**88. Zygnema sterile** Transeau 1934. *Trans. Amer. Micros. Soc.* **53**, p. 212.

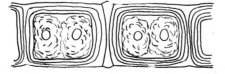

Fig. 228. *Z. sterile.* (after Transeau.)

Vegetative cells 44-54 × 22-69 $\mu$ with heavy cell walls, often with an outer pectic layer 6-15 $\mu$ in thickness.

Conjugation unknown; reproduction by akinetes ; akinetes heavy-walled, completely filling the cells, brown at maturity, often distinctly colligate.

*Distribution*: Greece; Asia Minor.

**89. Zygnema momoniense** W. WEST 1892. *Jour. Linn. Soc. London Bot.* **29**, p. 114, Pl. 24, Fig. 26.

Vegetative cells 20-22 $\mu$ in diameter.

Conjugation scalariform ; zygospores formed in the conjugating tubes, compressed-globose, with the longer diameter at right angles to the conjugating tubes ; 25-27 $\times$ 30-33 $\mu$ ; median spore wall brown, smooth.

*Distribution*: Ireland.

**90. Zygnema yunnanense** LI 1940. *Bull. Fan Mem. Inst. Biol.* **10**, p. 63.

Vegetative cells 16-18 $\times$ 50-104 $\mu$.

Conjugation lateral; receptive gametangia more or less enlarged ; zygospores globose to ovoid, 32-40 $\times$ 38-48 $\mu$ ; median wall thick, deeply scrobiculate, with pits 3-4.5 $\mu$ in diameter, 2-3 $\mu$ apart, yellow at maturity.

*Distribution*: Yunnan, China.

**91. Zygnema neocruciatum** TRANSEAU 1934. *Trans. Amer. Micros. Soc.* **53**, p. 212.

Vegetative cells 40-50 $\times$ 30-100 $\mu$.

Conjugation scalariform ; zygospores in one of the gametangia ; receptive gametangia cylindric or slightly enlarged ; zygospores globose to cylindric-ovoid, filling the gametangia, 40-45 $\times$ 40-50 $\mu$ ; median spore wall brown, scrobiculate ; pits about 2 $\mu$ in diameter, 3-4 $\mu$ apart ; aplanospores common and similar in size, rarely to 80 $\mu$ in length.

*Distribution*: U.S.A.

**92. Zygnema transeauianum** COUCH 1944. *Ohio Jour. Sci.* **44**, p. 277.

Vegetative cells 30-32 $\times$ 20-60 $\mu$.

Conjugation scalariform ; receptive gametangia enlarged or slightly inflated on the conjugating side ; zygospores globose to ovoid, 25-35 $\times$ 33-40 $\mu$ ; somewhat compressed; median spore wall yellow-brown, reticulate, with large irregular pits 7-12 $\mu$ across.

*Distribution*: U.S.A.

**93. Zygnema atrocoeruleum** W. & G. S. WEST 1879. *Jour. Roy. Micros. Soc. London*, p. 476.

Vegetative cells 14-17 $\times$ 40-70 $\mu$ in diameter.

Conjugation scalariform ; zygospores in one of the gametangia, receptive gametangia enlarged or inflated ; zygospores globose, 23-26 (—29) $\mu$ in diameter ; median spore wall dark blue, smooth.

*Distribution*:

*India*: Srinagar, Kashmir.

*Other countries*: England.

**94. Zygnema catenatum** TRANSEAU 1934. *Trans. Amer. Micros. Soc.* **53,** p. 213.

Vegetative cells 30-36 × 35-80 $\mu$.

Conjugation scalariform ; zygospores in one of the gametangia; receptive gametangia slightly enlarged on the conjugating side ; zygospores globose to ovoid, slightly compressed, 30-36 × 30-46 $\mu$ ; median spore wall blue, scrobiculate ; pits 1.5-2 $\mu$ in diameter, 2-4 $\mu$ apart ; aplanospores similar, 30-34 × 30-80 $\mu$, filling the cells.

*Distribution* : U.S.A.

**95. Zygnema laetevirens** KLEBS 1886. *Untersuch. Bot. Inst. Tubingen.* **2,** p. 333, Pl. 3, Fig. 14.

Vegetative cells 27-34 × 40-90 $\mu$.

Conjugation scalariform ; zygospores formed in the conjugating tubes, globose, 40-55 $\mu$ in diameter or ovoid, 34-41 × 54-68 $\mu$ ; median spore wall chestnut brown, of 2 layers, of which the inner is finely verrucose, the outer scattered-scrobiculate. It is probable that the ornamentation of the inner median wall arises from granules formed between the 2 layers.

*Distribution* : China; Europe; Australia; U.S.A.

**96. Zygnema skujae** CZURDA 1932. *Süsswasserflora Mitteleuropa.* **9,** p. 109; Skuja. *Acta Horti Bot. Univ. Latviensis.* **4.** p. 40. 1929.

Vegetative cells 20-27 × 40-100 $\mu$.

Conjugation scalariform ; gametangia slightly bent ; zygospores formed in the conjugating tubes, globose to ovoid, 40-55 $\mu$ ; median spore wall olive-brown, coarsely and thickly scrobiculate.

*Distribution* : Latvia.

**97. Zygnema carterae** CZURDA 1932. *Süsswasserflora Mitteleuropa.* **9,** p. 114; Carter, *Jour. Linn. Soc. London Bot.* **46,** p. 62.

Vegetative cells 13-16 $\mu$ in diameter.

Conjugation lateral or scalariform ; zygospores formed in the conjugating tubes, globose, 30-35 $\mu$ ; median spore wall brown scrobiculate.

*Distribution* : New Caledonia.

**98. Zygnema srinagarense** KOLKWITZ & KRIEGER 1944. *Rabenhorst's Kryptogamenflora,* **13,** p. 242, (=$Z$. *sphaerica* f. *crassa* Misra).

Vegetative cells 36-40 $\mu$ broad.

Conjugation scalariform; zygospores formed in the gametangia ; fructifying cells not swollen ; zygospores spherical or nearly spherical ; 36-40 $\mu$. Exospore thin, smooth and colourless. Mesospore smooth, thick and blue.

*Distribution* :

*India* : Srinagar, Kashmir.

**99. Zygnema insignisporum** COUCH 1944. *Ohio Jour. Sci.* **44,** p. 277.
Vegetative cells 24-28 × 39-71 $\mu$.

Conjugation scalariform ; receptive gametangia inflated on the conjugating side ; zygospores globose to ovoid 32-35 × 32-35 $\mu$ ; outer wall of 2 colourless layers, of which the outermost is smooth, the inner scrobiculate, with pits 4-5 $\mu$ in diameter and about 7 $\mu$ apart ; median wall punctate, yellow.

*Distribution* :   U.S.A.

**100.  Zygnema subtile** KUTZING 1849.   *Species Algarum.* p. 444.

Vegetative cells 14-20 × 30-85 $\mu$.

Conjugation scalariform or very rarely lateral ; zygospores in one of the gametangia ; receptive gametangia greatly enlarged or inflated on the inner side ; zygospores ovoid to subglobose, 20-29 × 22-30 $\mu$ ; median spore wall brown, punctate.

*Distribution* :   U.S.A.;   Finland;   Germany;   Bohemia.

## CHAPTER 14

# PLEURODISCUS Lagerheim 1895

Genus *Pleurodiscus* was established by Lagerheim in 1895. Filaments are simple or branched with rhizoids. Vegetative cells are cylindrical, 1-5 times as long as broad, characterised by purple colour, and by the presence of two distinct *disc-shaped chloroplasts*. The nucleus is situated in between the two chloroplasts in the cytoplasmic isthmus.

*Pleurodiscus* resembles *Zygogonium* in many respects, particularly in reproduction. Skuja (1932) favours the merger of *Pleurodiscus* with *Zygogonium* on the ground that the peculiar chloroplast is merely an expanded form of the *Zygogonium* chloroplast due to environmental conditions. Tiffany (1936) showed that the chloroplasts of this alga are really disc-shaped, and oriented at various angles to each other. *P. borinquinae* Tiffany is the only recognized species of this genus (Map F.).

**Pleurodiscus borinquinae** Tiffany 1936. *Brittonia.* **2,** p. 169, Figs. 31-39.

Vegetative cells 18-26 × 16-65 $\mu$, pectic sheath sometimes thick ; filaments either simple or branched and having rhizoids.

Zygospores ovoid to ellipsoid, within a sporangium partly formed by the tube papillae and partly by a collar between them ; zygospores 22-32 × 26-32 $\mu$ with a scrobiculate spore wall ; pits 3-5 $\mu$ in diameter.

*Distribution* : Puerto Rico ; West Indies.

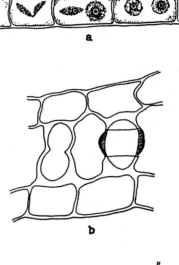

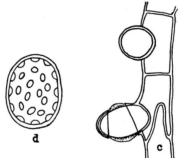

Fig. 229. a-d. *Pleurodiscus borinquinae.* a, vegetative cells showing disc-shaped chloroplasts ; b-c, zygospores ; d, zygospore showing the sculpturing of the spore wall. (after Tiffany.)

## CHAPTER 15

# ZYGOGONIUM Kutzing 1843

Genus *Zygogonium* was established by Kützing in 1843 and has been re-defined by Transeau (1933). The filaments are usually simple or sometimes branched. When branched, the horizontal branches and rhizoids are in the sub-soil with erect sub-aerial branches. The terrestrial forms have thick, opaque and lamellate cell walls which are yellow or brown in colour. In terrestrial specimens the cell sap is colourless or purple. The chloroplasts are compressed globular or pillow-shaped sometimes with short and irregular processes. In some cases they are ill-defined. In the terrestrial forms the accumulation of starch and fat globules often obscures the chloroplasts and the nucleus.

Reproduction is by zygospores, aplanospores, and akinetes. In terrestrial forms, sometimes all the cells of filaments are converted into akinetes. Conjugation is scalariform or lateral. In *Zygogonium ericetorum* secondary gametangia are formed *i.e.*, the gametes are separated by septa in conjugating papillae before the wall between the papillae dissolves. In other species, normal conjugation takes place. Cytoplasmic residues are present in the gametangia after the formation of zygospores. In fact, the presence of the cytoplasmic remains is the main feature which distinguishes this genus from *Zygnema*.

So far 14 species have been described of which three are from the U.S.A., one from China, five from India, three from Africa, two from South America and one from Australia. Of these *Zygogonium ericetorum* has been reported from all the continents (Map. H).

## KEY TO THE SPECIES OF ZYGOGONIUM

1a. Reproduction by zygospores
  2a. Mesopore smooth
    3a. Zygospores 13-17 $\times$ 9-32 $\mu$ ; sporangium
       suture distinct :                               3. **Z. mirabile**
    3b. Zygospores 15-26 $\times$ 20-36 $\mu$ ; sporangium
       suture indistinct                               2. **Z. ericetorum**
    3c. Zygospores 20-25 $\times$ 18-25 $\mu$ ; sporangium

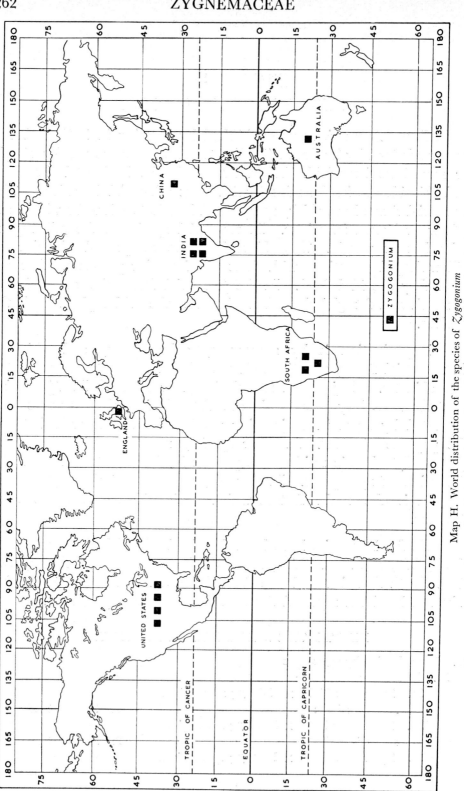

Map H. World distribution of the species of *Zygogonium*

with pectic wall — 7. **Z. pectosum**

2b. Mesopore not smooth, blue — 1. **Z. indicum**

2c. Mesopore not smooth, yellow to brown

    4a. Mesospore scrobiculate or punctate

        5a. Zygospores without distinct suture, mesospore punctate — 6. **Z. punctatum**

        5b. Zygospores without distinct suture, mesospore scrobiculate — 8. **Z. heydrichii**

        5c. Zygospores in gametangia having collars at both ends — 9. **Z. stephensiae**

        5d. Zygospores with distinct suture — 10. **Z. sinense**

    4b. Mesospore pitted or marginal arched ridges

        6a. Zygospores with scattered pits on the median wall — 11. **Z. exuvielliforme**

        6b. Zygospores with arching ribs on one side of suture — 13. **Z. plakountiosporum**

1b. Reproduction by aplanospores

    7a. Mesospore smooth

        8a. Vegetative cells 10-14 $\mu$ broad ; zygospores terminal — 14. **Z. kumaoense**

        8b. Vegetative cells 12-20 $\mu$ broad ; Zygospores usually lateral — 12. **Z. talguppense**

    7b. Mesospore not smooth

        9a. Vegetative cells 8-12 $\mu$ broad ; spore wall verrucose — 5. **Z. hansgirgii**

        9b. Vegetative cells 16-20 $\mu$ broad ; spore wall scrobiculate — 4. **Z. capense**

**1. Zygogonium indicum** (Randhawa) Transeau 1951. *The Zygnemataceae*, p. 68, (=*Zygnema Heydrichii* Schmidle. var. *indicum*. Randh 1938. *Proc. Indian Acad. Sci.* **8,** p. 140.)

Vegetative cells are 18-22 $\mu$ broad and 50-94 $\mu$ long. Each cell has two more or less stellate chloroplasts surrounding a centrally situated nucleus. The protoplasm of the cells is densely granular. On the exterior, the cells are surrounded by a hyaline mucilaginous covering (Fig. 230, a).

Conjugation both lateral and scalariform.

*Lateral Conjugation*: The predominant mode of conjugation is lateral. The neighbouring cells give out tube-like protuberances which ultimately meet forming a dome-like structure (Fig. 230, a). The dome-like space containing the zygospore is cut off by a partition wall from the remaining part of the conjugating cells (Fig. 230, e). In one case it was noticed that the partition wall was laid obliquely and the gametes instead of meeting had independently developed into parthenosporic bodies joined together by a very narrow isthmus (Fig. 230, c, d). Looked at laterally, these parthenospores with their swollen walls gave the filament the appearance of an *Oedogonium* (Fig. 230 d). In some cases the partition wall is obliterated entirely and the zygospore appears to lie in the swollen middle part of the cells, while in some cases the vertical septum separating the cells may be seen. Zygospores are greenish blue to dark blue in colour, and from oval to reniform in appearance. Zygospores are 22-27 $\mu$ broad and 31-37 $\mu$ long. Mesospore is scrobiculate with pits about 2 $\mu$ in diameter.

*Scalariform Conjugation*: This mode of conjugation is comparatively very rare. Zygospores are on the average 21 $\mu$ broad and 25 $\mu$ long and agreed in all details with those produced by lateral conjugation.

*Distribution*:

*India*: Found mixed with *Zygnemopsis minuta* var. *crassa* in a fresh-water stream near V. Mubarakpur, district Fyzabad, U.P.

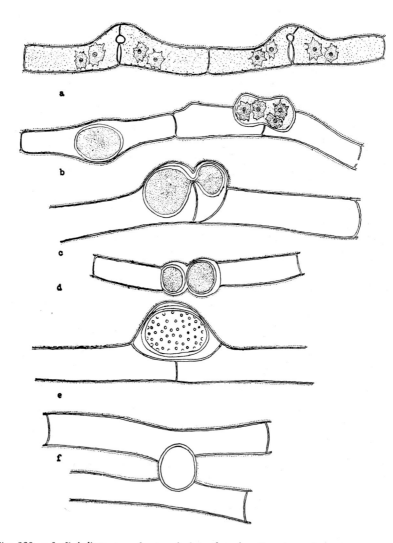

Fig. 230. a-f. *Z. indicum*. a, early stage in lateral conjugation; b, an immature zygospore and an aplanospore; c, d, azygospores; e, mature zygospore; f, scalariform conjugation. (after Randhawa)

**2. Zygogonium ericetorum** Kützing 1843. *Phycologia Generalis*, p. 446.

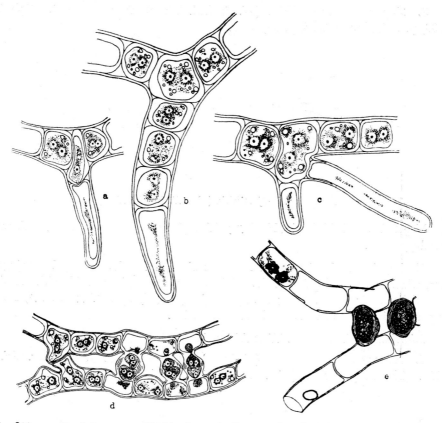
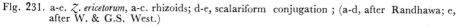

Flg. 231. a-e. *Z. ericetorum*, a-c. rhizoids; d-e, scalariform conjugation ; (a-d, after Randhawa; e, after W. & G.S. West.)

The filaments are simple with one to many-celled rhizoids. The vegetative cells are cylindrical 12-33 × 10-100 $\mu$ ; chloroplasts 2, stellate, rounded or indefinite, each with a central pyrenoid.

Perennation by akinetes which develop by thickening of cell walls. In some cases, the cells divide into two by ingrowth of septa from the side-walls and such akinetes have only a single chloroplast.

Conjugation scalariform, zygospores develop within definite sporangia formed by the conjugating tubes and cut off by a wall from the adjoining gametangia. The progametes are cut off from the gametangia by ingrowth of cell wall, leaving remants of protoplasm in the gametangia. A pore is formed between the progametes and it enlarges resulting in the fusion of gametes and the formation of a zygospore. Zygospores ovoid or ellipsoid, 15-26 × 20-36 $\mu$, thick-walled, smooth ; aplanospores globose or ovoid, occupying only a part of the original cell, 15-20 × 14-40 $\mu$ ; wall smooth.

*Distribution* :

*India* : On laterite soil on hill slopes and open ground at Makoot (altitude 4500 ft.) in Coorg, Western Ghats; Nandi Hills, Mysore State, Kodaikanal, Madras State, Deviculam, Kerala State.

*Other Countries*:   China, U.S.A., and from all continents.

**3. Zygogonium mirabile** (W. & G.S. WEST) Transeau 1933. *Ohio Jour. Sci.* 33, p. 158, *Jour. Bot.* **35,** p. 39, 1897.

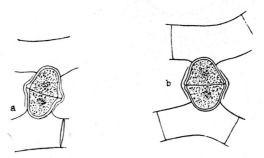

Fig. 232. a-b. *Z. mirabile.* (after W. & G.S. West.)

Vegetative cell 12-13·5×18-50 $\mu$ ; chloroplasts 2, rather indistinct, each with a central pyrenoid.

Conjugation scalariform ;   zygospores formed in the enlarged conjugating tubes, which are walled off from the original cells, sporangium ovoid, with prominent equatorial suture ; spores filling the sporangium, ovoid, 13·5-17 × 19-32 $\mu$, smooth, but possibly immature in the one known collection.

*Distribution*:   Portuguese West Africa, Huilla.

**4. Zygogonium capense** (Hodgetts) Transeau 1933. *Ohio Jour. Sci.* **33,** p. 159. *Trans. Roy. Soc. S. Africa.* **13,** p. 66. 1925 (=*Zygnema capense*).

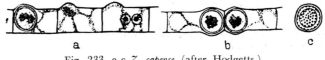

Fig. 233. a-c *Z. capense.* (after Hodgetts.)

Vegetative cells 16-20×20-60 $\mu$.

Conjugation unknown ; aplanospores globose, 19-26 $\mu$ in diameter, formed at the ends of the cells ; median spore wall brown, scrobiculate.

*Distribution*:   On damp soil, South Africa,.

**5. Zygogonium hansgirgii** (Schmidle) Transeau 1933. *Ohio Jour. Sci.* **33,** p. 159. *Hedwigia.* 39, p. 160. 1900 (=*Zygnema hansgirgii*).

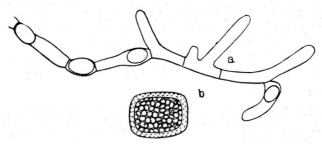

Fig. 234. *Z. hansgirgii.* (after Schmidle.)

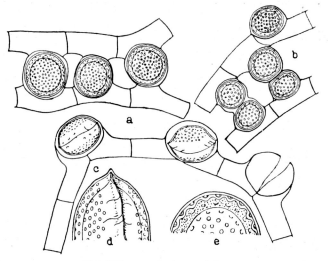

Fig. 239. a-e. *Z. sinense*. (after Jao.)

Vegetative cells 16-17 × 38-64 $\mu$ ; chloroplasts 2, irregularly globose bodies.

Reproduction by zygospores and parthenospores enclosed by sporangial walls. Conjugation scalarifom and lateral ; zygospores compressed-globose or subglobose, 29-38 × 22-25 $\mu$ ; median spore wall yellow to brown, sharply scrobiculate on the faces, only slightly scrobiculate or striate near the prominent equatorial suture ; parthenospores without prominent suture.

*Distribution*: Nanking and Chungking, China.

**11. Zygogonium exuvielliforme** JAO 1935. *Amer. Jour. Bot.* **22**, p. 768

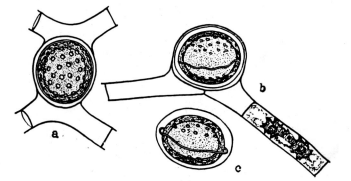

Fig. 240. a-c. *Z. exuvielliforme*. a, scalariform conjugation; b, lateral conjugation. (after Jao.)

Vegetative cells 13-22 × 48-105 $\mu$ ; chloroplasts two.

Conjugation lateral and scalariform ; spores formed in the greatly enlarged conjugating tubes ; zygospores compressed-globose with distinct or prominent sutures, 35-42 × 38-54 $\mu$ in diameter ; median wall yellow to brown, thick, lamellate, with scattered pits except near the equatorial suture.

*Distribution*:  South America, Columbia, at 14,400 feet altitude.

**12.  Zygogonium talguppense** IYENGAR 1932.  *Rev. Algolog.*  **6**, pp. 263-74.

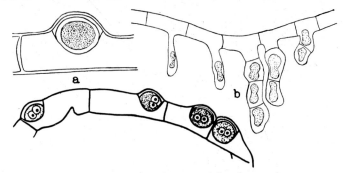

Fig. 241. a-c. *Z. talguppense*. (after Iyengar.)

Filaments forming a thick felt on soil, increasing in width upwards, often branching below ; lower cells of the filament 12-16 × 30-60 $\mu$ ; the upper 17-20 × 30-90 $\mu$.

Conjugation unknown ; aplanospores ellipsoid to subglobose, 12-26 × 13-34 $\mu$, developed in a lateral swelling and cut off from the parent cell by wall ; median spore wall smooth.

*Distribution* :

*India* :  On moist soil in plantation of Areca palm, Mysore; on laterite soils, Coorg.

**13.  Zygogonium plakountiosporum** JAO 1935.  *Amer. Jour. Bot.* **22**, p. 767.

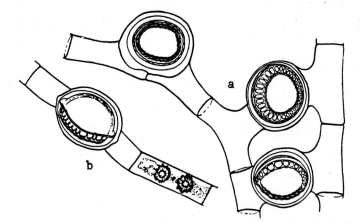

Fig. 242. a-b *Z. plakountiosporum*. Zygospores formed by lateral and scalariform conjugation. (after Jao.)

Vegetative cells 16-22 × 30-155 $\mu$, with 2 chloroplasts close to the nucleus.

Conjugation lateral and scalariform; tubes greatly distended containing the spores; zygospores compressed globose with colourless outer wall ; median wall brown, with equatorial suture more or less prominent, and with arching ridges forming a zone of pits on one side of the suture ; spore dimensions 35-41 × 40-68 × 14-20 $\mu$.

*Distribution*: South America, Colombia, at 14,000 feet altitude.

**14. Zygogonium kumaoense** RANDHAWA 1940. *Jour. Indian Bot. Soc.* **19**. pl 247.

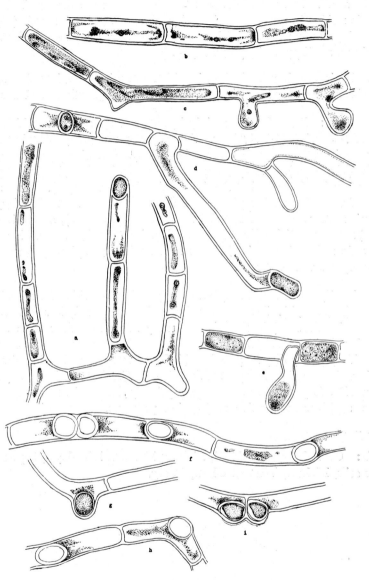

Fig. 243, a-i. *Z. kumaoense*. (after Randhawa.)

The thallus is composed of a creeping prostrate portion and a more or less erect projecting portion (Fig. 243, a). The function of the prostrate system is that of fixation and support, and its cells give out rhizoids of different shapes. In some plants, however, there is no such differentiation into prostrate and projecting portions. In shallow soil the rhizoids are more or less knob-like (Figs. 243, c,e) and deeper down they are fairly long (Fig. 243, d). In rare cases rhizoids may be even two-celled.

The vegetative cells are 10-14 $\mu$ broad and 2-10 times as long. The product of assimilation consists of both oil and starch; oil preponderates and stains slightly black with osmic acid, while reaction with iodine is very slight. The chloroplasts are proportionately small. In most of the cells the chloroplasts are disorganised and only protoplasmic residue in the form of irregular plate-like bodies is found (Fig. 243, a). The chloroplasts are small rounded bodies which may be close together or wide apart each bearing a small pyrenoid (Fig. 243, b).

This alga is an aplanosporic form in which no conjugation, lateral or scalariform has been observed. Only in one instance an abortive conjugation canal was observed.

*Aplanospores*: Reproduction mainly by means of aplanospores, which are ovoid bodies 12-17 $\mu$ broad and 15-24 $\mu$ long. Aplanospores are usually formed at the ends of cells and sometimes they may also be found centrally. Occasionally they are found terminally also (Fig. 243, a). They are usully produced subaerially, but in many instances they are produced underground at the tip of rhizoids (Fig. 243, d). In such cases migration of protoplasm takes place from the subaerial cell into rhizoids, and the protoplasmic matter accumulates at the lower end (Fig. 243 e), where it eventually rounds off, secretes a thick-cell-wall and develops into an aplanospore. Heavy deposit of cytoplasmic residue is seen in the cells surrounding the aplanospores on one side. Ripe aplanospores were not seen.

Occasionally aplanospores may be seen opposed to one side of a cell which shows geniculation (Fig. 243, h). In some cases these aplanospores may be seen in swellings on the side touching the soil (Fig. 243, g). One may as well consider these swellings as abbreviated rhizoids, though some would regard these as abortive conjugation processes. Very rarely they may be found lodged in these swellings in pairs cut off by a very thin wall from the other part of the cell as in *Z. talguppense* Iyengar (Fig. 243, i). Bodies found in this position are more appropriately described as azygospores, if we regard the swellings as abortive conjugation processes.

*Distribution*:

*India*: On red clay, Jariakhali, Almora, Kumaon Himalayas, September 1939; on laterite soils, Makoot, Western Ghats, Coorg.

## CHAPTER 16

# ENTRANSIA Elwyn Hughes 1943

The genus *Entransia* is one of the provisional genera of the Zygnemaceae, as its reproduction has not been observed. Vegetative cells are cylindrical with 1-2 laminate parietal chloroplasts with numerous finger-like processes, bearing many scattered pyrenoids.

The only species known is *Entransia fimbriata* described by Hughes from Nova Scotia (Canada), (Map. E.).

### KEY TO THE SPECIES OF ENTRANSIA

1. Vegetative cells with one or two laminate parietal chloroplasts.   Reproduction unknown          **E.fimbriata**

**Entransia fimbriata** HUGHES 1943.   *Abstracts of Doctoral Dissertations.* The Ohio State University, **40**, pp. 153-59 ; also in *Amer. Jour. Bot.*, **35** (1948), p. 487.

Fig. 243A.   *Entransia fimbriata*.   p. pyrenoid. (after Hughes)

Filaments with cylindrical vegetative cells 19-22.4 × 16-64 $\mu$ ; 1 or 2 parietal chloroplasts extending lengthwise of the cell, each with several lateral processes partly embracing the cell contents.   The nucleus, in young cells is located laterally and near the centre of the chloroplast ; in mature cells with 2 chloroplasts, the nucleus is in the bridge between them.

*Distribution* :   Canada.

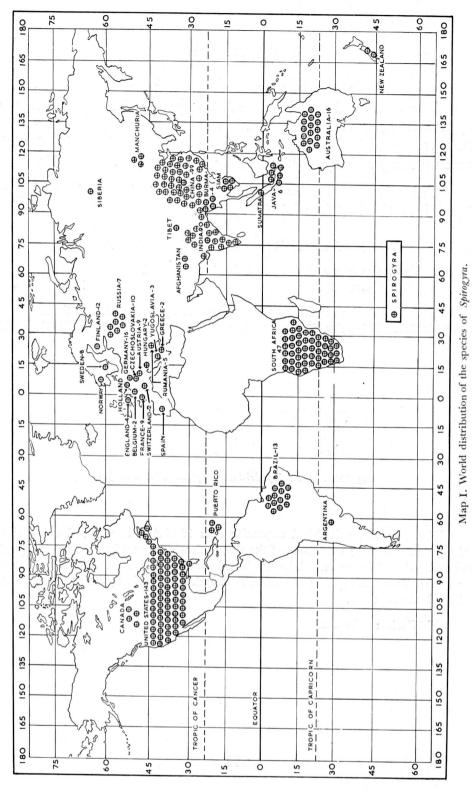

Map I. World distribution of the species of *Spirogyra*.

CHAPTER 17

# SPIROGYRA Link 1820

The genus *Spirogyra* was founded by Link in 1820. *Spirogyra* is represented by the largest number of species in the order Zygnemales. Filaments are free-floating, and rarely attached.

Cells are cylindrical, 0.5-30 (-50) times as long as broad, with plane, colligate, semi-replicate, replicate or unduliseptate septa. The chloroplasts are 1-16, spirally arranged, parietal ribbon-like bodies with numerous prominent pyrenoids. The nucleus is centrally situated in a protoplasmic strand.

Reproduction is by zygospores, parthenospores, aplanospores, akinetes or by fragmentation. Conjugation is scalariform or lateral.

Zygospores are usually ellipsoid, but rarely may be ovoid or lenticular. The median wall is pale yellow to chestnut brown in colour, and is either smooth or variously ornamented.

The species of *Spirogyra* have a more or less universal distribution, and they have been reported from all the continents and large islands. In all 289 species have been described so far (Map I).

### KEY TO THE SPECIES OF SPIROGYRA

1a. Reproduction by aplanospores
  2a. Cross walls plane
    3a. Chloroplast single
      4a. Gametangia cylindric; median spore wall scrobiculate    186. **S. oltmannsii**
      4b. Gametangia enlarged; median spore wall smooth    25. **S. mirabilis**
      4c. Gametangia and vegetative cells inflated; median spore wall smooth    161. **S. aplanospora**
      4d. Gametangia enlarged; median spore wall reticulate    288. **S. karnalae**
    3b. Chloroplasts 2 or more
      5a. Chloroplasts 2 to 3    204. **S. marvillosa**
      5b. Chloroplasts 6 to 8    192. **S. wrightiana**
      5c. Chloroplasts 5    163. **S. azygospora**
  2b. Cross walls semi-replicate    201. **S. narcissiana**

2c. Cross walls replicate     202. **S. articulata**

1b. Reproduction by zygospores

 6a. Cross walls plane

  7a. Conjugation canal formed by both gametangia

  8a. Chloroplast one in each cell

   9a. Mesospore smooth

    10a. Zygospores uniform

     11a. Zygospores ellipsoid

      12a. Gametangia cylindric or enlarged

       13a. Vegetative cells less than 40 $\mu$ broad

        14a. Vegetative cells 11-14.5 $\mu$ broad 237 **S. porangabae**

        14b. Vegetative cells 19-22 $\mu$ broad 5. **S. bullata**

        14c. Vegetative cells 18-26 $\mu$ broad 4. **S. communis**

        14d. Vegetative cells 25-29 $\mu$ broad 6. **S. intorta**

        14e. Vegetative cells 24-30 $\mu$ broad 7. **S. juergensii**

        14f. Vegetative cells 29-39 $\mu$ broad 8. **S. singularis**

        14g. Vegetative cells 32-40 $\mu$ broad 239. **S. silvicola**

       13b. Vegetative cells more than 40 $\mu$ broad

        15a. Zygospores 34-38 $\mu$ broad 2. **S. condensata**

        15b. Zygospores 42 $\mu$ broad 188. **S. variformis**

        15c. Zygospores 60-66 $\mu$ broad 3. **S. gallica**

      12b. Gametangia swollen on both sides

       16a. Vegetative cells less than 24 $\mu$ broad

        17a. Vegetative cells 15-19 $\mu$ broad; chloroplast one 206. **S. fennica**

        17b. Vegetative cells 17-20 $\mu$ ; chloroplasts 1-2 ; sterile cells bullate. 14. **S. pratensis**

17c.  Vegetative cells
    20-24 $\mu$ broad ;
    zygospores 48-60 $\mu$
    long          16. **S. parvula**

17d.  Vegetative cells
    20-25 $\mu$ broad; zygospo-
    res 52-72$\mu$ long   17. **S. macrospora**

16b.  Vegetative cells
    more than 24$\mu$ broad.

    18a.  Zygospores 28-
        33 × 30-50$\mu$;
        fertile cells glo-
        bose        18. **S. affinis**

    18b.  Zygospores 27-
        33 $\mu$ broad; yellow
        fertile cells fusi-
        form, inflated  19. **S. catanaeformis**

    18c.  Zygospores
        28-38 $\mu$ broad;
        brown; fertile
        cells fusiform,
        inflated     20. **S. subsalina**

12c.  Gametangia swollen
    on the conjugation side

  19a.  Vegetative cells less
      than 30 $\mu$ broad

    20a.  Vegetative cells    9. **S. gibberosa**
      19-21 $\mu$ broad

    20b.  Vegetative cells   10. **S. gracilis**
      16-24 $\mu$ broad

    20c.  Vegetative cells 23-
      30 $\mu$ broad

      21a.  Gametangia slightly  191. **S. fragilis**
        inflated

      21b.  Gametangia strongly  12. **S. teodoresci**
        inflated

      21c.  Vegetative cells   11. **S. woodsii**
        30-40 $\mu$ broad

  19b.  Vegetative cells 30-40 $\mu$
    broad

    22a.  Mesospore smooth,  180. **S. pseudovarians**
      exospore scrobiculate

    22b.  Mesospore smooth,  13. **S. varians**
      exospore smooth

22c.    Mesospore smooth    245.    **S. bicalyptrata**
with brown polar
caps

19c.    Vegetative cells more
than 40 $\mu$ broad

23a.    Zygospores 35-40 $\mu$
broad          230.    **S. supervarians**

23b.    Zygospores 40-50 $\mu$
broad          244.    **S. circumlineata**

12d.    Gametangia swollen on
the outer side

24a.    Vegetative cells 30-35 $\mu$
broad          21.    **S. borgeana**

24b.    Vegetative cells 37-42 $\mu$
broad          260.    **S. calcarea**

11b.    Zygospores cylindric or ovoid

25a.    Vegetative cells less than 40 $\mu$
broad

26a.    Vegetative cells less than
15 $\mu$ broad        22.    **S. flavescens**

26b.    Vegetative cells more than
15 $\mu$ broad

27a.    Zygospores less than
30 $\mu$ broad

28a.    Zygospores 18-20 $\mu$
broad          23.    **S. subsalsa**

28b.    Zygospores 24 $\mu$
broad          24.    **S. paludosa**

28c.    Zygospores 24-29 $\mu$
broad          25.    **S. mirabilis**

27b.    Zygospores more than
30 $\mu$ broad

29a.    Gametangia cylindric

30a.    Zygospores
28-38 $\mu$ broad   26,    **S. longata**

30b.    Zygospores
33-38 $\mu$ broad   27.    **S. indica**

30c.    Zygospores
36-42 $\mu$ broad   239.    **S. silvicola**

30d.    Zygospores
35-48 $\times$ 56-88 $\mu$   29.    **S. velata**

30e.    Zygospores
34-48 $\times$ 50-105 $\mu$   28.    **S. subvelata**

29b.    Gametangia swollen

31. Gametangia
    swollen on
    both sides        212. **S. suecica**
    31b. Gametangia
    swollen on the
    inner side        13. **S. varians**
25b. Vegetative cells more than 40 $\mu$
    broad
    32a. Vegetative cells 40-50 $\mu$ broad    30. **S. porticalis**
    32b. Vegetative cells 38-44 $\mu$ broad    31. **S. lacustris**
    32c. Vegetative cells 48-60 $\mu$ broad    32. **S. sahnii**
11c. Zygospores compressed globose or subglobose
    33a. Zygospores globose 85-95 $\mu$ broad  193. **S. sphaerospora**
    33b. Zygospores compressed globose,
    55-65 $\mu$ broad        187. **S. discoidea**
10b. Zygospores polymorphic
    34a. Chloroplast single
    35a. Vegetative cells 22-30 $\mu$ broad    34. **S. polymorpha**
    35b. Vegetative cells 27-40 $\mu$ broad    33. **S. lutetiana**
    34b. Chloroplasts 1-2        14. **S. pratensis**
9b. Mesospore variously ornamented
    36a. Zygospores ellipsoid
    37a. Vegetative cells less than 33 $\mu$ broad
    38a. Gametangia cylindric
    39a. Vegetative cells 25-33 $\mu$ broad ;
    sterile cells cylindric    223. **S. lagerheimii**
    39b. Vegetative cells 18-25 $\mu$ broad ;
    sterile cells bulliform    238. **S. taftiana**
    39c. Vegetative cells 14-18 $\mu$ broad;
    sterile cells not swollen    171. **S. perforans**
    39d. Vegetative cells 11-14 $\mu$ broad ;
    sterile cells inflated or bulliform  237. **S. porangabae**
    38b. Gametangia swollen on both sides
    40a. Mesospore grooved    227. **S. minutifossa**
    40b. Mesospore reticulate    41. **S. skujae**
    40c. Mesospore punctate    166. **S. hoehnei**
    40d. Mesospore coarsely punctate    42. **S. robusta**
    38c. Gametangia swollen on the inner
    side
    41a. Vegetative cells 12-16 $\mu$ broad  224. **S. taylorii**
    41b. Vegetative cells 22-26 $\mu$ broad  169. **S. subpapulata**
    41c. Vegetative cells 28-32 $\mu$ broad  43. **S. papulata**
    41d. Vegetative cells 30-40 $\mu$ broad  44. **S. scrobiculata**
    41e. Vegetative cells 17 $\mu$ broad  172. **S. sibirica**
    37b. Vegetative cells 33-45 $\mu$ broad
    42a. Gametangia swollen on the conjugating
    side

43a. Mesospore punctate | 45. **S. aphanosculpta**
43b. Mesospore scrobiculate | 44. **S. scrobiculata**
43c. Mesospore reticulate and granulate | 189. **S. kaffirita**
  42b. Gametangia swollen on both sides
43a. Mesospore verrucose | 281. **S. tuberculata**
44b. Mesospore irregularly corrugate | 46. **S. daedalea**
44c. Mesospore irregularly reticulate | 177. **S. daedaleoides**
44d. Mesospore broadly reticulate, mesospore separated by a considerable space | 47. **S. oudhensis**
  37c. Vegetative cells more than 45 $\mu$ broad
45a. Mesospore finely verrucose | 175. **S. australensis**
45b. Mesospore reticulate | 280. **S. labrynthica**
45c. Mesospore finely granulate | 48. **S. atasiana**
45d. Mesospore with irregular reticulate sides | 232. **S. pseudoreticulata**
36b. Zygospores globose | 35. **S. czurdae**
36c. Zygospore ovoid
46a. Mesospore scrobiculate | 36. **S. luteospora**
46b. Mesospore reticulate | 246. **S. sulcata**
46c. Mesospore wrinkled | 37. **S. westii**
46d. Mesospore punctate | 38. **S. obovata**
46e. Mesospore granulate | 40. **S. asiatica**
46f. Mesospore two layered, outer irregularly wrinkled and the inner irregularly reticulate | 39. **S. chekiangensis**

8b. Chloroplasts many in each cell
  47a. Zygospores laterally compressed
48a. Zygospores compressed-ellipsoid | 176. **S. crassoidea**
48b. Zygospores compressed ovoid
49a. Mesospore smooth | 216. **S. jassiensis**
49b. Mesospore verrucose | 267. **S. rectispira**
49c. Mesospore pitted
50a. Vegetative cells 80-95 $\mu$ broad | 248. **S. formosa**
50b. Vegetative cells 140-165 $\mu$ broad | 104. **S. crassa**
  48c. Zygospores lenticular
51a. Mesospore smooth
52a. Vegetative cells less than 50 $\mu$ broad
53a. Vegetative cells 22-24 $\mu$ broad | 105. **S. sinensis**
53b. Vegetative cells 32-36 $\mu$ broad | 261. **S. frankliniana**
53c. Vegetative cells 40-50 $\mu$ broad | 249. **S. pellucida**
53d. Vegetative cells 40-45 $\mu$ broad | 106. **S. subpellucida**
52b. Vegetative cells more than 50 $\mu$ broad
54a. Vegetative cells 50-80 $\mu$ broad ; chloroplasts 3-8 | 107. **S. majuscula**

54b. Vegetative cells 70-110 $\mu$ broad ; chloroplasts 8-9 ............................ 108. **S. submaxima**

54c. Vegetative cells 70-72 $\mu$ broad ; chloroplasts 6 ............................. 109. **S. lamellata**

54d. Vegetative cells 86-96 $\mu$ broad ; chloroplast 6-8 ............................ 110. **S. randhawae**

54e. Vegetative cells 145-155 $\mu$ broad ; chloroplasts 7 ........................... 196. **S. glabra**

54f. Vegetative cells 113-125 $\mu$ broad ; chloroplasts 5-6 ......................... 211. **S. peipingensis**

51b. Mesospore variously ornamented

  55a. Vegetative cells 32-40 $\mu$ broad ...... 111. **S. sphaerocarpa**

  55b. Vegetative cells 65-80 $\mu$ broad ...... 112. **S. bellis**

  55c. Vegetative cells 80-118 $\mu$ broad

    56a. Mesospore irregularly reticulate ... 262. **S. moebii**

    56b. Mesospore verrucose ............. 113. **S. oblata**

    56c. Mesospore pitted ................ 263. **S. hydrodictya**

    56d. Mesospore reticulate-verrucose ... 114. **S. manoramae**

  55d. Vegetative cells 118-200 $\mu$ broad

    57a. Vegetative cells less than 150 $\mu$
 broad

      58a. Vegetative cells 116-132 $\mu$
 broad ; mesospore smooth ...... 216. **S. jassiensis**

      58b. Vegetative cells 118-130 $\mu$
 broad ; mesospore verrucose ... 178. **S. jatobae**

      58c. Vegetative cells 118-140 $\mu$
 broad ; mesospore reticulate ... 115. **S. maxima**

      58d. Vegetative cells 130-150 $\mu$
 broad ; mesospore verrucose ... 219. **S. heeriana**

    57b. Vegetative cells more than 150 $\mu$ broad

      59a. Vegetative cells 150-170 $\mu$ broad ... 269. **S. crassiuscula**

      59b. Vegetative cells 170-200 $\mu$ broad ... 268. **S. magaspora**

      59c. Vegetative cells 150-162 $\mu$ broad ... 240. **S. lenticularis**

47b. Zygospores not laterally compressed

60a. Mesospore smooth

 61a. Chloroplasts less than 9 in each cell

  62a. Gametangia cylindric

   63a. Zygospores ellipsoid

    64a. Vegetative cells less than 45 $\mu$ broad

     65a. Vegetative cells 21-32 $\mu$ broad ;
 chloroplasts 2-3 ............... 279. **S. submarina**

     65b. Vegetative cells 32-37 $\mu$ broad ;
 chloroplasts 2-4 ............... 49. **S. irregularis**

     65c. Vegetative cells 36-41 $\mu$ broad ;
 chloroplasts 2-3 ............... 51. **S. rivularis**

     65d. Vegetative cells 35-38 $\mu$ broad ;
 chloroplasts 2 ................ 15. **S. microspora**

65e. Vegetative cells 38-48 $\mu$ broad ;
    chloroplasts (1) 2-3      52. **S. biformis**

65f. Vegetative cells 36-41 $\mu$ broad ;
    chloroplasts 2      247. **S. hollandiae**

65g. Vegetative cells 40-42 $\mu$ broad ;
    chloroplasts 3      50. **S. fuellebornei**

64b. Vegetative cells 45-60 $\mu$ broad

  66a. Chloroplasts 2-4 in a cell      53. **S. hyalina**

  66b. Chloroplasts 3 in a cell

    67a. Vegetative cells 48-54 $\mu$ broad      54. **S. columbiana**

    67b. Vegetative cells 49-62 $\mu$ broad      278. **S. angolensis**

    67c. Vegetative cells 55-60 $\mu$ broad      55. **S. pseudoneglecta**

64c. Vegetative cells more than 60 $\mu$ broad

  68a. Vegetative cells 60-80 $\mu$ broad

    69a. Zygospores less than 60 $\mu$ broad

      70a. Zygospores 57-58 $\mu$ broad      285. **S. welwitschii**

      70b. Zygospores 50 $\mu$ broad      252. **S. parvispora**

    69b. Zygospores more than 60 $\mu$ broad

      71a. Zygospores 63-68 × 120-140 $\mu$.      56. **S. turfosa**

      71b. Zygospores 57-68 × 100-210 $\mu$.      57. **S. szechwanensis**

      71c. Zygospores 60-80 × 90-170 $\mu$.      58. **S. nitida**

  68b. Vegetative cells 80-120 $\mu$ broad

    72a. Vegetative cells 86-92 $\mu$ broad ;
      chloroplasts 3(2)-(4)      59. **S. hymerae**

    72b. Vegetative cells 90-115 $\mu$ broad ;
      Chloroplasts 4      60. **S. setiformis**

    72c. Vegetative cells 115-128 $\mu$
      broad ; chloroplasts 4-6      61. **S. elliptica**

    72d. Vegetative cells 90-100 $\mu$
      broad ; chloroplasts 6-8      277. **S. wollnyi**

    72e. Vegetative cells 98-110 $\mu$
      broad ; chloroplasts 6-8      251. **S. yunnanensis**

  68c. Vegetative cells more than 120 $\mu$ broad

    73a. Vegetative cells 115-128 $\mu$
      broad      62. **S. hatillensis**

    73b. Vegetative cells 125-150 $\mu$
      broad      63. **S. ellipsospora**

    73c. Vegetative cells 158-166 $\mu$
      broad      195. **S. splendida**

63b Zygospores ovoid or cylindric-ovoid

  74a. Vegetative cells less than 60 $\mu$ broad

    75a. Chloroplasts 3 or less in a cell

      76a. Chloroplasts 2 in each cell

77a. Vegetative cells 27-30 $\mu$
    broad              64. **S. exilis**
77b. Vegetative cells 48-52 $\mu$
    broad              65. **S. distenta**
76b. Chloroplasts 3 in each cell
    78a. Zygospores 34-48 $\mu$ broad    66. **S. triplicata**
    78b. Zygospores 46-50 $\mu$ broad    276. **S. siamensis**
    78c. Zygospores 54-64 $\mu$ broad    67. **S. neglecta**
77c. Chloroplasts 2-3 in each cell
    79a. Vegetative cells 32-42 $\mu$
        broad          68. **S. decimina**
    79b. Vegetative cells 38-44 $\mu$
        broad          69. **S. plena**
    79c. Vegetative cells 40-50 $\mu$
        broad          209. **S. occidentalis**
75b. Chloroplasts 4-5 in a cell      241. **S. emilianensis**
74b. Vegetative cells more than 60 $\mu$ broad
    80a. Zygospores 54-64 $\mu$ broad ;
        chloroplasts 3          67. **S. neglecta**
    80b. Zygospores 57-68 $\mu$ broad ;
        chloroplasts 4          57. **S. szechwanensis**
    80c. Zygospores 87-108 $\mu$ broad;
        chloroplasts 3-4        70. **S. jugalis**
    80d. Zygospores 70-75 $\mu$ broad ;
        chloroplasts 3 ; lateral conju-
        gation direct          289. **S. jogensis**
62b. Gametangia swollen
    81a. Chloroplasts 3-4 in each cell    72. **S. paradoxa**
    81b. Chloroplasts 4-6 in each cell    73. **S. jaoensis**
    81c. Chloroplasts 2-3 in each cell
        82a. Vegetative cells 26-28 $\mu$ broad    75. **S. rhizoides**
        82b. Vegetative cells 40-50 $\mu$ broad    76. **S. dubia**
    81d. Chloroplasts 2 in each cell.
        83a. Vegetative cells 20-24 $\mu$ broad    234. **S. baileyi**
        83b. Vegetative cells 44-47 $\mu$ broad    274. **S. buchetii**
        83c. Vegetative cells 60-75 $\mu$ broad    74. **S. bichromatophora**
61b Chloroplasts more than 9 in each cell
    84a. Vegetative cells 100-120 $\mu$ broad    71. **S. margaritata**
    84b. Vegetative cells 150-189 $\mu$ broad    275. **S. polytaeniata**
60b. Mesospore variously ornamented
    85a. Vegetative cells 16-25 $\mu$ broad
        86a. Mesospore 2 layered, outer wrinkled
            and inner irregularly reticulate    77. **S. chungkingensis**
        86b. Mesospore 2 layered, outer wrinkl-
            led, and inner scrobiculate    272. **S. miamiana**
        86c. Mesospore punctate    78. **S. puncticulata**
        86d. Mesospore densely scrobiculate    200. **S. acquinoctialis**

85b. Vegetative cells 25-35 $\mu$
    87a. Zygospores ovoid
        88a. Mesospore irregularly reticulate.  80. **S. rhizopus**
        88b. Mesospore reticulate          79. **S. dictyospora**
        88c. Mesospore 2 layered, outer
            punctate, inner reticulate and
            finely verrucose          284. **S. notabilis**
        88d. Mesospore punctate and reti-
            culate               273. **S. natchita**
        88e. Mesospore corrugate      81. **S. fluviatilis**
    87b. Zygospores ellipsoid,
        89a. Zygospores less than 32 $\mu$
            broad               243. **S. fossa**
        89b. Zygospores 32-43 $\mu$ broad
            90a. Mesospore punctate or
                scrobiculate
                91a. Mesospore 2 layered,
                    punctate      77. **S. chungkingensis**
                91b. Mesospore single lay-
                    ered, scrobiculate  83. **S. orientalis**
            90b. Mesospore reticulate
            92a. Mesospore regularly reti-
                culate         84. **S. subcylindrospora**
            92b. Mesospore irregularly reti-
                culate         80. **S. rhizopus**
        89c. Zygospore more than 43 $\mu$
            broad
            93a. Zygospores 43-46 $\mu$ broad  82. **S. schmidtii**
            93b. Zygospores 45-52 $\mu$ broad  242. **S. smithii**
85c. Vegetative cells 35-60 $\mu$ broad
    94a. Zygospores ellipsoid
        95a. Chloroplasts 2-3 ; mesospore reticu-
            late             271. **S. castanacea**
        95b. Chloroplasts 2-3 granulose to ver-
            rucose          258. **S. mienningensis**
        95c. Chloroplasts 3 ; mesospore 2 layered
            outer wrinkled, inner irregularly re-
            ticulate         85. **S. shantungensis**
        95d. Chloroplasts 3 ; Mesospore minutely
            verrucose        86. **S. braziliensis**
        95e. Chloroplasts 3-5
            96a. Vegetative cells less than 54 $\mu$
                broad ;
                97a. Zygospores 48-64 $\mu$ broad  87. **S. pulchrifigurata**
                97b. Zygospores 76-72 $\mu$ broad  265. **S. torta**
                97c. Zygospores less than 54 $\mu$
                broad

98a. Mesospore 2 layered  
    99a. Outer wrinkled  
        inner smooth      89. **S. subreticulata**  
    99b. Outer wrinkled ;  
        inner punctate    88. **S. quadrilaminata**  
98b. Mesospore single  
    layered  
    100a. Spore-wall irre-  
        gularly reticulate   90. **S. rhizobrachialis**  
    100b. Spore-wall irre-  
        gularly corrugate  259. **S. paraguayensis**  
96b. Vegetative cells more than 54 $\mu$  
  broad  
101a. Gametangia cylindric    91. **S. minor**  
101b. Gametangia swollen  
    102a. Mesospore reticulate   92. **S. brunnea**  
    102b. Mesospore punctate  275. **S. scripta**  
94b. Zygospores ovoid  
103a. Gametangia cylindric  
    104a. Mesospore reticulate   89. **S. subreticulata**  
    104b. Mesospore scrobiculate  255. **S. novae-angliae**  
103b. Gametangia swollen  
    105a. Mesospore irregularly and  
        shallowly corrugate   93. **S. africana**  
    105b. Mesospore granulose  283. **S. ovigera**  
    105c. Mesospore irregularly cor-  
        rugate        94. **S. grossii**  
85d. Vegetative cells 60-125 $\mu$ broad  
106a. Zygospores ellipsoid  
107a. Mesospore verrucose  
    108a. Chloroplasts 2 in each cell  86. **S. braziliensis**  
    108b. Chloroplasts 2-3 in each  
        cell.        271. **S. castanacea**  
    108c. Chloroplasts 5 in each  
        cell        96. **S. verruculosa**  
    108d. Chloroplasts 4-8 in each  
        cell        96. **S. verrucosa**  
107b. Mesospore reticulate  
    109a. Zygospores 55-66 $\mu$ broad  92. **S. brunnea**  
    109b. Zygospores 65-83 $\mu$ broad  98. **S. malmeana**  
    109c. Zygospores 73.90 $\mu$ broad  99. **S. anomala**  
107c. Mesospore narrowly reticulate  
  with irregularly toothed ridges  102. **S. kundaensis**  
107d. Mesospore pitted, scrobiculate  
  or punctate  
    110a. Mesospore pitted    282. **S. propria**

110b. Mesospore scrobiculate     100. **S. trachycarpa**
110c. Mesospore punctate     101. **S. punctulata**
107e. Mesospore with irregularly
    raised ridges     97. **S. chakiense**
106b. Zygospores ovoid
    111a. Chloroplasts 4     164. **S. cylindrospora**
    111b. Chloroplasts 5     96. **S. verruculosa**
    111c. Chloroplasts 6-7     103. **S. ghosei**
    111d. Chloroplasts 3-8
      112a. Vegetative cells less than
       85 $\mu$ broad
       113a. Vegetative cells
        54-60 $\mu$ broad     93. **S. africana**
       113b. Vegetative cells
        56-71 $\mu$ broad     92. **S. brunnea**
       113c. Vegetative cells
        66-72 $\mu$ broad     254. **S. echinospora**
       113d. Vegetative cells
        70-85 $\mu$ broad     183. **S. diluta**
      112b. Vegetative cells more
      than 85 $\mu$ broad
       114a. Mesospore echinate     199. **S. echinata**
       114b. Mesospore reticu-
        late     167. **S. reinhardii**
       114c. Mesospore reticulate-
        echinate     212. **S. hunanensis**
7b. Conjugation canal formed by the male gametangia
   115a. Vegetative cells less than 30 $\mu$ broad
     116a. Zygospores ellipsoid
      117a. Vegetative cells less than 15 $\mu$ broad
       118a. Mesospore smooth     116. **S. liana**
       118b. Mesospore with foveolate reticu-
        lations     117. **S. reticuliana**
       118c. Mesospore coarsely punctate     266. **S. prescottii**
       118d. Mesospore reticulate to punctate     224. **S. taylorii**
      117b. Vegetative cells 15-25 $\mu$ broad
       119a. Mesospore smooth
        120a. Gametangia swollen on the
        conjugating side     9. **S. gibberosa**
        120b. Gametangia swollen on both
        sides     181. **S. chenii**
       119b. Mesospore coarsely punctate     170. **S. collinsii**
        121a. Mesospore irregularly pitted     286. **S. sirogonioides**
        121b. Mesospore reticulate     230. **S. lushanensis**
        121c. Mesospore finely scrobiculate     192. **S. sibirica**
      117c. Vegetative cells more than 24 $\mu$ broad
       122a. Mesospore coarsely punctate     118. **S. punctata**

122b. Mesospore irregularly reticulate    221. **S. esthonica**
116b. Zygospores ovoid
   123a. Mesospore punctate    119. **S. punctiformis**
   123b. Mesospore coarsely punctate    170. **S. collinsii**
115b. Vegetative cells 30-40 $\mu$ broad
   124a. Chloroplast one in each cell
     125a. Mesospore smooth    236. **S. reflexa**
     125b. Mesospore punctate    120. **S. micropunctata**
     125c. Mesospore irregularly reticulate    221. **S. esthonica**
     125d. Mesospore scrobiculate    121. **S. suomiana**
   124b. Chloroplasts 2-3 in each cell
     126a. Mesospore punctate    82. **S. schmidtii**
     126b. Mesospore 2-layered, outer layer
       corrugate, inner finely reticulate    122. **S. corrugata**
     126c. Mesospore 5-layered, irregularly
       crenulate    123. **S. crenulata**
115c. Vegetative cells more than 40 $\mu$ broad
   127a. Chloroplast one in each cell
     128a. Mesospore smooth ; vegetative
       cells 40-45 $\mu$ broad    215. **S. visenda**
     128b. Mesospore smooth ; vegetative
       cells 53-56 $\mu$ broad    210. **S. hungarica**
     128c. Mesospore punctate    124. **S. rugulosa**
   127b. Chloroplasts 2-5 in each cell
     129a. Mesospore irregularly corrugate    94. **S. grossii**
     129b. Mesospore areolate    173. **S. wabashensis**
     129c. Mesospore reticulate    250. **S. texensis**
   127c. Chloroplasts 5-10 in each cell
     130a. Zygospores ovoid    265. **S. conspicua**
     130b. Zygospores lenticular    253. **S. hydrodictya**
6b. Cross walls colligate    1. **S. colligata**
6c. Cross walls semi-replicate
   131a. Reproduction by aplanospores    201. **S. narcissiana**
   131b. Reproduction by zygospores    125. **S. tandae**
6d. Cross walls unduliseptate    126. **S. undulisepta**
6e. Cross walls replicate
132a. Conjugation canal formed by both gametangia
   133a. Chloroplast one in each cell
     134a. Gametangia cylindric
       135a. Zygospores ellipsoid
         136a. Mesospore smooth
           137a. Vegetative cells less than
             24 $\mu$ broad
             138a. Zygospores 22-26 $\times$
               51-103 $\mu$    128. **S. arta**
             138b. Zygospores 30-36 $\times$
               55-110 $\mu$    129. **S. spreeiana**

138c.  Zygospores 25-35 ×
48-86 μ                          130. **S. tumida**
137b.  Vegetative cells more than 24 μ
broad
139a.  Vegetative cells 45-50 μ
broad ; zygospores 32-35 ×
37-42 μ                  165. **S. tjibodensis**
139b.  Vegetative cells 29-32 μ
broad ; zygospores 32-42 ×
80-122 μ                 131. **S. lamellosa**
139c.  Vegetative cells 30-36 μ
broad ; zygospores 30-33 ×
60-82 μ                  132. **S. laxa**
139d.  Vegetative cells 27-32 μ
broad ; zygospores 35-46 ×
61-106 μ                 135. **S. semiornata**
136b.  Mesospore smooth, but
inner layer of the exospore scrobiculate     194. **S. venusta**
136c.  Mesospore reticulate                    127. **S. dentireticulata**
135b.  Zygospores ovoid
140a.  Mesospore smooth, outer wall smooth
141a.  Mesospore yellow           134. **S. weberi**
141b.  Mesospore yellow brown     135. **S. semiornata**
141c.  Mesospore smooth, exospore
2-layered, inner layer scrobiculate
142a.  Vegetative cells 25-27 μ
broad              194. **S. venusta**
142b.  Vegetative cells 28-34 μ
broad              225. **S. protecta**
142c.  Vegetative cells 36-40 μ
broad              136. **S. cleveana**
142d.  Vegetative cells 43-56 μ
broad              137. **S. denticulata**
140b.  Mesospore granulate                 133. **S. microgranulata**
134b.  Gametangia fusiform
143a.  Vegetative cells less than 20 μ broad
144a.  Mesospore smooth
145a.  Vegetative cells 8-13 μ broad  138. **S. tenuissima**
145b.  Vegetative cells 15-20 μ broad  139. **S. inflata**
144b.  Mesospore not smooth
146a.  Vegetative cells 11-13 μ broad  264. **S. rugosa**
146b.  Vegetative cells 13-17 μ broad  140. **S. kuusamoensis**
146c.  Vegetative cells 16-20 μ broad
147a.  Gametangia fusiform inflated  217. **S. discreta**
147b.  Gametangia cylindric          218. **S. amplectens**
143b.  Vegetative cells more than 20 μ broad
148a.  Mesospore smooth

149a.  Zygospores ellipsoid
    150a.  Vegetative cells 18-24 $\mu$ broad    129.  **S. spreeiana**
    150b.  Vegetative cells 24-30 $\mu$ broad    141.  **S. farlowii**
    150c.  Vegetative cells 34-38 $\mu$ broad    142.  **S. nyctigama**
149b.  Zygospores ovoid
    151a.  Outer wall single    143.  **S. grevilleana**
    151b.  Outer wall double
        152a.  Vegetative cells 20-25 $\mu$
            broad    263.  **S. latviensis**
        152b.  Vegetative cells 30-36 $\mu$
            broad    198.  **S. areolata**
148b.  Mesospore not smooth
    153a.  Mesospore wall single
        154a.  Zygospores 35-40 × 55-64 $\mu$    229.  **S. fritschiana**
        154b.  Zygospores 23-30 × 42-56 $\mu$    144.  **S. goetzii**
    153b.  Mesospore wall double
        155a.  Inner wall smooth    146.  **S. jaoi**
        155b.  Inner wall reticulate    145.  **S. lambertiana**
134c.  Gametangia cylindrically inflated
    156a.  Vegetative cells 18-23 $\mu$ broad    182.  **S. groenlandica**
    156b.  Vegetative cells 24-30 $\mu$ broad    147.  **S. quadrata.**

133b.  Chloroplasts more than one in each cell
    157a.  Mesospore smooth
        158a.  Gametangia cylindric
        159a.  Zygospores ellipsoid
            160a.  Vegetative cells 29-32 $\mu$
                broad    208.  **S. marchica**
            160b.  Vegetative cells 28-33 $\mu$
                broad    203.  **S. gratiana**
            160c.  Vegetative cells 37-40 $\mu$
                broad    207.  **S. proavita**
            160d.  Vegetative cells 42-58 $\mu$
                broad    154.  **S. transeauiana**
        159b.  Zygospores ovoid
            161a.  Zygospores 26-29 $\mu$ broad    214.  **S. tolosana**
            161b.  Zygospores 45-50 $\mu$ broad    205.  **S. hartigii**
        158b.  Gametangia swollen
        162a.  Zygospores ellipsoid
            163a.  Vegetative cells less than 35 $\mu$
                broad
                164a.  Zygospores 39-48 $\mu$ broad    155.  **S. hassallii**
                164b.  Zygospores 43-52 $\mu$ broad    179.  **S. incrassata**
                164c.  Zygospores 60-64 $\mu$ broad    156.  **S. wangi**
        163b.  Vegetative cells more than
            35 $\mu$ broad
            165a.  Zygospores 40-48 $\mu$ broad    226.  **S. insignis**
            165b.  Zygospores 45-60 $\mu$ broad    231.  **S. fallax**

162b. Zygospores ovoid
    166a. Chloroplasts 2-4 ; median spore wall smooth     185. **S. rectangularis**
    166b. Chloroplasts 1-2 ; second outer spore wall scrobiculate     198. **S. areolata**
157b. Mesospore not smooth
  167a. Zygospores ellipsoid
    168a. Chloroplasts 1-3 in each cell
      169a. Median spore wall single     270. **S nawashini**
      169b. Median spore wall double     168. **S tetrapla**
    168b. Chloroplasts 2-4 in each cell
      170a. Mesospore aculeate-reticulate     157. **S. incostans**
      170b. Mesospore reticulate-spinose     174. **S. acanthophora**
      170c. Mesospore mammilate-aculeate     197. **S. borysthenica**
      170d. Mesospore 2-layered; outer wrinkled, inner tuberculate     220. **S. crassispina**
  167b. Zygospores ovoid
    171a. Chloroplasts 3-4     190. **S. crassivallicularis**
    171b. Chloroplasts 2-3     158. **S. reticulata**
      172a. Median wall single     159. **S. regularis**
      172b. Median wall double
        173a. Inner wall granulate     162. **S. granulata**
        173b. Inner wall irregularly reticulate with crenulate to dentate ridges     160. **S. quinquilaminata**
        173c. Inner wall reticulate     233. **S. pseudogranulata**
132b. Conjugation canal formed by the male gametangia
  174a. Mesospore smooth
    175a. Gametangia fusiform ; inflated on both sides
      176a. Vegetative cells 16-19 $\mu$ broad     150. **S. pseudospreeiana**
      176b. Vegetative cells 28-39 $\mu$ broad     151. **S. chuniae**
      176c. Vegetative cells 30-36 $\mu$ broad

177a. Zygospores 24-28 μ
broad      228. **S. tsingtaoensis**
177b. Zygospores 30-36 μ
broad      129. **S. spreeiana**

175b. Gametangia cylindrically inflated
178a. Mesospore smooth    152. **S. cylindrica**
178b. Mesospore smooth with a
distinct suture     184. **S. pascheriana**

175c. Gametangia inflated on the
conjugating side
179a. Vegetative cells 17-25 μ
broad      235. **S. croasdaleae**
179b. Vegetative cells 21-25 μ broad 143. **S. grevilleana**
179c. Vegetative cells 26-29 μ broad 153. **S. hopeiensis**

174b. Mesospore not smooth
180a. Zygospores mostly ellipsoid
181a. Mesospore single, faveolate   149. **S. foveolata**
181b. Mesospore double, wrinkled
and reticulate     145. **S. lambertiana**
181c. Mesospore longitudinally scrobiculate      287. **S. anchora**

180b. Zygospore mostly ovoid, median
wall areolate     148. **S. laxistrata**

**1. Spirogyra colligata** HODGETTS 1920. *Ann. Bot.* **34**, p. 523, Pl. 22.

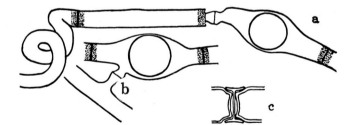

Fig. 244. a-c. *S. colligata.* (after Hodgetts.)

Vegetative cells 29-40 × 240-640 μ with conspicuous collars between the cells. 4 to 6 chloroplasts, usually 5, making 0.5 to 2.0 turns in the cell.

Conjugation scalariform, lateral, and terminal ; tubes formed by both gametangia ; fertile cells inflated at the middle up to 90-100 μ; zygospores lenticular to lenticular-globose, 50-80 (−90) μ in diameter ; median spore wall verrucose, brown.

*Distribution*: U.S.A. ; England.

**2. Spirogyra condensata** (VAUCHER) Kützing 1843. *Phycologia Generalis*, p. 279.

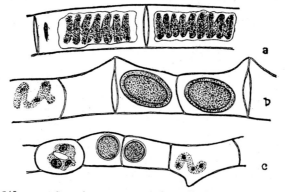

Fig. 245. a—c. *S. condensata.* a, vegetative cells; b, lateral conjugation;
c, azygospores. (after Randhawa.)

Vegetative cells 40-65 μ broad, 2.5 times as long. Septa of the cells plane. There is a single chloroplast of 1 to 2½ spirals in each cell.

Conjugation lateral as well as scalariform. In lateral conjugation the zygospores usually occur in pairs. Zygospores oval, 32-36 μ broad, and 60-70 μ long. Female cells containing zygospores are not swollen. Exospore hyaline, thick, mesospore brown, and endospore not known. The zygospores produced by lateral conjugation are slightly smaller than those of the type.

Zygospores in forms reproducing by means of scalariform conjugation are bigger, being 42-45 μ broad, and 70-75 μ long. Sterile cells with thickened mucilaginous walls frequently alternate with the male cells.

Azygospores may also be seen plentifully; rounded in appearance and 24-26 μ in diameter.

*Distribution*:

*India*: Specimens showing scalariform conjugation were found free-floating in a greenish mass, in a pond in V. Nowshera, district Hoshiarpur, about the middle of October 1930. Also found free-floating in a fresh-water spring at Tahli Sahib, district Hoshiarpur, in the first week of March 1931, reproducing by lateral conjugation.

*Other countries*: United States of America; Europe and South America.

**3. Spirogyra gallica** PETIT 1880. *Les Spirogyres des environs de Paris*, p. 23, Pl. 6. Figs. 1-3.

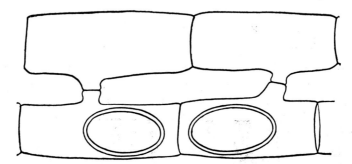

Fig. 246. *S. gallica.* (after Petit.)

Vegetative cells 72-75 × 150-500 $\mu$, with plane end walls ; 1 chloroplast making 4 to 8 turns in the cell.

Conjugation scalariform ; tubes formed by both gametangia ; fertile cells cylindric; zygospores ovoid to ellipsoid, 62-66 × 90-110 $\mu$; median spore wall yellow, smooth.

*Distribution* : France; Belgium and Germany.

**4. Spirogyra communis** (HASSAL) Kützing. 1849. *Species Algarum*. p. 439.

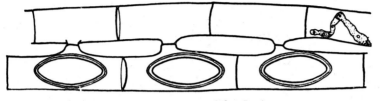

Fig. 247. *S.communis*. (after Jao.)

Vegetative cell 18-26 × 35-90 $\mu$ ; end walls plane ; chloroplast one, making 1.5 to 4 turns.

Conjugation scalariform and lateral ; conjugation canal formed by both gametangia ; fertile cells cylindric, rarely enlarged ; zygospores ellipsoid, 19-26 × 36-78 $\mu$ ; median spore wall yellow, smooth.

*Distribution* :

India : Gorakhpur, U.P. ; Hill stream, Assam.

*Other countries* : New Caledonia, U.S.A.

**5. Spirogyra bullata** JAO 1935. *Sinensia*. **6**, p. 588, Pl. 4, Fig. 55.

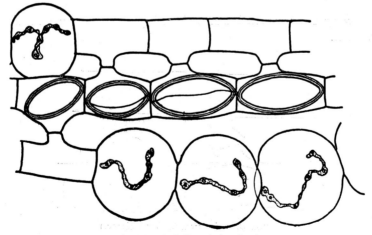

Fig. 248. *S. bullata*. (after Jao.)

Vegetative cells 19-22 × 41-83 $\mu$ ; end walls plane ; chloroplast 1, making 1.5 to 5.5 turns in the cell.

Conjugation scalariform ; conjugation canal formed by both gametangia ; sterile cells bullate up to 64$\mu$ in diameter and occurring in rows up to 25 cells long ; fertile cells cylindric or slightly enlarged ; zygospores ellipsoid,   22-29 × 31-35   (-51)  $\mu$, spore wall smooth, yellow at maturity.

*Distribution* :  Szechwan, China.

**6.  Spirogyra intorta** JAO 1935.   *Sinensia.*   **6**, p. 590, Pl.5, Fig. 58.

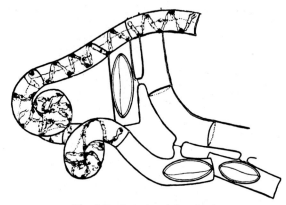

Fig. 249. *S. intorta.* (after Jao.)

Vegetative cells 25-29  ×  60-193 $\mu$, with plane end walls ; filaments generally cur‑ ved to spiral ; 1 chloroplast, making 3.5-6 turns in the cell.

Conjugation scalariform and lateral ; tubes formed by both gametangia ; fertile cells cylindric sometimes slightly enlarged ;  zygospores ellipsoid with  pointed ends, 22-29 × 41-68 $\mu$ ; median spore wall yellow smooth.

*Distribution* :   China and  United  States  of  America.

**7.  Spirogyra juergensii** KÜTZ. 1845. *Phycologia Germanica.* p. 222. (*S. juergen‑ sii* forma Singh).

Fig. 250. *S. juergensii.* (after Krieger.)

Vegetative cells 25-30 $\mu$ thick, $2\frac{1}{2}$ to 5 times as long.  Septa occasionally plane and swollen.   Each cell with one chloroplast making two to four turns.

Conjugation scalariform.   Fruiting cells not swollen on either side.   Zygospores ellipsoid, elongated, 30-32 $\mu$ thick and twice as long.   Mesospore smooth.

*Distribution* :

> *India and Pakistan* :   Free-floating in Badami Bagh Tanks, Lahore, Punjab, about the middle of March 1930.   Fairly common ; Goarakhpur, U.P.

> *Other countries* :   United States of America ; Europe ; South America and Australia.

**8.   Spirogyra singularis** NORDSTEDT. *Bot. Notiser* 1880. p. 118 ; Wittrock and Nordstedt, *Algae Exsiccatae*, No. 361 ; Transeau, 1951, p. 151.

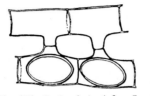

Fig. 251. *S. singularis*. (after Jao.)

Vegetative cells 29-39 × 60-240 $\mu$ ; end walls plane ; chloroplast 1, making 3 to 7 turns.

Conjugation scalariform ; tubes formed by both gametangia ; fertile cells cylindric, rarely enlarged ; zygospores ellipsoid, 27-36 × 46-70 $\mu$ ; median spore wall yellow, smooth.

*Distribution* :

> *India* :   In Powai lake, Bombay, August 1954 ; Banaras, U.P. 1953.

> *Other countries* :   China; South Africa ; Brazil ; Finland ; New Zealand and United States of America.

Forma *ventricosa* Venkataraman (1957) has ventricose fructifying cells.

**9.   Spirogyra gibberosa** JAO, *Sinensia*. **6**, p. 586. Pl. 4, Figs. 50-51.

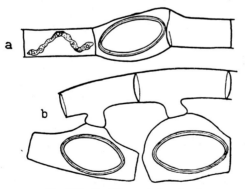

Fig. 252. *S. gibberosa*. (after Jao.)

Vegetative cells 19-21 × 48-104 $\mu$ ; end walls plane ; chloroplast 1, making 2 to 8 turns.

Conjugation scalariform, sometimes lateral ; tubes formed by the male gametangia, fertile cells inflated on the conjugating side, upto 45 $\mu$, often separating from each other as the spores mature ; zygospores ellipsoid with more or less pointed ends, 22-29 × 38-50 $\mu$ ; median spore wall smooth, yellow at maturity.

*Distribution* :

   *India* :  In  a  puddle  near  Parel,  Bombay.

   *Other  countries* :  Szechwan,  China.

**10.  Spirogyra gracilis** (HASSALL)  KUTZING 1849.  *Species Algarum*, p. 438.

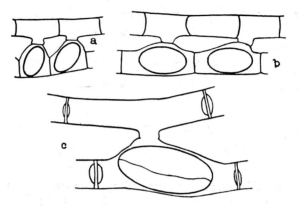

Fig. 253. a—c. *S. gracilis*. (c, after Czurda; a—b, after Krieger.)

Vegetative cells 16-24 × 50-100 $\mu$; end walls plane ; chloroplast 1 making 0.5 to 4 turns.

Conjugation scalariform ; conjugation canal formed by both gametangia ; fertile cells inflated, mostly on the conjugating side ; zygospores ellipsoid with rounded ends, 23-30 × 40-65 $\mu$ ; median spore wall yellow-brown, smooth.

*Distribution* :  Europe ;  China ;  Siam  and  U.S.A.

**11.  Spirogyra woodsii** (HASSALL)  CZURDA 1922 b, p. 171, Fig. 175 S. 171.

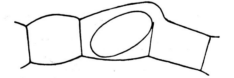

Fig. 254. *S. woodsii*. (after Petit.)

Vegetative cells 35-40 $\mu$ broad ; end walls plane ; chloroplast one.

Conjugation scalariform and lateral ; fertile cells swollen on the conjugating side. Zygotes ellipsoidal, 31-38 × 50-90 $\mu$ .  Exospore thin, smooth and colourless ; mesospore thick, smooth, yellowish-brown.

*Distribution* :  China ; Germany ; Yugoslavia.

**12.  Spirogyra teodoresci** TRANSEAU 1934.  *Ohio. Jour. Sci.* **34**, p. 420. (=*S. varians var. minor*) Teodoresco. *Beih. Bot. Centralbl.* **21**, abt. 2, 1907.

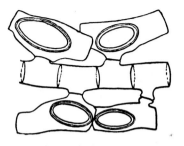

Fig. 255. *S. teodoresci.* (after Jao.)

Vegetative cells 24-30 × 42-80 $\mu$ ; end walls plane ; chloroplast 1, making 1 to 6 turns.

Conjugation scalariform and lateral ; tubes formed by both gametangia ; fertile cells strongly inflated on the conjugating side, zygospores ellipsoid, 26-33 × 45-55 $\mu$ ; median spore walls smooth, yellow.

*Distribution*: Nanking, Peiping, China ; Rumania ; U.S.A.

**13. Spirogyra varians** (HASSALL) KUTZING 1849. *Species Algarum,* p. 439 (=*S. varians* forma Rao).

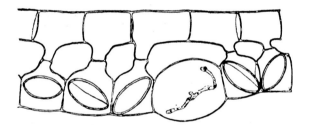

Fig. 256. *S. varians.* (after Jao.)

Vegetative cells (29) 30-40 × 30-120 $\mu$ ; end walls plane ; chloroplast 1, making 1 to 5 turns.

Conjugation scalariform and lateral ; tubes formed by both gametangia ; fertile cells usually inflated on the conjugating side only, rarely on both sides ; some of the sterile cells usually inflated, zygospores mostly ellispoid, usually some of them ovoid and very rarely globose, 32-40 × 50-100 $\mu$ ; median spore wall yellow ; smooth, aplanospores same as the zygospores.

*Distribution*:

    *India*: In a rain-water pool, Banaras, U.P. ; Hoshangabad, M.P.

    *Other countries*: Asia ; Africa ; Australia ; British Columbia ; Newfoundland ; U.S.A.

**14. Spirogyra pratensis** Transeau 1914. *Amer. Jour. Bot.* **1**, p. 292.

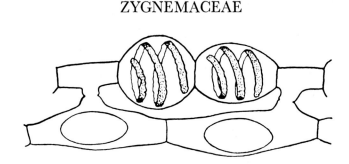

Fig. 257. *S. pratensis*. (after Transeau.)

Vegetative cells 17-20 × 80-240 $\mu$ ; with plane end walls ; 1 chloroplast (rarely 2), making 1 to 8 turns.

Reproducing commonly by both zygospores and aplanospores ; conjugation scalariform and lateral ; tubes formed by both gametangia ; fertile cells enlarged or fusiform-inflated to 38 $\mu$; sterile cells cylindric or inflated up to 90 $\mu$ in diameter; spores in most cells ellipsoid, in others ovoid, or cylindric ovoid, 24-36 × 50-70 $\mu$ ; median spore wall yellow, smooth.

*Distribution*: Peiping, Nanking, China ; U.S.A.

**15. Spirogyra microspora** Jao 1935. *Sinensia*, **6**, pp. 593-94, Pl. 6, Fig. 65 ; Transeau, 1951, p. 168, Pl. XXVI, Fig. 5.

Fig. 258. *S. microspora*. (after Jao.)

Vegetative cells 36-40 × 64-131 $\mu$ ; end walls plane ; chloroplasts 2, broad with large pyrenoids making 1.5-3.5 turns in the cell.

Conjugation lateral ; tubes formed by both gametangia ; fertile cells cylindric ; zygospores ellipsoid, 29-32 × 51-61 $\mu$ ; median spore wall smooth yellow.

*Distribution* :

    *India* : Ghatkopar, Bombay.

    *Other countries* : Szechwan, China.

**16. Spirogyra parvula** (Trans.) Czurda 1932. *Süsswasserflora Mitteleuropa*. **9**, p. 170, Fig. 174.

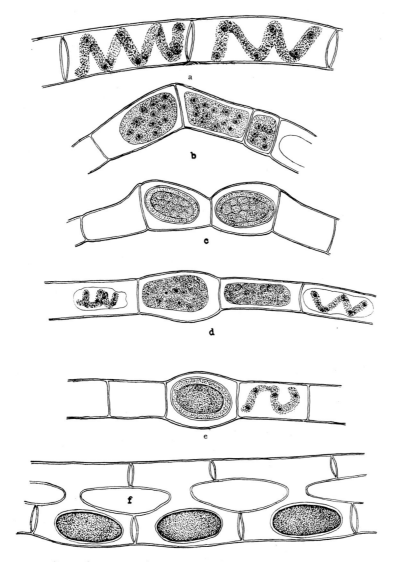

Fig. 259. *S. parvula.* a, vegetative cells with chloroplasts; b—e, stages in lateral conjugation; f, scalariform conjugation. (after Randhawa.)

Vegetative cells 20-24 $\mu$ broad, 2-5 times as long. Each cell with one chromatophore of 2-4 turns. Septa plane.

Both lateral and scalariform conjugation is seen in this species.

*Lateral conjugation*: The zygospores occur in pairs at regular intervals, and when they are found singly, they are separated by many vegetative cells. Lateral conjugation in this species is very interesting. The female cell becomes very much swollen, and its contents become rounded while the male cell is comparatively smaller in size. Thus there is not only a physiological difference between the gametes, but also a morphological one. The contents of both the male and female cells become very much granular and vacuolated. In some cases the female cells are swollen on both sides and present a flask-shaped appearance. The male gamete probably passes into the female cell through a pore in the middle of the cell-wall separating the two cells. The empty male cells may be seen adjoining the female cells containing zygospores.

*Scalariform conjugation*: This type of conjugation was seen in a material collected from Siah Baeen in the month of March 1941. The female cells are clearly swollen.

Zygospores ellipsoid to oval in shape, 22-24 $\mu$ broad, and 36-54 $\mu$ long. The zygospore wall is made up of three layers, a smooth and brown exospore, a smooth and bluish-green mesospore, and a light brown endospore.

*Distribution* :

*India* : Free-floating in a small fresh-water spring near V. Fatehpur, district Saharanpur, U.P. in the middle of February 1936, conjugating exclusively in a lateral fashion. Also collected from Siah Baeen, mixed with *Z. coeruleum* during March 1941, conjugating both in a lateral and scalariform fashion. In the lateral material the vegetative filaments were narrower ; in Uday Lodge tank, Srinagar, Kashmir.

*Other countries* : China; United States of America and Norway.

**17. Spirogyra macrospora** (RAO) KRIEGER 1944. *Rabenhorst's Kryptogamen-flora.* **13**, p. 243. ( =*S. subsalsa* var. *macrospora* Rao 1938).

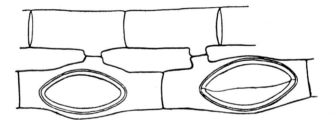

Fig. 260. *S. macrospora.* (after Rao.)

Vegetative cells 22-25 × 100-120 $\mu$, with plane end walls ; 1 chloroplast.

Conjugation scalariform ; receptive gametangia inflated ; conjugating tubes formed by both cells ; zygospores ellipsoid, with narrow end 28-33 × 52-73 $\mu$ ; median spore wall smooth and yellow-brown.

*Distribution* :

*India* : Central Provinces.

*Other countries* : Brandengburg, Germany.

**18. Spirogyra affinis** (Hass) PETIT 1880. *Les Spirogyres des environs de Paris,* p. 18, Pl. 3, Figs. 13-14.

Vegetative cells 22-30 $\mu$ broad. Septa not swollen. Chloroplast single with $2\frac{1}{2}$ to 4 spirals ; some of the vegetative cells give out rhizoids.

Conjugation both lateral as well as scalariform. Fruiting cells slightly swollen on both sides. Zygospores ellipsoid, 25-32 $\mu$ broad, 36-46 $\mu$ long, yellowish in colour. Spore-wall smooth.

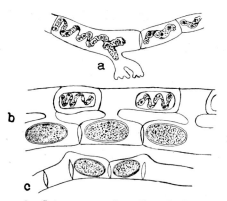

Fig. 261. a—c. *S. affinis.* a, vegetative cells with rhizoid; b, scalariform conjugation; c, lateral conjugation. (after Randhawa.)

Filaments showing lateral conjugation are attacked by rounded endophytic chytridiaceous fungi; 2-4 hyphae are invariably found in each cell which does not contain a zygospore.

*Distribution*:

*India*: Free-floating in a brownish mass in ponds near Hamira in the second week of March 1930, and mixed with *Oedogonium urbicum* at V. Jhingran, district Hoshiarpore, Punjab about the same time. Fairly common.

*Other countries*: China; United States; Europe, Jamaica and Kiangsi.

**19. Spirogyra catenaeformis** (Hassall) Kutzing 1849. *Species Algarum*, p. 438.

Vegetative cells 24-32 × 50-135 $\mu$, with plane end walls; 1 chloroplast making 1 to 6 turns.

Reproduction by both zygospores and aplanospores; conjugation scalariform and lateral; tubes formed by both gametangia; fertile cells enlarged or inflated, fusiform, sterile cells also inflated; zygospores and aplanospores ellipsoid, 27-33 × 55-90 $\mu$; median spore wall yellow, smooth.

*Distribution*: China; Europe; East and South Africa and U.S.A.

**20. Spirogyra subsalina** Cedercreutz. 1924. *Acta Soc. pro. Fauna et flora Fennica.* 55, (2), p. 4, Fig. 2; Transeau, 1951, p. 157, Pl. XXII, Fig. 9.

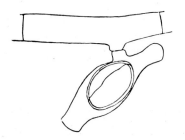

Fig. 262. *S. subsalina.* (after Mehra.)

Vegetative cells 28-38 × 70-190 $\mu$ ; end walls plane ; chloroplast 1, making 2 to 4.5 turns.

Conjugation scalariform ; tubes formed by both gametangia; fertile cells inflated to 49-56 $\mu$ ; zygospores ellipsoid, 28-38 × 42-76 $\mu$ ; median spore wall brown, smooth.

*Distribution* :

*India* :   Bombay.

*Other countries* :   Finland; United States of America.

**21.   Spirogyra borgeana** Transeau 1915.   *Ohio Jour. Sci.* **16**, p. 23.

Fig. 263. *S. borgeana.* (after Jao.)

Vegetative cells 30-45 × 50-200 $\mu$ ; end walls plane ; I chloroplast, making 1.5 to 5 turns.

Conjugation scalariform ; conjugation canal formed by both gametangia ; fertile cells inflated on the outer side, cylindric on the conjugating side ; zygospores ellipsoid, 30-40 × 54-70 $\mu$ ; mesospore yellow and smooth.

*Distribution* :   China ;   Tibet ;   Czechoslovakia;   U.S.A.

**22.   Spirogyra flavescens** (Hass.) Kütz. 1849.   *Species Algarum.* p. 438.

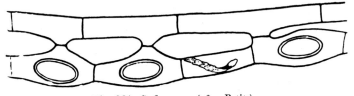

Fig. 264. *S. flavescens.* (after Petit.)

Vegetative cells 12-14 $\mu$ broad, and many times as long.   Septa plane.   There is only one very thin, more or less straight chloroplast in each cell.

Conjugation both scalariform and lateral.   The female cells are distinctly swollen.   The zygospores are long, ellipsoid in shape, 18-20 $\mu$ broad, and 40-50 $\mu$ long. The zygospore wall is composed of two layers only, a thin brownish exospore, and a bluish green mesospore.   The surface of the zygospore bears reticulate markings and depressions.

*Distribution* :

*India* :   Free-floating along with *Zygnema czurdae* and a species of *Oedogonium* during the third week of February 1931, in a fresh-water spring at Tahli Sahib district Hoshiarpur, Punjab ; in puddles, Banaras, U.P.

*Other countries*: United States of America ; Europe ; Australia.

**23. Spirogyra subsalsa** KUTZING 1845. *Phycologia Germanica*, p. 222. ( =*S. sublassa* forma Misra).

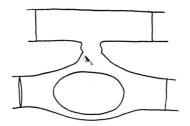

Fig. 265. *S. subsalsa*. (after Transeau.)

Vegetative cells 22-26 × 35-100 $\mu$, with plane end walls ; 1 chloroplast making 2 to 3 turns.

Conjugation sclariform ; tube formed largely by the male gametangia ; fertile cells inflated ; zygospores ovoid, 18-27 × 30-52 $\mu$ ; median spore wall yellow-brown, smooth.

*Distribution* :

*India*: In a puddle on the rock quarry of Hoshangabad M.P. ; in a road-side pond, Ramsu, Kashmir.

*Other countries*: Czechoslovakia ; Java ; France ; Holland ; Sweden ; U.S.A.

**24. Spirogyra paludosa** CZURDA 1932. *Süsswasserflora Mitteleuropa*. **9**, p. 167, Fig. 170.

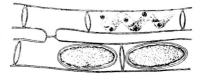

Fig. 266. *S. paludosa*. (after Randhawa.)

Vegetative cells 18-22 $\mu$ broad and 5-8 times as long. Chloroplast single in each cell. Septa plane.

Conjugation scalariform. Female cells containing zygospores slightly swollen. Zygospores ellipsoid, much longer than broad, being 24-26 $\mu$ broad and 44-46 $\mu$ long. Exospore hyaline and smooth, mesospore light brown in colour.

*Distribution* :

*India*: Found free-floating in a pond at V. Bodal, district Hoshiarpore, Punjab.

*Other countries*: Czechoslovakia.

**25. Spirogyra mirabilis** (HASSALL) KUTZING 1849. *Species Algarum*. p. 438.

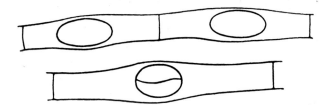

Fig. 267. *S. mirabilis*. (after Kolkwitz & Krieger.)

Vegetative cells 23-29 × 70-200 $\mu$ ; with plane end walls ; 1 chloroplast making 4 to 7 turns.

Reproduction by aplanospores, very rarely by scalariform conjugation, tubes formed by both gametangia ; sporangia enlarged or inflated ; aplanospores and zygospores ovoid, less frequent varying to ellipsoid, 23-29 × 50-83 $\mu$ ; median spore wall yellowish-brown, smooth.

*Distribution* :  China ; Afghanistan ; Europe ; Siberia ; Manchuria and U.S.A.

**26. Spirogyra longata** (Vaucher) Kutzing 1843. *Phycologia Generalis*, p. 279. Vaucher. *Histoire des Conferves* Pl. 6. 1603. Includes *S. circumscissa* Czurda 1932, and *S. longata* (Vaucher) Czurda.

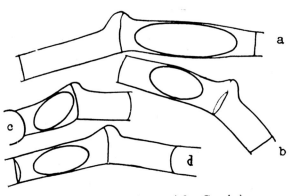

Fig. 268. a—d. *S. longata*. (after Czurda.)

Vegetative cells 26-38 × 45-280 $\mu$, with plane end walls ; 1 chloroplast, making 2 to 5 turns.

Conjugation scalariform and lateral ; tubes formed by both gametangia ; zygospores ovoid, varying in some cells to globose, 28-38 × 50-83 $\mu$ ; median spore wall yellow, smooth.

*Distribution* :  U.S.A. ; Europe ; East and South Africa; Asia ; South America and Australia.

**27. Spirogyra indica** Krieger 1944.  *Rabenhorst's Kryptogamenflora*, **13**, p. 317. (=*S. longata* forma Rao 1938. *J. Indian Bot. Soc.*, **17**, p. 342-3, Fig. 1. F,G.)

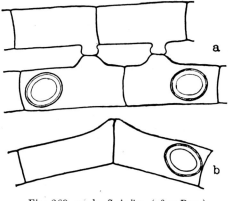

Fig. 269. a—b. *S. indica.* (after Rao.)

Vegetative cells 36-42 × 100-152 $\mu$, with plane end walls and 1 chloroplast.

Conjugating tubes formed by both gametangia : conjugation mostly lateral, less frequently scalariform ; receptive gametangia cylindric ; zygospores ovoid, 33-38 × 40-62 $\mu$ ; median spore wall thick, smooth, and brown.

*Distribution* :

    *India* :  Central Provinces.

    *Other countries* :  South America ; South Chile.

**28.  Spirogyra subvelata** KOLKWITZ & KRIEGER 1944. Rabenhorst's *Kryptogam-enflora* **13**, p. 363, Figs. 511, 512. (=*Spirogyra velata* var. *ellipsoidea* Wang.)

Fig. 270. *S. subvelata.* (after Wang)

Vegetative cells (34—) 40-50 $\mu$ broad ; cross walls plane ; chloroplasts 1 (2).

Conjugation scalariform and lateral ; fertile cells unswollen.  In the scalariform conjugation, conjugation canal is formed by both gametangia.  Zygospores ellipsoidal 34-48 × 50-105 $\mu$ ; exospore colourless, 2-layered ; outer thin and smooth, inner thick, pitted ; mesospore thin, smooth, yellow-brown ; endospore thin, smooth.

*Distribution* :  China.

**29.  Spirogyra velata** NORDSTEDT 1873. *Lunds Univ. Arsskrift.* **9**, p. 1. Pl. 1.

Fig. 271. a—b. *S. velata*. (after Nordstedt.)

Vegetative cells 29-41 × 60-200 $\mu$, with plane end walls ; 1 or rarely 2 chloroplasts, making 2.5 to 6 turns.

Conjugation scalariform ; tubes formed by both gametangia ; fertile cells cylindric or somewhat enlarged; zygospores mostly ovoid to cylindric-ovoid, rarely ellipsoid, 37-57 × 60-100 $\mu$ ; outer wall of 2 layers, of which the second is transparent and scrobiculate ; the median is chitinous, yellow-brown, smooth.

*Distribution* :

   *India* :   Dal Lake, Kashmir.

   *Other countries* :   China ; Germany ; Russia ; South Africa and U.S.A.

**30.   Spirogyra porticalis** (Müller) Cleve 1868. *Försök till en monografi. Nova Acta Reg. Soc. Sci. Upsali.* Ser, 3, **6**, p.22, Pl.5, Figs, 8-9.

Fig. 272. a—c. *S. porticalis*. a, vegetative cell; b—c, scalariform
conjugation. (after Petit.)

Vegetative cells 40-50 × 66-200 $\mu$, with plane end walls ; 1 chloroplast, making 3 to 5 turns.

Conjugation scalariform ; tubes formed by both gametangia; fertile cells cylindric or enlarged; zygospores mostly ovoid to globose-ovoid, 38-50 × 50-83 $\mu$; median spore wall yellow, smooth.

*Distribution* :   U.S.A.

**31.   Spirogyra lacustris** Czurda 1932. *Süsswasserflora Mitteleuropa.* **9**, p. 176, Fig. 182.

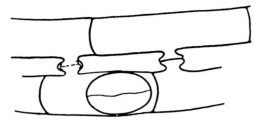

Fig. 273. *S. lacustris* (after Czurda.)

Vegetative cells 38-44 $\times$ 105-160 $\mu$, with plane end walls ; 1 chloroplast.

Conjugation scalariform ; tubes formed by both gametangia ; fertile cells cylindric or very slightly swollen ; zygospores ovoid, 42-35 $\times$ 80-80 $\mu$ ; median spore wall golden-brown, smooth, with suture more or less prominent.

*Distribution* : Austria.

**32.  Spirogyra sahnii** RANDHAWA 1938.  *Proc. Indian Acad. Sci.* **8**, pp. 339-41.

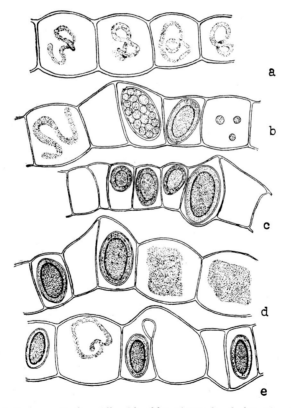

Fig. 274. a—e. *S. sahnii*. a, vegetative cell with chloroplasts; b—d, lateral conjugation (note the parthenospores in c), e, peculiar method of lateral conjugation by a tubular structure. (after Randhawa.)

Vegetative cells are 48-72 $\mu$ broad and 40-74 $\mu$ long.  Usually they are broader than long.  They are very much swollen and are barrel-like in appearance.  There is a single chloroplast which is more or less coiled in an irregular fashion. The septa of the cells are plane.

Conjugation lateral, and this is of a very interesting type. The neighbouring cells usualy give out tent-like protuberances in the usual way, and the female cells containing the zygospores almost always adjoin empty male cells. The female cells are usually of the same size, but in one case the empty male cell was considerably swollen and much bigger in size. It gave out a distinct tube which was continuous with a similar structure given out by the female cell, and appeared like a retort. Such conjugation tubes have been reported by de Bary in *Zygnema insigne* (Hassal) Kütz.

Zygospores are 22-36 $\mu$ broad, and 44-68 $\mu$ long. The zygospore-wall is composed of three layers, a smooth hyaline exospore, a thick bluish-green mesospore, and a smooth endospore.

*Parthenospores* : Parthenospores are also seen in larger numbers along with the zygospores. These are usually oval in shape like the zygospores, but are very much smaller in size, being 20-24 $\mu$ broad, and 22-36 $\mu$ long. In some cases these are spherical in shape.

*Some of the cells are infested with a fungal parasite, similar to a species of Myzocitium described on a material of Spirogyra affinis by Choudhari. Some of the zygospores also are full of the cells of this parasite. It is a curious coincidence that both the species of Spirogyra in which this form of Myzocitium has been seen reproduce by lateral conjugation.*

*Distribution* :

*India* : Free-floating in Siah Baeen, a fresh-water stream, mixed with *Sphaeroplea annulina* near Dasuya, district Hoshiarpore, Punjab, about the second week of March 1931.

**33. Spirogyra lutetiana** PETIT 1879. *Brebissonia*, **1**, p. 79, Pl. 6 ; Transeau, 1951, p. 160-61, Pl. XXIII, Figs. 11-13.

Fig. 275. *S. lutetiana*. (after Mehra.)

Vegetative cells 27-40 × 70-250 $\mu$ ; end walls plane ; chloroplast 1, making 3 to 7 turns.

Conjugation scalariform ; tubes formed by both gametangia ; fertile cells more or less variable, cylindric, enlarged, or slightly inflated; zygospore polymorphic, varying from globose to ellipsoid and irregular, 25-44 × 35-165 $\mu$ ; median spore wall yellow-brown, smooth.

*Distribution* :

*India* : Powai Lake, Bombay.

*Other countries* : Europe; South Africa ; United States of America.

**34. Spirogyra polymorpha** KIRCHNER 1879. *Algen. Kryptogamenflora Schlesien,*
p. 124.

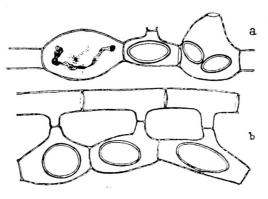

Fig. 276. a—b. *S. polymorpha.* (after Jao.)

Vegetative cells 22-30 × 45-230 $\mu$, with plane end walls ; 1 or rarely 2 chloroplasts
making 1 to 10 turns.

Conjugation scalariform ; tubes formed by both gametangia ; fertile cells inflated
to 26-64 $\mu$ ; zygospores polymorphic, varying from ellipsoid to ovoid and globose,
22-32 × 25-35 $\mu$ ; median spore wall, yellow, smooth.

*Distribution* : China and Europe.

**35. Spirogyra czurdae** MISRA 1937. *Proc. Indian Acad. Sci.* **5**, p. 115, Fig. 3.

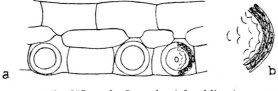

Fig. 277. a—b. *S. czurdae.* (after Misra.)

Vegetative cells 26-28 × 52-78 $\mu$, with plane end walls and 1 chloroplast.

Conjugation scalariform ; tubes formed by both gametangia ; receptive gametangia shortened and enlarged ; zygospores globose, 22-34 $\mu$ in diameter ; median spore
wall very thick, brown, and scrobiculate ; pits 3-4 $\mu$ in diameter.

*Distribution* :

*India* : Kashmir.

**36. Spirogyra luteospora** CZURDA 1932, *Süsswasserflora Mitteluropa,* **9**,
p. 181, Fig. 226.

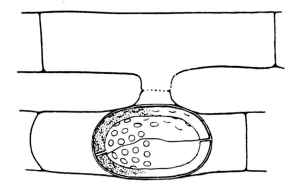

Fig. 278. *S. luteospora.* (after Czurda.)

Vegetative cells 22-24 $\mu$ broad ; end walls plane ; chloroplast one.

Conjugation scalariform ; fertile cells not or only very slightly swollen ; conjugation canal built by both the gametangia ; zygospore ellipsoidal with broad rounded ends, 25-26 × 33-40 $\mu$ ; exospore thin, smooth and colourless ; mesospore thick, yellowish brown, outer wall deeply pitted ; inner wall with clear ribs.

*Distribution* : Germany.

**37. Spirogyra westii** Transeau 1934. *Trans. Amer. Micros. Soc.* **53**, p. 224. *S. porticalis* var. *africana* G.S. West 1907. *Jour. Linn. Soc. London, Bot.* **38**, p. 105.

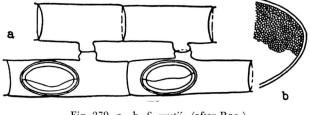

Fig. 279. a—b. *S. westii.* (after Rao.)

Vegetative cells 40-41 × 60-160 $\mu$, with plane end walls ; 1 chloroplast, making 3 to 5 turns in the cell.

Conjugation scalariform ; tubes formed by both gametangia ; fertile cells enlarged, zygospores ovoid, about 58 × 93 $\mu$; median spore wall finely wrinkled, or corrugate.

*Distribution* : Tanganyika, Africa.

**38. Spirogyra obovata** Jao. *Sinensia.* **6**, p. 596, Pl. 7, Fig. 73 ; Transeau, 1951, p. 162, Pl. XXIV, Fig. 5.

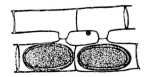

Fig. 280. *S. obovata.* (after Jao.)

Vegetative cells 24-26 × 90-95 $\mu$ ; end walls plane ; chloroplast 1, making 1.5 to 2.5 turns.

Conjugation scalariform ; conjugation canal formed by both gametangia ; receptive gametangia cylindrical or slightly enlarged ; zygospores ovoid, 30-32 × 60-64 $\mu$ ; median spore wall yellow, punctate.

*Distribution* :

*India* : In a pool on the way to Powai Lake, Andheri, Bombay.

*Other countries* : Szechwan, China.

**39. Spirogyra chekiangensis** JAO 1939. *Sinensia.* **10**, p. 152.

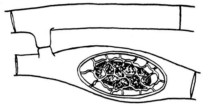

Fig. 281. *S. chekiangensis.* (after Jao.)

Vegetative cells 25-28 × 100-200 $\mu$, with plane end walls ; 1 chloroplast, making 1-2 turns in the cell.

Conjugation scalariform ; tubes formed by both gametangia ; receptive gametangia enlarged ; zygospores ovoid, 45-48 × 85-88 $\mu$ ; median spore wall of 2 layers, of which the outer is thin, irregularly wrinkled and yellow ; the inner coarsely and irregularly reticulate, yellow-brown at maturity.

*Distribution* : Wenchow, China.

**40. Spirogyra asiatica** CZURDA 1931. *Süsswasserflora Mitteleuropa.* **9**, p. 185, 1932.

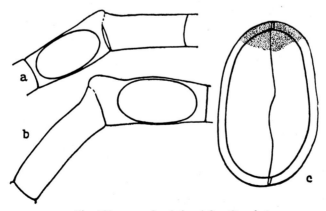

Fig. 282. a—c. *S. asiatica.* (after Czurda.)

Vegetative cells 46-51 × 100-160 $\mu$ , with plane end walls ; 1 chloroplast.

Conjugation lateral ; tubes formed by both cells ; fertile cells enlarged ; zygos-pores ovoid, 60-65 × 80-120 $\mu$ ; median spore wall dark brown, and minutely granu-lose ; suture more or less prominent.

*Distribution* :   Central Tibet.

**41.  Spirogyra skujae** RANDHAWA 1938.   *Proc. Indian Acad. Sci.* **8** (4), Sec. B, p. 338.

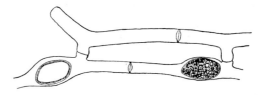

Fig. 283. *S. skujae.* (after Randhawa.)

Vegetative cells 14-17 $\mu$ broad 6-10 times as long, each with a single spiral ch-loroplast of 3 to 5 turns.   Septa plane and swollen.

Conjugation scalariform.   Fruiting cell swollen on both sides 26-34 $\mu$ in diameter. Zygospores oval, yellowish in colour, 24-30 $\mu$ broad and 40-42 $\mu$ long.   Zygospore wall composed of two layers, a thin and smooth exospore, and yellowish mesospore with reticulations and wavy lines on surface.

*Distribution* :

*India* :   Free-floating mixed with *Zygnemopsis lamellata* Randhawa and *Oedogonium* sp. in a Jhil near Tanda, district Fyzabad, U.P., on 7th February 1937.

**42.  Spirogyra robusta** (Nygaard)   Czurda   1932   *Süsswasserflora Mitteleuropa,* **9**, p. 187.

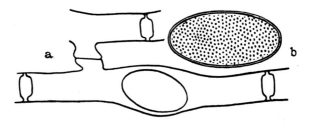

Fig. 284. a—b. *S. robusta.* (after Nygaard.)

Vegetative cells 29-35 $\mu$ broad, end walls plane ; chloroplast one.

Conjugation scalariform ; conjugation canal built by both gametangia ; fertile cells swollen on all sides,   bigger than the vegetative cells ; zygospore ellipsoidal, 32-60 × 54-104 $\mu$ ; exospore thin, smooth, colourless ; mesospore thick, yellowish brown, outer wall punctate.

*Distribution* :   South Africa.

**43.  Spirogyra papulata** JAO 1935.   *Sinensia.* **6**, p. 598, Pl. 7, Figs. 76-78.

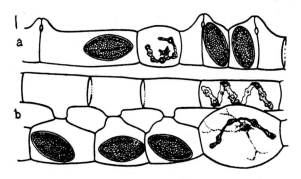

Fig. 285. a—b. *S. papulata.* (after Jao.)

Vegetative cells 28-32 × 64-176 $\mu$, with plane end walls ; chloroplast single, containing large pyrenoids.

Conjugation scalariform ; tubes formed by both gametangia ; fertile cells usually shortened and inflated on the conjugating side, up to 55 $\mu$ in diameter ; sterile cells sometimes swollen to 64 $\mu$ ; zygospores ellipsoid, very rarely subglobose, 22-32 × 35-55 $\mu$ median spore wall irregularly reticulate, golden yellow at maturity.

*Distribution* :   Szechwan, China.

**44.   Spirogyra scrobiculata** (STOCKMAYER) CZURDA   1932.   *Süsswasserflora Mitteleuropa.* **9**, p. 182.

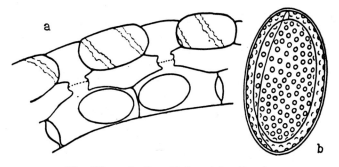

Fig. 286. a—b. *S. scrobiculata.* (after Czurda.)

Vegetative cells 30-40 × 30-90 $\mu$ ; with plane end walls ; 1 chloroplast.

Conjugation scalariform ; tubes formed by both gametangia ; fertile cells inflated on the conjugating side; zygospores ellipsoid, 34-38 × 58-68 $\mu$ ; median spore wall yellow to yellow-brown ; scrobiculate.

*Distribution* :   Australia ; U.S.A.

**45.   Spirogyra aphanosculpta** SKUJA 1937. *Hedwigia.* **77**, p. 55 ; Transeau, 1951, p. 166, Pl. XXV, Fig. 8.

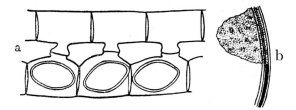

Fig. 287. a—b. *S. aphanosculpta*. (after Skuja.)

Vegetative cells 38-40 × 105-110 $\mu$ ; end walls plane ; chloroplast 1, making 1 to 4 turns.

Conjugation scalariform ; conjugation tube formed by both gametangia; receptive gametangia inflated on the conjugating side only; zygospores ellipsoidal with more or less rounded ends, 44-46 × 64-66 $\mu$ ; median spore wall yellow-brown, punctate with angular and irregular pits.

*Distribution* :

*India* :   In a cement tank, Institute of Science garden, Bombay, August 16, 1955.
*Other countries* :   Greece ; Tyagetus, Cape Colony, Africa; United States of America.

**46.  Spirogyra daedalea** LAGERHEIM 1888.  *Nuova Notarisia*, p. 592.

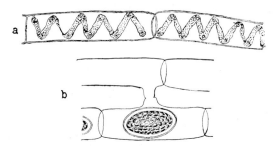

Fig. 288. a—b. *S. daedalea*. a, vegetative cells;
b, scalariform conjugation. (after Randhawa.)

Vegetative cells 30-38 $\mu$ broad, 6-10 times as long.  Septa of the  plane  type. Each cell with a single spiral chloroplast of 4-5½ turns.

Conjugation only scalariform.  The female cells are only very slightly swollen, or not swollen at all.  Zygospores oval to oval-ellipsoid in shape.  Zygospore wall is composed of two layers, a thin, smooth light blue exospore, and a very thick dark brown mesospore.  The zygospore wall has an irreuglarly network-like sculpturing  on it. Zygospores are 36-42 $\mu$ long and are brownish in colour.  Differs from the type in the absence of the horizontal suture on the spore-wall.

*Parthenosopores* :  A very interesting form of parthenospore formation was seen in this species.  In a part of two conjugating filaments zygospores of the normal type were seen, while in another part parthenospores were seen in both the male and the female cells, though conjugation canals are completely formed.  It seems that in this case the male and female gametes instead of fusing to form zygospores developed  independently

in their respective cells into parthenospores, due to some unknown reason.   The parthenospores developed from the female gemetes were much larger in size as compared
with those developed from male gametes and were devoid of any pigmentation, while
those developed from the male gametes were coloured brownish-green.   Such parthenospores have been reported by Rosenvinge in *S. groenlandica*.

Another very interesting type of parthenospore-formation was seen in a female
cell of one of the two conjugating fllaments, the remaining parts of which showed normal
conjugation.   In this case both the parthenospores, developed respectively from the
male and female gametes, were seen in the female cell.   In this case it seems, that the
male gamete successfully entered the female cell, but instead of fusing with the female
gametes developed independently into a parthenospore.   Even in this case difference
in the size of the parthenospore developed from the male and female gametes is noticeable, the former being very much smaller in size as compared with the latter.

*Distribution* :

*India* :   Free-floating in a fresh-water jhil near Baskhari tehsil Tanda, district
Fyzabad, U.P., mixed with *Debarya costata* Randh.   in the first week of December 1936
and free-floating in Tons Nadi near Akbarpur, Fyzabad, U.P., mixed  with  *Nodularia*
*spumigena* on 20th March 1937.

*Other countries* :   United States of America ; Germany ; Latvia ; Yugoslavia and
Finland.

**47.  Spirogyra oudhensis** RANDHAWA 1938.   *Proc. Indian Acad. Sci.* **8**, p. 348,
Fig. 41.

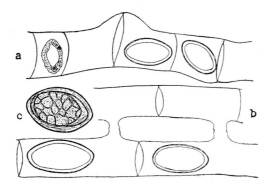

Fig. 289. a-c. *S. oudhensis*. a, lateral cojugation; b, scalariform
conjugation, c, zygospore, (after Randhawa.)

Vegetative cells 34-38 $\mu$ broad and 4 to 6 times as long, each containing a single
chloroplast of 3-4 spirals, septa plane.

Conjugation is both lateral and scalariform.   Zygospores are oval, 30-40 $\mu$ broad
and 55-86 $\mu$ long.   Spore-wall bears broad reticulations on surface, and mesospore is
separated from the other two layers by a considerable space (Fig. 289, c).

*Distribution* :

*India* :   Free-floating in a pond near V. Mhow Shivala, district Fyzabad, U.P.,
in October and November 1937.

**48. Spirogyra atasiana** Czurda 1939. *Arch. f. Hydrobiol. Suppl.* **16**, p. 417, Pl. 1, Fig. 3.

Vegetative cells 44-48 × 92-161 $\mu$, with plane end walls and 1 chloroplast.

Conjugation scalariform ; tubes formed apparently by the male gametangia ; receptive gametangia cylindric ; zygospores ovoid, 41-45 × 50-90 $\mu$ ; median spore wall thick, yellow-brown, outer surface granulose.

*Distribution* : Sumatra, Danau di Atas.

**49. Spirogyra irregularis** Nageli 1849. In Kützing, *Species Algarum* p. 440 ; also 1855, *Tab. Phycol.*, **5**, Pl. 23, Fig.2.

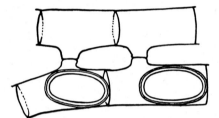

Fig. 290. *S. irregularis.* (after Jao.)

Vegetative cells 32-37 × 65-250 $\mu$, with plane end walls ; 2 to 4 chloroplasts making 0.5 to 1 turn.

Conjugation scalariform; tubes formed by both gametangia ; fertile cells cylindric ; zygospores ellipsoid to cylindric-ellipsoid, 30-36 × 45-90 $\mu$ ; median spore wall yellow- ish brown, smooth.

*Distribution* : Western and Central Europe, U.S.A.

**50. Spirogyra fuellebornei** Schmidle 1902. Engler's *Bot. Jahrb.* **32**, p. 76, Pl. 3, Fig. 2.

Fig. 291. *S. fuellebornei.* (after Schmidle.)

Vegetative cells 40-42 × 120-240 $\mu$, with plane end walls ; 3 chloroplasts making 1 to 2 turns.

Conjugation scalariform and lateral ; tubes formed by both gametangia ; fertile cells cylindric ; zygospores ellipsoid, more or less pointed, 32-44 × 50-80 $\mu$ ; median spore wall smooth, yellow-brown.

*Distribution* :

*India* : In a rain-water pond U.P. ; in a rain-water pool Hoshangabad, M.P. ; Banaras, U.P.

*Other countries* : Africa; Central America; Nyassa Lake region, Panama, U.S.A.

**51. Spirogyra rivularis** (HASSALL) RABENHORT'S 1868. *Flora Europaea Algarum.* **3**, p. 243 ; Transeau, 1951, *W.* 13, Pl. XXVI.

Fig. 292. a-c. *S. rivularis.* (after Mehra.)

Vegetative cells 36-41 × 100-400 $\mu$; end walls plane ; chloroplasts 2 to 3, making 2.5 to 3.5 turns.

Conjugation scalariform, rare ; tubes formed by both gametangia; fertile cells shortened, cylindric or enlarged; zygospores ellipsoid, 35-42 × 60-100 $\mu$ ; median spore wall yellow or brownish-yellow, smooth.

*Distribution* :

*India* : In the running water near Kanheri Caves, Borivli, Bombay, August 2, 1955.

*Other countries* : China; Europe; South Africa, New Guinea and United States of America.

**52. Spirogyra biformis** JAO 1935. *Sinensia* **6**, pp. 594-95, Pl. 6, Fig. 66. (=*S. biformis* forma Singh).

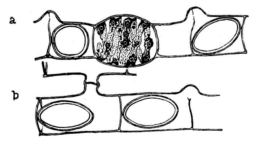

Fig. 293. a-b. *S. biformis.* (after Jao.)

Vegetative cells 38-48 × 64-150 (-190) $\mu$, with plane end walls, chloroplasts (1-) 2-3 making 1.5 to 4.5. turns.

Conjugation usually lateral, rarely scalariform; tubes formed by both gametangia; fertile cells cylindric or slightly enlarged, sometimes shortened to 38 $\mu$ ; sterile cells some times swollen to 58 $\mu$ in diameter ; zygospores ellipsoid with rounded ends, 36-51 × 60-83 $\mu$ ; median spore wall yellow, smooth.

*Distribution* :

*India* : Rice fields, Gorakhpur, U.P; Hoshangabad, M.P.

*Other countries* : Szechwan, China ; New Guinea ; Phillippines ; Leyte ; Brazil.

**53. Spirogyra hyalina** CLEVE 1868. *Nova Acta Reg. Soc. Sci. Upsali.* Ser. 3, **6,** p. 17, Pl. 3, Figs. 1-6.

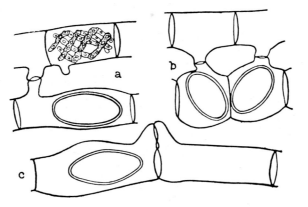

Fig. 294. a-c. *S. hyalina.* (after Cleve.)

Vegetative cells 45-60 × 80-240 $\mu$, with plane end walls; chloroplasts 2,3 or 4, making 0.5 to 3 turns.

Conjugation lateral or scalariform, tubes formed by both gametangia; fertile cells cylindric, or slightly inflated ; zygospores ellipsoid, more or less pointed, 45-60 × 60-130 $\mu$ ; median spore wall brown, smooth ; aplanospores similar, somewhat smaller.

*Distribution* :

   *India* :   Widely distributed.

   *Other countries* :   China ; Sweden ; Puerto Rico and U.S.A.

**54. Spirogyra columbiana** CZURDA 1942. *Süsswasserflora Mitteleropa.* **9,** p. 190. (=*S. columbiana* forma Rao).

Fig. 295. *S. columbiana.* (after Czurda.)

Vegetative cells 48-54 × 90-180 $\mu$, with plane end walls ; chloroplasts 1—3.

Conjugation scalariform ; tubes formed by both gametangia ; fertile and sterile cells cylindric; zygospores ellipsoid, about 50 × 70 $\mu$ ; median spore wall smooth, yellow-brown suture distinct.

*Distribution* :

*India* :   In a rain-water pool, U.P. ; Katni.

*Other countries* :   Columbia; Java; South America; South Africa.

**55.   Spirogyra pseudoneglecta** CZURDA 1932.   *Süsswasserflora Mitteleuropa.* **9**, p. 194.

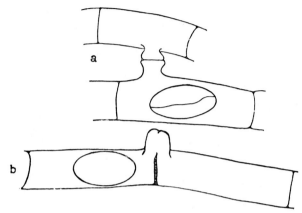

296. a-b. *S. pseudoneglecta.* (after Czurda.)

Vegetative cells 55-60 × 130-240 $\mu$, with plane end walls ; 3 chloroplasts.

Conjugation lateral and scalariform ; tubes formed by both gametangia ; fertile cells clylindric or slightly swollen; zygospores ellipsoid, 50-52 × 95-100 $\mu$; median spore wall reddish-brown, smooth.

*Distribution* :

*India* :   In pools, Jubbalpore, M.P.

*Other countries* :   Moravia.

**56.   Spirogyra turfosa** GAY 1884.   *Essai Monogr. Conjug.*, p. 187, Pl. 4, Fig. 3 ; Transeau, 1951, p. 171, PL. XXVI, Fig, 17.

297. *S. turfosa.* (after Mehra.)

Vegetative cells 68-78 × 68-350 $\mu$ ; end walls plane ; chloroplasts 3-4 making 1.5 to 4 turns  ; fertile cells cylindric.

Conjugation scalariform ;  tubes formed by both gametangia ; zygospores ellipsoid, pointed, 65-78 × 120-140 $\mu$ ; median spore wall smooth, yellow.

*Distribution*:

*India*:   In a puddle at Vile Parle, Bombay, August 19, 1955.

*Other countries*:   Galicia; United States of America.

**57.  Spirogyra szechwanensis** Jao 1946.   *Sinensia*. **6**, p. 595, Pl. 6, Fig. 69. *Amer. Jour. Bot.* **23**, p. 55, 1936.   (*S. szechwanensis* var. *varians* Singh)

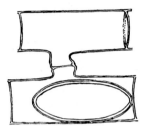

Fig. 298. *S.szechwanensis.* (after Jao.)

Vegetative cells 75-90 × 125-240 $\mu$, with plane end walls ; 4 chloroplasts, rarely 2 or 3, making 1-2 turns in the cell.

Conjugation scalariform ; tubes formed by both gametangia ; fertile cells cylindric ; zygospores ellipsoid to ovoid, 57-68 × 100-210 $\mu$ ; median spore wall smooth, yellow at maturity.

*Distribution*:

*India*:   Gorakhpur, U.P.

*Other countries*:   Chungking, China.

Var. *varians* Singh (1938) differs from the type in the narrower cells, smaller number of chloroplasts and in the cylindric obovoid zygospores filling the fructifying cells completely.

**58.  Spirogyra nitida** (Dillwyn) Link, 1833.   *Handbuch.* pt 3, p. 262 (=*S. nitida* forma Singh ; *S. nitida* forma Rao).

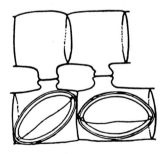

Fig. 299. *S.nitida.* (after Jao.)

Vegetative cells 70-90 $\mu$ in diameter, 1-3 time as long.   Septa plane, 3-5 chloroplasts with $\frac{1}{2}$ to $1\frac{1}{2}$ spiral in each cell.

Conjugation scalariform. Zygospores ellipsoid or even slightly ovoid. Fruiting cells slightly swollen on the outside. Mesospore thick, smooth and dark brown. Zygospores 50-55 $\mu$ in diameter, $1\frac{1}{2}$ times as long. Zygospores are slightly smaller than in the type.

*Distribution* :

*India* : Free-floating in a pond near Tahli Sahib district Hoshiarpore, Punjab ; Gorakhpur, Banaras, U.P.

*Other countries* : China; Europe ; Australia ; South Africa and United States of America.

**59. Spirogyra hymerae** BRITTON & SMITH 1942. *Ohio Jour. Sci.* **42**, p. 70, Transeau, 1951, p. 171-2 Pl. XXVII, Fig. 3.

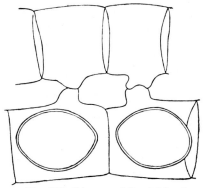

Fig. 300. *S.hymerae.* (after Mehra.)

Vegetative cells 83-92 × 43-256 $\mu$ ; end walls plane ; chloroplasts 2 to 4, making 0.5 to 2 turns in the cell.

Conjugation scalariform; tubes formed by both gametangia; receptive gametangia cylindric or slightly enlarged ; zygospores mostly ellipsoid, 53-79 × 83-128 $\mu$ ; median wall yellow, smooth.

*Distribution* :

*India* : In a puddle at Khar, Bombay, November 12, 1954.

*Other countries* : United States of America.

**60. Spirogyra setiformis** (ROTH). KÜTZING. 1845. *Phycologia Germanica.* p. 223. (*S. setiformis* forma Rao ; *S. setiformis* forma Dixit.)

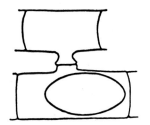

Fig. 301 *S.setiformis.* (after Czurda.)

Vegetative cells 100-120 $\mu$ in diameter $1\frac{1}{2}$ to $2\frac{1}{2}$ times as long, with plane septa. Each cell with 3-6 chloroplasts making 1-2 spirals.

Conjugation scalariform, fruiting cells not swollen. Zygospores oval or ovoid-rounded, 80-95 $\mu$ in diameter $1\frac{1}{2}$ times as long with a smooth mesospore.

*Distribution* :

*India* : Free-floating in Siah Baeen near Dasuya, district Hoshiarpore, Punjab, in big masses. A fairly common form. Hoshangabad, rock-quarry, M.P. ; rain-water pools U.P. ; Bombay.

*Other countries* : United States of America and European countries.

**61. Spirogyra elliptica** Jao 1935. *Sinensia.* **6**, p. 596, Pl. 6, Fig. 72 ; Transeau, 1951, p. 172, P. XXVII, Fig. 6.

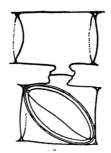

Fig. *S. elliptica.* (after Czurda.)

Vegetative cells 115-123 × 128-568 $\mu$ ; end walls plane ; chloroplasts 4 to 6, making 1 to 3 turns.

Conjugation scalariform ; tubes formed by both gametangia ; fertile cells cylindric and shortened ; zygospores ellipsoid with pointed ends, 82-106 × 144-202 $\mu$ ; median wall smooth, yellow-brown.

*Distribution* :

*India* : In a puddle at Kolwada, Bombay, September 2, 1955.

*Other countries* : Szechwan, China.

**62. Spirogyra hatillensis** Transeau 1936. *Brittonia,* 2, p. 171. (*S. setiformis* var. *maxima* Rao)

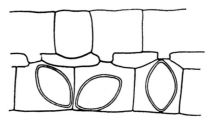

Fig. 303. *S. hatillensis.* (after Tiffany.)

Vegetative cells 120-130 × 108-450 μ, with plane end walls ; 6 to 8 chloroplasts, having 0.5 to 4 turns.

Conjugation scalariform ; tubes formed by both gametangia ; fertile cells cylindric, sterile cells more or less swollen ; zygospores ellipsoid, 85-125 × 130-160 μ ; median spore wall brown, smooth.

*Distribution* :

*India* : Rain-water pools, U.P.

*Other countries* : U.S.A., Puerto Rico, Hatillo.

**63. Spirogyra ellipsospora** Transeau 1914. *Amer Journ. Bot.* **1**, p. 294. (=*S. ellipsospora* forma *tenuis* Singh ; *S. setiformis* var. *maior* Biswas).

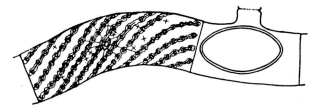

Fig. 304. *S. ellipsospora.* (after Transeau.)

Vegetative cells 125-150 × 125-500 μ ; end wall plane ; chloroplasts 3 to 8, making 4 to 5 turns.

Conjugation scalariform ; tubes formed by both gametangia ; fertile cells cylindric ; zygospores ellipsoid, more or less pointed, 100-140 × 160-255 μ ; median spore wall smooth, yellow-brown.

*Distribution* :

*India* : In a stream near National Park, Borivli, Kanheri caves, Salsette, Bombay ; Manipur, Assam; Gorakhpur, U.P.

*Other countries* : Central China and Eastern half of the United States of America.

**64. Spirogyra exilis** W. & G.S. West 1907. *Ann. Roy. Bot. Gard., Calcutta.* **6**, p. 186.

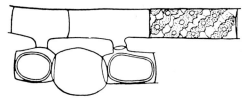

Fig. 305. *S. exilis.* (after W. & G.S. West.)

Vegetative cells 27-30 × 42-120 μ, with plane end walls ; 2 broad chloroplasts, making 1.5 to 2 turns.

Conjugation scalariform ; tubes formed by both gametangia ; fertile cells enlarged on the inner face, or cylindrical ; sterile cells often greatly inflated to 49 μ ; zygospores ovoid to oblong ; 27-30 × 36-45 μ ; median spore wall yellow, smooth.

*Distribution* :   Burma.

**65.  Spirogyra distenta** Transeau 1934. *Ohio Jour. Sci.* **34**, p. 420. *S. decimina* Fritsch. var. *inflata.* *Trans. Roy. Soc. S. Africa.* **9**, p. 46.

Fig. 306. a-b. *S.distenta.* (after Fritsch.)

Vegetative cells 48-52 × 81-180 μ, with plane end walls ; 2 chloroplasts, making 1.5 to 2 turns.

Conjugation scalariform; tubes formed by both gametangia ; fertile cells cylindric or enlarged ; sterile cells inflated to 75 μ ; zygospores ovoid, 49-55 × 50-100 μ ; median spore wall yellow, smooth.

*Distribution* :   U.S.A. and South Africa.

**66.  Spirogyra triplicata** (Collins) Transeau 1944. *Ohio. Jour. Sci.* **44** p. 243. *S. decima* var. *triplicata.* Collins. F.S. Phycoth. Bor.-Amer., No. 960.   *Green Algae of North America.* p. 110, 1912.

Fig. 307. *S. triplicata.* (after Mehra.)

Vegetative cells 35-45 × 140-200 μ ; end walls plane, chloroplasts 3, making 1.5 to 3 turns.

Conjugation scalariform ; tubes formed by both gametangia; fertile cells cylindric zygospores ovoid, 34-48 × 48-54 μ ; median spore wall yellow, smooth.

*Distribution* :

*India* :   In a pond at Khar, Bombay.

*Other countries* :   United States of America.

**67.  Spirogyra neglecta** (Hassall). Kutzing. 1849. *Species Algarum*, p. 441 (=*S. neglecta* f. *tenuis* Rao ; *S. neglecta* forma Rao).

Fig. 308. *S. neglecta.* (after Kolkwitz and Krieger.)

Vegetative cells 50-58 $\mu$ thick. 2-5 times as long, septa plane. Each cell with 3 chloroplasts making 2-2½ turns.

Conjugation scalariform. Fruiting cells only slightly swollen. Zygospore oval or even rounded, 54-58 $\mu$ in diameter, 1½ time as long as broad. Mesospore smooth and dark brown.

*Distribution*:

*India*: Found in a blackish mass, free-floating in a pond near V. Bhattain, district Hoshiarpore, in the second week of December 1929 ; Banaras, U.P. ; in Budgar Lake, Durie, M.P. ; Calcutta.

*Other countries*: China ; United States of America ; Germany ; Czechoslovakia ; Finland ; Macedonia ; Java ; Siam ; South Africa and West Indies.

**68. Spirogyra decimina** (MÜLLER) KÜTZING 1843. *Phycologia Generalis* p. 279. Wittrock and Nordstedt *Algae Exsiccatae*, No. 1372. (*S. communis* var. *intorta* Singh; *S. decimina* forma Rao ; *S. decimina* f. *longispora* Misra).

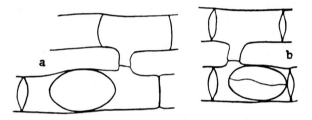

Fig. a-b. *S. decimina*. (after Czurda.)

Vegetative cells 32-42 × 66-150 $\mu$, with plane end walls ; 2-3 chloroplasts, making 1 to 2 turns.

Conjugation scalariform; tubes formed by both gametangia; fertile cells cylindric or enlarged ; zygospores ovoid to globose, 31-40 × 41-68 $\mu$ ; median spore wall yellow, smooth.

*Distribution*:

*India*: In a pond 22 miles off Srinagar towards Anantang, Kashmir ; in a roadside pool Hoshingabad, M.P. ; rice fields, Gorakhpur, Ganges, Banaras, U.P.

*Other countries*: Asia, Africa, Europe, Java, South America, U.S.A., West Indies.

**69. Spirogyra plena** (W. & G.S. WEST) CZURDA 1932. *Süsswasserflora Mitteleuropa.* **9**, p. 193. *Ann. Roy. Bot. Gard. Calcutta.* **6**, p. 187, 1907. (=*S. plena* forma Rao ; *S. plena* forma Singh)

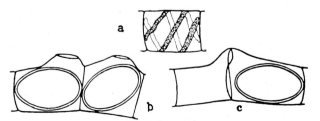

Fig. 310. a-c. *S. plena*. a, vegetative cell, b, scalariform conjugation; c, lateral conjugation. (after West.)

Vegetative cells 38-44 × 57-88 $\mu$, with plane end walls ; 2 to 3 chloroplasts.

Conjugation scalariform and lateral; tubes large and formed by both gametangia ; fertile cells cylindric or enlarged on the conjugating side; zygospores ovoid, 40-44 × 64-73 (—88) $\mu$ ; median spore wall yellow ; smooth.

*Distribution* :

*India* :   Bombay ; Gorakhpur, U.P. ;

*Other countries* :   Burma ; Yunnan, China ; U.S.A.

**70.  Spirogyra jugalis**  (FL.DAN). KÜTZING 1845. *Phycologia Germanica*, p. 223.

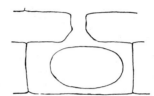

Fig. 311. *S. jugalis*. (after Transeau.)

Vegetative cells 75-103 × 80-300 $\mu$, with plane end walls ; 3 to 4 chloroplasts making 1 to 2 turns.

Conjugation scalariform; tubes formed by both gametangia ; fertile cells cylindric or enlarged; zygospores ovoid, 87-108 × 120-155 $\mu$; median spore wall brown, smooth.

*Distribution* :   China; Europe; U.S.A.

**71.  Spirogyra margaritata** WOLLNY 1877.   *Hedwigia*, **16**, p. 164.

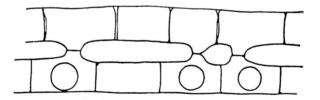

Fig. 312. *S.margaritata*. (after Wollny.)

Vegetative cells 100-120 × 150-400 $\mu$, with plane end walls ; 13-15 chlorolplasts making 0.25 to 0.5 turns.

Conjugation scalariform; tubes formed by both gametangia; fertile cells cylindric or inflated to 165 $\mu$ ; zygospores ovoid, 92-125 × 140-200 $\mu$ ; median spore wall smooth, brown.

*Distribution* :

*India* :   Gorakhpur, Banaras, U.P.

*Other countries* :   Dresden, Germany.

**72.  Spirogyra paradoxa** RAO 1937. *J. Indian Bot. Soc.*, **16**, p. 281.  Fig. 5. E.

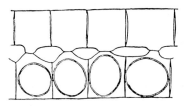

Fig. 313. *S. paradoxa*. (after Rao.)

Vegetative cells short, as long as, or sightly longer than broad ; end walls plane ; chloroplasts 3-4.

Conjugation scalariform ; fructifying cells swollen on the conjugating side and sometimes not swollen on both sides. Zygospores broadly ellipsoidal upto almost spherical ; exospore thin, smooth and hyaline ; mesospore thin, smooth and brown ; endospore indistinct ; 80-90 × 73-82 (-83) $\mu$.

*Distribution* :

*India* : In a rain-water pool, Sarnath, U.P. along with *Spirogyra weberi* forma, *S. neglecta*, *S. setiformis* var. *maxima* and also sterile filaments of *Oedogonium* and *Zygnema*.

The species is merely an attenuated form of *S. setiformis* (Rot) Kütz.

**73. Spirogyra jaoense** RANDHAWA 1938. *Proc. Indian Acad. Sci.* **8**, pp. 358-59.

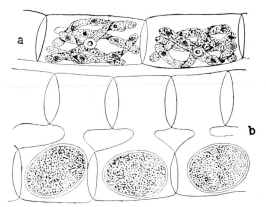

Fig. 314. a-b. *S. jaoense*. a, vegetative cells;
b, scalariform conjugation (after Randhawa.)

Vegetative cells are 44-56 $\mu$ broad and 2 to $2\frac{1}{2}$ times as long ; 4-5 chloroplasts in each cell ; nucleus conspicuous in the middle. The septa of the cells are plane.

Conjugation only scalariform. The female cells are only slightly swollen. The zygospores are oval to elliptical in shape and are 54-58 $\mu$ broad and 72-80 $\mu$ long. The zygospore wall is composed of two layers only, a thin and smooth exospore, and a comparatively thicker brownish mesospore.

*Distribution* :

*India* : Free-floating in a fresh-water stream flowing very slowly near Makrahi, district Fyzabad, U.P. about the second week of November 1936.

**74. Spirogyra bichromatophora** (Randhawa) Transeau 1944. *Ohio Jour. Sci.* **44,** p. 243. *Proc. Indian Acad. Sci.* **8,** pp. 353-54, Fig. 48. 1938 (=*S. gallica* var *bichromatophora*).

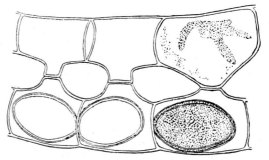

Eig. 315. *S. bichromatophora.* (after Randhawa.)

Vegetative cells 60-75 × 96-160 $\mu$, with plane end walls ; 2 chloroplasts, making 4 to 6 turns.

Conjugation scalariform; large tubes formed by both gametangia ; fertile cells cylindric or enlarged ; zygospores ellipsoid, 54-60 × 80-90 $\mu$ ; median spore wall smooth, brown,

*Distribution* :

*India* :   Fyzabad, U.P., May,   1938.

**75. Spirogyra rhizoides** Randhawa 1938. *Proc. Indian Acad. Sci.* **8,** pp. 354-56.

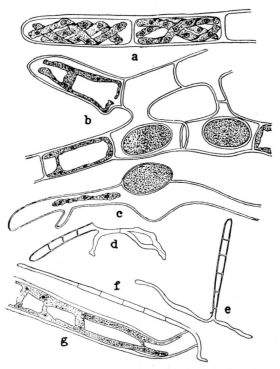

Fig. 316. a-g. *S. rhizoides.* a, vegetative cells ; b, scalarifom conjugation; c, azygospore; d-g, rhizoids. (after Randhawa.)

Vegetative filaments are usually 2 mm. to $2\frac{1}{2}$ cm. in length, and have a definite base and apex unlike other species of *Spirogyra*. The basal part bears rhizoids which are fixed in the mud. The apical cells are blunt and spatulate in appearance. The vegetative cells are 26-28 $\mu$ broad, have very thick brown walls, and 2 to 3 closely packed chloroplasts.

*Rhizoids* : Usually rhizoids are produced from the basal cells, but in some rare cases both ends of the filaments are elongated into rhizoidal structures. In this form, the rhizoids are not short and stumpy structures as in *Spirogyra affinis* Kütz. but are root-like, bifurcated organs, which are extraordinarily long. Other species of *Spirogyra* like *S. bellis* Cleve, and *S. affinis* Kütz. which produce rhizoidal structures were found growing on other water-plants, but never in mud, like the present species. The semi-terrestrial habit of this alga accounts for the advanced nature of its rhizoids. The chloroplasts, which are very closely packed in the apical cells, become very much attenuated in the upper part of the rhizoids and the extremities of the rhizoids are usually hyaline. An azygospore was seen lodged in the swollen part of a rhizoid. Zygospore like structures have been reported by Iyengar, as growing at the extremities of rhizoidal structures in *Mougeotia adnata* Iyeng. but the position in which this zygospore-like body was seen is most peculiar.

Conjugation scalariform. The zygospores are usually found in pairs, and nearly in all cases one of the conjugation canals is longer than its neighbour. The zygospores are oval in shape with a tendency towards roundness and are yellowish brown in colour. The fruiting cells are inflated on both sides. The zygospore wall is composed of two layers only, a thin and hyaline exospore, and a thick smooth bluish mesospore. Zygospores are 36-38 $\mu$ broad, and 52-58 $\mu$ long.

*Distribution* :

*India* : Attached in mud along with *Mougeotia* sp. and a species of *Oedogonium* near the banks of Pikia Nadi near Rajeh Sultanpur, district Fyzabad, U.P., in the last week of November 1936.

**76. Spirogyra dubia** Kützing 1849-69. Czurda 1932, *Süssawasserflora Mitteluropa* **9,** p. 188 (*S. dubia,* var *polymorphis* Rao; *S. dubia* forma Rao).

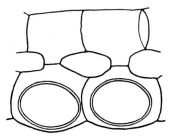

Fig. 317. *S. dubia.* (after Petkoff.)

Vegetative cells 40-50 $\mu$ broad; end walls plane; chloroplasts 2-3.

Conjugation scalariform; fertile cells largely swollen ; zygospore ellipsoid, $45\text{-}55 \times 75\text{-}90$ $\mu$ ; mesospore thick, smooth and brown.

*Distribution* :

*India* :   Jubbalpore, M.P. ; pools in U.P.

*Other Countries* :   Africa; Bulgaria ; Egypt ; North America.

**77.  Spirogyra chungkingensis** Jao 1935.   *Sinensia.*   **6**, p 600,   Pl. 8, Figs. 85-86.   *Amer. Jour. Bot.* **23**, p 58. 1936.

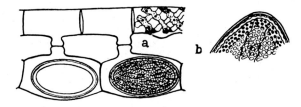

318. a-b. *S. chungkingensis.* (after Jao.)

Vegetative cells 22-26 × 80-170, *µ*, with plane end walls ; 3 chloroplasts, making 1 to 3 turns in the cell.

Conjugation scalariform ; tubes formed by both gametangia ; fertile cells inflated ; zygospores ellipsoid, 35-39 × 54-68 *µ* ; median spore wall of two layers, of which the outer is thin, brownish and wrinkled; the inner brown, and irregularly reticulate.

*Distribution* :   Chungking, China.

**78.  Spirogyra puncticulata** Jao 1935. *Trans Amer. Micros. Soc.* **54,** p. 4, Pl. 1, Fig. 9 ; Transeau, 1951, p. 178, Pl. XXVIII, Fig. 9.

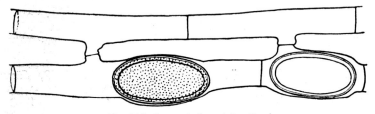

Fig. 319. *S. puncticulata.* (after Jao.)

Vegetative cells  16-22 × 48-240 *µ* ; end walls plane ; filaments attached by rhizoids ; chloroplasts 2 rarely 1, making 1.5 to 5 turns in the cell.

Conjugation scalariform; tubes formed by both gametangia; fertile cells fusiform or cylindrically inflated to 29-36 *µ* ; zygospores ovoid, 25-22 × 41-58 *µ* ; median spore wall densely punctate, yellow.

*Distribution* :

*India* :   In a stream near the National Park, Borivli, Bombay.

*Other countries* :   United States of America.

**79.  Spirogyra dictyospora** Jao 1935.   *Sinensia.*   **6**, p. 599, Pl. 8, Fig. 84 ; Transeau, 1951, p. 179, Pl. XXVIII, Fig. 14.

Fig. 320. a-b. *S. dictyospora.* (after Mehra.)

Vegetative cells 28-32 × 55-144 $\mu$ ; end walls plane ; chloroplasts 3, sometimes 2, making 2-5 turns.

Conjugation scalariform; tubes formed by both gametangia; fertile cells enlarged up to 55 $\mu$ ; zygospores ovoid, 41-55 × 61-103 $\mu$ ; median spore wall reticulate, yellow to yellow brown.

*Distribution* :

*India* : In a stream at Borivli, Bombay.

*Other countries* : Chungking, China.

**80. Spirogyra rhizopus** JAO 1936. *Amer. Jour. Bot.* **23**, p. 55, Figs. 10-12.

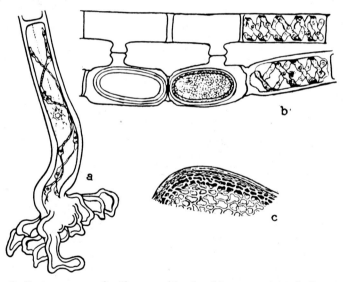

Fig. 321. a-c. *S. rhizopus.* a, part of a filament with a basal hapteron; b, scalariform conjugation; c, part of the zygospore showing the spore wall structure. (after Jao.)

Vegetative cells 25-32 × 80-250 $\mu$, with plane end walls ; 2 chloroplasts, making 1.5 to 4 turns; basal cell with much expanded and irregularly lobed holdfast.

Conjugation scalariform ; tubes formed by both gametangia; fertile cells quadrangularly inflated, sometimes oblong in form, to 57 $\mu$ ; zygospores ellipsoid, 35-42 × 64-100 $\mu$ ; outer spore wall thick, lamellose, colourless; median spore wall brown, irregularly reticulate.

*Distribution* : Peiping, China.

**81. Spirogyra fluviatilis** HILSE. 1863. In *Rabenhorst's Algen Europas*, No. 1476
*Flora Europa Algarum*. 3, p. 243, 1868 : Wolle. *Freshwater Algae*, p. 216, pl. 136, Figs. 1-3.

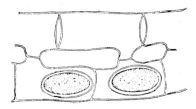

Fig. 322. *S. fluviatilis*. (after Randhawa.)

Vegetative cells 40-45 $\mu$ broad, 3-6 times as long. Only three irregular chloroplasts were seen in certain cells, as purely vegetative cells were rare and almost all the cells had conjugated in the material examined.

Conjugation scalariform, fertile cells not swollen. Zygospores oval-ellipsoid, 45$\mu$ broad, 70-75 $\mu$ long. Exospore thin hyaline, mesospore thick dark brown, endospore not known.

*Distribution* :

*India* : Free-floating almost filling a pond near V. Bhattian, district Hoshiarpore, in the third week of October 1929; epiphytic on rocks, Latif Shah, Chakia, Banaras, U.P.

*Other countries* : Brazil ; China; United States of America ; Germany and France.

**82. Spirogyra schmidtii** W. & G.S. WEST 1902. *Bot. Tiddsskr.* **24**, p. 161, Figs. 43-45.

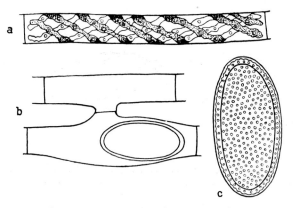

Fig. 323. a-c. *S. schmidtii*. (after West.)

Vegetative cells 30-35 × 210-350 $\mu$, with plane end walls ; 2 to 3(4) chloroplasts, making 2.5 to 4 turns; fertile cells inflated to 59 $\mu$.

Conjugation scalariform ; tubes formed by both gametangia ; zygospores ellipsoid, 43-46 × 88-118 $\mu$ ; median spore wall yellow-brown, scrobiculate.

*Distribution* : U.S.A.; Siam, Koh Chang.

**83. Spirogyra orientalis** W. & G.S. West 1907. *Ann. Roy. Bot. Gard.,
Calcutta.* **6,** p. 186 ; Transeau, 1951, p. 181, Pl.XXIX, Fig. 3.

Fig. 324. *S. orientalis.* (after Mehra.)

Vegetative cells 30-31 × 90-160 $\mu$ ; end walls plane ; chloroplasts 3, making 1 to
1.5 turns.

Conjugation scalariform ; tubes formed by both gametangia ; fertile cells inflated, 57-65 $\mu$ ; zygospores ellipsoid, more or less pointed, 38-42 × 67 $\mu$ ; median spore
wall minutely scrobiculate, brown.

*Distribution* :

*India* : In a stream at Dahisar, Bombay.

*Other countries* : Yunnan; China; Burma; Michigan, U.S.A.

**84. Spirogyra subcylindrospora** Jao 1935. *Sinensia.* **6,** p. 598, Pl. 7,
Figs. 79-80.

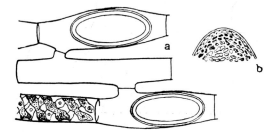

Fig. 325. *S. subcylindrospora.* (after Jao.)

Vegetative cells 25-32 × 96-228 $\mu$, with plane end walls ; 2 to 3 (rarely 4) chloroplasts making 1 to 1.5 turns in the cell.

Conjugation scalariform; tubes formed by both gametangia ; fertile cells
cylindric or enlarged; zygospores ellipsoid to cylindric-ellipsoid with rounded ends,
32-38 × 58-96 $\mu$ ; median spore wall brown, thick, reticulate.

*Distribution* : U.S.A. ; Szechwan, China.

**85. Spirogyra shantungensis** Li 1936. *Bull. Fan Mem. Inst. Biol., Botany.*
**7,** p. 60.

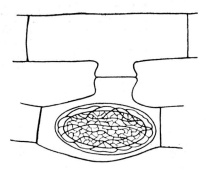

Fig. 326. *S. shantungensis.* (after Li.)

Vegetative cells 46-52 × 184-320 $\mu$, with plane end walls; chloroplasts 3, making 2 to 4 turns in the cell.

Conjugation scalariform ; tubes formed by both gametangia ; fertile cells inflated up to 70 $\mu$ and shortened ; zygospores ellipsoid, with somewhat rounded ends, 48-56 × 96-140 $\mu$ ; median spore wall of two layers outer nearly colourless, wrinkled; inner, brown, finely and irregularly reticulate.

*Distribution*:   Tsingtao, Shantung, China.

**86.  Spirogyra braziliensis** (NORDST) TRANSEAU 1915. *Ohio Jour. Sci.* **16,** p. 26 ; Transeau, 1951, p. 182.

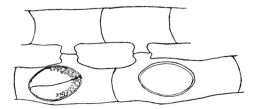

Fig. 327. *S. braziliensis.* (after Mehra.)

Vegetative cells 50-60 × 125-300 $\mu$ ; end walls plane; chloroplasts   3,  making 1 to 3   turns.

Conjugation scalariform ; tubes formed by both gametangia ; fertile cells cylindric, shortened ; zygospores ellipsoid, 54-60 × 80-90 $\mu$ ; median spore wall  minutely verrucose,   yellow   brown.

*Distribution*:

*India*:   In a puddle at Goregaon, Bombay.

*Other  countries*:   China;  U.S.A.;  South  America.

**87.  Spirogyra pulchrifigurata** JAO 1935.   *Sinensia.*   **6,** p. 601, Pl. 8, Figs. 91-92. *Amer. Jour. Bot.* **23,** p. 57, Figs. 15-17.   1936.

Fig. 328. a-b. *S. pulchrifigurata*. (after Jao.)

Vegetative cells 42-58 × 64-192 $\mu$, with plane end walls; 3 to 4 chloroplasts making 1.5 to 4 turns.

Conjugation scalariform; tubes formed by both gametangia ; fertile cells inflated upto 83 $\mu$; zygospores ellipsoid with more or less rounded ends, 48-64 × 70-109 $\mu$ ; median spore wall yellow-brown, irregularly reticulate.

*Distribution* : Szechwan, China ; U.S.A.

**88. Spirogyra quadrilaminata** JAO 1935. *Sinensia.* **6,** p. 600, Pl. 8, Figs. 87-88 ; *Amer. Jour. Bot.* **23,** p. 58 Figs. 25-26, 1936 ; Transeau, 1951, p. 183, Pl. XXIX, Figs. 11-13.

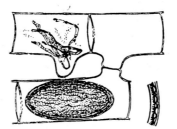

Fig. 329. *S. quadrilaminata*. (after Jao.)

Vegetative cells 38-58 × 112-256 $\mu$ ; end walls plane ; chloroplasts 3 to 4, making 1 to 3.5 turns.

Conjugation scalariform ; tubes formed by both gametangia ; fertile cells cylindric; zygospores ellipsoid to cylindric ellipsoid, with more or less rounded ends, 43-54 × 64-102 $\mu$ ; median spore wall of 2 layers ; outer brown and densely wrinkled ; inner brown finely punctate, and at times finely and irregularly reticulate.

*Distribution* :

*India* : In a pond near a temple at Thana, Bombay.

*Other countries* : Brazil; China; Puerto Rico, Tennessee and Texas, Florida, USA.

**89. Spirogyra subreticulata** FRITSCH 1921. *Trans. Roy. Soc. S. Africa.* **9,** p. 48.

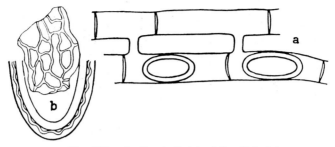

Fig. 330. a-b. *S. subreticulata.* (after Fritsch.)

Vegetative cells 50-54 × 150-400 $\mu$, with plane end walls ; 3 to 4 chloroplasts, making 0.5 to 3 turns.

Conjugation scalariform; tubes formed by both gametangia ; fertile cells cylindric or enlarged ; zygospores ellipsoid to somewhat ovoid, 42-54 × 60-124 $\mu$ ; outer median spore wall irregularly reticulate, yellow-brown ; inner wall brown, up to 9 $\mu$ thick.

*Distribution* :   Shantung, China ; South Africa ; U.S.A.

**90.  Spirogyra rhizobrachialis** Jao 1935. *Sinensia.* **6,** p. 599, Pl. 7, Figs. 81-83 ; *Amer. Jour. Bot.* **23,** p. 57, Figs. 18-21.   1936 ; Transeau, 1951, p. 18 P. 13, XXIX, Figs. 14-15.

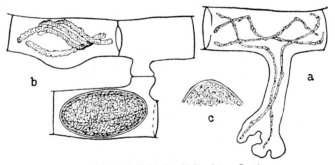

Fig. 331. a-c. *S.rhizobrachialis.* (after Jao.)

Vegetative cells 40-45 × 115-240 $\mu$ ; end walls plane ; chloroplasts 3 to 5, making 1.5 to 2.5 turns ; in some portions of the filament each sterile cell produces a lateral rhizoid-shaped attachment with a more or less lobed hapteron.

Conjugation scalariform; tubes formed by both gametangia ; fertile cells cylindric, sometimes shortened and enlarged ; zygospores ellipsoid with more or less rounded ends, 38-60 × 58-100 $\mu$ ; median spore wall yellow brown, finely and irregularly reticulate.

*Distribution* :

*India* :   In a streamlet near Khanheri Caves, Borivli, Bombay.

*Other countries* :   Chungking, China; United States of America.

**91.  Spirogyra minor** (Schmidle)  Transeau 1944.   *Ohio Jour. Sci.* **44,** p. 243. Schmidle 1901.   (*S. malmeana* var. *minor* Schmidle, *Hedwigia,* **40,** p. 46).

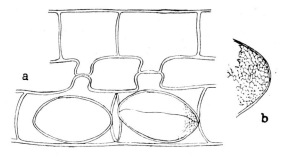

Fig. 332. a-b. *S. minor.* (after Mehra.)

Vegetative cells 55-60 × 150-300 $\mu$ ; chloroplasts 3, rarely 4.

Conjugation scalariform ; tubes formed by both gametangia fertile cells cylindric ; zygospores ellipsoid, 50-60 × 90-180 $\mu$ ; median spore wall irregularly reticulate, yellow brown.

*Distribution* :

*India* :   In a puddle at Vile Parle, Bombay.

*Other countries* :   China ; Brazil ; United States of America.

**92.   Spirogyra brunnea** CZURDA 1932. *Süsswasserflora Mitteleuropa.* **9,** p. 197. Fritsch & Rich. *Trans. Roy. Soc. S. Africa.* **18,** p. 51.   1929 (as *S. reinhardii* var. *africana*) (=*S. brunnea* f. *varians* Rao).

Fig. 333. a-b. *S.brunnea.* (after Fritsch & Rich.)

Vegetative cells 56-71 × 85-280 $\mu$, with plane end walls ; 3 to 5 chloroplasts making 2 to 3 turns.

Conjugation scalariform ; tubes formed by both gametangia ; fertile cells shortened, and slightly inflated on both sides ; zygospores ovoid, 55-66 × 73-94 $\mu$ ; median spore wall brown, intricately reticulate.

*Distribution* :

*India* :   In a shallow pond in U.P.

*Other countries* :   Transvaal, South Africa.

*S. brunnea* forma *varians* Rao 1937 (*J. Indian Bot. Soc.* **16,** p. 285.) differs from the type in narrower cells, unswollen fructifying cells and shorter zygospores.

**93. Spirogyra africana** (FRITSCH) Czurda 1932. *Süsswasserflora Mitteleuropa.* **9,** p. 201 ; Transeau, 1951, p. 185.

Fig. 334. *S. africana* (after Nygard.)

Vegetative cells 50-60 × 150-500 $\mu$ ; end walls plane ; chloroplasts 3 to 4, making 1.5 to 4 turns.

Conjugation scalariform; tubes formed by both gametangia ; receptive cells inflated or enlarged on both sides up to 96 $\mu$ ; zygospores ovoid, 60-67 × 78-90 $\mu$ ; median spore wall brown, irregularly and shallowly corrugate.

*Distribution :*

*India :*   In a pool at Ghatkopar, Bombay.

*Other countries :*   Cape Colony, Guatemala, Africa.

**94. Spirogyra grossii** SCHMIDLE 1901. *Allgem. Bot. Zeitschr.* **7,** p. 3.

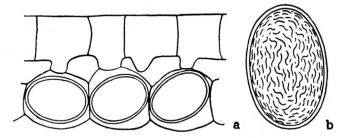

Fig. 335. a–b. *S. grossii.* (after Schmidle.)

Vegetative cells 40-42 × 50-120 $\mu$, with plane end walls ;  3 chloroplasts, making 2 to 4 turns in the cell.

Conjugation scalariform; tubes apparently formed by the male gametangia ; fertile cells inflated to 64 $\mu$ ; zygospores ovoid, 43-51 × 64-118 $\mu$ ; median spore wall irregularly corrugate.

*Distribution :*

*India :*   Widely distributed.

*Other countries :*   Yugoslavia ; Manchuria.

**95. Spirogyra verrucosa** (RAO) Krieger 1944. Rabenhorst's *Krypogamenflora*. 13, p. 398. *J. Indian Bot. Soc.* **17**, p. 358, Fig. 3.   (=*S. malmeana* var. *verrucosa* Rao).

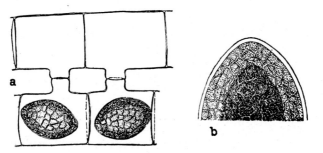

Fig. 336. a-b. *S. verrucosa.* (after Rao.)

Vegetative cells 108-126 × 144-190 $\mu$, with plane end walls and 4-8 chloroplasts.

Conjugation scalariform ; tubes formed by both cells ; receptive gametangia cylindric ; zygospores ellipsoid, 89-100 × 116-165 $\mu$ ; median wall thick, brown, minutely verrucose, and with coarse meshed reticulate ridges.

*Distribution* :

*India* :   Central Provinces.

**96. Spirogyra verruculosa** JAO 1936. *Amer. Jour. Bot.* **23**, p. 58. (=*S. verruculosa* forma Rao ; *S. verruculosa* var. *crassa* Singh).

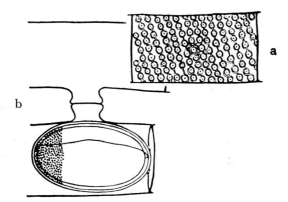

Fig. 337. a-b. *S. verruculosa.* (after Jao.)

Vegetative cells 105-120 × 259-400 $\mu$, with plane end walls; 5 chloroplasts making 2 to 5 turns.

Conjugation scalariform ; tubes formed by both gametangia ; fertile cells cylindric or slightly enlarged ; zygospores ellipsoid to ovoid, 105-120 × 168-200 $\mu$ ; median spore wall dark brown, distinctly verrucose.

*Distribution* :   Hangchow, China.

**97. Spirogyra chakiense** KOLKWITZ & KRIEGER 1944.   Rabenhorst's *Krypto-*

*gamenflora,* **13,** p. 390. (=*S. verruculosa* var. *chakianse* Rao 1937. *J. Indian Bot. Soc.* **5,** p. 283, Fig. 6.e).

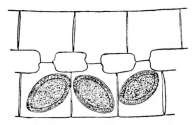

Fig. 338. *S. chakiense.* (after Rao.)

Vegetative cells 93-104 × 80-116 $\mu$ ; end walls plane ; chloroplasts 4-8.

Conjugation scalariform ; fructifying cells unswollen; zygospores ellipsoidal with more or less rounded ends, 50-66 × 73-122 $\mu$ ; exospore thin, smooth ; mesospore thick, yellowish-brown and verrucose ; endospore indistinct.

*Distribution* :

*India* :   Found in a pond, Chakia, Banaras, U.P., along with sterile species of *Bulbochaete* and *Spirogyra.*

**98.   Spirogyra malmeana** HIRN 1896. Wittrock and Nordstedt *Algae Exisccatae,* No. 1375.

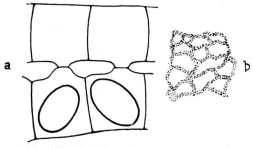

Fig. 339. a-b. *S. malmeana.* (after Borge.)

Vegetative cells 76-91 $\mu$ broad with plane end walls ; 3 to 4 chloroplasts making 4 turns.

Conjugation scalariform; tubes formed by both gametangia; fertile cells cylindric; zygospores ellipsoid, 65-83 × 75-100 $\mu$ ; median spore wall yellow-brown, irregularly reticulate.

*Distribution* :   Mato Grosso, Brazil.

**99.   Spirogyra anomala** RAO 1937. *J. Indian Bot. Soc.* **16,** p. 285.

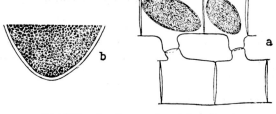

Fig. 340. a-b. *S. anomala.* (after Rao.)

Vegetative cells 108-125 × 72-165 $\mu$, with plane end walls ; chloroplasts 5 to 10.

Conjugation scalariform ; tubes formed by both gametangia ; fertile cells cylindric ; zygospores ellipsoid, more or less pointed, 73-90 × 108-138 (–165) $\mu$ ; median wall thick, brown, and finely reticulate.

*Distribution* :

*India* : Sarnath, U.P.

**100. Spirogyra trachycarpa** SKUJA 1932. *Acta Horti. Bot. Univ. Latviensis.* **7,** p. 63, Fig. 82.

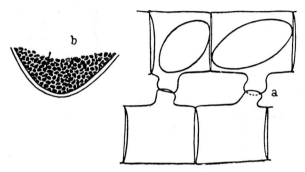

FIG. 341. a-b. *S. trachycarpa*. (after Rao.)

Vegetative cells 110-123 × 110-500 $\mu$, with plane end walls; chloroplasts 4 to 6 (8) making 1 to 2.5 turns.

Conjugation scalariform ; tubes formed by both gametangia ; fertile cells inflated on the inner side ; male gametangia 87-176 $\mu$ long, female 119-252 $\mu$ ; zygospores broadly ellipsoid, 87-108 × 117-172 (−204) $\mu$ ; median spore wall thick, irregularly scrobiculate, colour not given ; outer spore wall thick, hyaline.

*Distribution* : Latvia.

**101. Spirogyra punctulata** JAO 1936. *Amer. Jour. Bot.* **23,** p. 57, Figs. 13-14 ; Transeau, 1951, p. 187, Pl. XXX, Figs. 11-13.

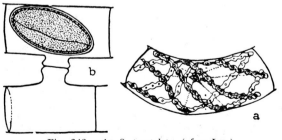

FIG. 342. a-b. *S. punctulata*. (after Jao.)

Vegetative cells 70-83 × 105-315 $\mu$ ; end walls plane ; filaments usually curved ; chloroplasts 3 to 7, making 0.5 to 1.5 turns.

Conjugation scalariform ; tubes formed by both gametangia ; fertile cells cylindric ; zygospores ellipsoid with pointed ends, 64-74 × 83-179 $\mu$ ; median spore wall thick, finely punctate, and yellow at maturity.

*Distribution* :

*India* :  In a puddle at Kowada, Bombay.

*Other countries* :  Poatin, China.

**102.  Spirogyra kundaensis** SINGH 1938.  *J. Indian Bot. Soc.* **17,**  p. 380-2 Fig. 5, A & B.

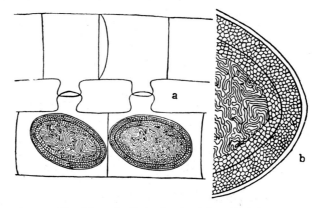

Fig. 343. a-b. *S. kundaensis*. (after Singh.)

Vegetative cells cylindrical, 105-120 × 150-180 $\mu$ ; end walls plane ; 4-5 chloroplasts.

Conjugation scalariform ; fructifying cells unswollen ; zygospores ellipsoidal with rounded ends, 75-90 × 105-135 $\mu$ ; exospore thin, smooth and hyaline ; mesospore thick, brown and reticulate, reticulations irregularly crenulate to dentate ; endospore indistinct.

*Distribution* :

*India* :  Kunda Ghat, Gorakhpore, U.P., (October 19, 1936).

**103. Spirogyra ghosei** SINGH 1938.  *J. Indian Bot. Soc.* **17,** p. 382, Fig. 5, C. & D.

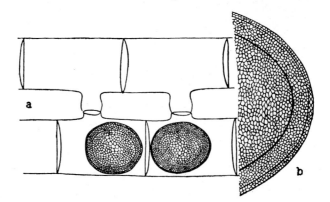

Fig. 344. a-b. *S. ghosei*. (after Singh.)

Vegetative cells cylindrical, longer than broad, 100-105 × 225-390 $\mu$ ; end walls plane ; 6 to 7 chloroplasts.

Conjugation scalariform; fructifying cells unswollen ; conjugation canal 45-60 $\mu$ broad. Zygospores ovoid with rounded ends, 90-102.5 × 105-120 $\mu$ ; exospore thin, reticulate ; mesospore thick and brown and reticulate ; both showing a close net-work ; reticulations thick and regular ; endospore indistinct.

*Distribution* :

*India* : Free-floating in a puddle along with sterile filaments of *Oedogonium*. Gorakhpur, U.P. (November 8, 1937).

**104.    Spirogyra crassa** KUTZING 1843. *Phycologia Generalis*, p. 280, Pl. 14, Fig. 4.

Fig. 345. *S. crassa*. (after Petit.)

Vegetative cells 108-118 $\mu$ thick, 1-2 times as long, squarish in shape. Chloroplasts 6-10 in number each with a half spiral, bearing numerous big pyrenoids.

Conjugation scalariform, fruiting cells not swollen. Zygospores brownish, oval to rounded in shape with smooth mesospore. Zygospores 90-110 $\mu$ in diameter, 1-1½ times as long. The alga is slightly smaller than *S. crassa* Kütz. where the zygospores are 144 $\mu$ thick, but in other respects resembles the type.

*Distribution* :

*India* : Free-floating along with *Oedogonium rivulare* in Shahniwala tank, Dasuya, district Hoshiarpore, in the second week of December 1929. A rather rare form.

*Other countries* : United States of America; Europe; Australia and South Africa.

**105.    Spirogyra sinensis** LI 1933. *Ohio Jour. Sci.* **33,** p. 153, Pl. 1, Figs. 7-8.

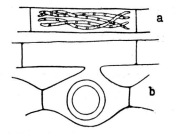

Fig. 346. a-b. *S. sinensis*. a, vegetative cell;
b, scalariform conjugation. (after Li.)

Vegetative cells 22-24 × 115-136 $\mu$, with plane end walls ; 2 to 4 chloroplasts, making 2.5 to 4.5 turns.

Conjugation scalariform ; tubes formed by both gametangia ; fertile cells inflated toward the middle to about 50 $\mu$ ; zygospores lenticular, 38-45 $\mu$ in diameter ; median spore wall smooth, brown.

*Distribution* :    Hangchow, China.

**106.   Spirogyra subpellucida** Jao 1939.   *Sinensia*.   **10.**   p. 157.

Fig. 347. *S. subpellucida*. (after Jao.)

Vegetative cells 40-45 × 62-225 $\mu$, with plane end walls ; chloroplasts 4 to 7, making 0.5 to 1.5 turns in the cell.

Conjugation scalariform ; tubes formed by both gametangia ; receptive gametangia inflated on the outer side only (up to 55-75 $\mu$) ; zygospores lenticular, 55-62 × 40-42 $\mu$ ; median spore wall smooth, yellow-brown at maturity.

*Distribution* :    China.

**107.   Spirogyra majuscula** Kutzing 1849.   *Species Algarum*, p. 441 ; Transeau, 1951, p. 190-1, Pl. XXXI, Figs. 14-15.

Fig. 348. a-b. *S. majuscula*. (after Czurda.)

Vegetative cells 50-80 × 80-500 $\mu$ ; end walls plane ; chloroplasts (3–)5 to 8, straight or making 0.3 turn.

Conjugation scalariform and lateral ; tubes formed by both gametangia ; fertile cells shortened, cylindric or slightly inflated ; zygospores lenticular, 57-62 × 45-60 $\mu$ ; median spore wall brown, smooth ; aplanospores similar but smaller.

*Distribution* :

*India* :    In a puddle at Kolwada, Bombay.

*Other countries* :    China; Brazil; Europe; Uruguay; South Africa; United States of America.

**108. Spirogyra submaxima** Transeau 1914. *Amer. Jour. Bot.* **1,** p. 295, Pl. 27, Figs. 3-4.

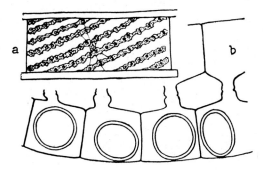

Fig. 349. a-b. *S. submaxima.* (after Transeau.)

Vegetative cells 70-110 × 100-300 $\mu$, with plane end walls ; 8 to 9 chloroplasts making 0.1 to 1 turn.

Conjugation scalariform ; tubes formed by both gametangia ; fertile cells cylindric, enlarged, or slightly inflated ; zygospores lenticular, 70-110 × 50-75 $\mu$ ; median spore wall brown, smooth.

*Distribution* :

*India* : Widely distributed.

*Other countries* : China and U.S.A.

**109. Spirogyra lamellata** (Rao) Kolkwitz & Krieger 1944. Rabenhorst's *Kryptogammenflora,* **13,** p. 412, Fig. 636. ( =*S. submaxima* var. *lamellata* Rao 1938).

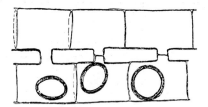

Fig. 350. *S. lamellata.* (after Rao.)

Vegetative cells with plane end walls, 70-72 × 75-80 $\mu$ ; 6 chloroplasts.

Conjugation scalariform ; conjugation canal built by both gametangia ; receptive gametangia cylindrical. Zygospores globose, 70-72 $\mu$ in diameter ; median wall thick, yellowish-brown, smooth.

*Distribution* :

*India* : In a puddle on the Hoshangabad rock-quarry, M.P. ; in a puddle at Ghatkopar, Bombay.

**110. Spirogyra randhawae** Kolkwitz & Krieger 1944. Rabenhorst's

*Kryptogamenflora.* **13,** p. 418, Fig. 650.    ( = *S. submaxima* var. *inflata* Randhawa 1938. *Proc. Indian Acad. Sci.* **8,** p. 361 fig. 56.)

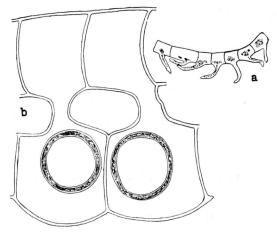

Fig. 351. a-b. *S. randhawae.* (after Randhawa.)

Vegetative cells 80-90 $\times$ 100-210 $\mu$ ; end walls plane ; chloroplasts 6-8.

Conjugation scalariform ; fertile cells are inflated on both sides ; conjugation canal built by both gametangia. In some cases the conjugation canals are lengthened into rhizoidal structures. Zygospores spherical, 70-75 $\mu$ ; exospore thin, smooth and colourless ; mesospore thick, smooth and brown.

*Distribution* :

*India* : Found free-floating in a fresh-water stream near Gonda—Balrampur Road, U.P., on 6th March 1938.

**111. Spirogyra sphaerocarpa** JAO 1939. *Sinensia.* **10,** p. 156.

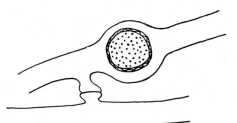

Fig. 352. *S. sphaerocarpa.* (after Jao.)

Vegetative cells 32-40 $\times$ 87-459 $\mu$, with plane end walls ; chloroplasts 4 or 5, making 0·5 to 1 turn in the cell.

Conjugation scalariform ; tubes formed by both gametangia ; receptive gametangia inflated towards the middle up to 75-87 $\mu$; zygospores lenticular, 62-75 $\times$ 37-57 $\mu$ ; median spore wall densely punctate, yellow-brown at maturity.

*Distribution* : China.

**112.   Spirogyra bellis** (HASSALL) CLEVE 1868.   *Nova Acta Reg. Soc. Sci. Upsali.*
*Ser.* 3, **6,** p. 18, Pl. 3, Figs. 2-5.

Fig. 353. *S. bellis.* (after Randhawa.)

Vegetative cells 60-65 $\mu$ broad, $1\frac{1}{2}$ times as long as broad, with plane septa.
Each cell with 5-7 chloroplasts closely packed.

Conjugation scalariform.   Zygospores oval or rounded in shape, 54-64 $\mu$ in
diameter, 80-85 $\mu$ long.   Mesospore   smooth,   thick,   brownish-yellow in colour.
Fruiting cells strongly swollen on both the sides.   This alga closely resembles *S. bellis*
Cleve in its dimensions but the mesospore is smooth in this case.

*Distribution* :

*India* :   Free-floating in a pond near V. Bodal, district Hoshiarpore, Punjab,
in the second week of March 1930.

*Other countries* :   Australia; Europe ; United States of America and South Africa.

**113.   Spirogyra oblata** JAO 1936.   *Amer. Jour. Bot.* **23,** p. 58, Figs. 29-31.

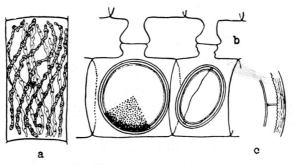

Fig. 354. a-c. *S. oblata.* (after Jao.)

Vegetative cells 96-118 $\times$ 80-256 $\mu$, with plane end walls ; 9 to 13 chloroplasts,
nearly straight, or making up to $0 \cdot 6$ turn.

Conjugation scalariform ;   tubes   formed   by   both   gametangia ;   fertile   cells
shortened, cylindric ; zygospores lenticular, 93-106 $\times$ 64-70 $\mu$ ; outer wall thick, smooth,
and lamellate ; median spore wall yellow-brown, verrucose.

*Distribution* :   China.

**114.   Spirogyra manoramae** RANDHAWA 1938.   *Proc. Indian Acad. Sci.* **8,**
p. 360.

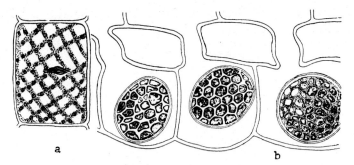

Fig. 355. a-b. *S. manoramae.* (after Randhawa.)

Vegetative cells 80-100 $\mu$ broad and 30-115 $\mu$ long, with thick walls sometimes as thick as 6 $\mu$.    Each cell contains 7-10 chloroplasts, each with a single turn and bearing numerous pyrenoids on its surface. The nucleus is lens-shaped. Septa plane.

Conjugation scalariform.    Zygospores oval to rounded in shape, lying loosely in the female cells which are inflated on outside.    Zygospore wall 5 $\mu$ thick, and is composed of two layers, a thin smooth exospore, and a thick yellowish-brown mesospore with polygonal reticulations.    Zygospores are 65-82 $\mu$ in diameter.

*Distribution* :

*India* : Free-floating in Manorama Nadi, a fresh-water stream in district Basti, U.P., on 23rd February 1937.

**115.  Spirogyra maxima** (HASSALL) WITTROCK 1882.  *Bot. Notiser.* p. 57.

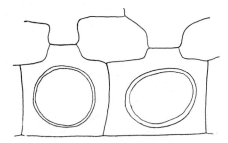

Fig. 356. *S. maxima.* (after Borge.)

Vegetative cells 118-140 × 100-250 $\mu$, with plane end walls ; 6 to 7 chloroplasts, making  0·2 to 0·8 turn.

Conjugation scalariform ; tubes formed by  both gametangia ; fertile  cells cylindric ; zygospores lenticular, 100-125 × 75-95 $\mu$ ; median  spore wall golden brown, reticulate.

*Distribution* :

*India* :  Widely distributed.

*Other countries* :  Australia; China; Europe; South America; U.S.A.,

Wests (West, W & West, G.S. 1907) say a  smaller  sterile species,  probably

*S. maxima* was observed from Vizagapatam, but this is doubtful.

**116. Spirogyra liana** Transeau 1934. *Trans. Amer. Micros. Soc.* **53**, p. 228.

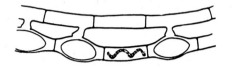

Fig. 357. *S. liana.* (after Jao.)

Vegetative cells 11-16 × 75-160 $\mu$, with plane end walls ; 1 chloroplast making 2 to 6 turns.

Conjugation scalariform and lateral ; tubes formed wholly by the male gametangia ; inflated single or paired fertile cells usually separated by 1 to 2 non-conjugating cells ; zygospores ellipsoid, 23-30 × 35-50 $\mu$ ; median spore wall yellow, smooth.

*Distribution* : Szechwan and Kiangsi, China; Sweden.

**117. Spirogyra reticuliana** Randhawa 1938. *Proc. Indian Acad. Sci.* **8**, p. 339, Fig. 33.

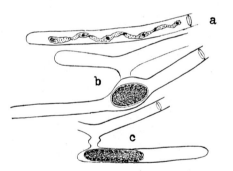

Fig. 358. a-c. *S. reticuliana.* a, vegetative cell; b,c, scalariform conjugation. (after Randhawa.)

Vegetative cells 14-16 × 140-160 $\mu$ ; end walls plane ; chloroplast 1, making 2-4 turns.

Conjugation scalariform ; conjugation canal formed by male gametangia alone; zygospores 23-26 × 40-45 $\mu$ ; exospore light-blue ; mesospore thick, brownish with foveolate reticulations.

*Distribution* :

*India* : Found in a stagnant drainage channel near V. Mamrezpur tehsil Tanda, district Fyzabad, U.P., in the middle of January 1937.

**118. Spirogyra punctata** Cleve 1868. *Nova Acta Reg. Soc. Sci. Upsali.* Ser. 3, **6**, p. 23, Pl. 4, Figs. 1-4.

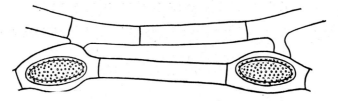

Fig. 359. *S. punctata*. (after Petit.)

Vegetative cells 24-30 × 70-360 μ, with plane end walls ; 1 chloroplast making 3 to 8 turns in the cell.

Conjugation lateral and scalariform ; tubes formed by the male gametangia ; gametangia single, or in pairs, separated by much longer sterile cells in each filament ; fertile gametangia inflated to 45 μ ; zygospores ellipsoid, 28-43 × 42-78 μ ; median spore wall coarsely punctate, yellow.

*Distribution* :   Afghanistan ; Australia ; China ; Europe and U.S.A.

**119. Spirogyra punctiformis** Transeau 1914. *Amer. Jour. Bot.* **1,** p. 294 ; Transeau, 1951, p. 200, Pl. XXXIV, Figs. 5-6.

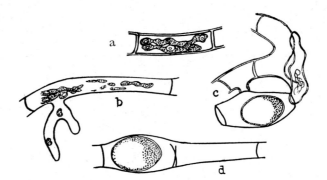

Fig. 360. a-d. *S. punctiformis*. a-b, vegetative cells, b, with a rhizoid; c, scalariform conjugation; d, azygospore. (after Mehra.)

Vegetative cells 27-30 × 120-390 μ ; end walls plane ; chloroplast 1 or 2, making 3 to 6 turns.

Conjugation scalariform ; conjugating tubes usually produced by the male gametangia ; fertile cells in pairs or singly between vegetative cells, inflated to 45-50 μ ; zygospores ovoid, 40-48 × 60-110 μ ; median spore wall yellow, punctate.

*Distribution* :

*India* :   In a puddle at Goregaon, Bombay ; Water Works drains, Assam.

*Other countries* :   United States of America.

**120. Spirogyra micropunctata** Transeau 1915. *Ohio. Jour. Sci.* **16,** p. 27 ; Transeau, 1951, p. 200-1, Pl. XXXIV, Fig. 9.

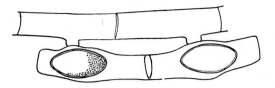

Fig. 361. *S. micropunctata.* (after Mehra.)

Vegetative cells 30-36 × 120-300 $\mu$; end walls plane; chloroplast 1, making 3 to 7 turns.

Conjugation scalariform; conjugating tubes formed almost wholly by the male gametangia; fertile cells in groups of 2 or 4, rarely continuous, inflated on the inner side to 50 $\mu$; zygospores ellipsoid, 37-42 × 57-100 $\mu$; median spore wall yellow, minutely punctate.

*Distribution:*

*India:* In a stream at Borivli, Bombay.

*Other countries:* United States of America.

**121. Spirogyra suomiana** Transeau 1934. *Ohio Jour. Sci.* **34,** p. 420. Hirn, Karl E. *Acta Soc. pro Fauna et Flora Fennica.* **11,** (10), p. 10, Pl. 1, Fig. 3. 1895. (=*S. scrobiculata* var. *inflata* Rao).

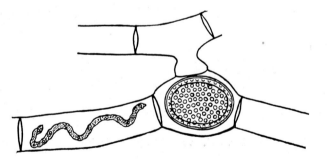

Fig. 362. *S. suomiana.* (after Hirn.)

Vegetative cells 33-40 × 100-240 $\mu$, with plane end walls; 1 chloroplast, making several turns in the cell.

Conjugation scalariform; tubes formed by the male gametangia; receptive gametangia inflated to 58-73 $\mu$; gametangia separated by much longer sterile cells; zygospores ovoid, 45-53 × 75-90 $\mu$; median wall golden yellow, coarsely punctate.

*Distribution:*

*India:* Rain-water pools, Katni.

*Other countries:* Tsingtao, Manchuria; China; Finnish Lapland.

**122. Spirogyra corrugata** Transeau 1934. *Trans. Amer. Micros. Soc.* **53,** p. 229.

Fig. 363. *S. corrugata.* (after Jao.)

Vegetative cells (30-) 32-36 (-40) × 140-280 (-400) $\mu$ ; with plane end walls ; 1 to 3 chloroplasts, making 2 to 4 turns.

Conjugation scalariform ; tubes formed by the male gametangia, usually long and broad; fertile cells solitary or in pairs (rarely in series) between vegetative cells, shortened and inflated to 40-60 $\mu$ ; zygospores ovoid, 42-60 × 80-120 $\mu$ ; median spore wall of 2 layers, outer thin, coarsely and irregularly corrugate ;  inner yellow or brownish-yellow, finely reticulate.

*Distribution* :   Szechwan, China ; U.S.A.

**123. Spirogyra crenulata** SINGH 1938.   *J. Indian Bot. Soc.* **17**, p. 378, Fig. 4, A & B

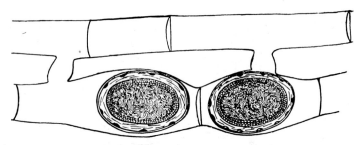

Fig. 364. *S. crenulata.* (after Singh.)

Vegetative cells cylindrical, seven to eight times as long as broad, 29-6-36.3 × 158-330 $\mu$ ; end walls plane ; chloroplasts two.

Conjugation scalariform, conjugation tubes formed wholly by the male gametangia ; fructifying cells swollen, nearly forming quadrangles.  Zygospores obovoid 52.8-60 × 67.5-93.3 $\mu$ ;  spore wall of five layers ; outer exospore thin and hyaline ;  inner exospore colourless, more or less lamellose, and upto 3.5 $\mu$ thick ; outer mesospore thin, yellow and a little wrinkled ;  inner mesospore yellowish-brown and reticulate, reticulations thick and irregularly crenulate to dentate ; endospore thin and distinct.

*Distribution* :

*India* :  Gorakhpur, U.P. (October, 15, 1936).

**124. Spirogyra rugulosa** IWANOFF 1902. From *Bot. Zentralbl.* **93**, p. 383. 1903. Teodoresco.  *Beih. Bot. Zent.* **21**, p. 192, Figs. 81-87. 1907.

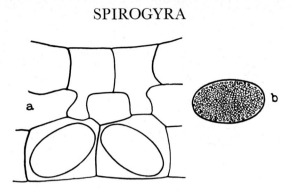

Fig. 365. a-b. *S. rugulosa*. (a, after Iwanoff ; b, after Teoderesco.)

Vegetative cells 47-57 × 100-350 $\mu$, with plane end walls ; 1 chloroplast, making 3 to 11 turns.

Conjugation scalariform; tubes formed by male gametangia; fertile cells shortened, inflated on the conjugating side ; zygospores ellipsoid or ovoid, 45-52 × 102-127 $\mu$ ; median spore wall yellow-brown, finely punctate.

*Distribution* :  China ; U.S.A. ; Russia ; Rumania.

**125. Spirogyra tandae** RANDHAWA 1938. *Proc. India Acad. Sci*, **8**, p. 350, Fig. 44.

Fig. 366. *S. tandae*. (after Randhawa.)

Vegetative cells 16-19 $\mu$ broad, 6-9 times as long, each cell containing a single spiral chloroplast with 3-6 turns, septa replicate.

Conjugation scalariform only. Conjugation canals very short and broad. Female cell cylindrically inflated. Zygospore oval to ellipsoid in shape, 25-32 $\mu$ broad and 56-62 $\mu$ long. Zygospore wall is composed of two layers only, a thin and smooth exospore, and a thick mesospore with foveolate reticulations.

*Distribution* :

*India* :  Free-floating in a fresh-water stream near Tanda, district Fyzabad, U.P., on 8th February 1937.

**126. Spirogyra undulisepta** RANDHAWA 1938. *Proc. Indian Acad. Sci.* **8**, p. 352, Fig. 46.

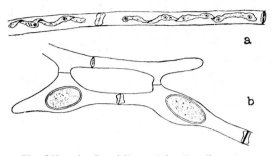

Fig. 367. a-b. *S. undulisepta*. (after Randhawa.)

Vegetative cells are 13-18 $\mu$ broad, and 8-12 times as long, each containing a single irregularly spiral chloroplast bearing 3-8 pyrenoids. The septa are peculiarly replicate and look like a parallelogram with the middle lamella as a diagonal, and the longer sides undulating in a wave-like manner.

Conjugation scalariform. The female cells are inflated on both sides with the zygospore lying loosely in the middle. Zygospores are ellipsoid 20-22 $\mu$ broad and 40-50 $\mu$ long. The spore-wall bears reticulations on its surface, and is composed of two layers, a thin, smooth and hyaline exospore, and a comparatively thicker yellowish-brown mesospore.

*Distribution* :

*India* : Collected from a jhil near Tanda, district Fyzabad, U.P., mixed with a species of *Oedogonium* on 8th February 1937.

**127. Spirogyra dentireticulata** Jao 1935. *Sinensia*. **6**, p. 611, Pl. 10, Figs. 114-15.

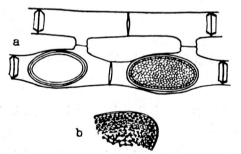

Fig. 368. a-b. *S. dentireticulata*. (after Jao.)

Vegetative cells 18-26 × 118-250 $\mu$, with replicate end walls ; 1 chloroplast making 2 to 7 turns.

Conjugation scalariform; tubes formed by both gametangia; zygospores ellipsoid, 29-41 × 42-80 $\mu$ ; median spore wall reticulate, with minute spines at the intersections of the network, yellow at maturity.

*Distribution* : Szechwan, China ; U.S.A.

**128. Spirogyra arta** Jao 1935. *Sinensia*. **6**, p. 602, Pl. 8, Fig. 93.

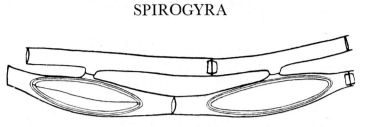

Fig. 369. *S. arta.* (after Jao.)

Vegetative cells 16-18 × 105-350 $\mu$, with replicate end walls ; 1 chloroplast, making 3-8 turns in the cell.

Conjugation scalariform; tubes formed by both gametangia; fertile cells enlarged, rarely inflated, zygospores ellipsoid to cylindric-ellipsoid, 22-26 (-32) × 51-103 $\mu$; median spore wall yellow smooth.

*Distribution* :

*India* : Bombay.

*Other countries* : Szechwan, China.

**129. Spirogyra spreeiana** Rabenhorst's 1863. *Die Algen Sachsens* No. 988. (*S. spreeiana* var. *kashiensis* Venkataraman ; *S. spreeiana* var. *crassa* Rao).

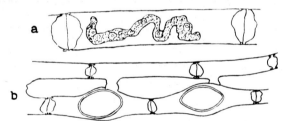

Fig. 370. a-b. *S. spreeiana.* (after Mehra.)

Vegetative cells 18-24 × 240-600 $\mu$, with replicate end walls; 1 chloroplast, making 1.5 to 4 turns.

Conjugation scalariform and lateral; tubes formed mostly by the male gametangia; fertile cells not shortened, enlarged and inflated toward the middle to 30-42 $\mu$; zygospores and aplanospores ellipsoid, 30-36 × 55-100 $\mu$; median spore wall yellow smooth.

*Distribution* :

*India* : Widely distributed.

*Other countries* : Europe ; Germany ; Finland ; Rumania ; South Africa ; U.S.A.

**130. Spirogyra tumida** Jao 1935. *Sinensia.* **6**, p. 602, Pl. 9, Fig. 96, Transeau, 1951, p. 201, Pl. XXXVII, Fig. 8.

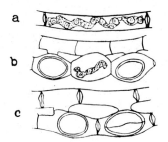

Fig. 371. a-c. *S. tumida.* (after Mehra.)

Vegetative cells 16-19 × 85-175 $\mu$; end walls replicate, chloroplast 1, making 2 to 9 turns.

Conjugation scalariform ; tubes formed by both gametangia ; sterile cells more or less cylindrically inflated up to 45 $\mu$ ; fertile cells enlarged ; zygospores ellipsoid, 25-35 × 48-86 $\mu$ ; median wall smooth, yellow at maturity.

*Distribution* :

*India* :   In  a  puddle  at  Goregaon,  Bombay.

*Other countries* :   Szechwan,  China.

**131.   Spirogyra lamellosa** Jao 1935.   *Sinensia.* **6**, p. 605, Pl. 9, Fig. 99.

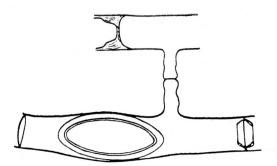

Fig. 372. *S. lamellosa.* (after Jao.)

Vegetative cells 29-32 × 188-280 $\mu$, with replicate end walls ; 1 chloroplast, making 4 to 6 turns in the cell.

Conjugation scalariform ; tubes narrow and long (32-96$\mu$), formed by both gametangia ; fertile cells cylindric or enlarged ; zygospores ellipsoid  to cylindric-ellipsoid, 32-42 × 80-102 $\mu$ ; outer wall colourless, lamellate, 3-4 $\mu$ in thickness ; median wall smooth,  yellow  at  maturity.

*Distribution* :   Szechwan,  China.

**132.   Spirogyra laxa** Kützing 1849.   *Species Algarum*, p. 438.   *Tabulae phycologicae.* **5**, pl. 30. Fig. 5.

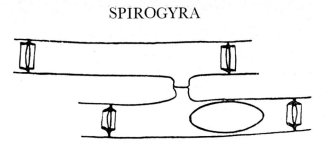

Fig. 373. *S. laxa*. (after Petit.)

Vegetative cells 30-36 × 120-320 $\mu$, with replicate end walls ; 1 chloroplast, making 3 to 5 turns.

Conjugation lateral and scalariform ; tubes formed by both gametangia ; fertile cells cylindric ; zygospores ellipsoid, with more or less pointed ends, 30-33 × 60-82$\mu$ ; median spore wall yellow and smooth.

*Distribution* :   Europe; Nova Scotia ; U.S.A.

**133. Spirogyra microgranulata** JAO 1935. *Sinensia*. **6,** p. 612, Pl. 10, Figs. 112-13.

Fig. 374. a-b. *S. microgranulata*. (after Jao.)

Vegetative cells 16-19 × 154-420 $\mu$, with replicate end walls ; 1 chloroplast, making 4.5 to 8 turns in the cell.

Conjugation scalariform ; tubes formed by both gametangia ; receptive gametangia enlarged ; zygospores ovoid, 24-26 × 51-77 $\mu$, with a double colourless outer wall, of which the inner layer is wrinkled ; median wall granulate to verrucose, yellow-brown at maturity.

*Distribution* :   Szechwan, China.

**134. Spirogyra weberi** KÜTZING 1843. *Phycologia Generalis*, p. 279. (*S. weberi* forma Rao ; *S. weberi* forma Singh).

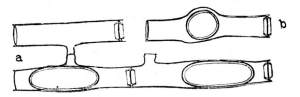

Fig. 375. a-b. *S. weberi*. a, scalariform conjugation; b, lateral
conjugation; (after Jao.)

Vegetative cells 19-30 × 80-480 $\mu$, with replicate end walls ; 1 chloroplast, making 3 to 6·5 turns ; fertile cells usually slightly enlarged.

Conjugation scalariform ; tubes formed by both cells ; zygospores ovoid to cylindric ovoid, 21-30 × 30-96 $\mu$ ; median spore wall yellow, smooth ; aplanospores similar.

*Distribution* :

*India* :   Rain-water puddles, U.P.

*Other countries* :   China; Europe; Java and U.S.A.

**135. Spirogyra semiornata** JAO 1935.   *Sinensia*.   **6,** p.   604,   Pl.   9, Figs.   97-98.

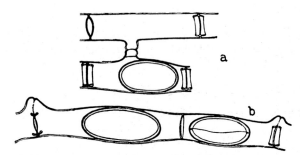

Fig. 376. a-b. *S. semiornata*. a, scalariform conjugation; b, lateral conjugation; (after Jao.)

Vegetative cells 27-32 × 96-245 $\mu$, with replicate end walls ; 1 chloroplast making 2 to 6 turns in the cell.

Reproduction usually by zygospores, rarely by aplanospores ; conjugation lateral and scalariform ; tubes formed by both gametangia ; fertile cells enlarged ; zygospores ovoid, 35-46 × 61-106 $\mu$ ; aplanospores subglobose to ovoid, 32-38 × 35-51 $\mu$ ; median spore wall yellow-brown, smooth.

*Distribution* :   Szechwan, China.

**136. Spirogyra cleveana** TRANSEAU 1934.   *Trans. Amer. Micros. Soc.* 53, p. 226. Jao. *Sinensia.* **6,** p. 614, Pl. 11, Fig. 120.

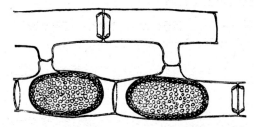

Fig. 377. *S. cleveana*. (after Jao.)

Vegetative cells 34-40 × 140-465 $\mu$, with replicate end walls ; 1 rarely 2, chloroplasts, making 3 to 6 turns in the cell.

Conjugation scalariform ; tubes formed by both gametangia ; sterile cells often greatly inflated ; fertile cells cylindric or enlarged ; zygospores ovoid to cylindric-ovoid, 34-50 × 70-125 $\mu$ ; outer spore wall  hyaline, of 2 layers, of which the inner is thick and coarsely scrobiculate ; median spore wall smooth, yellow.

*Distribution* :  Szechwan, China ; U.S.A.

**137.  Spirogyra denticulata** Transeau 1934.    *Trans. Amer. Micros. Soc.* **53,** p. 226.

Fig. 378. *S. denticulata.* (after Mehra.)

Vegetative cells 42-56 × 160-400 $\mu$ ; end walls replicate ; chloroplast 1, rarely 2, making 3 to 6 turns.

Conjugation scalariform ; tubes formed by both gametangia ; fertile cells cylindric or enlarged ; sterile cells sometimes inflated ;  zygospores ovoid, 45-60 × 76-130 $\mu$ ; outer spore wall hyaline of 2 layers ; the outer thin, smooth ; the inner thick, scrobiculate ; median spore wall yellow, smooth.

*Distribution* :

*India* :  In a pool at Andheri, Bombay.

*Other countries* :  United States of America.

**138.  Spirogyra tenuissima** (Hassall) Kützing 1849.    *Species    Algarum,* p. 437.

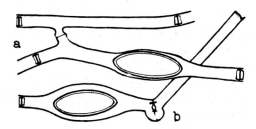

Fig. 379. a-b. *S. tenuissima.* a, scalariform conjugation; b, lateral conjugation. (after Jao.)

Vegetative cells 8-13 × 40-250 $\mu$, with replicate end walls; 1 chloroplast, making 3 to 6 turns.

Conjugation lateral and scalariform ; tubes formed by both cells ; fertile cells greatly inflated or enlarged towards the middle; zygospores and aplanospores ellipsoid, 25-32 × 40-70 $\mu$ ; median spore wall yellow, smooth.

*Distribution* :   Africa;  Asia;  Australia;  Canada;  Europe;   New Zealand; South America   and U.S.A.

**139.  Spirogyra inflata** (Vaucher) Kützing 1843. *Phycologia   Generalis,* p. 279.

Fig. 380. *S. inflata*. (after Jao.)

Vegetative cells 15-20 × 45-230 $\mu$, with replicate end walls ; 1 chloroplast, making 2.5 to 6 turns.

Conjugation lateral and scalariform ; tubes formed by both gametangia ; fertile cells inflated to 35-48 $\mu$ ; zygospores and aplanospores ellipsoid, 27-36 × 50-76 $\mu$ ; median spore wall yellow, smooth.

*Distribution* :   Asia ; Africa ; Europe ; Southern and eastern Canada ; U.S.A.

**140.  Spirogyra kuusamoensis** Hirn 1895.   *Acta Soc. pro Fauna et Flora Fennica*. **11,** p. 11, Fig. 4.

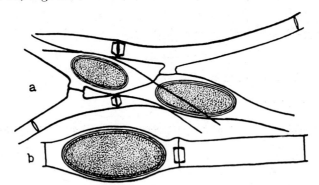

Fig. 381. a-b. *S. kuusamoensis*. (a, after Hirn; b, after Kolkwitz & Krieger.)

Vegetative cells 13-17 × 90-135 $\mu$, with replicate end walls ; 1 chloroplast.

Conjugation lateral and scalariform ; tubes formed by both gametangia ; fertile cells greatly enlarged towards the middle; zygospores ellipsoid, 23-33 × 45-75 $\mu$; median spore wall yellow, finely punctate.

*Distribution* :

*India* :   Bombay.

*Other countries* :   Finland.

**141.  Spirogyra farlowii** Transeau 1915.   *Ohio Jour. Sci.* **16,** p. 29. Phycoth. Bor.-Amer., No. 362.   (=*S. weberi* forma *inflata* Rao).

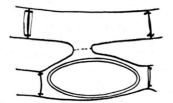

Fig. 382. *S. farlowii*. (after Wang.)

Vegetative cells 24-30 × 70-400 $\mu$, with replicate end walls; 1 chloroplast, making 2·5 to 6 turns.

Conjugation scalariform and lateral; tubes formed by both cells; fertile cells inflated to 39-60 $\mu$; zygospores and aplanospores ellipsoid, ends more or less pointed, 32-45 × 48-96 $\mu$; median spore wall yellow, smooth.

*Distribution*:

*India*: Rain-water pools, U.P.

*Other countries*: China and U.S.A.

**142. Spirogyra nyctigama** TRANSEAU 1938. *Amer. Jour. Bot.* **25**, p. 525, Fig. 11; Transeau, 1951, p. 205, Pl. XXXV, Fig. 18.

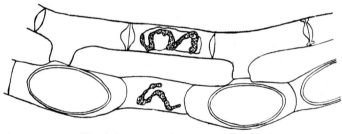

Fig. 383. *S. nyctigama.* (after Mehra.)

Vegetative cells 34-38 × 72-180 $\mu$; end walls replicate; chloroplast 1, making 2 to 5 turns.

Conjugation scalariform; tubes formed by both gametangia; receptive gametangia inflated to 65 $\mu$; zygospores ellipsoid, 45-54 × 80-98 $\mu$; median spore wall yellow-brown, smooth.

*Distribution*:

*India*: In a puddle near Parel, Bombay.

*Other countries*: Cape Town, South Africa.

**143. Spirogyra grevilleana** (HASSALL) KÜTZING 1849. *Species Algarum*, p. 438; Transeau, 1951, p. 205-6, Pl. XXXV, Figs. 19-20. ( =*S. chuniae* forma Rao).

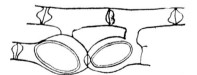

Fig. 384. *S. grevilleana.* (after Mehra.)

Vegetative cells 22-33 × 60-325 $\mu$; end wall replicate; chloroplast 1, in some cells 2, making 4 to 8 turns.

Conjugation scalariform and lateral; tubes formed largely by the male gametangia; fertile cells fusiform inflated to 36-43 $\mu$; zygospores ovoid, 30-37 × 60-90$\mu$; median spore wall yellow, smooth.

*Distribution* :

*India* :  In a stream at Dahisar, Bombay,.

*Other countries* :  Australia; China; Europe; United States of America.

**144. Spirogyra goetzei** SCHMIDLE 1902.  Engler's *Bot. Jahrb.* **30,** p. 251, Pl. 4, Fig. 8.

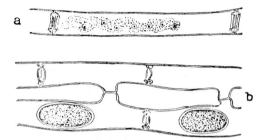

Fig. 385. a-b. *S. goetzei.* a, vegetative cell; b, scalariform
conjugation. (after Randhawa.)

Vegetative cells are 22-24 $\mu$ broad and 5-7 times as long ; each cell has a single spiral chloroplast bearing numerous conspicuous pyrenoids on it.  Septa of the walls are replicate.

Conjugation scalariform.  Female cells containing zygospores are slightly swollen. Zygospores are more or less oval in shape.  The zygospore wall is composed of two layers only, a thin hyaline exospore, and a brownish mesospore.  The zygospores are 24-28 $\mu$ broad and 50-56 $\mu$ long.

*Distribution* :

*India* :  Found mixed with *Zygnema giganteum*, *Z. coeruleum* and *Spirogyra parvula* in Siah Baeen, a fresh-water stream in district Jullundur, Punjab, during the second week of March 1931.

*Other countries* :  South Africa.

*The Indian form differs from the type in the absence of punctation of the mesospore.*

**145. Spirogyra lambertiana** TRANSEAU 1934.  *Trans. Amer. Microc. Soc.* **53,** p. 225, Pl. 21, Fig. 60.

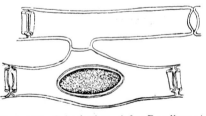

Fig.  386. *S. lambertiana.* (after Randhawa.)

Vegetative cells 24-30 $\mu$ broad 110-260 $\mu$ long, with replicate septa, each cell containing a single chloroplast.

Conjugation scalariform, fertile cells are inflated to 50-62 $\mu$.  Zygospores are ellipsoid, 32-36 $\mu$ broad and 72-80 $\mu$ long.  Mesospore is thick, yellow, reticulate.

*Distribution* :

*India* :   Free-floating in Tons Nadi near Akbarpur, district Fyzabad, on 12th February 1938.

*Other countries* :   United States of America.

**146.  Spirogyra jaoi** LEY 1944.   *Sinensia*, **15,** p. 99 ; Transeau, 1951, p. 220. Pl. XXXIX, Fig. 12.

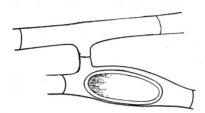

Fig.   387. *S. jaoi.* (after Mehra.)

Vegetative cells 19-22 × 64-216 $\mu$ ; end walls replicate ; chloroplast 1.

Conjugation scalariform; tubes formed by both gametangia, receptive gametangia; zygospores ovoid, 28-40 × 54-90 $\mu$ ; median spore wall of 2 layers,  the outer thin and wrinkled ; the inner smooth,  yellow.

*Distribution* :

*India* :   In a pool at Andheri, Bombay.

*Other countries* :   Tong-Kan, Kwangtung, China.

**147.  Spirogyra quadrata** (HASSALL) Petit 1874.  *Bull. Soc. Bot. de France.*  **21,** p. 41, Pl. 1, Fig. 2.

Fig.   388. *S. quadrata.* (after Randhawa.)

Vegetative cells 24-30 × 70-300 $\mu$, with replicate end walls ; 1 chloroplast, making 1.5 to 6 turns in the cell.

Reproduction by zygospores and aplanospores ; conjugation scalariform and lateral ; tubes formed by both gametangia ; receptive gametangia cylindrically inflated toward the middle up to 60 $\mu$ ; zygospores ellipsoid to cylindric-ellipsoid,  33-44 × 50-82 $\mu$ ; median wall smooth brown ; aplanospores similar but smaller.

*Distribution* :   Northern and Southern China; Europe and U.S.A.

**148.  Spirogyra laxistrata** JAO 1935.   *Sinensia.* **6,** p. 611, Pl. 10, Fig. 111.

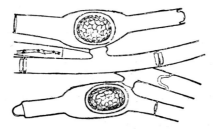

Fig. 389. *S. laxistrata*. (after Jao.)

Vegetative cells 18-201 × 12-147 $\mu$, with replicate end walls ; 1 chloroplast, making 2.5 to 4 turns.

Conjugation scalariform ; tubes formed by the male gametangia ; fertile cells ; cylindrically inflated toward the middle ; zygospores ovoid, 35-38 × 45-48 $\mu$ ; median spore wall double, of which the outer layer is thick, smooth, and yellow ; the inner coarsely areolate, yellow-brown at maturity.

*Distribution* : Szechwan, China.

**149. Spirogyra foveolata** (SKUJA) Czurda 1932. *Süsswasserflora Mitteleuropa.* **9,** p. 157.

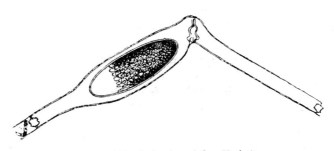

Fig. 390. *S. foveolata*. (after Skuja.)

Vegetative cells 12-18 $\mu$ thick, 7-10 times as long, septa replicate, chloroplast single with 3-6$\frac{1}{2}$ spirals, sometimes almost straight.

Conjugation both lateral and scalariform. A peculiar type of scalariform conjugation in which zygospores are seen in an alternate fashion in opposite cells of the conjugating filaments, known as cross-conjugation was quite commonly seen in the specimens collected from V. Shahpur in 1930. This is the only species which shows this peculiar type of conjugation. However, the specimens collected from a pond in the Military Grass Farm, Fyzabad, in February 1937 showed only the normal type of scalariform conjugation. Lateral conjugation was also seen in some of the filaments in the latter.

The fruiting cells are inflated on both sides. Zygospores are ellipsoid, 24-30 $\mu$ in diameter, and 48-54 $\mu$ long. Reticulate markings are seen on the surface of the zygospores. The zygospore wall is composed of two layers only, a smooth, thin and light bluish exospore, and a thick brownish mesospore.

*Distribution* :

*India* : Free-floating in a pond at V. Shahpur, district Hoshiarpore, Punjab, in the middle of April 1930, from ponds in Saharanpur in April 1935, and Military Grass Farm, Fyzabad U.P., in February 1937.

*Other countries* : China; Arkansas, Minnesota, U.S.A. and Latvia.

**150. Spirogyra pseudospreeiana** Jao 1935. *Sinensia*, **6,** p. 603.

Fig. 391. *S. pseudospreeiana.* (after Jao.)

Vegetative cells 16-19 × 140-210 $\mu$, with replicate end walls ; 1 chloroplast, making 2.5 to 8 turns in the cell.

Conjugation scalariform ; tubes formed by the male gametangia ; fertile cells inflated toward the middle up to 39 $\mu$, especially on the conjugating side ; zygospores ellipsoid, 27-35 × 45-64 $\mu$ ; median spore wall yellow-brown, smooth.

*Distribution* : Szechwan, China.

**151. Spirogyra chuniae** Jao 1935. *Sinensia*. **6,** p. 609, Pl 10, Fig. 105.

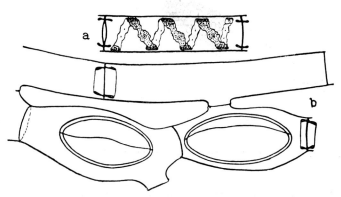

Fig. 392. a-b. *S. chuniae.* (after Jao.)

Vegetative cells 28-39 × 67-130 $\mu$, with replicate end walls ; 1 chloroplast, in some cells 2, making 2 to 5.5 turns in the cells ; fertile cells inflated ; reaching a diameter of 80 $\mu$.

Conjugation scalariform ; tubes very short, sometimes formed only by the male gametangia ; zygospores ellipsoid with pointed ends, 35-43 × 70-119 $\mu$ ; median spore wall yellow smooth.

*Distribution* : Chungking, China.

**152. Spirogyra cylindrica** Czurda 1932. *Süsswasserflora Mitteleuropa.* **9,** p. 150.

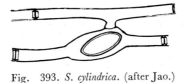

Fig. 393. *S. cylindrica.* (after Jao.)

Vegetative cells 13-16 × 140-350 $\mu$, with replicate end walls ; 1 chloroplast, making 2.5 to 6 turns in the cell.

Conjugation lateral and scalariform ; tubes formed almost wholly by the male gametangia ; fertile cells inflated toward the centre to 29-42 $\mu$ ; zygospores ellipsoid 22-23 × 50-71 $\mu$ ; median spore wall yellow-brown, smooth.

*Distribution* : Austria ; Szechwan, China ; South Africa ; Czechoslovakia.

**153. Spirogyra hopeiensis** Jao 1935. *Sinensia,* **6,** p. 608.

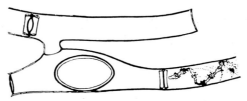

Fig. 394. *S. hopeiensis.* (after Jao.)

Vegetative cells 26-29 × 154-400 $\mu$, with replicate end walls ; 1 chloroplast, making 2 to 6 turns in the cell.

Conjugation scalariform ; tubes formed by the male gametangia ; fertile cells inflated on the conjugating side up to 55 $\mu$ ; zygospores ellipsoid, 32-48 × 61-96 $\mu$ ; median spore wall smooth, yellow.

*Distribution* : Hopei and Szechwan, China.

**154. Spirogyra transeauiana** Jao 1935. *Sinensia.* **6,** p. 610. Pl. 10, Fig. 107

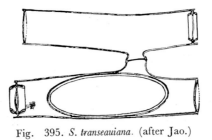

Fig. 395. *S. transeauiana.* (after Jao.)

Vegetative cells 42-61 × 160-304 $\mu$, with replicate end walls, 2 to 3 chloroplasts, making 2 to 5 turns.

Conjugation scalariform; tubes formed by both gametangia; fertile cells cylindric or slightly enlarged on the conjugating side ; zygospores ellipsoid with rounded ends, 41-58 × 96-183 $\mu$ ; median spore wall yellow smooth.

*Distribution*:  Szechwan, China.

**155.  Spirogyra hassallii** (JENN) Petit. 1880. *Lès Spirogyres des environs de Paris*, p. 13, Pl. 2, Figs. 6-8.

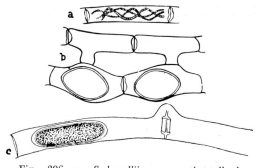

Fig. 396. a-c. *S. hassallii.* a, vegetative cell ; b, scalariform conjugation; c, lateral conjugation. (a·b. after Mehra; c, after Randhawa.)

Vegetative cells 30-32 $\mu$ broad, 6-8 times as long;  2 chloroplasts.  Septa of cells replicate.

Conjugation only lateral.  Cells containing the zygospores are only very slightly swollen, unlike typical specimens of the species.  Male and female cells always occur in pairs, which are separated by a plane wall.  Zygospores ellipsoid, and very much enlongated.  Exospore clear, smooth, light-blue in colour.  Many of the zygospores contain chytridiaceous fungi.  Zygospores 34-38 $\mu$ broad, and 64-106 $\mu$ long.

*Distribution* :

*India* :  Free-floating in a pond at Mangalur, tehsil Roorkee,  district Saharanpur, U.P. during the third week of February 1935.

*Other countries* :  Colorado, North Dakota, Iowa, Illinois, U.S.A.;  Europe and eastern Asia.

**156.  Spirogyra wangi** LI 1933.  *Ohio Jour. Sci.* **33,** p. 153, Pl. 1, Figs. 7-8.

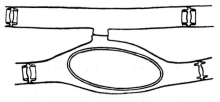

Fig. 397. *S. wangi.* (after Li.)

Vegetative cells 30-32 × 150-350 $\mu$, with replicate end walls ; 2 to 3 chloroplasts making 1.5 to 4.5 turns.

Conjugation scalariform ; tubes formed by both gametangia ; fertile cells inflated toward the middle, up to 72 $\mu$ ; zygospores ellipsoid, 60-64 × 112-124 $\mu$ ; median spore wall smooth, yellow.

*Distribution*: Hangchow, China.

**157. Spirogyra inconstans** COLLINS 1912. *Tufts College Studies.* **3,** p. 73; Phycoth. Bor. Amer., No. 1768. Wittrock and Nordstedt *Algae Exsiccatae*, No. 958. 1889 ; Transeau, 1951, p. 217, Pl. XXXVIII, Figs. 18-20.

Fig. 398. a-c. *S. inconstans.* (after Mehra.)

Vegetative cells 28-40 × 70-350 $\mu$ ; end walls replicate ; chloroplasts (2-) 3 to 4, nearly straight, or making 0.5 to 1.5 turns in the cell.

Conjugation scalariform or rarely lateral ; tubes formed by both gametangia ; at the time of tube formation both gametangia become reflexed and usually the conjugation between the same pair of filaments is limited to single or to 2 adjoining pairs of cells ; cross conjugation is not infrequent ; receptive gametangia shortened and inflated up to 50-75 $\mu$ ; zygospores ellipsoid to broadly ellipsoid, 45-70 × 75-140 $\mu$ ; median spore wall reticulate-areolate, brown.

*Distribution*:

*India* : In a streamlet, Kanheri Caves, Borivli, Bombay, August 17, 1955.

*Other countries* : Europe; Rumania; Sweden and United States of America.

**158. Spirogyra reticulata** NORDSTEDT 1880. *Bot. Notiser* 1880. p. 118. Wittrock and Nordstedt *Algae Exsiccatae*, No. 362.

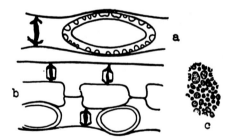

Fig. 399. a-c. *S. reticulata.* (after Kasanowsky.)

Vegetative cells 28-42 × 72-460 $\mu$, usually with replicate end walls ; 1 to 3 (usually 2) chloroplasts making 2 to 4 turns.

Conjugation scalariform and lateral ; tubes formed by both gametangia; fertile cells enlarged or inflated toward the middle to 48-60 $\mu$ ; zygospores mostly ovoid,

45-61 × 80-120 $\mu$ ; median spore wall yellow-brown, of 2 layers, of which the outer is thin and wrinkled ; the inner reticulate.

*Distribution* : Brazil; China; Europe; and U.S.A.

**159. Spirogyra regularis** (CEDERCREUTZ) KRIEGER 1944. Rabenhorst's *Kryptogamenflora.* **13,** p. 464. *Acta Soc. pro Fauna et Flora Fennica.* **55** (2), p. 3. 1924.

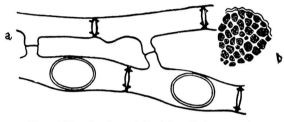

Fig. 400. a-b. *S. regularis.* (after Cedercreutz.)

Vegetative cells 28-32 × 110-380 $\mu$, with replicate end walls ; 2 chloroplasts, making 4 to 6 turns in the cell.

Conjugation scalariform ; tubes formed by both gametangia ; fertile cells enlarged or inflated ; zygospores ovoid, 39-45 × 60-90 $\mu$, yellow-brown ; median wall reticulate.

*Distribution* : Finland.

**160. Spirogyra quinquilaminata** JAO 1935. *Sinensia.* **6,** p. 615, Pl. 11, Figs. 121-22.

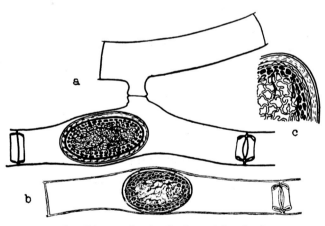

Fig. 401. a-c. *S. quinquilaminata.* (after Jao.)

Vegetative cells 41-45 × 154-280 $\mu$, with replicate end walls ; 2 chloroplasts making 2 to 4 turns in the cell.

Reproduction by zygospores and aplanospores ; conjugation scalariform ; tubes formed by both gametangia ; fertile cells enlarged toward the middle ; sterile cells sometimes inflated up to 70 $\mu$ ; zygospores ovoid, 51-55 × 83-144 $\mu$, with 5 layers in the spore wall; outer spore wall of 2 layers, of which the outer is thin and colourless; the inner up to 3.5 $\mu$ in thickness and distinctly lamellate ; median spore wall yellow-brown, also of 2 layers, of which the outer is thin and somewhat wrinkled ; the inner, coarsely and irregularly reticulate, the ridges being crenulate to dentate ; aplanospores subglobose, 41-48 × 41-67 $\mu$, with similarly marked walls.

*Distribution* :   Szechwan, China.

**161. Spirogyra aplanospora** Randhawa 1938. *Proc. Indian Acad. Sci.* **8,** pp. 336-37.

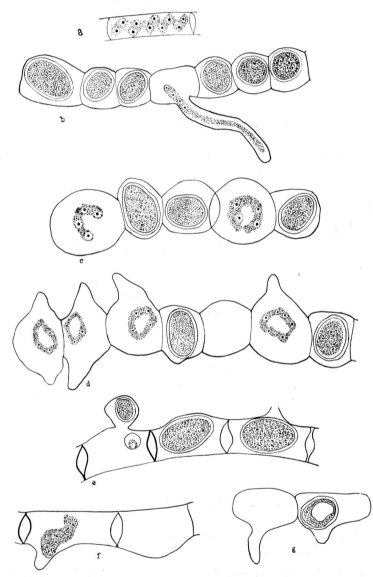

Fig. 402. a-g. *S. aplanospora*. a, vegetative cell; b-g. aplanospores ;
b, filament showing a rhizoid. (after Randhawa.)

Vegetative cells 20-26 $\mu$ broad, and 2-4 times as long.  Septa plane.  Each cell contains a single spiral chloroplast with 3-6 spirals

Reproduction in this species takes place exclusively by means of aplanospores.

In most filaments the fertile cells become swollen on both sides, appearing almost globose in shape, while in some filaments these become swollen on one side only. Abortive conjugation tubes are given out by some of the cells, which may be closed or ruptured, presenting the appearance of a broken conjugation canal.    In one peculiar case the tube had become swollen in a balloon-like manner and an aplanospore was found lodged in it.    The aplanospores are globose to ellipsoid in shape, and are 24-30 $\mu$ broad and 30-54 $\mu$ long.    The spore-wall is composed of two layers, a light-blue exospore and a brown mesospore, both of which are smooth.    In most cases the sterile cells become swollen in a globose fashion and the chloroplast is in the shape of a ring or a loop.    In some cases even the sterile cells give out conjugation canal-like protuberances, on one or both sides.    The sterile swollen cells may be as broad as 54$\mu$ in some cases.

*Distribution* :

*India* :    In a pond near Dasuya, Punjab, in January 1929.

**162.    Spirogyra granulata** Jao 1935.    *Sinensia*.   **6,** p. 613, Pl. 11, Figs. 116-17.

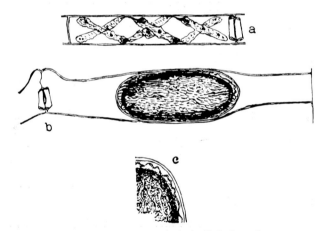

Fig. 403. a-c. *S. granulata*, a, vegetative cell; b, lateral conjugation; c, part of the zygospore showing ornamentation of the spore wall. (after Jao.)

Vegetative cells 32-35 × 147-280 $\mu$, with replicate end walls ; 2 chloroplasts making 2.5 to 6 turns in the cell.

Conjugation lateral ; tubes formed by both gametangia ; receptive gametangia enlarged toward the middle ; zygospores ovoid to cylindric-ovoid, 45-55 × 93-131 $\mu$ ; median wall double, of which the outer layer is thin and irregularly wrinkled ; the inner, granulate and slightly wrinkled, yellowish-brown.

*Distribution* :    Szechwan, China.

**163.    Spirogyra azygospora** Singh 1938.    *Jour. Indian Bot. Soc.* **17,** p. 372.

Fig. 404. *S. azygospora.* (after Singh.)

Vegetative cells 85-90 × 270-300 $\mu$, with plane end walls ; chloroplasts 5.

Conjugation unknown ; reproduction by aplanospores which are compressed-globose, 71-77 × 60-67 $\mu$ ; median wall thick, brown, and smooth.

*Distribution* :

India : Gorakhpur, U.P., October, 1936.

**164.  Spirogyra cylindrospora** W. & G.S. WEST 1897. *Jour. Bot.* **35**, p. 42.

Vegetative cells 70-77 × 100-300 $\mu$, with plane end walls ; 4 chloroplasts making 1 to 3 turns.

Conjugation scalariform and lateral ; tubes formed by both gametangia ; fertile cells cylindric ; zygospores cylindric-ovoid, 70-77 × 78-98 $\mu$ ; median spore wall yellow, punctate-scrobiculate, thick.

*Distribution* :  Central Africa.

**165.  Spirogyra tjibodensis** FABER 1912. *Ann. Jard. Bot. Buitenzorg.* **26**, p. 265.

Vegetative cells 45-50 × 80-130 $\mu$, with replicate end walls ; 1 chloroplast making about 4 turns.

Reproduction by zygospores and aplanospores ; conjugation scalariform ; tubes formed by both gametangia ; fertile cells cylindric ; zygospores ellipsoid, 32-35 × 37-42 $\mu$ ; median wall brown ; aplanospores, similar, 30-34 × 35-40 $\mu$.

*Distribution* :  Java, Tjibodas.

**166.  Spirogyra hoehnei** BORGE 1925. *Ark. Bot.* **19**, p. 13, Pl. 2, Fig. 1.

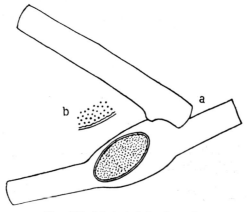

Fig. 405. *S. hoehnei.* (after Borge.)

Vegetative cells 26-29 × 150-350 $\mu$, with plane end walls ; 1 chloroplast, making 4 to 9 turns.

Conjugation scalariform ; tubes formed by both cells ; fertile cells inflated towards the middle to 52 $\mu$ ; zygospores ellipsoid, 32-37 × 50-65 $\mu$ ; median spore wall yellow, irregularly and coarsely punctate.

*Distribution* : South Africa ; South America; United States of America.

**167. Spirogyra reinhardii** CHMIELEVSKI 1903. In Borge's *Süsswasserflora Deutschland.* **9,** p. 31, Fig. 41.

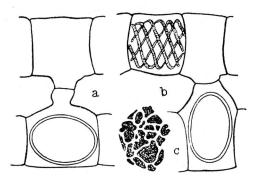

Fig. 406. a-c, *S. reinhardii.* (after Borge.)

Vegetative cells 108-117 × 85-310 $\mu$, with plane end walls ; 4 to 6 chloroplasts, making 0.5 to 2 turns.

Conjugation scalariform ; tubes formed by both gametangia ; fertile cells inflated on the conjugating side ; zygospores ovoid, 78-100 × 115-175 $\mu$ ; median spore wall chestnut brown, irregularly reticulate.

*Distribution* : Brazil ; Russia.

**168. Spirogyra tetrapla** TRANSEAU 1938. *Amer. Jour. Bot.* **25,** p. 528, Fig. 6.

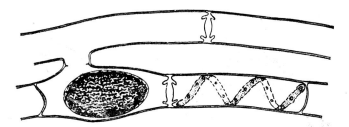

Fig. 407. *S. tetrapla.* (after Transeau.)

Vegetative cells 30-40 × 100-250 $\mu$, with replicate end walls ; 1 to 2 chloroplasts, making 2 to 8 turns in the cell.

Conjugation scalariform ; tubes formed by both gametangia ; fertile cells inflated, up to 66 $\mu$ ; zygospores ellipsoid 48-58 × 68-88 $\mu$ ; median wall of 2 layers, of which the outer is thin and irregularly corrugate ; the inner, finely reticulate, yellow.

*Distribution* :   United  States  of  America.

**169.   Spirogyra subpapulata** JAO 1935.   *Sinensia.* **6,** p. 569, Pl. 7, Figs. 74-75.

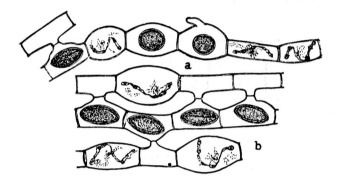

Fig. 408. a-b. *S. subpapulata.* (after Jao.)

Vegetative cells 22-26 × 41-166 $\mu$, with plane end walls ; 1 chloroplast, making 2-7 turns in the cells ; reproduction by either zygospores or aplanospores.

Conjugation scalariform ; tubes formed by both cells ; sterile cells usually swollen to 58 $\mu$ in diameter ; zygospores ellipsoid, with pointed ends, 21-29 × 41-60 $\mu$ ; aplanospores subglobose or ellipsoid, 22-26 × 32-48 $\mu$ ; median wall finely and densely punctate, yellow  at  maturity.

*Distribution* :   China.

**170.   Spirogyra collinsii** (Lewis) PRINTZ 1927.   In Engler and Prantl., *Pflazenfamilien.* Second edition, **3,** p. 371, *Amer. Jour. Bot.* **12,** p. 251, 1935 (as *Temnogyra collinsii*).

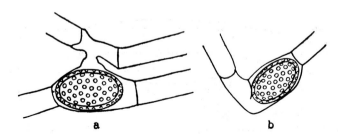

Fig. 409. a-b. *S. collinsii.* (after Lewis.)

Vegetative cells 18-22 × 100-200 $\mu$, with plane end walls ; 1 chloroplast, rarely in some cells, making from 3 to 9 turns in the wall.

Conjugation usually lateral, sometimes scalariform ; tubes formed mostly by the male gametangia ; fertile cells inflated, 25-39 × 45-110 $\mu$ ; zygospores ellipsoid, or sometimes ovoid, 26-27 × 52 (-110) $\mu$ ; median spore wall coarsely punctate, yellow.

*Distribution* :   United States of America.

**171.   Spirogyra perforans** Transeau 1934.   *Trans. Amer. Micros. Soc.* **53,** p. 228, Pl. 21, Fig. 57.

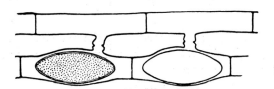

Fig. 410. *S. perforans.* (after Transeau.)

Vegetative cells 14-18 × 72-120 $\mu$, with plane end walls ; 1 chloroplast, making 3 to 6 turns.

Conjugation scalariform ; tubes formed by both gametangia ; fertile cells enlarged, zygospores ellipsoid, 25-29 × (50-) 65-69 $\mu$ ; median spore wall yellow-brown, coarsely punctate.

*Distribution* :   United States of America.

**172.   Spirogyra sibirica** Skvortzow 1927.   *Jour. Bot.* **65,** p. 252, Fig.1.

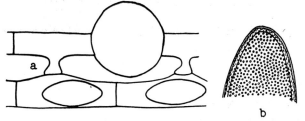

Fig. 411. a-b. *S. sibirica.* (after Skvortzow.)

Vegetative cells about 17 $\mu$ broad, with plane end walls and 1 chloroplast.

Conjugation scalariform ; tube formed by male cells ; receptive gametangia slightly swollen on the inner side ; many sterile cells bullate ; zygospores ellipsoid, 20 × 32-40 $\mu$ ; median spore wall yellow, scrobiculate.

*Distribution* :   Russia.

**173.   Spirogyra wabashensis** Tiffany 1927.   *Bot. Gaz.* **83,** p. 202, Pl. 8, Fig. 1.

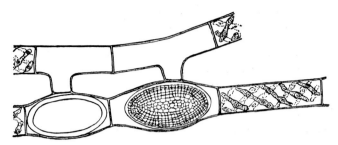

Fig. 412. *S. wabashensis.* (after Tiffany.)

Vegetative cells 40-50 × 120-400 $\mu$ ; with plane end walls ; 2 to 4 chloroplasts, making 0.5 to 4.5 turns.

Conjugation scalariform ; tubes formed by the male gametangia ; fertile cells inflated, single or in groups of 2, alternating with vegetative cells ; zygospores ellipsoid, 56-76 × 110-150 $\mu$ ; median spore wall yellow, areolate.

*Distribution* :   United States of America.

**174.  Spirogyra acanthophora** (Skuja) Czurda 1932, *Süsswasserflora Mitteleuropa.* **9,** p. 160. Skuja. *Acta. Horti Bot. Univ. Latviensis.* **3,** p. 114, 1928 (as *S. willei* var. *acanthophora*).

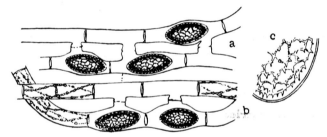

Fig. 413. a-c. *S. acanthophora.* (after Skuja.)

Vegetative cells 30-38 × 75-350 $\mu$, with replicate end walls ; 3 to 4 chloroplasts, making 0.5 to 1.5 turns in the cell.

Conjugation scalariform ; tubes formed by both gametangia ; receptive gametangia inflated to 50-70 $\mu$ ; zygospores ellipsoid, 42-60 × 80-140 $\mu$ ; median wall irregularly spinose-reticulate, yellow-brown.

*Distribution* :   Latvia.

**175.  Spirogyra australensis** Moebius 1895.   In Bailey, *Queensland Flora. Dept. of Agric. Bot. Bull.* **1,** p. 34, Pl. 9, Fig.1.

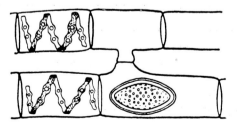

Fig. 414. *S. australensis.* (after Moebius.)

Vegetative cells about $50 \times 100$-$150$ $\mu$, with plane end walls; 1 chloroplast, making 2.5 to 3 turns.

Conjugation scalariform; tubes formed by both gametangia; fertile cells cylindric or enlarged; zygospores ellipsoid, 40-50 $\times$ 74-77 $\mu$; median spore wall yellowish-brown finely verrucose.

*Distribution*:  Australia.

**176. Spirogyra crassoidea** Transeau 1937. *Amer. Midland Naturalist.* **18,** p. 936, Pl. 5, Fig. 77. *Amer. Jour. Bot.* **1,** p. 295, Pl. 27, Fig.2.

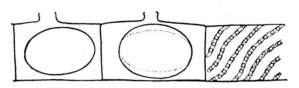

Fig. 415. *S. crassoidea.* (after Tiffany.)

Vegetative cells 140-150$\times$140-560 $\mu$, with plane end walls; 3 to 8 chloroplasts, making 0.5 to 3 turns in the cell.

Conjugation scalariform; tubes formed by both gametangia; fertile cells cylindric, zygospores compressed-ellipsoid, 120-140 $\times$ 145-255 $\mu$; median spore wall smooth, yellow-brown.

*Distribution*:  United States of America.

**177. Spirogyra daedaleoides** Czurda 1932. *Susswasserflora Mitteleuropa,* **9,** pp. 180-81. Skuja. *Acta. Horti. Bot. Univ. Latviensis.* **4,** p. 39. 1929.

Fig. 416. *S. daedaleoides.* (after Skuja.)

Vegetative cells 30-44 $\times$ 65-240 $\mu$, with plane end walls; 1 chloroplast, making 2 to 8 turns.

Conjugation scalariform and lateral; tubes formed by both gametangia; fertile cells enlarged or slightly inflated (-50$\mu$); zygospores ellipsoid, 30-46 $\times$ 46-90 $\mu$; median spore wall, brown, with prominent irregular reticulate ridges.

*Distribution*:  Latvia; United States of America.

**178. Siprogyra jatobae** Transeau 1938. *Amer. Jour. Bot.* **25,** p. 527, Figs. 14-15.

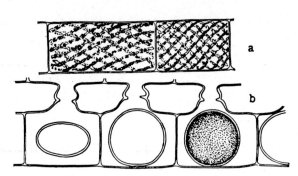

Fig. 417. a-b. *S. jatobae.* (after Transeau.)

Vegetative cells 118-130 × 108-500 $\mu$, with plane end walls and 8-11 chloroplasts straight or making 1 turn in the cell.

Conjugation scalariform; tubes formed by both gametangia; receptive gametangia slightly inflated, especially on the conjugating side; zygospores compressed-spherical 108-140 × 70-90 $\mu$; median wall yellow-brown, irregularly and minutely verrucose.

*Distribution*:  Brazil.

**179.  Spirogyra incrassata** Czurda 1930.  *Beih. Bot. Centralbl.* **47,** p. 38. Fig. 10.

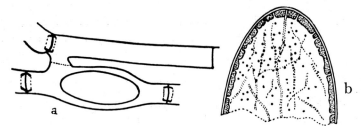

Fig. 418. a-b. *S. incrassata.* (after Czurda.)

Vegetative cells 26-30 × 200-250 $\mu$, with replicate end walls (1-) 2 chloroplasts.

Conjugation lateral and scalariform; tubes formed by both cells; fertile cell greatly inflated towards the middle; zygospores ellipsoid, 42-52 × 110 $\mu$; median spore wall yellow-brown irregularly punctate, and inwardly channeled.

*Distribution*:  Germany.

**180.  Spirogyra pseudovarians** Czurda 1930.  *Beih. Bot. Zentralbl.* **47,** p. 32,

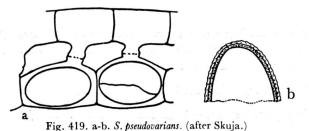

Fig. 419. a-b. *S. pseudovarians.* (after Skuja.)

Vegetative cells 36-39 × 35-75 $\mu$ ; with plane end walls ; chloroplast 1 (rarely 2).

Conjugation scalariform ; tubes formed by both gametangia; fertile cells swollen, mostly on the conjugating side; zygospores ellipsoid, 33-37 × 47-57 $\mu$; outer spore wall thick, transparent, scrobiculate ; median spore wall reddish-brown, smooth ; sterile cells more or less swollen.

*Distribution*: Austria ; Czechoslovakia.

**181. Spirogyra chenii** Jao 1935. *Sinensia.* **6,** p. 587, Pl. 4, Fig. 52.

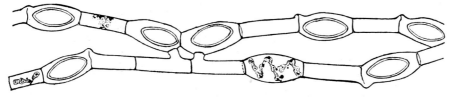

Fig. 420. *S. chenii.* (after Jao.)

Vegetative cells 18-22 × 38-115 $\mu$ , with plane end walls ; 1 chloroplast making 1 to 5 turns in the cell.

Conjugation lateral and scalariform; conjugating tubes formed by the male gametangia; fertile cells inflated up to 42 $\mu$, usually separated by 1 or more sterile cells; zygospores ellipsoid, 25-32 × 45-61 $\mu$ ; median spore wall smooth, yellow at maturity.

*Distribution*: China.

**182. Spirogyra groenlandica** ROSENVINGE 1883. *Ofvers. Kgl. Vet.-Akad. Förhandl.* Stockholm, 1883, No. 8, p. 37, Pl. 8, Figs, 1-11.

Fig. 421. *S. groenlandica.* (after Kolkwitz & Krieger.)

Vegetative cells 18-24 × 360-600 $\mu$, with replicate end walls; 1 chloroplast, making 8 turns in the cell ; reproduction by zygospores and aplanospores.

Conjugation lateral and scalariform; tubes formed by both gametangia; receptive gametangia more or less cylindrically inflated up to 51 $\mu$ towards the middle; zygospores ellipsoid to cylindric-ellipsoid, 34-48 × 100- 130 $\mu$; median wall smooth, chestnut brown; aplanospores similar, 34-44 × 60-90 $\mu$.

*Distribution*: United States of America.

**183. Spirogyra diluta** WOOD 1869. *Proc. Amer. Phil. Soc.* p. 139. Phycoth, Bor.-Amer., No. 513.

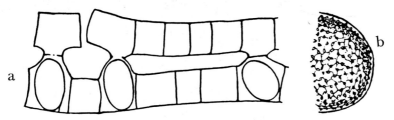

Fig. 422. a-b. *S. diluta.* (after Transeau.)

Vegetative cells 70-85 × 80-160 $\mu$, with plane end walls; 5 to 8 chloroplasts, straight or making 1 turn.

Conjugation scalariform ; tubes formed by both gametangia; fertile cells enlarged or inflated on the inner side ; zygospores ovoid, 66-90 × 90-130 $\mu$ ; median spore wall chestnut brown, verrucose-reticulate to verrucose.

*Distribution* :　United States of America.

**184. Spirogyra pascheriana** CZURDA 1932. *Süsswasserflora Mitteleuropa.* **9,** p. 150.

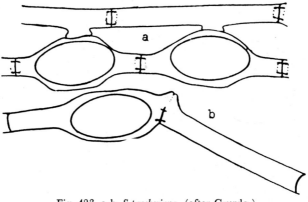

Fig. 423. a-b. *S. pascheriana*. (after Czurda.)

Vegetative cells 18-21 × 120-170 $\mu$, with replicate end walls; 1 chloroplast.

Conjugation lateral and scalariform; tubes formed mostly by the male gametangia; fertile cells more or less cylindrically inflated, up to 60 $\mu$; zygospores ellipsoid, 45-50 × 80-95 $\mu$ ; median wall yellow-brown, smooth, with distinct suture.

*Distribution* :　Czechoslovakia ; United States of America.

**185. Spirogyra rectangularis** TRANSEAU 1914.　*Amer. Jour. Bot.* **1,** p. 291. Pl. 25, Figs. 9-11.

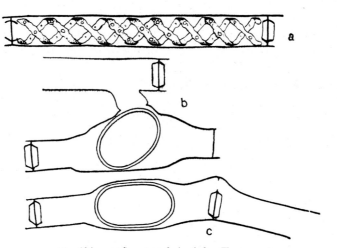

Fig. 424. a-c. *S. rectangularis*. (after Transeau.)

Vegetative cells 35-40 × 150-320 $\mu$, with replicate end walls ; 2 to 4 chloroplasts, making 2 to 5 turns.

Conjugation lateral and scalariform; tubes formed by both gametangia; fertile cells cylindrically inflated to 48-70 $\mu$ ; zygospores ovoid to cylindric-ovoid, 45-65 × 75-120 $\mu$ ; median spore wall yellow-brown smooth.

*Distribution* : Austria ; United States of America.

**186. Spirogyra oltmannsii** Hurber-Perstalozzi 1930. *" Algen aus dem Knysnawalde in Sudafrica."* *Zeitsch f. Bot.* **23,** p. 448.

Fig. 425. *S. oltmannsii.* (after Hurber-Perstalozzi.)

Vegetative cells 23-27 × 70-125 $\mu$, with plane end walls ; 1 chloroplast.

Zygospores unknown ; sporangia cylindric ; aplanospores ovoid, 22-26 × 30-42 $\mu$; median spore wall outwardly scrobiculate.

*Distribution* : South Africa.

**187. Spirogyra discoidea** Transeau 1934. *Trans. Amer. Micros. Soc.* **53,** p. 228.

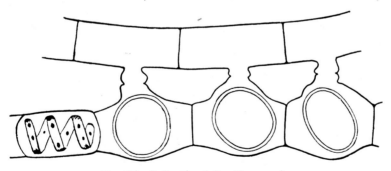

Fig. 426. *S. discoidea.* (after Transeau.)

Vegetative cells 39-42 × 72-115 $\mu$, with plane end walls ; 1 chloroplast.

Conjugation scalariform; tubes formed by both gametangia; receptive gametangia enlarged or inflated toward the middle ; zygospores compressed-globose, 40-44 × 56-65 $\mu$ ; median spore wall brown, smooth.

*Distribution* : South Africa.

**188. Spirogyra variformis** Transeau 1938. *Amer. Jour. Bot.* **25,** pp. 526-27.

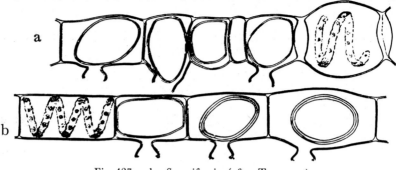

Fig. 427. a-b. *S. variformis.* (after Transeau.)

Vegetative cells 43-50 × (70-)108-140(-200) $\mu$ with plane end walls ; 1 chloroplast making 2 to 5 turns in the cell.

Conjugation scalariform; tubes formed by both gametangia and widest at the middle ; some sterile cells inflated to 72-100 $\mu$ ; fertile cells mostly cylindric but sometimes enlarged or inflated ; zygospores ellipsoid or ovoid 45-54 × 58-90 $\mu$, rarely spherical, 52-60 $\mu$ in diameter ; median wall brown, smooth.

*Distribution* : Africa.

**189. Spirogyra kaffirita** Transeau 1934. *Trans. Amer. Micros. Soc.* **53,** p. 228, Fig. 59.

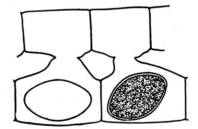

Fig. 428. *S. kaffirita.* (after Transeau.)

Vegetative cells 39-45 × 65-140 $\mu$, with plane end walls ; 1 chloroplast.

Conjugation scalariform; tubes formed by both gametangia; fertile cells inflated on the inner side ; zygospores ellipsoid, 32-40 × 45-60 (-75) $\mu$ ; median spore wall yellow, shallow-granulate, reticulate.

*Distribution* : Africa.

**190. Spirogyra crassivallicularis** Jao 1935. *Trans. Amer. Micros. Soc.* **54,** p. 2, Pl. 1, Fig. 4.

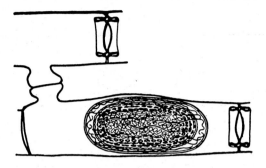

Fig. 429. *S. crassivallicularis*. (after Jao.)

Vegetative cells 54-58 × 168-420 $\mu$ ; end walls replicate ; chloroplasts usually 4 rarely 3, making 1.5 to 3.5 turns in the cell.

Conjugation scalariform; tubes formed by both gametangia; fertile cells enlarged, or inflated up to 80 $\mu$ ; zygospores ovoid, 52-71 × 90-144 $\mu$ ; median wall of 2 layers, of which the outer is thin, wrinkled, and yellow ; the inner thick, yellow-brown and reticulate with thick irregularly crenulate ridges.

*Distribution*: United States of America.

**191. Spirogyra fragilis** JAO 1935. *Sinensia*. **6,** p. 590, Pl. 6, Fig. 64.

Fig. 430. *S. fragilis*. (after Jao.)

Vegetative cells 24-29 × 54-160 $\mu$, with plane end walls; chloroplast 1 (rarely 2), making 1.5-6 turns.

Conjugation scalariform ; tubes formed by both gametangia ; fertile cells slightly inflated, usually a little more on the conjugating side ; the female gametangia often separate from each other after conjugation ; zygospores ellipsoid with more or less rounded ends, 22-28 × 36-67 $\mu$ ; median spore wall yellow, smooth.

*Distribution*: United States of America.

**192.  Spirogyra wrightiana** Transeau 1938.  *Amer. Jour. Bot.* **25,** p. 527. Fig.  16-17.

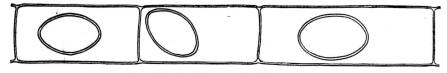

Fig. 431. *S. wrightiana.* (after Transeau.)

Vegetative cells 130-165 × 275-430 (-690)$\mu$, with plane end walls; 6-8 chloroplasts, making  1-3  turns  in  the  cell.

Conjugation unknown ; aplanospores mostly ellipsoid, 100-126 × 158-206 $\mu$ ; sporangia cylindric and of the same dimensions as the vegetative cells ; spore walls mature,  smooth  and  colourless.

*Distribution* :   South  America.

**193.  Spirogyra sphaerospora** Hirn 1895.  *Acta. Soc. pro. Fauna et Flora Fennica.* **11,** (10), p. 10.

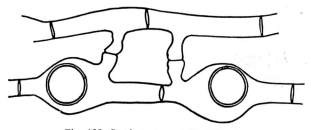

Fig. 432. *S. sphaerospora.* (after Hirn.)

Vegetative cells 43-45 × 180-320 $\mu$, with plane end walls ; 1 chloroplast, making about  3  turns.

Conjugation scalariform; tubes formed by both gametangia; fertile cells greatly inflated (to 93-100 $\mu$ towards the middle) ; zygospores compressed-globose, 85-95 $\mu$ in diameter, median  spore  wall  yellowish-brown, smooth.

*Distribution* :   Finland.

**194.  Spirogyra venusta** Jao 1935.  *Sinensia.* **6,** p. 614, Pl. 10, Figs. 118-19.

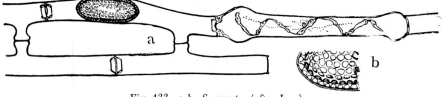

Fig. 433. a-b. *S. venusta.* (after Jao.)

Vegetative cells 25-27 ×175-350 $\mu$, with replicate end walls; 1 chloroplast, making 3  to  6  turns  in  the  cell.

Conjugation scalariform; tubes formed by both gametangia; sterile cells inflated at the ends ; fertile cells cylindric or enlarged ; zygospores cylindric-ellipsoid, 26-32 ×

67-84 $\mu$; outer spore wall of 2 layers, of which the inner is colourless, strongly scrobiculate; median spore wall smooth and yellow.

*Distribution*: China.

**195. Spirogyra splendida** G.S. WEST 1914. *Mem. Soc. Neuchateloise Sci. Nat.* **5,** pp. 1013-51.

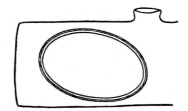

Fig. 434. *S. splendida.* (after G.S. West.)

Vegetative cells 158-168 × 210-330 $\mu$, with plane end walls; 5 to 6 chloroplasts, making 1.5 to 2 turns in the cell.

Conjugation scalariform; tubes formed by both gametangia; fertile cells cylindric, zygospores ellipsoid, about 135 × 216 $\mu$ ; median spore wall yellow smooth.

*Distribution*: South America.

**196. Spirogyra glabra** CZURDA 1932. *Süsswasserflora Mitteleuropa.* **9,** p. 206, Fig. 222.

Fig. 435. *S. glabra.* (after Czurda.)

Vegetative cells 145-153 × 120-220 $\mu$, with plane end walls ; 7 chloroplasts.

Conjugation scalariform; tubes formed by both gametangia; fertile cells cylindric zygospores lenticular, about 120 × 170 $\mu$ ; outer spore wall about 10 $\mu$ thick, colourless; median spore wall about 20 $\mu$ thick, yellow-brown, smooth.

*Distribution*: Austria.

**197. Spirogyra borysthenica** KASANOFSKY & SMIRNOFF 1913. *Oesterr. Bot. Zeitschr..* **63.** p. 137, Pl. 3.

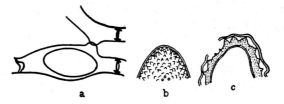

Fig. 436. a-c. *S. borysthenica.* (after Kasanofsky.)

Vegetative cells 30-40 × 180-450 $\mu$, with replicate end walls; 2 to 4 chloroplasts, straight or making up to 2.5 turns in the cell.

Conjugation scalariform; tubes formed by both gametangia; fertile cells inflated up to 70 $\mu$ ; zygospores ellipsoid, 52-62 × 110-160 $\mu$ ; median spore wall with spine-like or mammiform papillae, yellow-brown.

*Distribution*:   Russia; United States of America.

**198.   Spirogyra areolata** LAGERHEIM 1883.   *Ōfvers. Kal. Vet.-Akad. Forhandl.* Stockholm. **40,** p. 56, Pl. 1, Figs. 18-20.

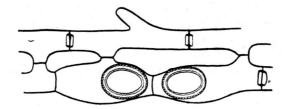

Fig. 437. *S. areolata.* (after Lagerheim.)

Vegetative cells 30-36 × 120-600 $\mu$, with replicate end walls ; 1 or 2 chloroplasts, making 3 to 9 turns.

Conjugation scalariform; tubes formed by both gametangia; fertile  cells  inflated up to 67 $\mu$; zygospores ovoid to ovoid globose, 40-57 × 60-103 $\mu$; outer spore wall of 2 layers, of which the inner is hyaline, scrobiculate, median spore wall yellow-brown, smooth.

*Distribution*:   Germany ; Latvia ; United States of America.

**199.   Spirogyra echinata** TIFFANY 1924.   *Ohio. Jour. Sci.* **24,** p. 180, Pl. 1, Fig. 1.

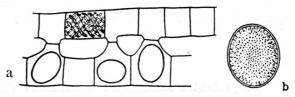

Fig. 438. a-b.  *S. echinata.* (after Tiffany.)

Vegetative cells 88-96 $\times$ 84-106 $\mu$, with plane end walls ; 4 to 7 chloroplasts, making 0.5 to 1.5 turns.

Conjugation scalariform; tubes formed by both gametangia; fertile cells shortened and inflated on the conjugating side ; zygospores ovoid, 68-85 $\times$ 76-120 $\mu$, often placed transversely to the filament; median spore wall reticulate-echinate, brown.

*Distribution* :   South Africa ;  United States of America.

**200.   Spirogyra aequinoctialis** G.S. WEST 1907. *Jour. Linn. Soc. London, Bot.* **38,** p. 105, Pl. 5, Figs. 1-2.

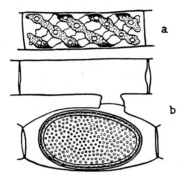

Fig. 439. a-b. *S. aequinoctialis*. (after G.S. West.)

Vegetative cells 23-25 $\times$ 90-150 $\mu$, with plane end walls ; 3 (rarely 2) chloroplasts, making 1-1.5 turns.

Conjugation scalariform ; tubes formed by both gametangia ; fertile cells inflated, oblong ; zygospores ovoid, or oblong-ovoid, 41-43 $\times$ 52-71 $\mu$ ; median wall densely scrobiculate.

*Distribution* :   Central Africa ;  United States of America.

**201.   Spirogyra narcissiana** Transeau 1914.      *Amer. Jour. Bot.* **1,** p. 290. Pl. 25, Figs. 4-6.

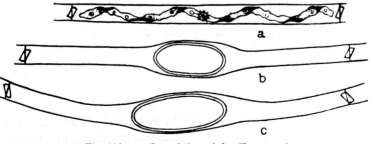

Fig. 440. a-c. *S. narcissiana*. (after Transeau.)

Vegetative cells 12-14 $\times$ 200-400 $\mu$, with semireplicate end walls ; 1 chloroplast making 2 to 5 turns ; zygospores unknown ; sporiferous cells inflated towards the middle up to 25-53 $\mu$ ; aplanospores ellipsoid to ovoid, 23-30 $\times$ 50-120 $\mu$ ; median spore wall, yellow, smooth.

*Distribution* :   United States of America.

**202.  Spirogyra articulata** Transeau 1934.   *Trans. Amer. Micros. Soc.* **53,** p. 226, Pl. 22, Figs. 67-69.

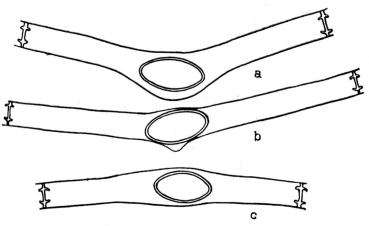

Fig. 441. a-c.  *S. articulata.* (after Transeau.)

Vegetative cells 24-28 $\times$ 300-600 $\mu$, with replicate end walls ; 1 chloroplast, making 3 to 8 turns in the cell.

Zygospores unknown; reproducing by ellipsoid aplanospores, 36-40 $\times$ 60-88 $\mu$; median spore wall yellow, smooth ; sporangia cylindric, enlarged or slightly inflated, sometimes straight, often bowed or bent toward the middle.

*Distribution* :   United States of America.

**203.  Spirogyra gratiana** Transeau 1938.   *Amer. Jour. Bot.* **25,** p. 528, Figs. 12-13.

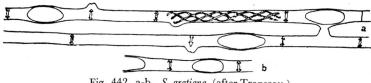

Fig. 442. a-b.  *S. gratiana.* (after Transeau.)

Vegetative cells 28-33 $\times$ 144-400 $\mu$, with replicate end walls; usually 3 chloroplasts (rarely in some cells 2 or 4)

Conjugation lateral and scalariform; tubes formed by both gametangia; receptive gametangia cylindric or enlarged; zygospores ellipsoid, 35-47 $\times$ 108-223 $\mu$ ; all walls smooth ; median wall yellow ; aplanospores infrequent, smaller, 38-40 $\times$ 47-72 $\mu$.

*Distribution* :   United States of America.

**204.  Spirogyra maravillosa** Transeau 1938.   *Amer. Jour. Bot.* **25,** p. 525.

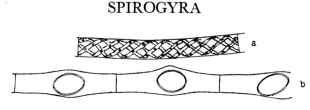

Fig. 443. a-b. *S. maravillosa*. (after Transeau.)

Vegetative cells 24-29 × 108-260 $\mu$, with plane end walls ; 2 to 3 chloroplasts, making 2 to 5 turns in the cell.

Conjugation unknown ; aplanospores broadly ellipsoid, 28-36 × 43-60 (-72) $\mu$ ; median wall smooth, yellow-brown ; sporangia enlarged or slightly inflated.

*Distribution* : Brazil.

**205. Spirogyra hartigii** Kützing 1855. *Tabulae Phycologicae.* **5**, p. 33.

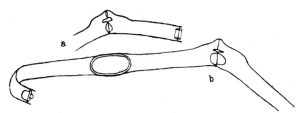

Fig. 444. a-b. *S. hartigii*. (a, after Langer; b, after Kützing.)

Vegetative cells about 45 × 500-675 $\mu$, with replicate end walls ; 2 chloroplasts, making 2 turns.

Conjugation lateral and scalariform; tubes formed by both gametangia, longer than usual ; in lateral conjugation the tube primordia arise 4 to 5 $\mu$ from the end wall ; receptive gametangia enlarged or slightly inflated at the middle ; zygospores ovoid, 45-50 × 80-105 $\mu$ ; median spore wall smooth.

*Distribution* : Germany.

**206. Spirogyra fennica** Cedercreutz 1924. *Acta. Soc. pro Fauna et Flora Fennica.* **55**, (2), p. 4.

Fig. 445. *S. fennica*. (after Jao.)

Vegetative cells 15-19 × 60-260 $\mu$, with plane end walls; 1 chloroplast.

Conjugation scalariform ; tubes formed by both gametangia ; fertile cells shortened and inflated to 34-39 $\mu$ ; zygospores ellipsoid, 24-31 × 45-55 $\mu$ ; median spore wall yellow-brown, smooth.

*Distribution* :   China ; Finland ; South Africa.

**207.  Spirogyra proavita** Langer 1913.   *Bot. Közlemenyek.* **12,** p. 166.

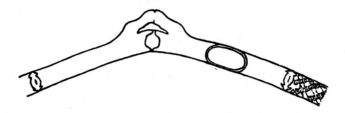

Fig. 446. *S. proavita.* (after Langer.)

Vegetative cells 37-40 $\times$ 330-560 $\mu$, with replicate end walls ; 2-3 chloroplasts, making 1 to 3.5 turns in the cell.

Conjugation lateral; tubes arising from primordia several microns away from the end wall, thus forming a distant tube outside the filament ; fertile cells cylindric ; zygospores ovoid, 38-40 $\times$ 83-86 $\mu$; median spore wall smooth, brownish-yellow when mature.

*Distribution* :   Hungary.

**208.  Spirogyra marchica** Kolkwitz & Krieger 1944. Rabenhorst's *Kryptogamenflora.* **13,** p. 459.

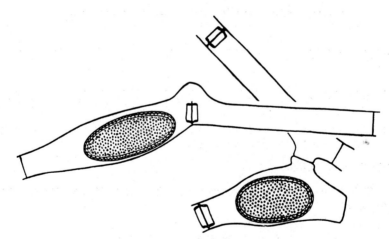

Fig. 447. *S. marchica.* (after Kolkwitz & Krieger.)

Vegetative cells 29-32 $\times$ 150-250 $\mu$, with replicate end walls, and 2 chloroplasts.

Conjugation lateral and scalariform ; tubes formed by both cells ; receptive gametangia inflated on both sides ; zygospores ovoid to ellipsoid with rounded ends, 36-53 $\times$ 86-170 $\mu$ ; median spore wall brown coarsely verrucose.

*Distribution* :   Germany.

**209.  Spirogyra occidentalis** (Transeau) Czurda 1932. *Süsswasserflora Mitteleuropa.* **9,** p. 183.

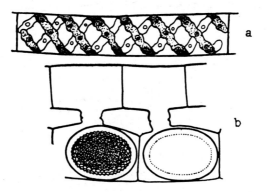

Fig 448. a-b. *S. occidentalis*. (after Transeau.)

Vegetative cells 4-5 × 125-300 $\mu$, with plane end walls ; chloroplasts, 1,2 or 3, making 2 to 6 turns in the cell.

Conjugation scalariform ; tubes formed by both gametangia ; fertile gametangia cylindric or inflated to 66 $\mu$ ; zygospores ovoid to cylindric-ovoid, 36-56 × 57-105 $\mu$ ; median spore wall smooth, yellow-brown ; outer wall of 2 layers, of which the inner is hyaline, scrobiculate.

*Distribution* :   Canada; British Columbia; United States of America.

**210.   Spirogyra hungarica** LANGER 1932.   *Folia Crypt.* **1,** p. 10, Figs. 1-8

Fig. 449. *S. hungarica*. (after Langer.)

Vegetative cells 53-56 × 150-400 $\mu$, with plane end walls ; 1 chloroplast, making 6 to 10 turns in the cell.

Conjugation scalariform ; tubes obconical, formed wholly by the male gametangia ; receptive gametangia slightly inflated on the conjugating side ; zygospores ellipsoid, 45-53 × 120-148 $\mu$ ; median spore wall smooth, yellow-brown.

*Distribution* :   Hungary.

**211.   Spirogyra peipingensis** JAO 1939.   *Sinensia.* **10,** p. 155.

Fig. 450. *S. peipingensis*. (after Jao.)

Vegetative cells 113-135 × 82-332, $\mu$, with plane end walls, chloroplasts 5 or 6.

Conjugation scalariform ; tubes formed by both gametangia ; gametangia cylindric and shortened ; zygospores lenticular, 100-128 × 82-100 $\mu$ ; mesospore smooth, yellow-brown.

*Distribution* :    China.

**212.  Spirogyra suecica** Transeau 1934.   *Ohio. Jour. Sci.* **34,** p. 420. (=*S. varians* var. *gracillis* Borge 1923. *Ark. Bot.* **6,** p. 11, Pl. 1, Fig. 2.)

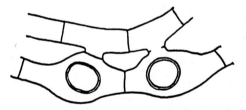

Fig. 451. *S. suecica* (after Borge.)

Vegetative cells 26-29 × 80-175 $\mu$, with plane end walls ; 1 chloroplast, making 1 to 4.5 turns.

Conjugation scalariform or rarely lateral between some cells ; tubes formed by both gametangia ; fertile cells inflated on both sides, usually more on the conjugating side, up to 60 $\mu$ ; zygospores usually ovoid, 32-39 × 38—60 $\mu$ ; median spore wall yellow, smooth.

*Distribution* :    France ; Sweden ; United States of America.

**213.  Spirogyra supervarians** Transeau 1934.   *Trans. Amer. Micros. Soc.* **53,** p. 208.

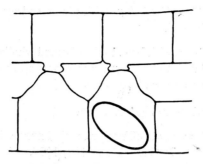

Fig. 452. *S. supervarians*. (after Transeau.)

Vegetative cells 50-57 × 50-144 $\mu$ ; 1 chloroplast ; cells with plane end walls.

Conjugation scalariform ; tubes formed by both gametangia ; receptive gametangium inflated on the inner side ; zygospores ellipsoid, small in proportion to the gametangia 35-40 × 54-74 $\mu$ ; median spore wall smooth, yellow.

*Distribution* : Africa.

**214. Spirogyra tolosana** COMERE 1899. *Bull. soc. bot. de France.* **46,** p. 168, Pl. 3, Figs. 1-3.

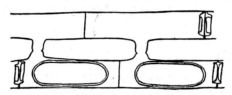

Fig. 453. *S. tolosana*. (after Transeau.)

Vegetative cells 28-30 × 225-300 $\mu$, with replicate end walls ; 2 chloroplasts, making 3.5 to 4 turns.

Conjugation lateral ; fertile cells cylindric or enlarged and shortened ; zygospores cylindric-ovoid, with ends more or less truncate when filling the gametangium, 26-29 × 95-108 $\mu$ ; median wall yellow-brown, smooth.

*Distribution* : France ; United States of America.

**215. Spirogyra visenda** TRANSEAU 1944. *Ohio. Jour. Sci.* **44,** p. 243.

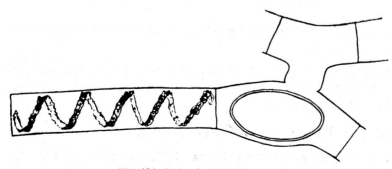

Fig. 454. *S. visenda*. (after Transeau.)

Vegetative cells 40-45 × 130-300 $\mu$, with plane end walls ; 1 narrow chloroplast, making 4 to 9 turns in the cell.

Conjugation scalariform, with broad tubes formed wholly by the male gametangia; receptive gametangia inflated to 60-80 $\mu$ ; zygospores ellipsoid, sometimes ovoid, 35-65 × 92-124 $\mu$ ; median spore wall yellow, smooth.

*Distribution* : United States of America.

**216. Spirogyra jassiensis** (TEODORESCO) CZURDA 1932. *Süsswasserflora Mitteleuropa* **9**, p. 203. *Beih. Bot. Centralbl.* **21**, p. 189, 1907.

Fig. 455. *S. jassiensis.* (after Teodoresco.)

Vegetative cells 116-132 × 116-250 $\mu$, with plane end walls ; 8 to 9 chloroplasts, making 0.5 to 1 turn.

Conjugation lateral ; tubes formed by both gametangia ; fertile cells cylindric ; zygospores lenticular to compressed-ovoid, 102-126 × 140-154 × 72-97 $\mu$ ; median spore wall brown, smooth.

*Distribution* : Russia.

**217. Spirogyra discreta** TRANSEAU 1934. *Ohio. Jour. Sci.* **24**, p. 420. *Amer. Jour. Bot.* **1**, p. 291, 1914 (=*S. inflata* var. *foveolata*).

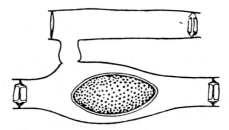

Fig. 456. *S. discreta.* (after Transeau.)

Vegetative cells 16-20 × 50-220 $\mu$, with replicate end walls ; 1 chloroplast, making 3 to 6 turns in the cell.

Conjugation lateral and scalariform ; tubes formed by both gametangia ; fertile cells greatly inflated towards the middle; zygospores ellipsoid, 28-36 × 50-75 $\mu$ ; median spore wall scrobiculate, yellow.

*Distribution* : China ; United States of America.

**218. Spirogyra amplectens** SKUJA 1937. *Symbolae Sinicae.* **1**, p. 85, Figs. 9-11.

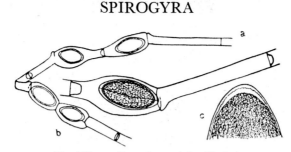

Fig. 457. a-c. *S. amplectens*. (after Skuja.)

Vegetative cells 15-20 × 60-200 $\mu$, with replicate end walls ; 1 chloroplast.

Conjugation lateral ; receptive gametangia cylindrically inflated to 30-50 $\mu$ ; zygospores ellipsoid, 32-40 × 53-73 $\mu$ ; outer spore wall thick, hyaline, inwardly scrobiculate-punctate ; median wall thick, yellow-brown, outwardly reticulate, inwardly scrobiculate-punctate ; inner wall thin, hyaline and externally rugose.

*Distribution* : China.

**219. Spirogyra heeriana** NAEGELI 1849. In Kützing, *Species Algarum*, p. 442. *Tabulae Phycologicae*. **5,** pl. 28, Fig. 3.

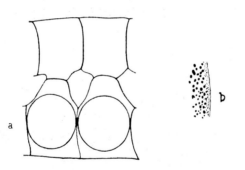

Fig. 458. a-b. *S. heeriana*. (after Czurda.)

Vegetative cells 130-150 × 130-250 $\mu$, with plane end walls ; about 8 chloroplasts, making 0.5 to 1 turn in the cell.

Conjugation scalariform ; tubes formed by both gametangia ; fertile cells not inflated, although the tubes become very wide ; zygospores lenticular, about 150 $\mu$ in diameter ; median wall yellow-brown, thick, with round brown papillae irregularly distributed over the surface.

*Distribution* : Austria ; France.

**220. Spirogyra crassispina** JAO 1939. *Sinensia*. **10,** p. 153.

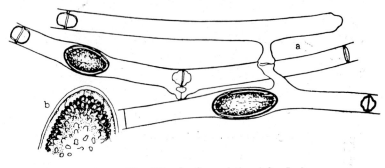

Fig. 459. a-b. *S. crassispina*. (after Jao).

Vegetative cells 30-35 × 326-351 $\mu$, with replicate end walls ; chloroplasts 2, making 1 to 3.5 turns in the cell.

Conjugation lateral and scalariform ; tubes formed by both cells ; receptive gametangia enlarged ; zygospores ellipsoid or sometimes cylindric-ellipsoid, 42-50 × 80-137 $\mu$ ; median spore wall of 2 layers, of which the outer is thin, yellow, and wrinkled; the inner coarsely dentate or tuberculate, yellow-brown at maturity.

*Distribution* :   China.

**221.   Spirogyra esthonica** (SKUJA) CZURDA 1932. *Süsswasserflora Mitteleuropa*. **9,** p. 180, Fig. 191. *Acta Horti Bot. Univ. Latviensis*. **3,** p. 109 ( =S. *punctata* var *esthonica*.)

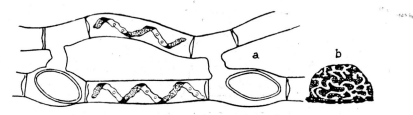

Fig. 460. a-b. *S. esthonica*. (after Skuja).

Vegetative cells 27-33 × 90-360 $\mu$, with plane end walls ; 1 chloroplast,   making 3 to 9 turns in the cell.

Conjugation scalariform ; tubes formed largely by the male gametangia ; receptive gametangia inflated up to 60 $\mu$ ; gametangia usually separated by sterile cells ; zygospores ellipsoid, 39-50 × 64-115 $\mu$ ; median spore wall irregularly corrugate with minute punctations between the ridges.

*Distribution* :   Estonia.

**222.   Spirogyra hunanensis** JAO 1940.   *Sinensia*. **11,** p. 297, Pl. 4, Figs. 4-5.

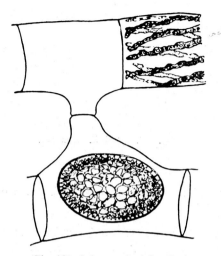

Fig. 461. *S. hunanensis.* (after Jao).

Vegetative cells 88-100 × 75-210 $\mu$, with plane end walls ; and 8-10 nearly straight or slightly spiralled chloroplasts.

Conjugation scalariform ; tubes formed by both gametangia ; receptive gametangia inflated on the conjugating side up to 150 $\mu$ ; zygospores ovoid, 88-105 × 142-163 $\mu$ ; median spore wall yellow-brown, reticulate and verrucose, with verrucae up to 13 $\mu$ in length.

*Distribution* : China.

**223. Spirogyra lagerheimii** WITTROCK 1889. In Wittrock and Nordstedt Nos. 961 and 962. *Bot. Notiser.* 1889. p. 165.

Fig. 462. *S. lagerheimii.* (after Wittrock).

Vegetative cells 25-33 × 75-150 $\mu$, with plane end walls ; 1 chloroplast, usually narrow, making 0.5 to 4 turns.

Conjugation scalariform and lateral ; tubes formed by both cells ; fertile cells cylindric or enlarged ; zygospores ellipsoid with more or less pointed ends, 25-38 × 50-100 $\mu$ ; median spore wall yellowish-brown, finely punctate.

*Distribution* : Finland ; Germany ; Latvia ; Sweden ; United States of America.

**224. Spirogyra taylorii** JAO 1935. *Trans. Amer. Micros. Soc.* **54,** p. 4, Pl. 1, Figs. 2-3.

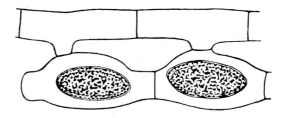

Fig. 463. *S. taylorii.* (after Jao.)

Vegetative cells 12-16 × (48-) 70-193 $\mu$, with plane end walls ; 1 chloroplast making 2.5 to 6 turns in the cell.

Conjugation scalariform ; tubes formed by the male gametangia ; fertile cells inflated towards the middle and usually more on the conjugating side, up to 33 $\mu$ ; zygospores ellipsoid, 19-29×39-45 $\mu$ ; median spore wall finely reticulate to punctate, yellowish-brown at maturity.

*Distribution :* United States of America.

**225. Spirogyra protecta** Wood 1872. *Smithson. Contribu. Knowledge.* **19,** p. 165, Pl. 14, Fig. 3. Cleve. *Nova Acta Reg. Soc. Sci. Upsali,* Ser. 3, **6,** p. 26. 1868 (=*S. calospora* forma *gracilior*). Czurda 1932. *Süsswasserflora Mitteleuropa* **9,** p. 147 (=*S. calospora* Cleve).

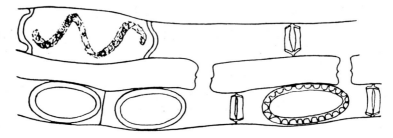

Fig. 464. e-b. *S. protecta.* (after Transeau.)

Vegetative cells 28-34×120-425 $\mu$, with replicate end walls ; 1 rarely 2 chloroplasts, making 2 to 6 turns ; reproduction by zygospores and aplanospores.

Conjugation scalariform ; tubes formed by both gametangia ; receptive gametangia cylindric or enlarged ; zygospores ovoid, 30-38 × 66-90 $\mu$ ; outer spore wall of 2 layers, of which the inner is thick, scrobiculate ; median spore wall yellow, smooth ; aplanospores similar but smaller.

*Distribution :* Finland ; France ; Ukraine ; United States of America.

**226. Spirogyra insignis** (Hassall) Kützing 1849. *Species Algarum,* p. 438.

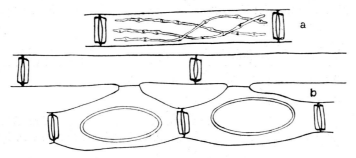

Fig. 465. a-b. *S. insignis.* (after Petit.)

Vegetative cells 39-42 × 150-590 $\mu$, with replicate end walls ; 2 to 4 (usually 3) chloroplasts, making 0.5 to 1.5 turns.

Conjugation scalariform and lateral ; tubes formed by both gametangia ; fertile cells shortened and inflated ; zygospores ellipsoid, 40-48 × 60-128 $\mu$ ; median spore wall yellow-brown, smooth.

*Distribution* :   China ; Europe ; United States of America.

**227. Spirogyra minutifossa** Jao 1935. *Trans. Amer. Micros. Soc.* **54,** pp. 3-4, Pl. 1, Fig. 5.

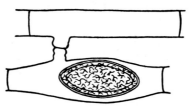

Fig. 466. *S. minutifossa.* (after Jao.)

Vegetative cells 16-19 × 55-176 $\mu$, with plane end walls ; 1 choloroplast making 2-6·5 turns.

Conjugation scalariform ; tubes formed by both gametangia ; fertile cells fusiform-inflated ; zygospores ellipsoid with rather pointed ends, 22-26 × 35-48 $\mu$ ; median spore wall irregularly and minutely grooved, yellow at maturity.

*Distribution* :   Nova Scotia ; United States of America.

**228. Spirogyra tsingtaoensis** Li 1936.   *Bull. Fan Mem. Inst. Biol.* **7,** p. 61, Pl. 1, Figs. 3-4.

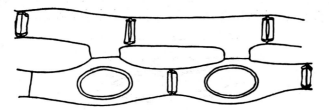

Fig. 467. *S. tsingtaoensis.* (after Li.)

Vegetative cells 20-25 × 54-80 $\mu$, with replicate end walls ; 1 chloroplast, making 0.5 to 2 turns in the cell.

Conjugation scalariform and lateral ; tubes formed by the male gametangia ; fertile cells inflated up to 35 $\mu$ and shortened ; zygospores ellipsoid with rounded ends, 24-28 × 46-52 $\mu$ ; median spore wall smooth, yellow.

*Distribution* :   China.

**229.   Spirogyra fritschiana** Czurda 1932. *Süsswasserflora Mitteleuropa.* **9,** p. 156. *Trans. Roy. Soc. S. Africa.* **18,** p. 50, Fig. 14A-B (=*S. protecta* var. *inflata*).

Fig. 468. *S. fritschiana.* (after Fritsch & Rich.)

Vegetative cells 17-24 × 80-260 $\mu$, with replicate end walls ; 1 chloroplast.

Conjugation lateral and scalariform ; tubes formed by both gametangia ; fertile cells inflated toward the middle ; zygospores ellipsoid, 35-40 × 55-64 $\mu$ ; median spore wall brown, coarsely punctate.

*Distribution* :   South Africa.

**230.   Spirogyra lushanensis** Li 1938. *Bull. Fan Mem. Inst. Biol.* **8,** p. 92, Pl. 2, Figs. 4-5.

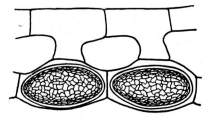

Fig. 469. *S. lushanensis.* (after Li.)

Vegetative cells 17-23 × 84-158 $\mu$, with plane end walls ; 1 chloroplast making 3·5 to 7 turns in the cell.

Conjugation scalariform ; tubes formed wholly by the male gametangia ; fertile cells inflated to 38 $\mu$ and shortened ; zygospores ellipsoid, 26-36 × 42-78 $\mu$ ; median wall irregularly reticulate, yellow.

*Distribution* :   China.

**231.   Spirogyra fallax** (Hansgirg) Wille 1900. *Nyt Magaz. f. Naturw.* **38,** p. 16.   Hansgirg. *Hedwigia.* **27,** p. 253. 1888 (as *S. insignis* var. *fallax*).

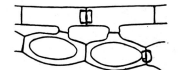

Fig. 470. *S. fallax.* (after Hansgirg.)

Vegetative cells 36-45 × 80-165 $\mu$, with replicate end walls ; 3 to 4 chloroplasts, straight, or making 0.5 to 1.5 turns in the cell.

Conjugation scalariform ; tubes formed by both cells ; fertile cells inflated to 48-75 $\mu$ ; zygospores ellipsoid, 45-60 × 75-120 $\mu$ ; median spore wall brown, smooth.

*Distribution* : Czechoslovakia ; United States of America.

**232. Spirogyra pseudoreticulata** KRIEGER 1944. Rabenhorst's *Kryptogamen-flora.* **13,** p. 400.

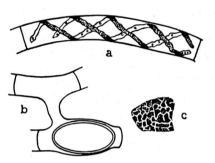

Fig. 471. a-c. *S. pseudoreticulata.* (after Borge.)

Vegetative cells 20-25 × 75-170 $\mu$, with plane end walls and 2 chloroplasts.

Conjugation lateral and scalariform ; tubes formed by both cells ; receptive gametangia enlarged ; zygospores ellipsoid, 30-33 × 64-68 $\mu$ ; median spore wall brown, with rather fine, irregular, reticulate ridges.

*Distribution* : Brazil.

**233. Spirogyra pseudogranulata** LEY 1944. *Sinensia,* **15,** p. 99.

Fig. 472. *S. pseudogranulata.* (after Li)

Vegetative cells 36-40 × 152-378 $\mu$, end walls replicate ; chloroplasts 2.

Conjugation lateral ; tubes formed by both gametangia ; receptive gametangia enlarged or inflated ; zygospores ovoid, 46-68 × 100-140 $\mu$ ; median spore wall of 2 layers ; the outer thick, irregularly corrugate ; the inner minutely reticulate, yellow-brown.

*Distribution* : China.

**234. Spirogyra baileyi** SCHMIDLE 1896. *Flora.* **82,** pp. 302-3, Pl. 9, Fig. 2.

Fig. 473. *S. baileyi*. (after Schmidle.)

Vegetative cells 20-24 × 128-200 $\mu$, with plane end walls ; 2 chloroplasts, making 3 to 4 turns.

Conjugation scalariform ; tubes formed by both gametangia ; fertile cells inflated to 32 $\mu$ ; zygospores ellipsoid, 28 × 48-50 $\mu$ ; median spore wall smooth.

*Distribution* :   Australia.

**235.  Spirogyra croasdaleae** BLUM 1943.   *Amer. Jour. Bot.* **30,** p.  783, Figs. 6-8.

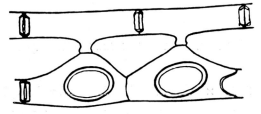

Fig. 474. *S. croasdaleae*. (after Blum.)

Vegetative cells 17-25 × 120-300 $\mu$, with replicate end walls; 1 chloroplast making 4 to 8 turns in the cell.

Conjugation scalariform ; tubes formed by the male gametangia ; fertile cells much inflated on the conjugating side ; zygospores ellipsoid, 26-33 × 46-62 $\mu$ ; median wall yellow, smooth.

*Distribution* :   United States of America.

**236.  Spirogyra reflexa** TRANSEAU 1915.   *Ohio Jour. Sci.* **16,** p. 28.

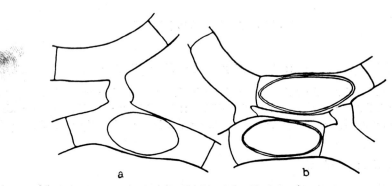

Fig. 475. a-b. *S. reflexa*. (after Transeau.)

Vegetative cells 30-44 × 120-300 $\mu$, with plane end walls ; 1 chloroplast, making 3 to 8 turns.

Conjugation scalariform ; tubes formed by the male gametangia ; fertile cells inflated or enlarged and strongly reflexed, single or in groups of 2 or 4; zygospores and aplanospores ellipsoid, 44-64 × 90-150 $\mu$ ; median spore wall yellow-brown, smooth.

*Distribution* : United States of America.

**237. Spirogyra porangabae** Transeau 1938. *Amer. Jour. Bot.* **25,** p. 525.

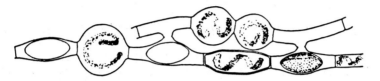

Fig. 476. *S. porangabae.* (after Transeau.)

Vegetative cells 11-15 × 65-145 $\mu$, with plane end walls ; 1 chloroplast making 4 to 9 turns in the cell.

Conjugation scalariform ; tubes formed by both gametangia ; receptive gametangium enlarged or slightly inflated ; sterile cells inflated, often bulliform ; zygospores ellipsoid, 21-27 × 47-54 $\mu$ ; median wall at first smooth, at maturity irregularly but distinctly punctate, yellow-brown.

*Distribution* : Brazil.

**238. Spirogyra taftiana** Transeau 1944. *Ohio Jour. Sci.* **44,** p. 243.

Fig. 477. *S. taftiana.* (after Taft.)

Vegetative cells 18-25 × 50-96 $\mu$, with plane end walls ; 1 chloroplast making 2-4 turns in the cell.

Conjugation scalariform ; tubes formed by both gametangia ; receptive gametangia enlarged or fusiform-inflated ; sterile cells often bulliform ; zygospores ellipsoid, 24-34 × 42-80 $\mu$ ; median wall distinctly and densely punctate; pits more or less angular, yellow.

*Distribution* : United States of America.

**239. Spirogyra silvicola** Britton 1943. *Amer. Jour. Bot.* **30,** p. 799, Fig. 1.

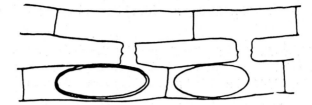

Fig. 478. *S. silvicola*. (after Britton.)

Vegetative cells 32-42 × 63-267 $\mu$, with plane end walls ; 1 chloroplast making 1.5 to 3 turns in the cell.

Conjugation scalariform ; tubes formed by both gametangia ; receptive gametangia cylindric or slightly enlarged : zygospores ellipsoid to cylindric-ovoid, 36-43 × 56-103 $\mu$ ; all walls smooth ; median wall yellow or brown at maturity.

*Distribution* : United States of America.

**240. Spirogyra lenticularis** Transeau 1938. *Amer. Jour. Bot.* **25**, p. 528, Figs. 18-19.

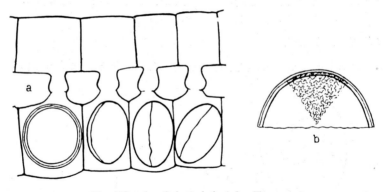

Fig. 479. a-b. *S. lenticularis*. (after Transeau.)

Vegetative cells 150-162 × (80-) 125-200 (-300) $\mu$, with plane end walls ; 9 or 10 chloroplasts, straight, or making 1 turn in the cell.

Conjugation scalariform ; tubes formed by both gametangia ; receptive gametangia shortened and cylindric or slightly enlarged on the inner side ; zygospores compressed-spheroid, 136-145 × 90-100 $\mu$ ; outer wall thin, smooth, transparent ; median wall thick, minutely verrucose and with reticulations, brown.

*Distribution* : South Africa.

**241. Spirogyra emilianensis** Bonhomme 1858. *Sur quelques algues d'eau douce*, p. 7, Pl. 2, Fig. 2.

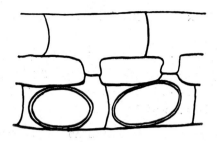

Fig. 480. *S. emillianensis*. (after Transeau).

Vegetative cells 50-60 × 100-200 $\mu$, with plane end walls ; 4 to 5 chloroplasts, making 0.2 to 2.5 turns.

Conjugation scalariform ; tubes formed by both gametangia ; fertile cells cylindric ; zygospores ovoid, 52-60 × 90-124 $\mu$ ; median spore wall brown, smooth.

*Distribution* : France; United States of America.

**242. Spirogyra smithii** TRANSEAU 1934. *Trans. Amer. Micros. Soc.* **53,** p. 225.

Flg. 481. a-b. *S. smithii*. (after Transeau).

Vegetative cells 30-35 × 220-360 $\mu$, with plane end walls ; 3 to 4 chloroplasts making 1 to 3 turns in the cell.

Conjugation scalariform ; tubes formed by both gametangia : fertile cells enlarged; zygospores ellipsoid, 45-52 × 75-102 $\mu$ ; median spore wall yellow-brown, of 2 layers ; outer, thin, wrinkled ; inner, reticulate.

*Distribution* : United States of America.

**243. Spirogyra fossa** JAO 1935. *Trans. Amer. Micros. Soc.* **54,** p. 3, Pl. 1, Fig. 6.

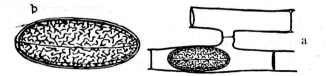

Fig. 482. a-b. *S. fossa*. (after Jao).

Vegetative cells 19-22 × 96-192 $\mu$, with plane end walls ; 2 chloroplasts making 1 to 5 turns.

Conjugation scalariform ; tubes formed by both gametangia ; fertile cells enlarged to 33 $\mu$ ; zygospores ellipsoid, 27-32 × 48-77 $\mu$ ; median spore wall yellow-brown at maturity, with irregular, tortuous grooves, or corrugations.

*Distribution* : United States of America.

**244. Spirogyra circumlineata** TRANSEAU 1914. *Amer. Jour. Bot.* **1,** p. 293.

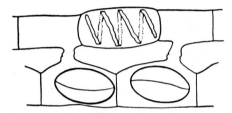

Fig. 483. *S. circumlineata*. (after Transeau.)

Vegetative cells (38-) 40-48 × 120-240 $\mu$, with plane end walls ; 1 chloroplast, slender, making 4 to 8 turns.

Conjugation scalariform ; tubes formed by both gametangia : fertile cells inflated on the conjugating side only ; zygospores ellipsoid, 40-50 × 70-125 $\mu$ ; median spore wall yellow-brown, smooth ; suture more or less prominent.

*Distribution* : United States of America.

**245. Spirogyra bicalyptrata** CZURDA 1930. *Beih. Bot. Centralbl.* **47,** p. 31.

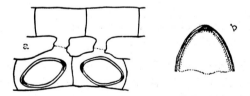

Fig. 484. a-b. *S. bicalyptrata*. (after Czurda.)

Vegetative cells 36-39 × 60-110 $\mu$, with plane end walls ; chloroplast 1 (rarely 2).

Conjugation scalariform ; tubes formed by both gametangia; fertile cells swollen on the conjugating side ; zygospores ellipsoid, 31-34 × 55-70 $\mu$ ; median spore wall brown, smooth, with dark brown polar thickenings.

*Distribution* : Austria ; Czechoslovakia ; Greece.

**246. Spirogyra sulcata** BLUM 1943. *Amer. Jour. Bot.* **30,** p. 783, Figs. 9-11.

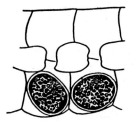

Fig. 485. *S. sulcata*. (after Blum.)

Vegetative cells 37-46 × 50-160 $\mu$, with plane end walls ; 1 (-2) chloroplast, with prominent median furrow, making 2 to 5 turns in the cells.

Conjugation scalariform ; tubes formed by both gametangia ; fertile cells inflated on the outer side ; zygospores ovoid, 43-46 × 52-62 $\mu$ ; median spore wall thick, brown, and reticulate.

*Distribution* : United States of America.

**247. Spirogyra hollandiae** TAFT 1947. *Ohio Jour. Sci.* **47**, p. 173.

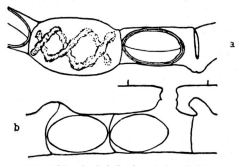

Fig. 486. a-b. *S. hollandiae*. (after Taft.)

Vegetative cells 36-41 × 60-192 $\mu$, with plane end walls ; 2 chloroplasts, broad with large pyrenoids, making 1.5-2.5 turns in the cell.

Conjugation usually lateral ; tubes formed by both gametangia ; sterile cells sometimes inflated ; receptive gametangia cylindric or enlarged ; zygospores ellipsoid with rounded ends, 38-42 × 62-78 $\mu$ ; median wall smooth, bright yellow at maturity.

*Distribution* : Dutch New Guinea.

**248. Spirogyra formosa** (TRANSEAU) CZURDA 1932. *Süsswasserflora Mitte-leuropa.* **9**, p. 203. ( =*S. crassa* var. *formosa. Ohio Jour. Sci.* **16**, p. 27, 1915).

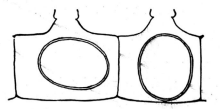

Fig. 487. *S. formosa*. (after Transeau.)

Vegetative cells 80-95 × 80-270 $\mu$, with plane end walls ; 6-12 chloroplasts, making 0.5 to 1 turn in the cell.

Conjugation scalariform ; tubes formed by both gametangia ; fertile cells cylindric ; zygospores compressed-ovoid, 88-100 × 120-150 $\mu$ × 70-90 $\mu$ ; median spore wall brown, with irregular, shallow pits.

*Distribution* :   United States of America.

**249.   Spirogyra pellucida** (HASSALL) KUTZING 1849.   *Species Algarum*, p. 439. Hassall. *History of British Freshwater Algae*. p. 143, Pl. 25, Figs. 1-2. 1844.

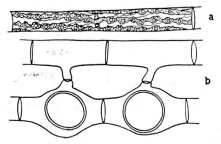

Fig. 488. a-b. *S. pellucida*. (after G.S. West).

Vegetative cells  40-50 × 100-400 $\mu$, with plane end walls ; 3 to 4 chloroplasts straight, or making 0.5 to 4 turns.

Conjugation scalariform ; tubes formed by both gametangia ; fertile cells inflated toward the middle ; zygospores lenticular, 77-86 $\mu$ in diameter ; median spore wall smooth, brown.

*Distribution* :   China;  England;  Finland ;  United States of America.

**250.   Spirogyra texensis** TAFT 1944.   *Ohio Jour. Sci.* **44**, p. 238.

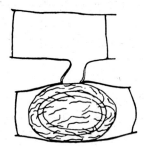

Fig. 489. *S. texensis*. (after Taft).

Vegetative cells 50-55 × 90-530 $\mu$, with plane end walls ;  3 to  5 chloroplasts making 1.5 to 3.5 turns in the cell.

Conjugation scalariform ; tubes formed by the male gametangia ; fertile cells shortened and enlarged ; zygospores ovoid,  66-76 × 99-124 $\mu$ ;  outer  spore wall transparent, irregularly corrugate ; median wall yellow-brown, conspicuously reticulate.

*Distribution*: United States of America.

**251. Spirogyra yunnanensis** LI 1939. *Bull. Fan Mem. Inst. Biol., Botany.* **9,** p. 224, Pl. 27, Fig. 2.

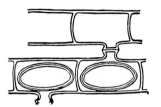

Fig. 490. *S. yunnanensis.* (after Li.)

Vegetative cells 98-110 × 224-268 $\mu$, with plane end walls ; chloroplasts 6-8, making 2-4 turns in the cell.

Conjugation scalariform ; tubes formed by both gametangia ; fertile cells cylindric and shortened ; zygospores ellipsoid, 88-96 × 120-180 $\mu$ ; median spore wall smooth, yellow.

*Distribution*: China.

**252. Spirogyra parvispora** WOOD 1869. *Proc. Amer. Phil. Soc.* **11,** p. 139. 1872. *Smithson. Contribu. Knowledge,* **19,** p. 169, Pl. 15, Fig. 7.

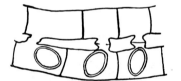

Fig. 491. *S. parvispora.* (after Wood.)

Vegetative cells about 75 × 150-300 $\mu$, with plane end walls ; 4 chloroplasts making 1.5 turns.

Conjugation scalariform ; tubes formed by both gametangia ; fertile cells not inflated ; spores ellipsoid, 50 × 75-100 $\mu$ ; median spore wall brown, smooth.

*Distribution*: Galicia ; United States of America.

**253. Spirogyra hydrodictya** TRANSEAU 1915. *Ohio Jour. Sci.* **16,** p. 28.

Vegetative cells 75-100 × 210-360 $\mu$, with plane end walls ; 7 to 10 chloroplasts, straight or making 0.1 to 0.5 turn.

Conjugation scalariform and lateral ; tubes formed by the male gametangia ; fertile cells shortened and enlarged, or slightly inflated ; zygospores lenticular to lenticular-globose, 80-120 × 110-195 $\mu$; median spore wall brown, pitted.

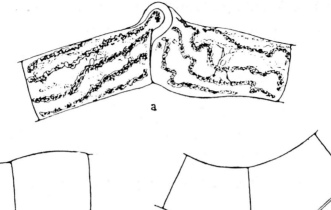

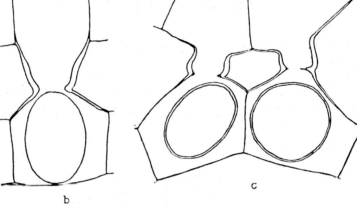

Fig. 492. a-c. *S. hydrodictya*. (after Transeau.)

*Distribution*: United States of America.

**254. Spirogyra echinospora** BLUM 1943.    *Amer. Jour. Bot.* **30**, p. 783, Figs. 1-2.

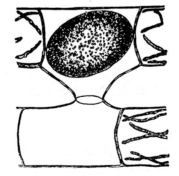

Fig. 493. *S. echinospora*. (after Blum.)

Vegetative cells 66-72 × 50-125 $\mu$, with plane end walls; 6-7 (-8) chloroplasts, making 0,5 to 1,5 turns in the cell.

Conjugation scalariform; tubes wide and formed by both gametangia; fertile cells more or less inflated on the conjugating side; zygospores ovoid, 67-82 × 98-150 $\mu$; median spore wall thick, brown-black, echinate.

*Distribution*: United States of America.

**255.  Spirogyra novae-angliae** Transeau 1915.  *Ohio Jour. Sci.* **16,** p. 26.

Fig. 494. *S. novae-angliae.* (after Blum.)

Vegetative cells 48-60 × 150-390 $\mu$ ; with plane end walls ; 3 to 5 chloroplasts, making 2.5 to 4.5 turns.

Conjugation scalariform ; fertile cells cylindric or enlarged ; tubes formed by both gametangia ; zygospores ovoid, 50-65 × 70-120 $\mu$ ; median spore wall yellow, reticulate and finely punctate.

*Distribution* :  United States of America.

**256.  Spirogyra torta** Blum 1943.  *Amer. Jour. Bot.* **30,** p. 783, Figs. 3-5.

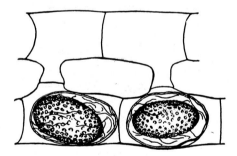

Fig. 495. *S. torta.* (after Blum.)

Vegetative cells 49-56 × 270-600 $\mu$, with plane end walls ; 3 to 5 chloroplasts, making 1 to 4 turns in the cell.

Conjugation scalariform ; tubes formed by both gametangia ; fertile cells cylindric or enlarged ; zygospores ellipsoid, 67-72 × 110-135 $\mu$; outer spore wall wrinkled, loose ; median spore wall dark yellow, conspicuously pitted-reticulate.

*Distribution* :  United States of America.

**257.  Spirogyra scripta** Nygaard 1932.  *Trans. Roy. Soc. S. Africa,* **20,** p. 144, Fig. 48.

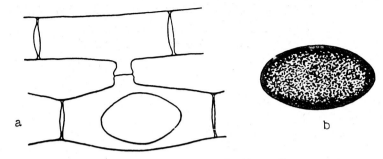

Fig. 496. a-b. *S. scripta.* (after Nygaard).

Vegetative cells 51-64 × 220-300 $\mu$, with plane end walls ; 4 to 5 chloroplasts, making about 2 turns.

Conjugation scalariform ; tubes formed by both gametangia ; fertile cells inflated to 67-71 $\mu$, shortened ; zygospores ellipsoid, more or less pointed, 54-60 × 91-107 $\mu$; median spore wall brown, with an intricate pattern of branched, short, dark crevices and corrugations.

*Distribution* :   South Africa.

**258.  Spirogyra mienningensis** Li 1940.   *Bull. Fan Mem. Inst. Biol., Botany.* **10,** p. 61.

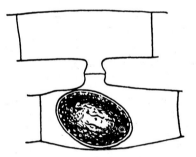

Fig. 497. *S. mienningensis.* (after Li.)

Vegetative cells 42-48 × 102-208 $\mu$, with   plane end walls ; chloroplasts 2 or 3, making 1-4 turns in the cell.

Conjugation scalariform ; tubes formed by both gametangia ; fertile cells inflated up to 74 $\mu$ ; zygospores ellipsoid, 52-59 × 70-88 $\mu$ ; outer spore wall of 2 layers, the outermost thin, smooth, transparent ; the inner thin and wrinkled ; median  spore wall granulose to verrucose, yellow-brown at maturity.

*Distribution* :   China.

**259.  Spirogyra paraguayensis** Borge 1903.   *Ark. Bot.* **1,** p. 280.

Fig. 498. a-b. *S. paraguayensis*. (after Borge.)

Vegetative cells 41-45 × 80-200 $\mu$, with plane end walls ; 3 to 4 chloroplasts, nearly straight, or making 0·5 turn.

Conjugation scalariform ; tubes formed by both gametangia ; fertile cells cylindric, shortened ; zygospores ellipsoid, 37-42 × 58-65 $\mu$ ; median spore wall irregularly corrugate, yellow-brown.

*Distribution* : South America.

**260. Spirogyra calcarea** TRANSEAU 1934. *Trans. Amer. Micros. Soc.* **53,** p. 226.

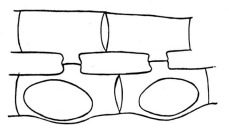

Fig. 499. *S. calcarea*. (after Kolkwitz & Krieger.)

Vegetative cells 37-42 × 40-120 $\mu$, with plane end walls ; 1 chloroplast, making 2 to 5 turns in the cell.

Conjugation scalariform ; tubes formed by both gametangia ; receptive gametangia inflated only on the outer side ; zygospores ellipsoid, 40-55 × 58-80 $\mu$ ; median spore wall smooth, yellow.

*Distribution* : United States of America.

**261. Spirogyra frankliniana** TIFFANY 1934. *Trans. Amer. Micros. Soc.* **53,** p. 225. *Ohio Jour. Sci.* 24, p. 65.

Fig. 500. *S. frankliniana*. (after Tiffany.)

Vegetative cells 32-36 × 80-120 $\mu$, with plane end walls ; 3 to 4 chloroplasts, making 1 to 3 turns in the cell.

Conjugation scalariform ; tubes formed by both gametangia ; fertile cells inflated towards the middle ; zygospores lenticular, 40-56 $\mu$ in diameter ; median spore wall smooth, brown.

*Distribution* :    United States of America.

**262.   Spirogyra moebii** Transeau 1934.   *Trans. Amer. Micros. Soc.* **53,** p. 225. (*S. maxima* var. *minor* Moebius. *Flora.* **75,** p. 421.1892 ; *S. bimorphis* Dixit).

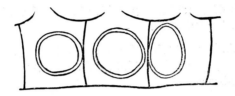

Fig. 501. *S. moebii.* (after Borge.)

Vegetative cells 80-117 × 130-240 $\mu$, with plane end walls; 6 to 8 chloroplasts, making 0·5 to 1 turn.

Conjugation scalariform ; tubes formed by both gametangia ; fertile cells cylindric ; zygospores lenticular, 74-100 × 56-65 $\mu$ ; median spore wall yellow-brown, reticulate.

*Distribution* :

    *India* :   Bombay.

    *Other countries* :   Australia ; Europe ; United States of America.

**263.   Spirogyra latviensis** (Skuja) Czurda 1932.   *Süsswasserflora Mitteleuropa.* **9,** p. 147. Skuja. *Acta Horti Bot. Univ. Lativiensis.* **3,** p. 109. 1928 (as *S. protecta* forma). It is also described as *S. petitiana* Transeau 1934.

Vegetative cells 20-25 × 100-250 $\mu$, with replicate end walls ; 1 chloroplast, making 3 to 5·5 turns in the cell.

Conjugation scalariform ; tubes formed by both gametangia ; fertile cells inflated to 30-40 $\mu$ ; zygospores ovoid to cylindric-ovoid, 29-39 × 75-115 $\mu$; outer hyaline spore wall of 2 layers, of which the outer is thin ; the inner, thick, verrucose, with short, pointed elevations ; median spore wall smooth, yellow-brown.

*Distribution* :   Latvia; United States of America.

**264.   Spirogyra rugosa** (Transeau) Czurda 1932.   *Süsswasserflora Mitteleuropa.* **9,** p. 156. *Amer. Jour. Bot.* **1,** p. 291. 1914. Phycoth. Bot. Amer., No. 456 (as *S. tenuissima* var. *rugosa*).

Vegetative cells 10-13 × 50-210 $\mu$, with replicate end walls ; 1 chloroplast, making 2 to 6 turns.

Conjugation lateral and scalariform ; tubes formed by both gametangia ; fertile cells greatly inflated towards the middle ; zygospores ellipsoid, 28-32 × 55-66 $\mu$ ; median spore wall yellow-brown, minutely scrobiculate.

*Distribution*: United States of America.

**265. Spirogyra conspicua** GAY 1884. *Essai d'une monographie locale des Conjuguées*, p. 91, Pl. 4, Fig. 5.

Vegetative cells about $45 \times 45\text{-}135$ $\mu$, with plane end walls; 5 chloroplasts making 0.5 to 1.5 turns.

Conjugation scalariform; tubes formed by the male gametangia; fertile cells inflated; zygospores ovoid, about $55 \times 82$ $\mu$; median spore wall brown, smooth.

*Distribution*: France.

**266. Spirogyra prescottii** (PRESCOTT) Transeau 1944. *Ohio Jour. Sci.* **44,** p. 243. *Amer. Midland Naturalist*, **27,** p. 673, Pl. 4, Figs. 15-17. 1942 (as *S. collinsii* var. *minor*).

Vegetative cells $13\text{-}14 \times 115\text{-}140\,\mu$; with plane end walls; 1 chloroplast, loosely spiralled.

Conjugation scalariform; tubes formed by the male gametangia; fertile cells inflated to 33 $\mu$; zygospores ovoid to ellipsoid, $29 \times 39\text{-}40$ $\mu$; median spore wall coarsely punctate, yellow.

*Distribution*: United States of America.

**267. Spirogyra rectispira** MERRIMAN 1922 (Char. amend). *Amer. Jour. Bot.* **9,** p. 283.

Vegetative cells $150\text{-}180 \times 75\text{-}320$ $\mu$; with plane end walls; 11-16 chloroplasts, straight or making 0.1 to 1 turn.

Conjugation scalariform; tubes formed by both gametangia; fertile cells cylindric or enlarged on the inner side; zygospores compressed ovoid, $140\text{-}152 \times 168\text{-}185 \times 110\text{-}130$ $\mu$; median spore wall minutely verrucose, brown.

*Distribution*: United States of America.

**268. Spirogyra megaspora** (LAGERHEIM) Transeau 1934. *Ohio Jour. Sci,* **34,** p. 420. Wittrock and Nordstedt, *Algae Exsiccatae*, No. 745.

Vegetative cells $170\text{-}200 \times 150\text{-}400$ $\mu$, with plane end walls; 6 to 7 chloroplasts, making 0.5 to 1 turn in the cell.

Conjugation scalariform; tubes formed by both gametangia; fertile cells cylindric; zygospores lenticular, $135\text{-}170 \times 90\text{-}120$ $\mu$; median spore wall yellow-brown, reticulate.

*Distribution*: Sweden; Uruguay.

**269. Spirogyra crassiuscula** (Wittrock & Nordstedt.) TRANSEAU 1934. *Ohio Jour. Sci.* **34,** p. 420. Wittrock and Nordstedt, *Algae Exsiccatae*, No. 746.

Vegetative cells $145\text{-}170 \times 140\text{-}300$ $\mu$, with plane end walls; 6 to 7 chloroplasts making 0.5 to 1 turn in the cell.

Conjugation scalariform; tubes formed by both gametangia; fertile cells cylindric; zygospores lenticular, $120\text{-}150 \times 85\text{-}100$ $\mu$; median spore wall yellow-brown, reticulate.

*Distribution*: England; South Africa.

**270. Spirogyra nawashini** KASANOFSKY 1913. *Ber. deutsch. Bot. Gesells.* **31,** p. 55, Pl. 3.

Vegetative cells 27-41 × 170-325 $\mu$, with replicate end walls ; 2 (rarely 1) chloroplasts, with 0.5 to 1.5 turns.

Conjugation scalariform ; tubes formed by both gametangia; fertile cells fusiform, inflated to 50-55 $\mu$ ; zygospores ellipsoid to cylindric-ellipsoid, 30-49 × 45-100 $\mu$ ; median spore wall reticulate, yellow-brown.

*Distribution*: China ; South Africa ; Ukraine ; United States of America.

**271. Spirogyra castanacea** G.C. COUCH 1944. *Ohio Jour. Sci.* **44,** p. 277.

Vegetative cells 34-37 × 100-173 $\mu$, with plane end walls ; 2 to 3 chloroplasts, making 2 to 3 turns in the cell.

Conjugation scalariform ; tubes formed by both gametangia ; receptive cell inflated on both sides ; zygospores mostly broadly ellipsoid, rarely ovoid, 48-52 × 69-73 $\mu$ ; median spore wall chestnut brown, strongly reticulate.

*Distribution*: United States of America.

**272. Spirogyra miamiana** TAFT 1944. *Ohio Jour. Sci.* **44,** p. 238.

Vegetative cells 20-25 × 150-340 $\mu$, with plane end walls ; 3 chloroplasts (rarely 2), making 1.5 to 5 turns.

Conjugation scalariform ; tubes formed by both gametangia ; fertile cells enlarged to 41 $\mu$, length 71 to 172 $\mu$ ; zygospores ellipsoid to cylindric-ellipsoid, 30-39 × 92 $\mu$ ; median spore wall composed of 2 layers ; the outer layer wrinkled ; the inner layer finely scrobiculate, yellow-brown at maturity.

*Distribution*: United State of America.

**273. Spirogyra natchita** TRANSEAU 1934. *Trans. Amer. Micros. Soc.* **53,** p. 225.

Vegetative cells 32-36 × 120-200 $\mu$, with plane end walls ; 1 to 3 (mostly 2) chloroplasts.

Conjugation scalariform ; tubes formed by both gametangia ; fertile cells inflated to 62 $\mu$ ; zygospores ovoid, 56-60 × 90-114 $\mu$ ; median spore wall yellow-brown, punctate and reticulate.

*Distribution*: United States of America.

**274. Spirogyra buchetii** PETIT 1913. *Bull. Soc. Bot. de France.* **60,** pp. 40-43.

Vegetative cells 44-48 × 100-140 $\mu$, with plane end walls ; 2 chloroplasts, making 2.5 to 4 turns.

Conjugation scalariform ; tubes formed by both gametangia ; fertile cells shortened and inflated to 51 $\mu$ ; zygospores ellipsoid with rounded ends, variously placed in the fertile cells giving the appearance of being polymorphic, 48-51 × 72 $\mu$; median spore wall smooth, yellow.

*Distribution*: China ; Morocco ; United States of America.

**275. Spirogyra polytaeniata** STRASBURGER 1888. *Ueber Kern-und Zell-teilung. Jena.*

Vegetative cells 150-189 × 180-240 $\mu$, with plane end walls ; 12 to 14 chloroplasts making 0.5 turn.

Conjugation scalariform ; tubes formed by both gametangia ; fertile cells cylindric ; zygospores ellipsoid, about 120 × 158 $\mu$ ; median spore wall smooth, brown.

*Distribution*: Switzerland.

**276. Spirogyra siamensis** NOM NOV. *Bot. Tidsskrift*. **24**, p. 161 (=*S. decimina* var. *tropica* W. & G.S. West.) Transeau 1944. *Ohio Jour. Sci.* **44**, p. 243 (=*S. tropica*.)

Vegetative cells 46-50 × 100-250 $\mu$ with plane end walls ; 3 chloroplasts, making 2.5 to 4.6 turns.

Conjugation scalariform ; tubes formed by both gametangia ; fertile cells cylindric ; zygospores ovoid, 46-50 × 81-124 $\mu$ ; median spore wall yellow, smooth.

*Distribution*: Siam.

**277. Spirogyra wollnyi** de TONI 1889. *Sylloge Algarum*. **2,** p. 754. Woollny. *Hedwigia*. 1887, p. 166 (as *S. elegans*).

Vegetative cells 90-100 × 270-350 $\mu$, with plane end walls ; 6 to 8 chloroplasts making 2 to 2.5 turns in the cell.

Conjugation scalariform ; tubes formed by both gametangia ; fertile cells cylindric ; zygospores ellipsoid, 90-100 × 140-190 $\mu$ ; median wall yellow-brown, smooth, with distinct suture.

*Distribution*: South Africa.

**278. Spirogyra angolensis** WELWITSCH 1897. *Jour. Bot.* **35**, p. 41.

Vegetative cells 49-62 × 60-200 $\mu$, with plane end walls ; 2 or 3 chloroplasts making 2 to 3 turns.

Conjugation scalariform ; tubes formed by both gametangia ; fertile cells cylindric or enlarged ; zygospores ellipsoid with somewhat pointed ends, 52-57 × 84-100 $\mu$ ; median spore wall smooth, yellow.

*Distribution*: China ; South Africa ; United States of America.

**279. Spirogyra submarina** (COLLINS) TRANSEAU 1915. *Ohio Jour. Sci.* **16,** p. 25. Collins. 1909. *Green Algae of North America*, p. 110.

Vegetative cells 21-32 × 65-175 $\mu$, with plane end walls ; 2 to 3 chloroplasts making 1.5 to 3 turns.

Conjugation scalariform ; tubes formed by both gametangia ; fertile cells enlarged ; zygospores ellipsoid, 31-37 × 56-120 $\mu$ ; median spore wall yellowish-brown, smooth.

*Distribution*: Bermuda ; China ; United States of America.

**280. Spirogyra labyrinthica** TRANSEAU 1934. *Ohio Jour. Sci.* **34**, p. 420. (*S. daedalea* var. *major* Hirn 1913) in Borge, *Zygnemales. Süsswasserflora Deutschland*. **9,** p. 27.

Vegetative cells 50-63 × 150-400 $\mu$, with plane end walls ; 1 chloroplast.

Conjugation scalariform ; tubes formed by both gametangia ; fertile cells cylindric or enlarged ; zygospores ellipsoid, 43-58 × 80-118 $\mu$ ; median spore wall brown, distinctly reticulate.

*Distribution* : Germany.

**281. Spirogyra tuberculata** LAGERHEIM 1896. Wittrock and Nordstedt, *Algae Exsiccatae*, No. 1379.

Vegetative cells 35-37 × 70-165 $\mu$, with plane end walls ; 1 chloroplast.

Conjugation scalariform ; tubes formed by both gametangia ; fertile cells inflated on both sides; zygospores ellipsoid with rounded ends, 30-38 × 50-67 $\mu$ ; median spore wall yellow, irregularly verrucose.

*Distribution* : Sweden.

**282. Spirogyra propria** TRANSEAU 1915. *Ohio Jour. Sci.* **16,** p. 25.

Vegetative cells 60-68 × 80-150 $\mu$, with plane end walls ; 3 chloroplasts, making 0.5 to 1 turn.

Conjugation lateral ; tubes formed by both gametangia ; fertile cells cylindric; zygospores ellipsoid, 42-60 × 80-120 $\mu$ ; median spore wall irregularly pitted, yellow-brown.

*Distribution* : United States of America.

**283. Spirogyra ovigera** MONTAGNE 1850. *Ann. sci. nat.* p. 305. *Sylloge generum specierumque*, Paris, p. 463. 1856.

Vegetative cells 38-42 × 60-280 $\mu$, with plane end walls ; 3 chloroplasts, making 2 to 3 turns in the cell.

Conjugation scalariform ; tubes formed by both gametangia ; fertile cells inflated ; zygospores ovoid, sometimes nearly ellipsoid, 45-52 × 75-100 $\mu$ ; median spore wall granulose, brown.

*Distribution* : South America ; United States of America.

**284. Spirogyra notabilis** TAFT 1944. *Ohio Jour. Sci.* **44,** p. 238.

Vegetative cells 30-37 × 92-230 $\mu$. with plane end walls ; 2, 3, or 4 chloroplasts, making 1 to 3 turns in the cell ; at conjugation the cell walls are notably thickened.

Conjugation scalariform between short gametangia ; tubes formed by both gametangia, but more by the male ; receptive gametangia enlarged near the spore ; zygospores ovoid, 48-57 × 78-105 $\mu$ ; median spore wall of 2 yellow-brown layers, of which the outer is conspicuously punctate, the inner, reticulate and finely verrucose.

*Distribution* : United States of America.

**285. Spirogyra welwitschii** W. & G.S. WEST 1897, *J. Bot.* **35,** p. 41.

Vegetative cells 65-75 × 40-150 $\mu$ ; end walls plane ; chloroplasts 2, making 1 to 2 turns.

Conjugation scalariform ; conjugation canal formed by both gametangia ; gametangia cylindric ; zygospores ellipsoid, 57-58 × 69-71 $\mu$ ; mesospore smooth.

*Distribution* : South Africa.

**286. Spirogyra sirogonioides** HUGHES 1943. Abstracts of Dotoral Dissertations. The Ohio State University, **40,**

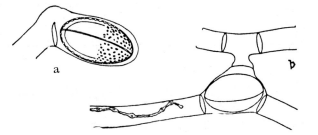

Fig. 502. a-b. *S. sirogonioides*. a, lateral conjugation;
b, scalariform conjugation. (after Hughes.)

Vegetative cells $17-22 \times 160-220$ $\mu$ ; end walls plane ; chloroplast 1, making 3 to 6 turns.

Conjugation lateral and scalariform ; conjugating tubes formed mostly by the male gametangia ; gametangia inflated on the conjugating side ; zygospores ellipsoid, $35-39 \times 58-67$ $\mu$ ; mesospore yellow-brown, irregularly scrobiculate.

*Distribution* : Canada.

**287. Spirogyra anchora** SKUJA. *Nova Acta Reg. Soc. Sci. Upsal.* **14,** p. 101, Pl. XXI, Figs. 5-8.

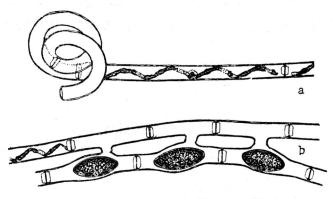

Fig. 503. a-b. *S. anchora*. a, vegetative filament with basal spirals; b, scalariform conjugation. (after Skuja.)

Vegetative filaments spirally twisted at the base ; $12-15 \times 70-240$ $\mu$ ; end walls replicate ; chloroplast single, making 2-6 turns.

Conjugation scalariform ; conjugation tubes formed by male gametangia ; female gametangia swollen in the middle up to 65 $\mu$ ; zygospores ellipsoid, $22-26 \times 38-43$ $\mu$ ; median spore wall longitudinally scrobiculate.

*Distribution* : Burma.

**288. Spirogyra karnalae** RANDHAWA 1958. *Joun. Indian Bot. Soc.,* **37** (3), p. 380, Figs. 1 & 2.

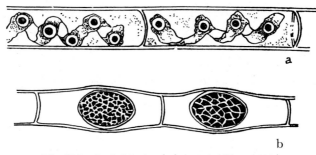

Fig. 504. a-b. *S. karnalae.* a, vegetative filament; b, aplanospores. (after Randhawa.)

Vegetative cells 28.5-30.4 × 106.4-224.2 (-304) $\mu$; end walls plane; chloroplast single, making 3 to 5 turns.

Reproduction by aplanospores; aplanosporangia slightly inflated in the middle; aplanospores ellipsoid, 30.4-34.2 × 41.8-64.6 $\mu$; yellow brown; median spore wall reticulate.

*Distribution* :

*India* : In a pond near mile stone 46 from Delhi on the Grand Trank Road, Karnal District, Punjab.

This form differs from the other apalanosporic forms with a single chloroplast like *S. oltmannsii, S. mirabilis* and *S. aplanospora*, in having reticulate median spore wall.

**289. Spirogyra jogensis** IYENGAR 1958. *J. Indian Bot. Soc.* **37** (3), p. 387, Fig. 1-12.

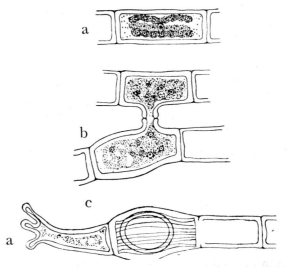

Fig. 505. a-c *S. jogensis.* a, vegetative cell with chloroplast ; b, scalariform conjugation; c, lateral conjugation. (after Iyengar.)

Filaments attached by the lower end of the hapteroid basal cell. Vegetative cells 70-80 $\mu$ broad and 2-6 times as long as broad ; end-walls plane. Cell-walls thick, obscurely finely ribbed longitudinally. Chloroplasts six, generally straight, often slightly coiled to the right, making 0.1-0.3 turn.

Conjugation lateral, though very rarely scalariform ; in the latter case tubes formed by both the gametangia. Lateral conjugation direct, the male gamete fusing with the female gamete by perforating the septum. Male cell cylindrical ; female cell generally inflated all round, with a thick longitudinally ribbed refractive mucilage layer below the cell-wall. Zygospores broadly ovoid ; zygospore wall thick and smooth ; mesospore dark brown, 70-76 × 90-122 $\mu$.

*Distribution :*

*India :* On sprayed rocks near the pool, Jog Falls, Mysore State.

**289a. Spirogyra jogensis** IYENGAR, VAR. **minor** Iyengar 1958 *J. Indian Bot. Soc.* **37** (3), p. 391, Figs. 13-21.

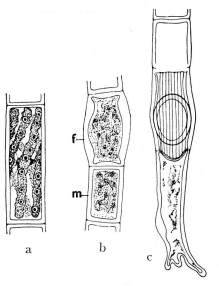

Fig. 506. a-c. *S. jogensis* var. *minor*. a, vegetative cells with chloroplasts ; b-c, lateral conjugation. f, female; m, male. (after Iyengar.)

Similar to the type but differing from it in being smaller in dimensions all round and in having only three chromatophores. Vegetative cells 38-48 $\mu$ broad and $2\frac{1}{2}$-4 times as long as broad. Zygospores broadly ovoid but often ellipsoid, 42-52 × 68-88 $\mu$.

*Distribution :*

*India :* Attached to stones in a tiny shallow seepage channel at the base of the dam of the Periyar Reservoir, Kerala.

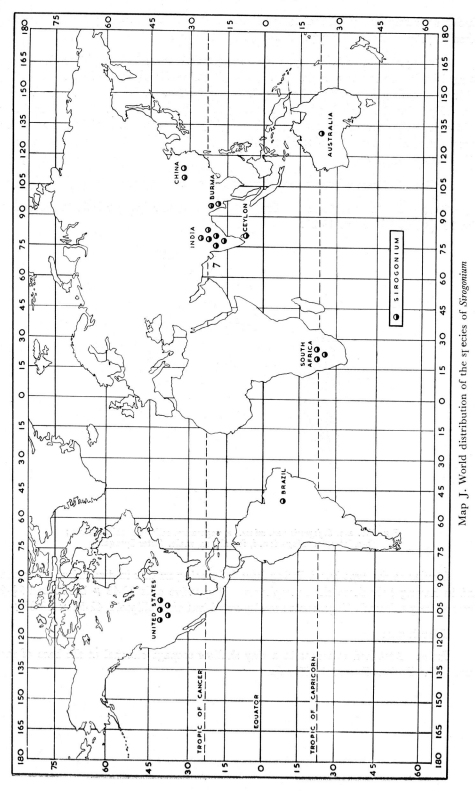

Map J. World distribution of the species of *Sirogonium*

CHAPTER 18

# SIROGONIUM Kützing 1843

The genus *Sirogonium* was established by Kützing in 1843. Czurda (1932) followed by Krieger (1944) included species of this genus under *Spirogyra*. Transeau (1951) recognized it as a distinct genus.

The vegetative cells have plane septa, and several narrow chloroplasts which are more or less straight. The cell wall lacks an external pectose layer.

Conjugation takes place directly between the gametangia without the formation of conjugation tubes. The progametangia divide into unequal gametangia ; the smaller behaves as a male, and the larger as a female. Sometimes progametangia may conjugate without division. Flexing of filaments takes place during conjugation.

Zygospores are ellipsoid or ovoid, and yellow brown, or black in colour. The median wall is smooth or variously ornamented.

So far, 14 species have been described of which 5 are from U.S.A., 6 from India, 3 from South America, 3 from South Africa, 2 from China, 2 from Burma, and 1 from Ceylon. (Map. J).

### KEY TO THE SPECIES OF SIROGONIUM

1a. Zygospores ellipsoid to ellipsoid-ovoid
  2a.  Spore wall smooth
    3a.  Vegetative cells less than 36 $\mu$ broad     11.  **S. tenuis**
    3b.  Vegetative cells 36-56 $\mu$ broad
      4a.  Zygospores 40-67 $\mu$ broad     2.  **S. sticticum**
      4b.  Zygospores 70-85 $\mu$ broad     3.  **S. megasporum**
    3c.  Vegetative cells 56-66 $\mu$ broad     12.  **S. floridanum**
  2b.  Spore wall not smooth
    5a.  Median wall single
      6a.  Mesospore punctate     13.  **S. ceylanicum**
      6b.  Mesospore granulose and finely
        corrugate     7.  **S. pseudofloridanum**

6c.   Mesospore verrucose
    7a.   Vegetative cells 65-72 $\mu$ broad        10.   **S. ventersicum**
    7b.   Vegetative cells 70-90 $\mu$ broad        8.   **S. melanosporum**
    7c.   Vegetative cells 82-99 $\mu$ broad        9.   **S. inflatum**
6d.   Mesospore reticulate
    8a.   Mesospore with scattered
        protuberances        5.   **S. illinoiense**
    8b.   Mesospore without scattered
        protuberances        14.   **S. reticulatum**
6e.   Mesospore scrobiculate        6.   **S. indicum**

5b.   Median wall double
    9a.   Outer layer smooth;  inner
        verrucose        4.   **S. hui**
    9b.   Outer layer granulate; inner
        finely reticulate        15.   **S. vandalurensis**

1b.   Zygospore lenticular        1.   **S. phacosporum**

**1.   Sirogonium phacosporum** SKUJA 1949.   *Nova Acta Soc. Sci. Upsali.* Ser. 3, **14,** p. 103, Pl. 22, Figs. 1-5.

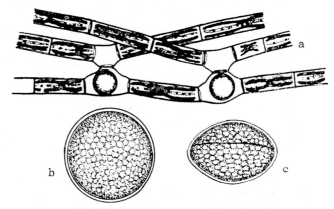

Fig. 507. a-c. *S. phacosporum.* (after Skuja.)

Vegetative cells 54-60 × 100-370 $\mu$ ; chloroplasts usually 4, rarely 3, straight or slightly curved.

Conjugation direct ; receptive gametangia inflated, 95-110 × 150-190 $\mu$; zygospores lenticular, 70-100 × 60-70 $\mu$; median spore wall 2-3 $\mu$ thick, yellow or brownish-yellow, finely reticulate-scrobiculate.

*Distribution* :   Burma.

**2.   Sirogonium sticticum** (Engl. Bot.) KÜTZING 1843. *Phycologia Generalis,* p. 278.   (=*S. sticticum* var. *microsporum* Venkataraman 1957. *J. Bombay Nat. Hist. Soc.* **54,** p. 914, figs. 9-11 = *Spirogyra stictica* var. *minor* Pignatti 1958.   *Atti,* **15**(5), p. 33, fig. 3.)

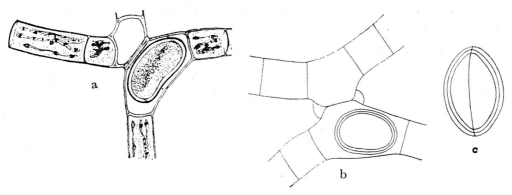

Fig. 508. *S. sticticum*. (after Jao.)

Vegetative cells 38-56 × 80-300 $\mu$ ; chloroplasts 3-6, nearly straight, or making 0·5 turn.

Conjugation direct between usually shortened and more or less reflexed gametangia ; receptive gametangia inflated to 72 $\mu$; spores ellipsoid, sometimes more or less ovoid, 40-67 × 68-127 $\mu$; median spore wall smooth, yellow.

*Distribution* :

*India* : Freshwater stream, Tanda, Fyzabad Dt., U.P. ; Banaras, U.P.

*Other countries* : Africa ; Australia ; Europe ; South America and United States of America; Pavia, Italy.

**3. Sirogonium megasporum** (JAO) TRANSEAU 1944. *Ohio Jour. Sci.* **44,** p. 244. ( =*S. sticticum* var. *megasporum* Jao 1935. *Sinensia*, **6,** p. 645, Pl. 12).

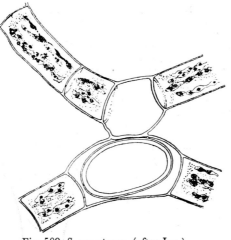

Fig. 509. *S. megasporum*. (after Jao )

Vegetative cells 48-55 × 90-385 $\mu$ ; chloroplasts 3 to 4, sometimes 2, straight, or making 0·5 turn in the cell.

Conjugation direct, gametangia shortened, reflexed, and more or less inflated on the inner side ; receptive gametangia inflated up to 100 $\mu$ ; zygospores ellipsoid to ovoid, 70-85 × 100-122 $\mu$ ; median spore wall smooth, yellowish-brown at maturity.

*Distribution* :    China ; South America and United States of America.

**4. Sirogonium hui** (LI) TRANSEAU 1944. *Ohio Jour. Sci.* **44**, p 244. Li, *Bull. Fan Mem. Inst. Biol., Botany*, **8**, p 91 ( =*Spirogyra hui* Li. 1938.)

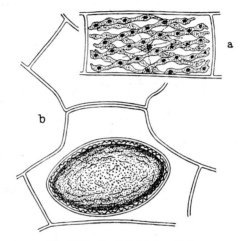

Fig. 510. a-b. *S. hui* (after Li.)

Vegetative cells 82-108 × 140-256 $\mu$ , with plane end walls ; 5 to 10 chloroplasts.

Receptive gametangia inflated to 150 $\mu$ ; zygospores ellipsoid to ovoid, 88-115 × 133-192 $\mu$ ; outer spore wall thin, colourless ; median wall of 2 layers ; outer layer thin, irregularly wrinkled ; inner layer yellow, verrucose ; the inner wall thin and transparent.   Akinetes 86-92 × 64-96 $\mu$ are common.

*Distribution* :   China.

**5. Sirogonium illinoiense** (TRANSEAU) G.M. SMITH 1933.   *Freshwater Algae of the United States*, p 557. Transeau. 1914.   *Amer. Jour. Bot.* **1**, p 296, Figs. 1-3.

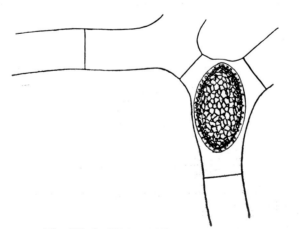

Fig. 511. *S. illinoiense.* (after Transeau.)

Vegetative cells 65-85 × 100-310 $\mu$; 6 to 9 chloroplasts, nearly straight or making up to 1 turn in the cell.

Both gametangia more or less reflexed, the receptive one inflated ; zygospores ellipsoid, 85-115 × 140-190 $\mu$ ; median wall yellow with scattered protuberances connected by a more or less prominent reticulum.

*Distribution*: United States of America.

**6. Sirogonium indicum** Singh 1938. *Jour. Indian Bot. Soc.* **17,** p 384, Fig. 6B.

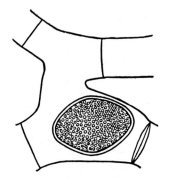

Fig. 512. *S. indicum.* (after Singh.)

Vegetative cells 65-80 $\mu$ in diameter, with approximately 7 chloroplasts which are nearly straight.

Conjugation scalariform between reflexed gametangia ; receptive gametangia greatly inflated ; zygospores ellipsoid, 75-90 × 135-165 $\mu$ ; median spore wall thick, yellow, and scrobiculate.

*Distribution*:

*India*: Gorakhpur, U.P.

**7. Sirogonium pseudofloridanum** (Prescott) Transeau 1944. *Ohio Jour. Sci.* **44,** p 243. *Farlowia.* **1,** pp 360-61, Fig. 1. 1944.

Fig. 513. *S. pseudofloridanum.* (after Prescott.)

Vegetative cells 51-60 × 150-275 $\mu$, each with 4 to 5 chloroplasts ; straight, or making up to 1·5 turns in the cell.

Receptive gametangia somewhat inflated ; zygospores ellipsoid, 63-70 × 100-120 $\mu$;

median wall brown, finely corrugate and granulate.

*Distribution*:   United States of America.

**8.   Sirogonium melanosporum** (Randhawa) Transeau 1944.   *Ohio Jour. Sci.* **44,** p 243.   (=*S. ventersicum* var. *melanosporum* Randhawa.   1938.   *Proc. Indian Acad.* **8,** p 364.)

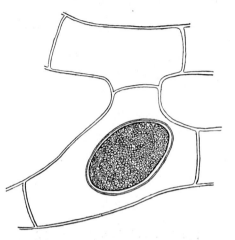

Fig. 514. *S. melanosporum.* (after Randhawa.)

Vegetative cells 70-90 × 140-260 $\mu$, each with 6 to 9 nearly straight chloroplasts.

Conjugation direct; receptive gametangia inflated up to 120-166 $\mu$; zygospores usully ellipsoid, 90-110 × 140-160 $\mu$ ; median spore wall  brown to black, verrucose.

*Distribution* :

*India* :   Fyzabad, U.P.

*Other countries* :   United States of America.

**9.   Sirogonium inflatum** Dixit 1937. *Proc. Indian. Acad. Sci.,* **5,** p 23, Fig. 6. *S. Dixitii* nom. nov. Kolkwitz and Krieger 1944.   Rabenhorst's *Kryptogammenflora,* **13,** p 432,  Fig. 682.

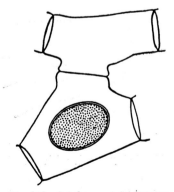

Fig. 515. *S. inflatum.* (after Dixit.)

Vegetative cells 82-99 $\mu$ broad ; end walls plane ; 6-10 chloroplasts mostly straight.

Conjugation scalariform. Fertile cells swollen on the conjugating side. Conjugation canal is broad and short ; conjugation canal built by both the gametangia. Zygospores ellipsoid with rounded ends, 81-110 $\times$ 111-160 $\mu$; exospore thin, smooth and colourless ; mesospore thick, brown and verrucose.

*Distribution* :

*India* :   In a rain water pool, Petlad, North Gujerat.

**10.   Sirogonium ventersicum** Transeau 1934. *Trans. Amer. Micros. Soc.* **53,** p. 229.   (*S. ventersicum* var. *megaspora* Rao ; *S. ventersicum* var. *variabilis* Singh).

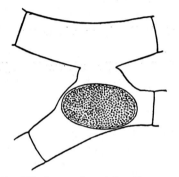

Fig. 516. *S. ventersicum.* (after Transeau.)

Vegetative cells 65-72 $\times$ 110-250 $\mu$; 5 to 8 chloroplasts, straight, or making 1 turn.

Conjugation direct; receptive gametangia inflated to 100-140 $\mu$; zygospores mostly ellipsoid, rarely somewhat ovoid, 80-90 $\times$ 133-152$\mu$ ; median spore wall brown, densely and irregularly verrucose.

*Distribution* :

*India* :   Gorakhpur, U.P., Hoshangabad, M.P.

*Other countries* :   South Africa.

**11.   Sirogonium tenuis** (Nordstedt) Transeau 1934. *Ohio Jour. Sci.* **34,** p. 420.   Nordstedt. *Bot. Notiser* 1882. p. 47 (=*Spirogyra stictica* var. *tenuior*).

Vegetative cells 32-36 $\times$ 50-135$\mu$ ; 2 to 5 chloroplasts nearly straight.

Conjugation direct between shortened and more or less reflexed gametangia separated by vegetative cells ; receptive gametangia inflated to 60$\mu$ ; zygospores ellipsoid varying to ovoid, 47-50 $\times$ 60-88$\mu$ ; median spore wall yellow, smooth.

*Distribution* :   Cordoba ; Argentina ; Mato Grosso ; Brazil ; Burma and United States of America.

**12.   Sirogonium floridanum** (Transeau) G.M. Smith 1933. *Freshwater Algae of the United States*, p. 557.   Transeau 1915.   *Ohio Jour. Sci.* **16,** p. 30.

Vegetative cells 56-66 $\times$ 120-335$\mu$ ; 4-5 chloroplasts nearly straight, or making a half turn.

Conjugation direct ; gametangia shortened and reflexed ; receptive gametangia inflated up to 135$\mu$ ; zygospores ellipsoid, 75-105 × 95-135$\mu$ ; median spore wall yellow and smooth.

*Distribution*:   South Africa and United States of America.

**13.  Sirogonium ceylanicum** WITTROCK 1889.  Wittrock and Nordstedt, *Algae Exsiccatae*, No. 358.  ( =*S. floridanum* forma Rao).

Vegetative cells 69-75 × 140-300 $\mu$ ; 7 chloroplasts nearly straight.

Conjugation direct between reflexed gametangia ; receptive gametangia inflated, 120-165 × 135-300 $\mu$ ; zygospores ellipsoid, 100-110 × 135-195$\mu$ ; median spore wall thick, yellow-brown with minute shallow depressions that have no distinct edges but are easily seen when viewed edgewise.

*Distribution*:

*India*:   In rain water pools, Bombay ; rain water puddle, M.P.

*Other countries*:   Ceylon.

**14.  Sirogonium reticulatum** RANDHAWA 1958. *J. Indian Bot. Soc.* **37,** p 380, Figs. 3-5.

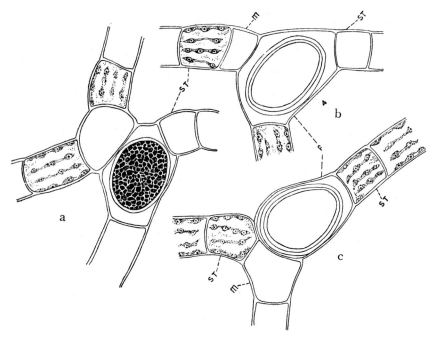

Fig. 517. a-c. *S. reticulatum*. a, scalariform conjugation; b-c, fusion of terminal cells. m. male; f, female; st, sterile cell. (after Randhawa.)

Vegetative cells 45·6-53·2 × 91.2-102·6$\mu$ ; chloroplasts 4, straight.

Conjugating cells geniculate and shortened ; fertile cells inflated ; zygospores ellipsoid, 76×91·2-102·6$\mu$ ; median spore wall reticulate and yellowish brown at maturity.

*Distribution*:

India:   Free-floating in a pond along the Grand Trunk Road near V. Shanjpur Bahana, Karnal District, Punjab.

### 15. Sirogonium vandalurensis IYENGAR.

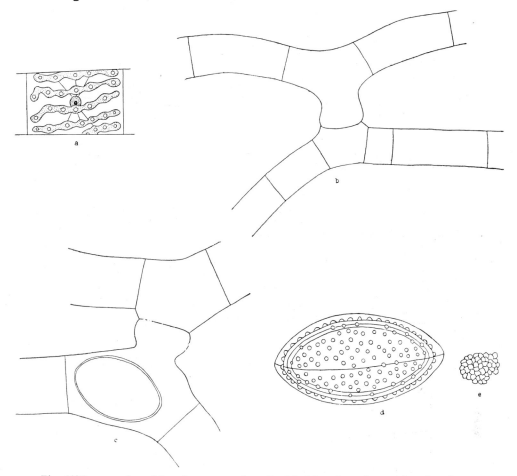

Fig. 517A, a-e. *S. vandalurensis.* a, vegetative cell with chloroplasts; b-c, conjugation, show-ing the swollen receptive gametangium produced into a broadly cylindrical piece; d, mature zygospore with the outer median spore layer densely covered by round brown granules ; e, reticulate sculpturing of the inner median spore layer. (after Iyengar.)

Vegetative cells 76-86 × 64-294 $\mu$ ; chloroplasts 7−9.

Conjugation direct ; receptive gametangia inflated to 108-160 $\mu$ ; swollen end of the receptive gametangia on the conjugation side finally becoming produced into a broadly cylindrical piece, 70-72 × 32-51 $\mu$ ; zygospores ellipsoid, 70-89 × 124-148 $\mu$ ; median spore wall made up of two layers, an outer hyaline layer densely covered by round brown granules and an inner thick golden brown layer with an extremely fine reticulation.

*Distribution :*

> *India :* In paddy fields, ponds, pools and irrigation tanks at Vandalur, Madras State.

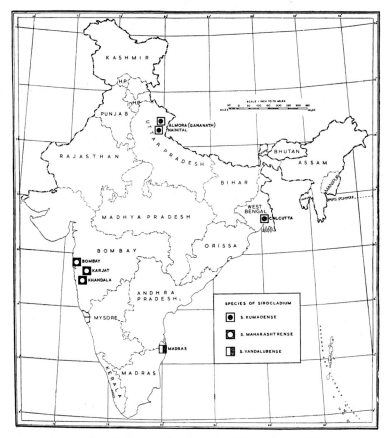

Map K. Distribution of the species of *Sirocladium* in India.

## CHAPTER 19

# SIROCLADIUM Randhawa 1941

The genus *Sirocladium* was established by Randhawa in 1941 on a solitary species described from Kumaon, Himalayas. In 1958 he described two more species from India.

The cells are rectangular in outline, 45-64 $\mu$ broad and 120-210 $\mu$ long. Septa are plane. Most of the subaerial cells have two flat, broad plate-shaped, or ribbon-like parietal chloroplasts. When plate-shaped, the margin of the chloroplasts may be smooth or laciniate, and on the surface there are numerous conspicuous pyrenoids scattered irregularly. When ribbon-like, the pyrenoids are in a row. Caryoids are found in the chloroplasts, as in some species of *Mougeotia* with broad chloroplasts.

All the species are terrestrial. The subterranean cells are usually much elongated and are narrower as compared with the subaerial cells. Rhizoids are short pillar-like bodies usually unseptate. Sometimes terminal cells are drawn out into rhizoidal structures.

Conjugation as in *Sirogonium* without the formation of conjugation tubes, between geniculate gametangia which are differentiated into short and long cells. Monoecism is seem in two species *viz.*, *S. kumaoense* and *S. maharashtrense*, and conjugation between male and female cells in the same filament takes place by coiling. Zygospores are ellipsoid, yellowish-brown in colour. Spore-wall is smooth or reticulate.

So far 3 species have been described, all from India, one from North India, and two from South India. (Map K).

### KEY TO THE SPECIES OF SIROCLADIUM

| | | |
|---|---|---|
| 1a. | Margin of the chloroplast straight | |
| | 2a. Spore wall smooth | 1. **S, kumaoense** |
| | 2b. Spore wall reticulate | 3. **S. maharashtrense** |
| 1b. | Margin of the chloroplast laciniate | 2. **S. vandalurense** |

# 1. **Sirocladium kumaoense** RANDHAWA 1941. *Bot. Gaz.* **103,** p. 196.

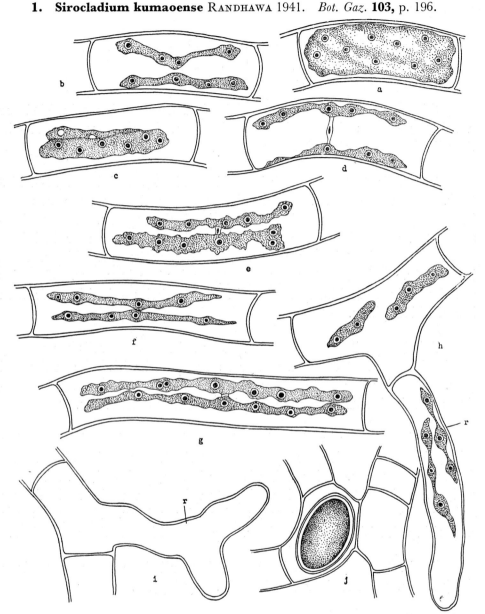

FIG. 518. a—j. *S. kumaoense* Randh. a—g, vegetative cells showing chloroplasts in different positions; h-i, rhizoids (r); j, conjugating filaments with mature zygospore (after Randhawa.)

Vegetative cells cylindric, 45-64 × 120-210 $\mu$ ; more or less irregularly bent, with 2 parietal plate-like chloroplasts, 15-20$\mu$ broad. Pyrenoids 4-12, irregularly scattered.

Conjugation between 2 geniculate gametangia. Receptive gametangia are inflated. Zygospores are ellipsoid, 42-70 × 90-108 $\mu$. Median spore wall is yellow brown and smooth. Parthenospores and aplanospores present.

*Distribution* :

*India* : On moist clay under a shady rock Gananath, and Nainital, Kumaon Hills, Himalayas, Almora, U.P. and Calcutta.

**2. Sirocladium vandalurense** RANDHAWA. 1958. *Bot. Gaz.* **119,** pp 25-26,
Figs. 1-10.

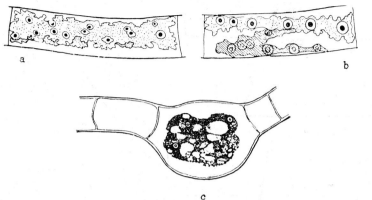

Fig. 519. a-c *S. vandalurense*. a-b, vegetative cells with chloroplasts (note the forked chloroplats
in fig. b) ; c. immature aplanospore. (after Randhawa.)

Vegetative cells cylindrical, 38-49·4 × 114-323 $\mu$. Chloroplasts 2, flat, axial,
plate-like. The margin of the chloroplast is finely laciniate. Pyrenoids several and
scattered irregularly. In rare instances the chloroplast is forked.

Reproduction is by aplanospores. Mature spores not observed.

*Distribution* :

*India* : On the moist soil from Vandalur near Madras.

**3. Sirocladium maharashtrense** RANDHAWA 1958. *Bot. Gaz.* **119,** pp.201-202,
Figs. 3-10.

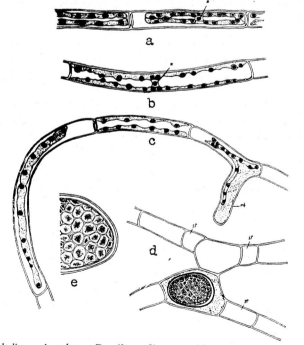

FIG. 520 a-e. *Sirocladium maharashtrense* Randh. a, filament with chloroplasts and nucleus (*n*); b, chloroplasts in basal cell; c, showing a rhizoid (*rh*); d, conjugation; note sterile (*st*) cells and brownish contents
of female gametangium; e, ripe zygospore with reticulate sculpturing of mesospore. (after Randhawa.)

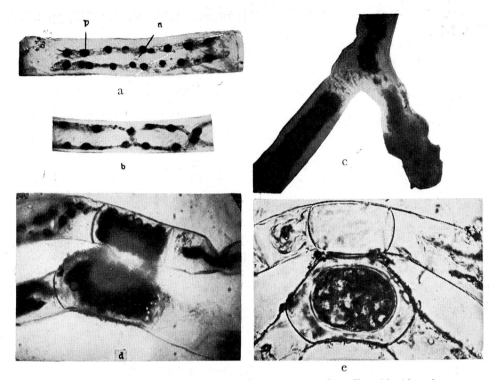

FIG. 521, a—e. *Sirocladium maharashtrense* Randh. a-b, vegetative cells with chloroplasts ; c, vegetative cell with rhizoid ; d, e, stages in conjugation, n, nucleus ; p, pyrenoid. (after Randhawa.)

Vegetative cells cylindric with plane end walls, $37 \cdot 5\text{-}41 \cdot 25 \times 108 \cdot 75\text{-}207 \cdot 5\mu$ ; chloroplasts 2 ; parietal ribbons $9\text{-}11 \cdot 2 \ \mu$ broad, each with 4-14 pyrenoids arranged in a row.

Conjugation occurs between two geniculate gametangia without the formation of the conjugating tubes. Receptive gametangia swollen. Zygospores ellipsoid, $56 \cdot 2\text{-}65 \cdot 2 \times 75\text{-}112 \cdot 5\mu$. Mesospore reticulate.

*Distribution* :

    *India* : Terrestrial, in wet fields, Khandala, and Karjat, Western Ghats, Bombay.

# BIBLIOGRAPHY

Ackley, A.B. (1929) : New Species and Varieties of Michigan Algae. Trans Amer. Micr. Soc. **48.**

Adolph, E.F. (1925) : Some Physiological Distinctions between Freshwater and Marine Organisms. Biol. Bull. **43.**

Agardh, C.A. (1817) : Synopsis Algarum Scandinaviae. Lund.

—(1824) : Systema algarum. Lund.

Allen, W.E. (1921) : A Quantitative and Statistical Study of the Plankton of the San Joaquin River and its Tributaries in and near Stockton, California, in 1913. Univ. Calif. Publ. Zool. **22.**

Allorge, P. (1925a) : Sur quelques groupements aquatiques et hygrophiles des Alpes du Brainçonnais. Festschr. Carl Schröter. Zürich.

—(1925b) : Algues des étangs de la Brenne. Cpt. Rd. Congr. Soc. Sav.

—(1925c) : Chlorophycées récoltées dans quelques étangs de la forêt d'Orléans. Bull. ass. natura Valée du Loing **8**

—(1926) : Algues du Briançonnais. Bull. Soc. Bot. France. **63.**

—(1928) : Note préliminaire sur la flore des algues d'eau douce de la Galice. Bolet. Soc. espanol. Hist. nat. **28.**

—(1930) : Hétérocontes, Euchlorophycées et Conjuguées de la Galice. Rev. Algol. **5.**

Allorge, P. and Denis, M. (1920) : Remarques sur la distribution des Algues dans la Haute-Maurienne. Bull. Soc. Bot. France. **57.**

Allorge, P. and Gaume, R. (1931) : Esquisse phytogéographique de la Sologne. *Ibid.* **72.**

Allorge, P. and Lefévre, M. (1931) : Algues de Sologne. *Ibid.*

Alten, H. von (1910) : Beiträge zur Kenntnis der Algenflora der Moore der Provinz Hannover. Mitt. Nat-hist. Ges. Hannover. **58/59.**

—(1912) : Die Algen der Umgebung von Braunschweig. Jahresber. Ver. Naturw. z. Braunschweig. **17.**

Anderson, I.P. (1905) : Decatur County Algae. Iowa Natural. **1.**

Andersson. O.F. (1890) : Bidrag till kännedomen om Sveriges Chloro-phyllophyceer. I. Chlorophyllophyceer frän Roslagen, K. Sv. Vet. Akad. Handl. **16.**

Andrews, F.M. (1911) : Conjugation of two different Species of *Spirogyra*. Bull. Torrey Bot. Club. **38.**

—(1912/13) : Conjugation in *Spirogyra*. Proc. Indiana Acad. Sci.

Ardissone, F. and Strafforello, J. (1877) : Enumerazione delle Alghe di Liguria. Mailand.

Areschoug. J.E. (1853) : Copulationen hos Zygnemaceerne. Oefvs. Kgl. Vetensk. Akad. Förhandl. **10.**

Arrondeau, S. (1852) : Observations sur l'organisation du *Zygnema orbiculare* Hassall. Sess. Congr. sc. France. **19.**

—(1861) : Etude sur les Conferves des environs de Toulouse.

Askenasy, E. (1889) : Algen. Die Forschungsreise S.M.S. Gazelle v. J. 1874-78. Berlin.

Askenasy, F. and Förster, F. (1892) : Beiträge zur badischen Algenflora. Mitt. bad. bot. Ver.

Assfahl, E. (1892) : Ueber die Ernährung der Pflanzenzellen mit Glycerin. Diss. Erlangen.

Atkins, W.R.G. and Harris, G.T. (1924) : Seasonal Changes in the Water and Heleoplankton of Fresh water Ponds. Sci. Proc. R. Dublin Soc. N.S. **18.**

Atkinson, G.F. (1903) : The Genus *Harpochytrium* in the United States. Ann. Mycol **1.**

—(1904) : Note on the Genus *Harpochytrium*. Jour. Mycol. **10.**

—(1909) : Some Fungus Parasites of Algae. Bot. Gaz. **48.**

Atwell, C.B. (1889) : A Phase of Conjugation in *Spirogyra*. Bot. Gaz. **14.**

Bachmann, H. (1921) : Beiträge zur Algenflora des Süsswassers von Westgrönland. Mitt. Naturf. Ges. Luzern. **8.**

Bachmann, H. and Birrer (1932) : Uber die Giftwirkung von chemischen Substanzen auf niedere Wasserorganismen, Z. f. Hydrol. **6.**

Bailey, F.M. (1895, 1898) : Contributions to the Queensland Flora. Depart. Agriculture, Brisbane. Bot. Bull. **11.**

Bailey, E.L. (1936) : A Survey of the Filamentous Algae of Labette County, Kansas. Trans. Kansas Acad. Sci.

Bajkow, A.D. (1934) : The Plankton of Lake Winnipeg Drainage System. Intern. Rev. d. ges. Hydrogr. u. Hydrobiol. **31.**

Balachonzew, E.N. (1909) : Phytobiologie des Ladoga-Sees. Petersburg.

Barnes, T.C. and Larson, E.J. (1934) : The Influence of Heavy Water of Low Concentrations on *Spirogyra, Planaria* and on Encyme Action. Protoplasma. **22.**

Batard, Ch. (1932) : Phytoplankton estival des cours d'eau de la region de Saint-Malo. Bull. Soc. Bot. France. **79.**

—(1933) : Le Phytoplancton de l'Adour et de ses Affluents : la Douze et le Midou. Proces-Verb. Soc. Linn. Bordeaux.

Bates, F. (1884) : On the *Zygnemaceae*. Midland Naturalist.

—(1885) : On Sexuality of the *Zygnemaceae*. Journ. Queckett Micr. Club. Sect. 2. **2.**

Baumgärtel, O. (1924) : Algologische Studien im Gebiete des mittleren Kamnitzbaches. Lotos. **62.**

Beal, W. (1885) : *Mesocarpus pleurocarpus*. The Microscope (Trenton, New Jersey).

Beck-Mannagetta, G. (1886) : Flora von Südbosnien und der angrenzenden Herzegowina. Ann. k.k. naturh. Hofmus. **1.**

—(1887) : Uebersicht der bisher bekannten Kryptogamen Niederösteuiechs. Verh. k.k. zool-bot. Ges. i. Wien. **37.**

—(1901) : Die Vegetationsverhältnisse der illyrischen Länder. Veg. d. Erde. **4.**

—(1926a) : Algenfunde im Riesengebirge. Kral. Ces. Spol. Nauk. Tr. **2.**

—(1926b) : Neue Grünalgen aus Kärnten. Arch. Protisten. **55.**

—(1929) : Neue Grün-und Blaualgen aus Kärnten und den Sudeten. Ibid. **66.**

—(1931) : Die Algen Kärntens. Beih. Bot. Centralbl. **47,** Abt. 2.

Behning, A. (1928) Das Leben der Wolga. Die Binnengewasser. **5.** Stuttgart.

Behre, K. (1939) : Die Algenbesiedlung der Truper Blänken bie Bremen. Abh. Nat. Ver. Bremen. **31.**

Behrens, J. (1890) : Zur Kenntnis einiger Wachstums-und Gestaltungsvorgänge der Vegetabilischen Zelle. Bot. Zeitg. **48.**

Beijerinck, W. (1927) : Over verspreiding en perioliiteit van de zoetwaterwieren in Drentsche heideplassen. Diss. Wigeningen.

Bêlâr, K. (1926) : Der Formwechsel der Protistenkerne. Berlin.

Belloc, E. (1893) : Recherches sur les Algues des eaux douces, des eaux thermales et des eaux salées de l'Algérie, de Tunisie et du Maroc. Rev. Biol. N. de la France. **5.**

Benecke, W. (1898) : Mechanismus und Biologie des Zerfalles der Conjugatenfäden in die einzelnen Zellen. Jahrb. wiss. Bot. **31.**

—(1907) : Ueber die Giftwirkung verschiedener Salze auf *Spirogyra* Ber. Deutsch Bot. Ges. **25.**

—(1908) : Über die Ursachen der Periodizität im Auftreten der Algen auf Grund von Untersuchungen über die Bedingungen der Zygotenbildung bei *Spirogyra communis*. Intern. Rev. Hydrob. u. Hydrogr. **1.**

—(1925) : Zur Frage der Bedingungen der Konjugation bei *Spirogyra*. Flora. **118/119.**

Bennet, A.W. (1883) : Reproduction of the *Zygnemaceae*, a Contribution towards the solution of the Question.—Is it of Sexual Character? Jour. Linn. Soc. Bot. **20.**

—(1886) : Freshwater Algae of the English Lake District. Jour. R. Micr. Soc.

—(1888) : Freshwater Algae of the English Lake District. *Ibid.*

—(1889) : Freshwater Algae and *Schizophyceae* of Hampshire and Devonshire. Jour. R. Micr. Soc.

—(1891a) : Freshwater Algae and *Schizophyceae* of S.W. Survey. *Ibid.*

—(1891b) : Sexuality among the *Conjugatae*. Jour. Bot. **29.**

—(1891c) : Non-sexual Formation of Spores in the *Desmidiaceae* Rep. Brit. Assoc. Advanc. Sci. **61.**

Berdan, H. (1939) : Two New Genera of Operculate Chytrids. Amer. Jour. Bot. **26.**

Berghs, I. (1906) : Le noyau et la cinése chez le *Spirogyra* La Cellule. **23.**

Berkeley, M.J. (1832) : Gleanings of British Algae. London.

Bernard. Ch. (1903) : Protococcacées et Desmidiées d'eau douce récoltees a Java. Départ. de l'agricult. aux Indes Néerl.

Berthold, G. (1886) : Studien über Protoplasmamechanik. Leipzig.

Bessey, C.E. (1884a) : Preliminary List of Zygophytes, Protophytes, Oophytes, and Charophytes of the Ames Flora. Bull. Iowa Agric. College, Dpt. Bot.

—(1884b) : Hybridism in *Spirogyra*. Amer. Naturalist. **18.**

—(1885a) : Attempted Hybridisation between Pond-scums of Different Genera. *Ibid.* **191.**

—(1885b) : The Question of Bisexuality in the Pond-scums (*Zygnemaceae*). Bot. Gaz. **10.**

—(1886) : The Question of Bisexuality in the Pond-scums. Proc. Amer. Ass. **34.**

—(1891) : Note on Cross-conjugation. Journ. Bot. **29.**

Bigelow, N.K. (1923) : The Plankton of Lake Nipigon and Environs. Univ. Toronto Stud. Biol. Ser. **22.**

Bishop, A.S. (1935) : Algunas Zygnemataceas de Chapultapec. Ann. Inst. Biol. Mexico. **6.**

Biswas, K.P. (1930) : Contributions to our Knowledge of the Freshwater Algae of Manipur, Assam Jour. Bombay Natural Hist. Soc. **34.**

Blackman, F.F. and Tansley, A.G. (1902) : A Revision of the Classification of the Green Algae. New Phyt. 1.

Blum, J. (1956) : Zygnemataceae of Western New York I. Mich. Acad. Sci. Arts & Lett. 41.

Bode, H.R. (1926) : Untersuchungen über die Abhängigkeit der Atmungsgrösse von der H-Ionenkonzentration bei einigen *Spirogyra*-Arten. Jahrb. wiss. Bot. **65.**

Bohlin, K. (1901a) : Utkast till de gröna algernas och arkegoniaternas fylogeni (m. dutsch. Rés.). Akad. Afhandl.

—(1901b) : Etude de la flore algologique des Açores. Bih. K. Sv. Vet. Akad. Handl. **27.**

Bokorny, Th. (1886) : Das Wasserstoffsuperoxyd und die Silberabscheidung durch aktives Albumin Jahrb. wiss. Bot. **17.**

—(1888) : Über die Einwirkung basischer Stoffe auf das lebende Protoplasma. *Ibid.* **19.**

—(1889) : Eine bemerkenswerte Wirkung oxydierter Eisenvitriollösungen auf lebende Pflanzenzellen, Ber. Deutsch Bot. Ges. **7.**

—(1892) : Ernährung grüner Pflanzenzellen mit Formaldehyd. Landwirtsch. Jahrb.

—(1893) : Uber die physiologische Wirkung der tellurigen Säure. Chemikerzeitung.

—(1895) : Uber den Einfluß des Calciums und Magnesiums auf die Ausbildung der Zellorgane. Beih. Bot. Zentralbl. **62.**

—(1896) : Einige Versuche über die Stickstöffernahrung grüner Pflanzen. Chemikerzeitung.

—(1897) : Die Grenze der wirksamen Verdünnung bei Algen und Pilzen. Biol. Centralbl. **17.**

—(1908) : Über die Assimilation des Formaldehyds und die Versuche, dieses Zwisch-enproduk bei der Kohlensäureassimilation nachzuweisen. Assimilation von Glycerin und Zucker. Arch. d. ges. Physiol. **125.**

—(1917) : Organische Kohlenstoffernährung der Pflanzen. Zentralbl. f. Bakt. Abt. II, **47.**

—(1918) : Zur Kenntnis der physiologischen Fähigkeiten der Algengattung *Spirogyra*. Hedwigia. **49.**

Boldt, R. (1885) : Bidrag till kannedomen om Sibiriens Chlorophyllophyceen. K. Vet. Akad. Förhandl. Stockholm.

Bonhomme, J. (1858) : Notes sur quelques algues d'eaudouce. Rodez (Carriéres).

Borge, O. (1891) : Ett litet bidrag till Sibiriens Chlorophyllophycé-flora. Bih. Sv. Vet. Akad. Handl. **17.**

Borge, O. (1894a) : Über die Rhizoidbildung bei einigen fadenförmigen Chlorophyceen. Upsala.

—(1894b) : Süsswasserchlorophyceen, gesammelt von Dr. A. Osw. Kihlmann im nördlichen Russlandy Gouvernement Archangel. K. Sv. Vet. Akad. Handl. **19.**

—(1895a) : Bidrag till kännedomen om Sveriges Chlorophyllophyceer. II. Chlorophyllophyceen aus Falbygden in Vestergötland. Bih. Sv. Vet. Akad. Handl. **21.**

—(1895b) : Algologische Notizen 5. Schweizerische Algen.

—(1896) : Australische Süsswasserchlorophyceen. Bih. K. Sv. Vet. Akad. Handl. **22.**

—(1899) : Über tropische und subtropische Süsswasserchlorophyceen. *Ibid.* **24.**

—(1901) : Süsswasseralgen aus Südpatagonien. *Ibid.* **27.**

—(1903) : Die Algen der ersten Regnellschen Expedition. III. Zygnemaceen und Mesocarpaceen. Ark. f. Bot. **1.**

—(1906) : Süsswasserchlorophyceen von Feuerland und Isla Desolacion. Bot. Stud. F.R. Kjellmann.

—(1906a) : Beiträge zur Algenflora von Schweden. Ark. f. Bot. **6.**

—(1906b) : Algen aus Argentina und Bolivia. *Ibid.*

—(1911a) : Algologische Notizen 6. Süsswasseralgen aus Queensland. Bot. Not.

Borge, O. (1911b): Die Süsswasseralgenflora Spitzbergens. Videnskapsselskapets Skrifter. I. Mat.-Naturv. Kl. **11.**

—(1913a): Beitrage zur Algenflora von Schweden. 2. Die Algenflora um den Torne-Träsk-See in Schwedisch-Lappland. Bot. Not.

—(1913b): *Zygnemales*; in Pascher's Süsswasserflora H. 9. 1. Aufl.

—(1918): Die von Dr. A. Löfgren in São Paulo gesammelten Süsswasseralgen. Ark. f. Bot. **15.**

—(1921): Die Algenflora des Takernsees, Sjön Täkerns fauna och flora. H.4. Utgiven: K. Sv. Vet. Akad. No. 4.

—(1923): Beiträge zur Algenflora von Schweden. Ark. f. Bot. **18.**

—(1925): Die von Dr. F.C. Hoehne während der Expedition Roosevelt-Rondon gesammelten Süsswasseralgen. Ibid. **19.**

—(1928): Süsswasseralgen in: Zellpflanzen Ostafrikas. Hedwigia. **68.**

—(1930): Beitrage zur Algenflora von Schweden 4, Ark,. f. Bot. **23A.**

—(1933): Schwedisch-Chinesische wissenschaftliche Expedition nach den norwestlichen Provinzen Chinas, Algen. Ibid. **25A.A.**

—(1936): Beiträge zur Algenflora von Schweden 5. Süsswasseralgen aus den Stockholmer Schären. Ibid. **28A.**

Börgesen, F. (1894): Ferskvandsalger fra Ostgronland. Med. om Gronland **18.**

—(1898): Nogle Freskvandsalger fra Island. Bot. Tidskr. **22.**

Bornet, M.E. (1891): Algues du département de la Haute-Vienne contenues dans l'herbier d'Edouard Lamy de la Chapelle. Bull. Soc. Bot. France. **38.**

Bory De S. and Vincent, J.B. (1822-31) in: Dictionnaire classique d'histoire naturelle. Paris.

Bourrelly, P. (1948): Microflorale algole de la region maritime de concarne neau Mem. Soc. Nat. et Math. Cherbourg.

—and Manguin, E. (1956): Algues d'eau douce de la Guadeloupe et dependances recueilles par la Mission P. Allorge in 1936. Sades, Paris.

—(1957): Alegues d'eau douce du soudan Francais region du Macina (A.O.F.) Bull. l'I.F.A.N. **19,** ser. A. no. 4.

Bourquin, H. (1917): Starch Formation in *Zygnema*. Bot. Gaz. **64.**

Boytschenko, E.A. (1935): Réduction du ritrate d'argent par les chromatophores de *Zygnema* et autres algues vertes. Bull. Soc. Natural. Moscou N.S. **44.**

Brauner, L. (1933): Zur Frage der postmortalen Farbstoffaufnahme von Pflanzenzellwänden. Flora. **127.**

Brand, F. (1899a): Über einen neuen Typus der Algenchlorophoren. Ber. Deutsch Bot. Ges. **17.**

—(1899b): *Mesogerron*, eine neue Chlorophyceengattung. Hedwigia **38.**

Braun, A. (1851): Betrachtungen über die Erscheinung der Verjüngung in der Natur. Leipzig.

—(1855): Algarum unicellularum genera nova vel minus cognita. Leipzig.

Britton, M.E. and Smith, B.H. (1936): Additions to the Algae of the Lower Wabash Valley. Proc. Indiana Acad. Sci. **45.**

Brown, H.G. (1908): Algal Periodicity in Certain Ponds and Streams. Bull. Torrey Bot. Club. **35.**

—(1918): Abnormal Conjugation in *Spirogyra*. Bot. Gaz. **66.**

Brundza, K. (1937): Kamanos. Aufbau und Pflanzendecke. Jahrb. Dd. landw. Ak. Dotnuva. kaunas.

Brühl, P. and Biswas, K. (1926): Algae of the Loktak Lake. Mem. Asiat. Soc. Bengal. **8.**

Brunel, J. (1932): Etudes sur la flore algologique du Québec. I. Contr. Laborat. de Bot. Univ. de Montréal. H.22-23.

Brunnthaler, J. (1907): Die Algen und Schizophyceen der Altwässer der Donau bei Wien. Verh. Zool. Bot. Ges. Wien.

—(1914): Beitrag zur Süsswasseralgenflora von Agypten. Hedwigia. **54.**

Brutschy, A. (1921): Die Vegetation und das Zooplankton des Hallwiler Sees. Jahrb. Aargau. Naturf. Ges

(1929): Die Algenflora des Val Piora. Zeitschr. f. Hydrol. **5.**

Buchanan, R.E. (1907): Notes on the Algae of Iowa. Proc. Iowa Acad. Sci. **14.**

Budde, H. (1929): Beitrag zur Algenflora der fliessenden Gewässer Spaniens. Arch. f. Hydrobiol. **20.**

—(1934): Algenuntersuchungen in westfälischen Mooren, insbesondere algensoziologischer Art. Abh. Westfäl. Prov. Mus. f. Naturk. **5.**

—(1935): Die Algenflora der Eder. Arch. f. Hydrobiol. **28.**

Bukatsch, F. (1939) : Uber die Rolle der Ascorbinsaure in den Chloroplasten. Planta. **30.**

—(1940) : Uber die Rolle der Ascorbinsäure in den Chloroplasten II. Planta. **31.**

Butscher, R.W. (1932) : Studies in the Ecology of Rivers II. Ann. Bot. **46.**

Büttner, R. (1890) : Über Gerbsäurereaktionen in der lebenden Pflanzenzelle. Diss. Erlangen.

Burge, W.E. and E.L. (1924) : Effect of Temperature and Light on Catalasé Content of *Spirogyra*. Bot. Gaz. **77.**

Carnoy (1884) : La Biologie cellulaire.

Carter, M. (1800) : On misdirected Efforts to Conjugation in *Spirogyra*. Ann. & Mag. Nat. Hist., Ser. 5, **6.** London.

Carter, N. (1922) : Freshwater Algae in : A. Systematic Account of the Plants collected in New Caledonia and the Isles of Pines. Jour. Linn. Soc. Bot. **46.**

—(1926) : Freshwater Algae from India. Bot. Survey of India. **9.**

Cederereutz, C. (1924) : Finnländische Zygnemalen. Acta Soc. Faun. & Flora Fenn. **55.**

—(1929a) : Süsswasseralgen aus Petsamo. Mem. Soc. Faun. & Flora Fenn. **5.**

—(1929b) : Algvegetationen i träsken pa Aland. *Ibid.* **6.**

—(1930) : *Spirogyra fluviatilis* Hilse, neu für Finnland. *Ibid.*

—(1932) : Süsswasseralgen aus Petsamo II. *Ibid.* **7.**

—(1934a) : *Spirogyra scrobiculata* (Stockmayer) Czurda ny för Finland. *Ibid.* **9.**

—(1934b) : Die Algenflora und Algenvegetation auf Aland. Act. Bot. Fenn. **16.**

—(1935) : Die Zygnemaceen Finnlands. Mem. Soc. Fauna. & Flora. Fenn. **11.**

—(1936) : Algen aus Kuusamo. *Ibid.* **12.**

Cedergren, G.R. (1913) : Bidrag till kännedomen om sötvattensalgerna i Sverige. I. Algflora vid Upsala. Ark. f. Bot. **13.**

—(1926) : Beiträge zur Kenntnis der Süsswasseralgen von Schweden. II. Die Algen aus Bergslagen und Wästerdalarne. Bot. Notiser.

—(1932) : Die Algenflora der Provinz Härjedalen. Ark. f. Bot. **25A.**

—(1938) : Ein kurzer Beitrag zur Algenflora Meddelpads. Bot. Notiser.

Cejp, K. (1932) : Some Remarks to the Knowledge of the Parasitic Phycomycetes of Conjugates in Bohemia. Bull. Int. Acad. Sc. Bohême.

—1933) : Further Studies on the Parasites of Conjugates in Bohemia. *Ibid.*

—(1935) : The Parasites of Conjugates in Bohemia III. *Ibid.*

Chadefaud, M. (1945) : Caracters Cytologiques remarquables d'une *Spirogyra*. C.R. Acad. Sci. Paris.

Chaudhuri, H. (1931) : On a Myzocytium parasitic on *Spirogyra affinis*. Arch. Protistenk. **57.**

Chesterman, D.R. and Forster, C.L. (1936) : Creeping Movements of *Spirogyra*. Nature.

Chmielevsky, V. (1890) : Über Conjugation bei *Spirogyra*. Sitz.-prot. biol. Sect. Warschau. naturf. Ges.

—(1890) : Eine Notiz über das Verhalten der Chlorophyllbänder in den Zygoten der *Spirogyra*-Arten. Bot. Zeitung.

—(1890) : Materialien zur Morphologie und Physiologie des Sexualprozesses bei niederen Algen. Charkow.

Chodat, R. (1910) : Etudes sur les Conjuguées. I. Sur la copulation d'un *Spirogyra*. Bull. Soc. Bot. Genève Ser. 2, **2.**

—(1913) : Monographies d'algues en culture pure, Mat. p. I. flore crypt. suisse. **4** (Fasc. **2**).

—(1914) : Etudes sur les Conjugees. II. Sur la copulation d'un *Mouges. tia.* Bull. Soc. Bot. Geneve. Ser. 2 **6.**

—(1916) : Sur l'isogamie, l'heterogamie, la conjugaision et la superfétation chez une algue verte. Arch. sc. phys. nat. **41.**

Chodat, R. and Zender. M.J (1924) : Algues de la region du Grand-Saint-Bernard. Bull. Soc. Bot. Genève. Ser. 2 **15.**

Cholnoky, B. v. (1927) : Untersuchungen über die Ökologie der Epiphyten. Arch. f. Hydrobiol. **18.**

—(1929) : Einige Bemerkungen zur Zygotenbildung der Conjugaten. Arch. Protistenk. **65.**

—(1930) : Untersuchungen über den Plasmolyseort der Algenzellen. I, II. Protoplasma. **11.**

—(1931a) : Untersuchungen über den Plasmolyseort der Algenzelle III. Protoplasma. **12.**

—(1931b) : Zur Kenntnis der Physiologie einiger fadenbildender Conjugaten. Arch. Protistenk. **75.**

—(1932) : Vergleichende Studien über Kern und Zellteilung der fadenbildenden Conjugaten. Arch. Protistenk. **68.**

Clemens, W.A., Dymond, J.R. and Bigelow, N. K. (1925) : Univ. Toronto Stud. 1924. Publ. Ontario Fisheries Lab. **25.**

Cleve, P. Th. (1868): Försök till en monografi öfver de Svenska Arterna af algfamilien *Zygnemaceae*. Nov. Act. Reg. Soc. Sci. Upsaliensis. Ser. 3 **6.**

Cohn, F. (1850): Zur Lehre vom Wachstum der Pflanzenzelle. Nov. Act. **22.**

—(1852): Über Keimung der Zygnemaceen. Schles. Ges. f. vaterl. Cultur.

Collins, F.S. (1905): Phycological Notes of the Late Isaac Holden. Rhodora. **7.**

—(1906): Algae in: Flora of Mount Desert.

—(1909): The Green Algae of North America. Tufts Coll. Stud. Sci. Ser. 2

—(1912): The Green Algae of North America. Suppl. I. *Ibid* 3

—(1918): The Green Algae of North America. Suppl. II. *Ibid* **4.**

—(1920): A working key to the Genera of North American Algae. *Ibid.*

Comère, J (1899): Conjuguées des environs de Toulousc. Bull. Soc. Bot. France, Ser. 3 **6.**

—(1901a): La florule des Conjuguees des environs de Toulouse. C.R. Congr. Soc. Sav. en 1900. Paris.

—(1901b): La flore du canal du midi dans la région toulousaine. *Ibid.*

—(1903): De l'action des eaux salées sur la végétation de quelques Algues d'eau douce. Nuov. Notorisia. **14.**

—(1905): De l'influence de la composition chimique du milieu sur la végétation de quelques Algues Chlorophycées. Bull. Soc. Bot. France. **52.**

—(1906): Observations sur lap ériodicité du développement de la flore algologique dans la région toulousaine. *Ibid.* **53.**

—(1909): De l'action des Arséniates sur la végétation des Algues. Bull. Soc. Bot. France. **56.**

—(1913a): De l'action du milieu considérée dans ses rapports avec la distribution générale des Algues d'eau douce. *Ibid.* **60.**

—(1913b): De l'influence exercèe par les matiéres colorantes dérivées de l'aniline sur la végétation des Algues d'eau douce. Nuov Notorisia. **28.**

Comère, J. and Vuathier, Ch. (1927): Influence de la concentration en ions hydrogene sur la flore de Algues des environs de Toulouse. Bull. Soc. Bot. France. **78.**

Conard, A. (1929): Sur la division cellulaire chez *Spirogyra*. C.R. Soc. Biol. **102.**

—(1931a): Sur la formation de la membrane chez certaines especes de *Spiroygyra*. C.R. congr. national d. sc. Liege.

—(1931b): Il n'ya pas d',,amphinucléole" chez les *Spirogyra*. C.R. Soc. Biol. **107.**

—(1931c): Quelle est la signification du nucléole chez *Spirogyra*? C.R. Soc. Biol. **107.**

—(1931d): Sur les characteres présentées par *Spirogyra majuscula*. *Ibid.*

—(1931e): Observation sur la zygote de *Spirogyra majuscula*. *Ibid.*

—(1931f): Les formes à noyeau lenticulaire doivent être séparées des *Spirogyra* et réunies en u genre nouveau. *Ibid.*

—(1931g): Sur le rôle des suspensures dans la division chez *Degagnya majuscula* (Kütz.) Conard et sur la formation des fibres du fuseau. *Ibid.*

—(1931h): Dans la plantule de *Degagnya majuscula* (Kütz.) Conard les cytoplasmes de deux gametes qui ont formé le zygote gardent leur individualité. *Ibid.*

—(1932a): Sur la croissance du noyeau chez *Degagnya majuscula* (Kütz.) Conard. *Ibid.* **110.**

—(1932b): Sur le mécanisme de la séparation dicentrique des plaques anaphasiques chez *Degagnya majuscula* (Kütz.) Conard (*Spirogyra majuscula*). *Ibid.*

—(19333a): Sur la vitesse de croissance des membranes chez le *Degagnya* et le *Spirogyra*. *Ibid.* **113.**

—(1933b): Sur l'association temporaire de la caryotine et de la substance nucléolaire au cours des phénomenes de division chez les Degagnyas et les Spirogyras. C.R. Soc. Biol. Paris. **111.**

—(1936a): Sur la variation du volume du noyeau au cours de la division. Beih. Bot. Centralbl 55 Abt. A.

—(1936b): Sur la germination des zygotes de *Degagnya majuscula* (Kütz) Conard. *Ibid.*

—(1936c): Sur la germination der zygotes de *Degagnya maxima* (Hass. Czurda) Conard (*Spirogyra maxima* (Hass.) Czurda. *Ibid.*

—(1936d): Quelques remarques sur la fécondation chez les *Spirogyra* et les *Degagnya*. *Ibid.*

—(1936e): Contribution à l'étude du genre *Degagnya* (*Spirogyra* à noyeau plat) Conard. *Ibid.*

—(1939): Sur le mécanisme de la division cellulaire et sur les bases morphologiques de la cytologie. Brüssel.

Conn, H.W. and Webster, C.W. (1908): A Preliminary Report on the Algae of the Fresh Waters of Connecticut. State of Conn, State Geol. a. Nat. Hist. Surv. Bull. Nr. 10.

Conrad, W. and Kufferath, H. (1912) : Additions à la florule algologique de Belgique. Bull. Soc. R. Bot. Belg. **49.**

Cook, A.B. (1945) : Algal pigments and their significance. Camb. Phil. Soc. Biol. Rev. **20.**

Cooke, M.C. (1882-84) : British Freshwater Algae. London.

Copeland, E.B. (1902) : The Conjugation of *Spirogyra crassa* Kütz. Bull. Torrey Bot. Club. **29.**

—(1909) : Periodicity in *Spirogyra*. Bot. Gaz. **47.**

Cornu, M. (1869) : Note sur un genre nouveau du groupe des Zygnémacées. Bull. Soc. Bot. France. **16.**

Cornu, P. (1939) : Contribution la flore algologique de la tourbière des Tenasses-Prantins (Vaud), Mém Soc. Vaud Sc. Nat. No. **44.**

Couch, J.N. (1935) : New or little known *Chytridiales*. Mycologia. **27.**

Coulter, S. (1887) : *Spirogyra* under Shock. Bot. Gaz.

Craaf, F. de. (1955) : Contribution to our knowledge of Dutch freshwater algae. I. Acta. Bot. Neerland. **4.**

Craveri, M. (1913) : Catalogo delle Alghe italiane e francesi del Museo "Rosmini" di Domodossola. Malpighia. **26.**

Croasdale, H.T. (1935) : The Fresh Water Algae of Woods Hole, Massachusetts, Philadelphia.

Crouan (1870-77) in Mazé, H. u. Schramm, A., Algues de la Guadeloupe. II. A ufl.

Crow, W.B. (1923) : Freshwater Plankton Algae from Ceylon. Jour. Bot. **61.**

—(1924) : Variation and Hybridization in *Isokontae* and *Akontae* in Relation to Classification. Jour. Genetics.

Cunningham, B. (1917) : Sexuality of filament of *Spirogyra*. Bot. Gaz. **63.**

—(1918) : Cross-conjugation in *Spirogyra Weberi*. *Ibid.* **66.**

—(1921) : The Occurence of unlike Ends of the Cells of a single Filament of *Spirogyra*. Jour. Elisha Mitchell Sci. Soc. **36.**

Cunningham, D.D. (1888) : On an Endophytic Alga occuring in the Leaves of *Limnanthemum indicum*. Sc. Mem. by Medic. Offic. of the Army of India. **3.**

Czurda, V. (1922a) : Zur Frage der Nucleuslöslichkeit bei *Spirogyra*. Arch. Protistenk. **44.**

—(1922b) : Über ein bisher wenig beachtetes Gebilde und andere Erscheinungen im Kern von *Spirogyra setiformis* Kütz. *Ibid.* **45.**

—(1924) : Über die Kultur der Konjugaten. Lotos. **72.**

—(1925a) : Zur Kenntnis der Kopulationsvorgänge bei *Spirogyra*. Arch Protistenk. **51.**

—(1925b) : Zur Kenntnis der Geschlechtsverhältnisse bei *Spirogyra*. Ber. Deutsch. Bot. Ges. **42.**

—(1926a) : Die Reinkultur der Konjugaten. Arch. Protistenk. **53, 54.**

—(1926b) : Wachstum und Stärkebildung einiger Konjugaten auf Kosten organisch gebundenen Kohlenstoffs. Planta. **2.**

—(1928) : Morphologie und Physiologie des Algenstärkekornes. Beih. Bot. Centralbl. **45.** Abt. 1.

—(1929) : Über Pyrenoidveränderung bei der Stärkebildung der *Spirogyra*-Zellen. Ber. Deutsch. Bot. Ges. **47.**

—(1930) : Experimentelle Untersuchungen über die Sexualitätsverhältnisse der Zygnemalen. Beih. Bot. Centralbl. **47.** Abt. 1.

—(1931a) : Zur Morphologie und Systematik der Zygnemalen. *Ibid.* **48.**

—(1931b) : Ein neuer, eigenartiger Kopulationsverlauf bei einer *Mougeotia* (*M. oedogonioides* Czurda). Beih. Bot. Centralbl. **48.**

—(1932a) : *Zygnemataceae* in : W. Bosshard, Botanische Ergebnisse der Deutschen Zentralasien-Expedition 1927-28. Fedde, Rep. spec. nov. **31.**

—(1932b) : *Zygnemales* in A. Pascher's Süsswasserflora von Mitteleuropa **9.**

—(1933) : Experimentelle Analyse der kopulationsauslösenden Bedingungen bei Mikroorganismen. I· Untersuchungen an Algen. Beih. Bot. Centrabl. **51.** Abt. A.

—(1934) : Chemisch-ökologische und experimentelle Untersuchungen natürlilcher Gewässer und ihrer Organismengesellschaften. Deutsche Forschung.

—(1937) : *Conjugatae* in : Handbuch der Pflanzenanatomie. II. Abt. 6. 2. Teil. Algen. B,b.

(1939) : *Zygnemales* der Deutschen Limnologischen Sundaexpedition. Arch. f. Hydrobiol. Suppl. **16,** Trop. Binnengewasser.

Dalla Torre, K.W. and Sarntheim, L.V. (1901) : Die Algen von Tirol, Vorarlberg und Liechtenstein. Flora der gefürsteten Grafschaft Tirol, des Landes Vorarlberg und des Fürstenthums Liechtenstein. **2,** Innsbruck.

Danforth, C.H. (1910) : Periodicity in *Spirogyra* with special Reference to the Work of Benecke. Rep. Missouri Bot. Gard. **21.**

Dangeard, P. (1886) : Recherches sur les organismes inférieures. Ann. Sci. Nat. Bot. Sér. 7. **4.**

—(1889) : Mémoire sur les Chytridinées. Le Botaniste. **1.**

—(1891a) : Sur la présence de crampons dans les Conjuguees. *Ibid*. **2.**

—(1891b) : Mémoire sur quelques maladies des algues et des animaux. *Ibid.*

—(1909) : Sur les phénomènes de fécondation chez les *Zygnema*. C.R. Acad. Sci. Paris. **148.**

—(1921) : Sur le chondriome des Conjuguées et des Diatomées. C.R. Soc. Biol. Paris.

—(1924) : Quelques remarques nouvelles sur le cytoplasme des Spirogyres. Rev. Algol. **1.**

—(1930) : Sur l'existence de deux variétés du *Spirogyra fluviatilis*. Le Botaniste. **22.**

Dannenberg. W. (1927) : Vorarbeiten zu einer Algenflora des Ostbaltischen Gebietes. Korr.-bl. Naturf. Ver. Riga. **59.**

De Bary, A. (1857) : Über die Copulation der Desmidiaceen, Zygnemaceen und Pilze, über die Keimung der Copulationsprodukte und die Ansichten über die Bedeutung der Copulation. Bot. Zeitg. **15.**

—(1858) : Untersuchungen über die Familie der Conjugaten. (Zygnemeen and Desmidieen) Leipzig.

—(1860) : Einige neue Saprolegnieen. Jahrb. wiss. Bot. **2.**

—(1888) : Species der Saprolegniaceen. Bot. Zeitg.

Debray, F. (1893) : Liste das Algues marines et d'eau douce récoltées jusqu'a ce jour en Algérie. Bull. Sc. d. 1. France et d. 1. Belg. **25.**

—(1897) : Catalogue des Algues du Maroc, d'Algérie et de Tunisie. Alger.

Deflandre. G. (1926a) : Algues d'eau douce du Venezuela récoltées par la Mission M. Grisol. Rev. algol. **3.**

—(1926b) : Contribution à la flore algologique de la Basse-Normandie. Bull. Soc. Bot. France. **63.**

—(1928) : Contribution à la flore algologique de France II, III. Bull. Soc. Bot. France. **65.**

Degagny, Ch. (1890) : Sur la division celluaire chez le *Spirogyra orthospira* et sur la réintégration des matieres chromatiques refoulées aux pôles du fuseau. C.R. Acad. Sci. Paris. **114.**

—(1893a) : Sur les matieres formées par le nucléole chez le *Spirogyra setiformis*. *Ibid.* **116.**

—(1893b) : Sur la morphologie du noyau cellulaire chez les *Spirogyra*. *Ibid.*

—(1893c) : Sur la concordance des phénomenes de la division du noyeau chez les lis et les *Spirogyra. Ibid.*

Delf, E.M. (1913) : Note on an attached Species of *Spirogyra* Ann. Bot. **27.**

Denis, M. (1924) : Observations algologiques dans les Hautes-Pyrénées I. Rev. Algol. **2.**

—(1925a) : Contribution à la flore algologique de l'Auvergne I, Bull. Soc. Bot. France. **72.**

—(1925b, 1926) : Revue des travaux parus sur les algues de 1910 à 1920. Rev. gén. Bot. **37**,38.

—(1926a) : La castration des Spirogyres par des champignons parasites. Rev. Algol. **3.**

Derry, B.H.E. (1929) : Plasmolyseform-und Plasmolysezeitstudien. Protoplasma. **8.**

Desmaziéres, J.B.H.J. (1825-31) : Plantes cryptogamiques de la France. Exsiccaten. I. Ausg. II. Ausg. 1836-51. Neue Ausg. 1853-60. Lille.

De Toni, J.B. (1889) : Sylloge Algarum. **6,** Padua.

De Toni, G.B. and Forti, A. (1898/99) : Contributo alla conoscenza della flora pelagica del Lago Vetter. Bull. Soc. Bot. Ital.

—(1900) : Contributo alla conoscenza del Plankton del Lago Vetter. Att. Real. Ist. Veneto. di sc., lett. and art. **59.**

—(1914) : Terza contribuzione alla flora algologica della Libia. Att. Real. Ist. Veneto di sc., lett. and art. **73.**

—(1916) : Catalogo delle Alghe raccolte nella regione di Bengasi dal R.P.D. Vito Zanon. *Ibid.* **76.**

De Toni, G.B. and Levi, D. (1888) : L'Algarium Zanardini, Civ. Mus. e racolt. corr. in Venezia. Coll. d. Stor. nat.

Dickie, G. (1880a) : Notes on Algae from Lake Nyassa, East Africa. Jour. Linn. Soc. Bot. **17.**

—(1880b) : On the Algae found during the Arctic Expedition. *Ibid.*

—(1881) : Notes on Algae from the Amazonas and its Tributaries. Jour. Lenn. Soc. Bot. **81.**

Dillenius, J.B.H.J. (1741) : Historia muscsrorum. London.

Dillwyn (1809) : British *Confervae*. London.

Dixit. S.C. (1937) : The *Chlorophyceae* of the Bombay Presidency, India I. Proc. Indian Acad. Sci., **5.**

Drew, K.M. (1948) : Genetics and algal life-histories. Nature. **161.**

Drouet, F. (1932) : A list of Algae from Missouri. Bull. Torrey Bot. Club. **59.**

Duplakow. K. (1925) : Contribution a la connaissance des biocenoses des objects submergies. Rev. russ. Hydrobiol. **4.**

Duplakow, S.N. (1933) : Materialien zur Erfoechung des Periphytont. Arb. Limnol. Stat. Kossino. **16.**

Dupray (1889) : Note sur une nouvelle espece de *Spirogyra*. Rev. gén. de Bot. **1.**

Durand. Th. and Wildeman. E. de (1897) : Prodrome de la flore belge. **1.**

Dvorák. R. (1917) : Tretí príspevek ku kvetene moravskych ras. V Trebici.

—(1919) : Ctvrty príspevek ku kvetene moravskych ras. Ibid.

—(1921) : Paty príspevek ku kvetene moravskych ras. Vestnik, Klub. Prirod. d. Prostejové. (1920/21).

—(1924) : Sesty prispevek ku kvetene moravskych ras. Sborniku kulbu. Prirod. v. Brne. **7.**

—(1931) : Príspevek ku pzonání ras tuni a jejich rosireni v oblasti západmoravské. Vedy prirodni. **12.**

Dvorák, R. and Novácek, F. (1926) : Sedmy príspevek ku kvetene moravskych ras. Sborniku klubu. Prirod. v. Brne. **9.**

Eckert, F. (1932) : Algenbeobachtungen I. Die Keimung und Zellteilung bei *Zygnema.* Mikroskcp. f. Naturfr. **10.**

—(1935/36) : Kopulation bei *Zygnema*. Mikroakosmos. **29.**

Eibl, K. (1939a) : Das Verhalten der *Spirogyra*-Chloroplasten bei Zentrifugierung. Protoplasma. **33.**

—(1939b) : Plasmolytische Untersuchungen an den Plastiden von *Spirogyra*. Ibid.

—(1940) : Lipophanerose der Plastiden von *Spirogyra* durch K-Oleat und andere Seifen. Protoplasma. **34.**

Eichler. B. (1892-1895, 1896) : Materaly do flory wodorostów okolic miedzyrzeca. Pamietnik Fizyograficzyny. **12, 13, 14.**

Eiselsberg, C. v. (1937) : Ionenantagonismus und Giftwrikung an *Spirogyra*. I. Über Ionenantagonismus ein-und zwiewertiger Kationen und deren Giftwrikung auf *Spirogyra*-Zellen. Biol. Generalis. **13.**

—(1938) : Ionenantagonismus und Giftwrikungen an *Spirogyra*. II. Über die Wirkung von Kaliumarsenit, Akonitin und Wasserstoffsuperoxyd. Ibid. **14.**

Eldaroff-Serguéeff, M. (1913) : Le phytoplankton dans le delta du Wolga en 1909. Ichthyol. Labor. D. Kaspi-Volgaschen Fisch, Verw. i. Astrachan. **2.**

El. Nayal, A.A. (1932) : An Enumeration of Egyptian *Chlorophyceae* and *Cyanophyceae*. Rev. Algol. **6.**

—(1936) : Contributions to our Knowledge of the Freshwater Algae of Egypt. The Egypt. Univ. Bull. Fac. Sci. Nr. **9.**

Emig, W.H. (1917) : The Travertine Deposits of the Arbuckei Mountains, Oklahoma, with Reference to the Plant Agencies concerned in their Formation. Bull. Oklah. Geol. Surv. Nr. 29.

Engelmann. Th. W. (1881) : Neue Methode zur Untersuchung der $O_2$-Ausscheidung pflanzlicher und tierischer Organismen. Bot. Zeitg. **39.**

—(1882) : Zur Biologie der Schizomyeceten. *Ibid.* **40.**

—(1883) : Farbe und Assimilation. *Ibid.* **41.**

—(1894) : Die Erscheinungsweise der Sauerstoffausscheidung chlorophyllhaltiger Zellen im Licht bei Anwendung der Bakterienmethode. Verh. K. Akad. Wiss. Amsterdam. Sket. **2. 3.**

Ernst, A. (1918) : Bastardierung als Ursache der Apogamie im Pflanzenreich. Jena.

Escoyez. E. : Le noyan et la caryocinese chez le *Zygnema*. La Cellule. **24.**

Faber, F.C. (1912) : *Spirogyra tjibodensis* n. sp. Ann. Jard. Bot. Buitenzorg. **26.**

Fagerstrom, L. (1937) : Sötvattensalger fran Ik Terijoki. Mem. Soc. pro Fauna. et Flora. Fenn. **13.**

Famintzin, A.S. (1865a) : Die Wirkung des Kerosinlampenlichtes auf *Spirogyra orthospira* Naeg. Bull. Acad. St. Petersb. **10.**

—(1865b) : Über die Wirkung des Lampenlichts auf *Spirogyra orthospira* Naeg. Ibid.

—(1867a) : Die Wirkung des Lichtes auf Algen und einige andere ihnen verwandte Organismen. Jahrb. wiss. Bot. **6.**

—(1867b) : Die Wirkung des Lichtes auf *Spirogyra*. Bull. Acad. Imp. Sci. St. Petersbourg. **6.**

—(1868) : Die Wirkung des Lichtes auf die Zellteilung der *Spirogyra*. Ibid. **7.**

Famintzin, A. (1871) : Die anorganischen Salze als ausgezeichnete Hilfsmittle zum Studium der Entwicklungsgeschichte der niederen Pflanzenformen. Beih. Bot. Centralbl. **74.**

Filarszky, N. (1899) : Adatok a Pieninek mo szatvegetatiójátus. Math.-és. termeszet. Közlem. **27.**

—(1900) : Beiträge zur Algenvegetation des Pieninen-Gebirges auf ungarischer Seite. Hedwigia. **39.**

Fischer, A. (1883) : Über das Vorkommen von Gipskristallen bei den Desmidiacceen. Jahrb. wiss. Bot. **14.**

Fischer, A. (1905) : Die Zelle der Cyanophyceen. Bot. Zeitg.

Fischer, R. (1920) : Die Algen Mährens und iher Verbreitung. Verh. d. Naturf. Ver. in Brünn. **57.**

—(1924) : Ökologische Skizzen zur Algenvegetation des mährisch-schlesischen Gesenkes. Schirift. f. Susswasser-und Meeresk. **2.**

—(1925) : Ökologische Skizzen zur Algenflora des mährisch-schlesischen Gesenkes. Verh. ber. naturf. Ver. Brünn. **59.**

Fitschen, J. (1905) : Das pflanzliche Plankton zwiern nordhannoverschen Seen. Jahrb. Ver. f. Naturk. Unterweser f. 1903 and 1904.

Flemming. W. (1882) : Zellsubstanz, Kern-und Zellteilung. Leipzig.

Fling. E.M. (1939) : One hundred Algae of West Virginia. Castanea, Journ. South Appalach. Bot. Club. **4.**

Flint, E. (1949) : An ecological study of some freshwater algae. (Abst). Trans. Roy. Soc. New Zealand. **77** (5).

Fluri, M. (1909) : Einfluss von Aluminiumsalzen auf das Protoplasama. Flora. **99.**

Forel, E. (1904) : Le Léman **3.**

Forni, D.B. (1925) : Contributo alla ficologia del Verbano. Atti dell'Ist. Bot. Univ. Pavia. 3 Ser. **2.**

Forti A (1902) : Contributo 4. alla conoscenza della florula ficologica Veronese. Nuov. Notorisia **13.**

—(1913) : Primi studi per un'exploration limnobiologico dell'oriente. Nuov. Notorisia **24.**

—(1926) : La alghe delle republica di San Marino in : R. Pampanini, Flora della Republica di San Marino. San Marino.

—(1931) : Osservazioni biologiche spora alcune laghi dell'Albania orientale. Att. dell' Acad. Veneto-Trent-Istr. **21.**

Forti, A. Marcello, A. and Pampanini, R. (1932) : Una escursione botanica in Tripolitania. Att. del Real. Ist Veneto di scienze, lett, et art. **98.**

Fragoso, R.G. (1925) : *De Tonisia* gen. nov. de hongo parasitico en une *Spirogyra*. Nuov. Notorisia **40.**

Fremineur, F. (1923) : Les Spirogyres, Les Natur. belges **4.**

Frémy, P. (1924) : Contribuition à la flora algologique de l'Afrique équatoriale francaise. Rev. Algol. **1.**

—(1926) : Excursions botaniques de la Société Linnéenee de Normandie, la 1 juin 1925 aux environs de Lessay (Manche). Bull. Soc. Linn. Normandie. 7. Ser. **9.**

Frémy, P. (1930) : Algues provenant des récoltes de M. Henri Gadeau de Kervelli dans le canton de Bagueres-de-Luchon (Jaute-Garonne). Bull. Soc. Amis· Sc. nat. Rouen.

—(1933) : Seconde contribution à la flore algologique du Congo Belge. Bull. Jard. Bot. Bruxelles. **9.**

Frémy, P. and Meslin, R. (1927) : Excursion botanique dans la lande de la Mauffe (Manche), 12, Juillet 1926. Bull. Soc. Bot. Normandie. 7. Sér. **91.**

Fritsch, F.E. (1903) : Algological Notes IV. Remarks on the Periodical Development of the Algae in the Artificial Waters at Kew. Ann. Bot. **17.**

—(1907) : The Subaerial and Freshwater Algal Flora of the Tropics. A Physiographical and Ecological Study. *Ibid.* **21.**

—(1914) : Contributions to our knowledge of the Freshwater Algae of Africa. 1. Some Freshwater Algae from Madagascar. Ann. Biol. Lacustre. **7.**

—(1916) : The Morphology and Ecology of an Extreme Terrestrial Form of *Zygnema* (*Zygogonium*) *ericetorum* (Kütz.) Hansg. Ann. Bot. **30.**

—(1918) : Contributions to our Knowledge of the Freshwater Algae of Africa. 2. A first Report of the Freshwater Algae mostly from the Cape Peninsula in the Herbarium of the South African Museum. Ann. S. Afr. Mus. **9.**

—(1931) : Some Aspects of the Ecology of Freshwater Algae (with special reference to static waters). Journ. Ecol. **19.**

—(1935) : The Structure and Reproduction of the Algae I. Cambridge.

—(1945) : Studies in the comparative morphology of the algae. Ann. Bot. (N.S.). **9.**

Fritsch, F.E. and Rich, F. (1907) : Studies on the Occurence and Reproduction of British Freshwater Algae in Nature I. Preliminary Observations in *Spirogyra*. Ann. Bot. **21.**

—(1913) : Studies of the Occurence and Reproduction of British Freshwater Algae in Nature. Ann. Biol. Lacustre, **6.**

—(1924) : Contributions to our Knowledge of the Freshwater Algae of Africa. 4. Freshwater and Subaerial Algae from Natal. Trans. Roy. Soc. S. Afr. **11.**

Fritsch, F.E. and Rich, E. (1927): The Reproduction and Delimination of the Genus *Zygnema*. New Phytologist. **26.**

—(1928): Contributions to our Knowledge of the Freshwater Algae of Africa 7. Freshwater Algae from Griqualand West. Trans. Roy. Soc. S. Afr. **18.**

—(1937): Contributions to our Knowledge of the Freshwater Algae of Africa. 13. Algae of the Belfast Pan, Transvaal. *Ibid.* **25.**

Fritsch, F.E. and Stephens, E. (1921): Contributions to our Knowledge of the Freshwater Algae of Africa. 3. Freshwater Algae, mainly from the Transkei Territories, Cape Colony. *Ibid.* **9.**

Fritsch, F.E. and West, G.S. (1927): A treatise on the British Freshwater Algae. Cambridge.

Gaidukow, N.N. (1925): Ökologische Untersuchungen der Süsswasseralgen. Zapisok Belorussk. Gosudarstv. Inst. Selsjk i. Lesnogo Chozjajstva. Minsk.

Gams, H. (1916): La Grande Gouille de la Sarvaz. Bull. Soc. Murithienne. **39.**

—(1927): Von der Follatères zur Dent de Morcles. Beitr. z. geobot. Landesaufn. d. Schweiz. **15.**

—and Ruoff, S. (1929-1930): Geschichte, Aufbau und Pflanzendecke des Zehlaubruches. Schrift. Physik-ökonom. Ges. zu Königsberg, **66.**

Gates, R.R. (1932): Notes on Zygospore Formation in *Spirogyra*. Jour. Roy. Micr. Soc. **102.**

Gau, B. (1935): Beiträge zue Morphologie und Biologie von *Zygogonium ericetorum*. Diss. Köningsberg.

Gauthier-Lievre, H. (1924): Algues d'Afrique du Nord. Bull. Soc. Sci. Nat. Afrique Nord. **15.**

—(1931): Recherches sur la flora des eaux continentales de l'Afrique due Nord. Soc. d'Hist. Nat. Afr. Nord. Mém. Hors-série.

—(1941): Algues des eaux continentales africanes I. Bull. Soc. Hist. nat. Afr. du Nord. p. **32.**

Gay, F. (1884a): Essai d'une monographie locale des Conjuguées. Rev. Sc. nat. Ser. 3 **3.**

—(1884b): Note sur les Conjuguées due Midi de la France. Bull. Soc. Bot. France. **31.**

—(1891): Algues de Baguerres-de-Bigorre. *Ibid.* **38.**

Geissbühler, J. (1930): Grundlagen zu einer Algenlora einiger oberthurgauischer Moore. Mitt. Thurgau. Naturf. Ges. **28/29.**

Geitler, L. (1926): Zur Morphologie und Entwicklungsgeschichte der Pyrenodie. Arch f. Prot. **56.**

—(1930a): Über Apomixis bei *Mougeotia*. Arch. Protistenk. **70.**

—(1930b): Über die Kernteilung von *Spirogyra*. *Ibid.* **71.**

—(1934): Grundrib der Cytologie. Berlin.

—(1935): Untersuchungen über den Kernbau von *Spirogyra* mittles Feulgens Nuklealfärbung. Ber. Deutsch. Bot. Ges. **53.**

—(1935): Neue Untersuchungen über die Mitose von *Spirogyra*. Arch Protistenk. **85.**

—(1938): Chromosomenbau. Protoplasmamonogr. **14.**

—(1941): Algues des eaux continentales africones I. Bull. Soc. Hist. nat. Afr. du Nord, p. 32.

—(1949): Das kopulationsverhalten von *Mougeotia polymorpha* n. sp. und die Azygotenbildung von *Spirogyra dimorpha* n. sp. Oester. Bot. Zeitschr. **96.**

—(1958): Isogames Bewegungsverhalten unter morphologischer Anisogamic bei einer Konjugaten Alge. Biol. Centralbl. **77.**

—(1958): Sexualler dimorphismus bei einer Konjugate (*Mougeotia heterogama* n. sp.) Oester. Bot. Zeitschr. **105.**

Gemeinhardt, K. (1926): Uber Wirkung von aktivem Chlor auf Wasserpflanzen. Nachr. üb. Sc Schädlingsbek. **1.**

Gerassimoff, J.J. (1890): Einige Bemerkungen über die Funktion des Zellkerns. Bull. Soc. imp. Nat. Moscou.

—(1892): Über kernolose Zellen bei einigen Konjugaten. *Ibid.*

—(1896): Über ein Verfahren kernlose Zellen zu erhalten. *Ibid.*

—(1898): Über die Kopulation der zweikernigen Zellen bei *Spirogyra*. Bull. Soc. Imp. Nat. Moscou.

—(1900): Über die Lage und Funktion des Zelkernes. *Ibid.*

—(1901): Über den Einfluss des Kernes auf das Wachstum der Zelle. *Ibid.*

—(1902): Die Abhiängigkeit der Grosse der Zellen von der Menge ihrer Kernmasse. Zeitschr, f. allg. Physiol. **1.**

—(1904): Über die kernolsen und einen Übfluss an Kernlaasse enthaltenden Zellen bei *Zygnema*. Hedwigia. **44.**

—(1905a): Atherkulturen von *Spirogyra*. Flora. **94.**

—(1905b): Über die Grösse des Zellkerns. Beih. Bot. Centralbl. **18** Abt. 1.

Gertz. O. (1927) :   Untersuchungen über die Verbretiung der Jodidoxydasen.   Bot. Not.

Gessner, F. (1930) :   Gestaltänderung an *Spirogyra*-Chromatophoren.   Mikroskop. f. Naturfr.   **8.**

Gibbs, R.D. (1926) :   The Action of Ultraviolet Light in *Spirogyra*.   Trans.   Proc. R. Soc. Canada.

Giklhorn, J. (1933) :   Über aktive Chloroplasten-Kontraktion bei *Spirogyra* und den Aggregatzustand der Spiralbander.   Protoplasma.   **17.**

Gilbut, W.J. (1946) :   Studies on Phillipine Chlorophyceae.   II Survey of literature and list of record-ed species prior to 1940.   Bull. Torrey Bot. Club.   **B.**   **73.**

Gillis, J. (1923) :   Zetmeelvorming bij *Spirogyra* onder den invloed van organische stoffen.   Natuurweten-sch. Tijdschr.   **5.**

Giroud, A. (1938) :   L'acide ascorbique dans la cellule et les tissus.   Protoplasmamonogr.   **16.**

Godward, M. (1937) :   An Ecological and Taxonomic Investigation of the Littorial Algal Flora of Lake Windermere.   Jour. Ecol.   **25.**

Godward, M.B.E. (1954) :   Cytological criteria in the taxonomy of *Spirogyra*.   Proc. 7th Int. Bot. Congr.

—(1954) :   The ' Diffuse ' centromere or polycentric chromosomes in *Spirogyra*.   Ann. Bot. n.s. **18.**

—(1954) :   The centromere, with special reference to the Conjugales.   Rapp. Comm. 8me Congr. Int. Bot. **9.**

—(1954) :   Cytotaxonomy of *Spirogyra*.   (Abstr). Rapp. Comm. 8me Congr. Int. Bot. **17.**

Gonzales, P. (1927) :   Contribucion al estudo de las algas y esquizofites de Espana.   Trab. Mus. Nat. Cienc. Nat. Ser. Bot. **22.**

—(1929) :   De la ficoflora Hispano-Marroqui (Agua dulce).   Bull. R. Soc. espanol. Hist. Nat. **29.**

—(1931) :   Algunas datos algologicos de la peninsula iberica, de Baleares y de Marruecos (agua dulce).   *Ibid.* **31.**

Gonzalves, E.A. & Joshi, D.B. (1946) :   Freshwater algae near Bombay.   I. The seasonal succession of the algae in a tank at Bandra.   Jour. Bombay Nat. Hist. Soc. **46.**

Graff, P.W. (1928) :   Contribution to our knowledge of Western Montana Fungi II. Mycologia.   **20.**

Gratzky, E. u. Weber, F. (1931) :   Plasmolyseort und Membranwachstum.   Protoplasma.   **12.**

Gray, I.E. (1821) :   A Natural Arrangement of British Plants.   London.

Graudina, A. (1928) :   Die Algenflora des Stadtkanalas von Riga.   Act. Hort. Bot. Univ. Latviensis. **3.**

Greger, J. (1910) :   Beitrag zur Algenflora des Kustenlandes.   Hedwigia.   **52.**

—(1914) :   Die Algenflora der Komotau-Udwitzer Teichgruppe.   Lotos.   **62.**

—(1920) :   Die Algenflora der Komotau-Udwitzer Teichgruppe II. Beih. Bot. Centralbl.   **37**, Abt. 2

Gregory, E.L. (1892) :   Abnormal Growth of *Spirogyra* Cells. Bull. Torrey. Bot. Club. **19.**

Griffiths, B.M. and Cooke, R.B. (1924) :   Tyton Willows Pool. Trans. Nat. Hist. Soc., Nothumberland, Durham and Newcastle-upon-Tyne.   N. Ser. **6.**

Grilli, C. (1897) :   Algae nonnullae in regoine Picena lectae.   Bull. Soc. Bot. Taal.

Gronglad, R. (1934) :   A short Report of the Freshwater Algae recorded from the Neighbourhood of the of the Zoological Station at Tvarminne. Mem. Soc. Fauna et. Flora. Fenn.   **10.**

Grunow (1896) :   Algen von der Welterise der Novara.   Wien.

Gulliermond. M. (1921) :   Sur le chondriome des Conjuguees et des Diatomees.   D.R. Soc. Biol.

Gutwinski, R. (1890) :   Materyali do flory glonow galicyi II, Sprawozdan Komisyi fizyjograiczny Akad. Umiejetuosci.   **25.**

—(1891) :   Flora algarum agri Leopoliensis, *Ibid* **27.**

—(1892a) :   Materylay do flory glonow Galicyi III. *Ibid.* **28.**

—(1892b) :   Der Teich von Tarnopol.   Beschreibung. Thiere und Pflanzen mit besonderer Beruck-sichtigung der Algen.   Nadbitka z. I. Rocznika Kokaamauknowego tranopolskiego.

—(1893) :   Glony stawow na Zyburuczu. Sprawozd. Kom, fisyogr. Akad. Umeij. w Krakow. **29.**

—(1894) :   Flora algarum gri Tarnopolienisis.   *Ibid.* **30.**

—(1895) :   Produdromus Florae Algarum Galiciensis.   Rospraw Wydzialu. Mathpryzrod. Akad. Umiej. w. Krakow. **28.**

—(1897a) :   Wykaz glonow zebranych w. okolicy Wadowic-Makowa. Sprawozd. Kom. fizyogr. Akad. Umiej. w. Krakow. **32.**

—(1897b) :   Über die bis jetzt in Bosnien und der Hercegowina entdeckten Algen.   Wiss. Mitt. Bosn Herzeg. **5.**

—(1898) :   Algae in itinere per montem Babia Gora collectae. Sprawozd. Kom. fizyogr. Akad. Umiej. w. Krakow. **33.**

Gutwinski, R. (1899): Systematische Übersicht der von Dr. Justin Karlinski in der Umgebung von Gracanica während des Herbstes 1879 gesammelten Algen. Wiss. Mitt. Bosn. u. Herzeg. **6.**

—(1902): De Algis a Dr. M. Raciborski anno 1899 in insula Java collectis. Bull, intern, Acad. Sci., Cracovie. Cl. Sci., Math. et Nat., Nr. 9.

—(1903): De algis, praecipue Diatomaceis, a D.J. Holder in Asia centrali utque in China colectis. *Ibid.*

—(1909): Flora Algarum montium Tatrensium. *Ibid.* **4.**

Haberlandt. G. (1890): Zur Kenntnis der Conjugation bei *Spirogyra*. Sitz. Ber. d. Akad. Wiss. Wien, math-naturw. Kl. **99**, Abt. 1.

Hallas, E. (1895): Om en ny *Zygnema*-Art med Azygosporer. Bot. Tidsskr. **20.**

Handa, R. (1927a): A contribution of our Knowledge of the Green Algae of Rangoon. Jour. Burma Research Soc. **17.**

—(1927b): Some Peculiar Features of the Sub-aerial *Zygnemales* of Rangoon. Jour. Indian. Bot. Soc. **6.**

Hansgirg, A. (1882a): Beitrage zur Kenntnis der Böhmischen Algen. Sitz. Ber. Bohm. Ges. d. Wiss.

—(1883a): Neue Beitrage zur Algenkunde Böhmens. *Ibid.*

—(1883b): Beitrage zur Kenntnis böhmischer Algen. *Ibid.*

—(1886): Prodromus der Algenflora von Böhmen. Arch. d. naturw. Durchforsch, in Böhmen. **5.**

—(1888): De *Spirogyra insigni* (Hass). Nov. var. *fallaci Zygnemate chalybeospermo* nov. sp. et *Z. rhynchonemate* nov. sp. adjecto conspectu subgenerum, sectionum et subsectionum generis *Spirogyrae* Link et *Zygnematis* (Ag.) De. Bary. Hedwigia. **27.**

—(1890): Physiologische und algologische Mitteilungen. Sitz. Ber. böhm. Ges. d. Wiss.

—(1891): Algologische und bacteriologische mitteilungen. *Ibid.*

—(1892): Bieträge zur Kenntnis der Susswasseralgen und Bakterienflora von Tirol und Böhmen. Sitz. Ber. k. böhm. Ges. d. Wiss.

—(1893): Physiolgische und phycophysiologische Untersuchungen. Prag.

—(1905): Grundzüge der Algenflora von Niederösterreich. Beih. Bot. Centralbl. **18** Abt. 2.

Hariot. P. (1913): Algues d'eau douce du Maroc. Bull. Soc. Bot. France. **60.**

Harnisch, O. (1929): Die Biologie der Moore. Die Binnengewasser. **7.** Stuttgart.

Harper, R.M. (1950): Algae on animals: A bibliographical note. Ecology. **31.**

Hartig, F. (1846,47): Über die Conjugation der Spirogyren. Ver. d. naturhist. Vereins D. Harzes.

Hartmann, M. (1939): Geschlecht und Geschlechtsbestimmung im Tier, und Pflanzenreich. Samml. Göschen. Nr. 427.

Harvey, F.L. (1892): The Freshwater Algae of Maine III. Bull. Torrey Bot. Club. **19.**

Hassall, A.H. (1842): Observations on the Genera *Zygnema*, *Tyndaridea* and *Mougeotia* with description of new species. Ann and Mag. Nat. Hist. **10.**

—(1843a): Description of British Freshwater *Confervae*, mostly new. *Ibid.* **11.**

—(1843b): Observations on the Genus *Mougeotia*, on two New Genera of Freshwater Algae and on *Tyndaridea*. *Ibid.* **12.**

—(1845): A History of British Frewhwater Algae. London.

Hattori, H. (1917): Mikrobiologische Untersuchungen über einige japanische Wasserleitungen. Jour. Coll. Sc. Imp. Univ. Tokyo. **40.**

Häydén, A. (1910): The Algal Flora of the Missouri Botanical Garden. Rep. Missouri Bot. Garden. **21.**

Hayren, E. (1902): Studier öfver vegetationen patil landningsomradena i Ekenäs skärgard. Act. Soc. Fauna. et Flora. Fenn. **23.**

—(1909): Algologische Notizen aus der Gegend von Björneborg. Medd. Soc. Fauna. et Flora. Fenn. **35.**

—(1936): Algenfunde 1935 von der Insel Ösel und von einigen Nachbarinseln. Mem. Soc. Fauna. et Flora. Fenn. **12.**

Hecht, K. (1912): Studien über den Vorgang der Plasmolyse. Diss. Marburg.

Heering, W. (1904): Über einige Süsswasseralgen Schleswig-Holsteins. Mitt. Altonaer Mus. H.1.

Heering, W. and Homfeld, H. (1904): Die Algen des Eppendorfer Moores bei Hamburg. Verh Naturw. Ver. Hamburg. 3 Folg. **12.**

Heiden, H. (1887, 1888): Beitrag zur Algenflora Mecklenburgs.

Heidt. K. (1937): Beitrag zur Kenntnis der Gattung *Micromyces*. Ber. Deutsch Bot. Ges. **55.**

Heidt. K.(1939a): Über das Auftreten von Zygnemaceen in der Ostsee, Vitter Bodden. Mitt. Naturw. Ver. Neuvorpommern und Rügen.

—(1939b): Zytomorphologie und Zytogenese bei *Mougeotia* normaler und abnormer Konstitution. Arch. f. exper. Zellforsch. **23**.

Hemleben, H. (1922): Über den Kopulationsakt und die Geschlechtsverhältnisse der *Zygnemales*. Bot. Arch. 2.

—1923): Einige Bemerkungen über Generationswechsel, Abstammung und Geschlechtsverhältnisse der *Zygnemales*. Zietschr. f. indukt. Abstammungsu. Vererbungslehre. **31**.

Hempel, C.E. (1881): Algenflora der Umgebung von Chemnitz. Ber. naturw. Ges. Chemnitz. 1878-80.

Hennings, P. (1893): Die Algenflora des Müggelsees. Naturw. Wochenschr. **8**.

Henriques. J. (1881): Contributiones ad floram cryptogamicam ilusitanicum. Coimbra.

—(1886): Contribuçoes para o estudo da flora d'Africa. Bot. Soc. Broter. **4**.

Heydrich, F. (1894): Beiträge zur Kenntnis der Algenflora von Ostasien. Hedwigia. **33**.

Hieronymus, G. (1895): Algen in: Engler, Die Pflanzenwelt Ostafrikas und der Nachbargebiete. Teil C. Berlin.

Hill, G.A. (1916): *Spirogyra gigantea* n. sp. Publ. Puget Sound Biol. Stat. **1**.

—(1916): *Spirogyra dubia longiarticulata* Kütz. in. Washington. *Ibid*.

—(1916): Origine of the Second Spiral in *Spirogyra lutetiana*. *Ibid*.

Hilse (1863): Neue Beiträge zur Algen-und Diatomeenkunde Schlesiens, insbesondere Strehlens. Abh. Schles. Ges. vaterl. Cult. Abt. f. Naturwiss. u. Med. 1862.

Hirn, K.E. (1895): Die finnländischen Zygnemaceen. Act. Soc. Fauna. et Flora. Fenn. **9**.

—(1896): Algologische Notizen I, II. Ofvers. Finska Vet. Soc. Förhandl. **38**.

—(1900): Einige Algen aus Centralasien. *Ibid*. **42**.

Hobby, C.N. (1880): List of Species of Freshwater Algae found in Iowa. Proc. Iowa Acad. Si. Append.

Hodgetts, W.J. (1918): The Conjugation of *Zygogonium ericetorum* Kütz. New Phytolog. **17**.

—(1920): A New Species of *Spirogyra*. Ann. Bot. **34**.

—(1925): Some Freshwater Algae from Stellenbosch, Cape of Good Hope. Trans. R. Soc. S. Africa. **13**.

Höfler, K. (1933): Stärkespeicherung kopulierender *Spirogyra*. Protoplasma. **18**.

—(1939): Nekroseformen pflanzlicher Zellen. Ber. Deutsch. Bot. Ges. **56**.

Hofmeister, L. (1937): Die Wirkung von Athylenglykol auf die Plastiden von *Spirogyra*, Protoplasma. **20**

Hofmeister, W. (1867): Die Lehre von der Pflanzenzelle. Hdb. d. physiol. Bot. **1**.

Hofmeister. W. (1874): Über die Bewegungen der Faden der *Spirogyra princeps* (Vauch) Link, Württ, naturw. Hajresh. **30**.

Hooker, J.D. (1855): Flora Novae Zelandiae II. The Botany of the Antarctic Voyage of Erebus and Terror II. London.

Hoyt, W.D. (1913): Some Toxic and Antitoxic Effects in Culture of *Spirogyra*. Bull. Torrey Bot. Club. **40**.

Huber, G. (1906): Monographische Studien im Gebiete der Montigglerseen (Südtirol) mit besonderer Berücksichtigung ihrer Biologie. Arch. f. Hydrobiol. **1**.

—(1908): Biologische Notiz über das Langmoos bei Montiggl. (Südtirol). *Ibid*. **3**.

Huber-Pestalozzi, G. (1928): Beiträge zur Kenntnis der Süßwasseralgen von Korsika. *Ibid*. **19**.

—(1930): Algen aus dem Knysnawalde in Südafrika. Zeitschr, f. Bot. **23**.

—(1931): Infektion einer *Mougeotia*-Population durch *Micromyces Zygogonii* Dangeard an einem alpine Standort. Hedwigia. **71**.

Hunter, S.J. (1885): Unusual Form of attempted Conjugation in *Spirogyra*. Jour. Bot. **23**.

Hurter, E. (1928): Beobachtunlgen an Litoralagen des Vierwaldstättersees. Mitt. Naturf. Ges. Luzern. **10**.

Hutchinson, G.E. Picford, G.E. and Schuurmann. I. (1932): A Contribution to the Hydrobiology of Pans and other Inland Waters of South Africa, Arch. f. Hydrobiol. **24**.

Huzel, C. (1936): Beitrag zur Kenntnis der Mikroskopischen Pflanzenwelt der Rauhen Wiesen bei Böhmenkrich, Veröff. Württ. Landesstelle f. Natursch. H. 13.

Hylander, C.J. (1928): The Algae of Connecticut. State of Connecticut. State Geol. a. Bat. Hist. Survey, Bull. Nr. **42**.

Hymlö, D.E. (1916) :  Studien über die marinen Grunalgen der Gegend yon Malmö.  Ark. f. Bot. **14.**

Israel and Klingmann (1897) :  Oligodynamische Erscheinungen anpflanzlichen und tierischen Zellen. Virchows Arch. f. pathol. Anat. u. Phys. **147.**

Istvanffi, J. (1884) :  Hibernatio Zygnemacearum.  Magyar növénytani Lapok. **8.**

—(1892) :  Florula algarum aquae thermalis insulae St. Margarethae Buda Péstini.  *Ibid.* **15.**

—(1893) :  Adatok Romania Algeflorajakoz.  Természet. Fezelek. **16.**

—(1898) :  Die Kryptogamenflora des Balaton und seiner Nebengewässer.  Res. d. wiss. Erforsch d. Balaton II, 2, 2, 1.

Itzigsohn, H. (1853a) :  Die Fruktiflikation der *Mougeotia.*  Bot. Zeitg.

—(1853b) :  Über den männlichen Geschlechtsapparat bie *Spirogyra* und einigen anderen Konferven.  *Ibid.*

—(1856) :  De fabirica sporae *Mougeotiae genu exae.*  Neudamm.

Iwanoff, L. (1899) :  Über neue arten von Algen und Flagellaten, welche an der biologischen Station zu Bologoje gefunden wurden.  Bull. Soc. imp. Natural. Moscou. N.F. **13.**

—(1902) :  Beobachtungen über die Wasservegetation des Seengebietes.  Von den Biol. Stat. Bologoje. **2.**

Iyengar. M.O.P. (1923) :  Note on some attached Forms of *Zygnemaceae.*  Jour. Indian Bot. Soc. **3.**

—(1932) :  Studies on Indian Zygnemales.  Rev. Algol. **6.**

(1958) :  "Algology" Proc. Nat. Inst. Sci. Part **4.**

(1958a) :  Three new species of *Temnogametum* from South India.  J. Indian Bot. Soc. **37** (2)

(1958b) :  A new type of lateral conjugation in *Spirogyra. Ibid.* **37** (3)

Jaag. O, (1938) :  Die Kryptogamenflora des Rheinfalls und des Hochroheins von Stein bis Eglisau.  Mitt. Naturf. Ges. Schaffhausen.

Janse, J.M. (1887) :  Plasmolytische Versuche an Algen.  Bot. Zentralbl. **32.**

—(1888) :  Die Permeabilitat des Protoplasmas.  Versl. en Medeel. d.k. Akad. Wetensch. Amsterdam. R. 3, **4.**

Jao. C.C. (1925a) :  New *Zygnemataceae* from Woods Hole.  Trans. Amer. Microsc. Soc. **54.**

—(1935b) :  New *Zygnemataceae* collected in China.  Amer. Jour. Bot.

—(1935) :  Studies on the Freshwater Algae of China I.  *Zygnemataceae* from Szechwan. Sinensia. **6.**

Japp. G. (1930) :  Rasy v zupe olomoucké.  Vlastivéda sterdinía severení Moravy. **1.**

Jenner, E. (1845) :  Flora of Tunbridge Wells.  Tunbridge Wells.

Joyet-Lavergne, P. (1932) :  Sur quelques chracteres de sexulisation cytoplasmique chez les Algues et les Champignons.  D.R. Acad. Sc. **145.**

Jürgensen, CH. (1934) :  Die Mainalgen bei Würzburg.  Arch. f. Hydrobiol. **28.**

Kaiser, P.E. (1907) :  Beiträge zur Kryptogamenflora von Schönebeck an der Elbe.  Wiss. Beil. z. Jahresber, d. Realsch, z. Schönebeck.

—(1914) :  Beiträge zur Kenntnis der Algenflora von Traunstein und dem Chiemgau I. Ber. d. Bayr. Bot. Ges. **14.**

—(1916)  Beiträge zur Kenntnis der Algenflora von Traunstein und dem Chiemgau III. Krypt. Forsch. Nr. 1.

—(1918) :  Beiträge zur Kenntnis der Algenflora von Traunstein und dem Chiemgau IV. *Ibid.* Nr. 3.

—(1926) :  Beiträge zur Kenntnis der Algenflora von Traunstein und dem Chiemgau V. *Ibid.* Nr.7.

Kann, E. (1933) :  Zur Ökologie des litoralen Algenaufwuchses im Lunzer Untersee.  Intern. Rev. ges. Hydrob. u. Hydrogr.

Karling, J.S. (1935) :  A further Study of *Cladochytrium replicatum* with special reference to its Distribution, Host Range and Culture on Artificial Media.  Amer. Jour. Bot. **22.**

Karsten, G. (1909) :  Entwicklung der Zygoten von *Spirogyra jugalis.*  Flora, **99.**

—(1912)  Konjugaten In Handbuch der Naturwissenschaften, **2.** Jena.

—(1918) :  Über die Tagesperiode der Kern-und Zellteilungen.  Zeitschr. f. Bot. **10.**

Kasanowsky, V. (1913) :  Die Chlorophyllbänder und die Verzweigung derselben bei *Spirogyra Nawashini* n. sp. Ber. Deutsch Bot. Ges. **31.**

Kasanowsky, V. and Smirnoff, S. (1913) :  *Spirogyra borysthenica* nov. sp. Österr. Bot. Zeitschr. **43.**

Kirchner, O. (1878) :  Algen, in Kryptogamenflora von Schlesien. **2,** 1. Hälfte.

—(1880) :  Beiträge zur Algenflora von Württemberg.  Württ. naturw. Jahresh. **36.**

—(1888) :  Nachträge zur Algenflora von Württemberg.  Jahresh. Ver. f. vaterl. Naturk. in Württemberg.

Kirchner, O. (1891): Die mikroskopische Pflanzenwelt des Süsswassers. 2. Aufl. Hamburg.

—(1896): Das Pflanzliche Plankton des Bodensees. Das pflanzliche Benthos. Bodenseeforschungen. **9.**

—(1899): Florula phycologica Benacensis. Publ. Civ. Mus. Rovereto. Nr. 36.

Kisselew, J.A. (1927): Zur Kenntnis der Algen des Aralsees. Bull. Bureau apl. Ichthyol. **5.** Leningrad.

—(1930): Periodicity of the "Nau" Pond Plankton (Old Buchara, Usbekistan) :. Tran. Usbekistan Inst. Trop. Medicine. **1.**

—(1931): Materialien zur hydrobiologischen Charakteristik einiger typischen Wasserbecken Mittelasiens. *Ibid.*

—(1932): Zur Kenntnis des Phytoplanktons des Issykul-Sees. Mem. Inst. Hydrol. **7.**

Klebahn, K. (1888): Über die Zygosporen einiger Conjugaten. Ber. Deutsch Bot. Ges. **6.**

Klebs, G. (1886); Über die Organisation der Gallerte bei einigen Algen und Flagellaten. Unt. a. d. Bot. Inst. Tubingen. **2.**

—(1887a): Beiträge zur Physiologie der Pflanzenzelle. *Ibid.* **2.**

Klebs, G. (1887b): Beiträge zur Physiologie der Pflanzenzelle. Ber. Deutsch Bot. Ges. **5.**

—(1896): Die Bedingungen der Fortpflanzung bei einigen Algen und Pilzen. Jena.

Klein, J. (1877): Algologische Mitteilungen. 4. Über oxalsauren Kalk und globoidartige Körper bei Algen. Flora. **35.**

Klemm, P. (1892): Beitrag zur Erfchung der Aggregationsvorgänge in lebenden Pflanzenzellen. Flora. **75.**

Klopfer, T. (1934): Die Teilung der Chloroplasten während der Zytokinese bei *Spirogyra*. Act. Soc. Bot. Polon. **11.**

Kniep, H. (1928): Die Sexualität der niederen Pflanzen. Jena.

Knoche, H. (1921): Flora Balearica. **1.** Montpellier.

Kny, L. (1893): Membranwachstum gegen den Turgor. Ber. Deutsch Bot. Ges. **11.**

—(1897): Die Abhängigkeit der Chlorophyllfunktion von den Chromatophoren und vom Cytoplasma. Ber. Deutch Bot. Ges. **15.**

—(1906): Botanische Wandtafelr. T. 103. Er.-Text.

Kohl, F.G. (1891): Protoplasmaverbindungen bei Algen. Ber. Deutsch Bot Ges. **9.**

Kol, E. (1925): Vorarbeiten zur Kenntnis der Algenflora des Ungarischen Nagy Alföld (grosse Tiefebene). I. Szeged und Umgebung. Folia Crypt. 1 H.2.

—(1927): Fragmenta Algologica Hungarica I. "Ewidge Regen" vallis Felkaensis. Ung. Bot. Blätter.

—(1931a): Zur Hydrobiologie eines Natronsees bei Szeged in Ungarn. Ver. Intern. Ver. theoret. u. angew. Limnol. **5.**

—(1931b): Vorarbeiten zur Kenntnis der Algenvegetation des Nagy Magyar Alföld II. Arch. Biol. **2.**

—(1932a): Uber die Algenvegetation der Hajduszoboszloer Therme. Arch. Protistenk.

—(1938): Die Algenvegetation des Balaton-Sees. Arb. d. Ung. Biol. Forsch.-Inst. **10.**

Kolkwitz, R. (1899): Die Wachsthumsgeschichte der Chlorophyllbänder von *Spirogyra*. Festschr. Schwendener. Berlin.

—(1923): Methoden zum Nachweis und zur Rohkultur der Wasser-und Abwasserorganismen. —Handb. mikrobiol. Technik.

—(1940): Phosphorsäure, Kali aund Algenökologie. Verh. Int. Ver. theor. u. angew. Limnol. **9.**

Kolkwitz, R. and Krieger, H. (1944): *Zygnemales*. In Rabenhorst's Kryptogamen-Flora von Deutschland und der Schweiz. **13,** Abt. 2.

Kolkwitz, R. and Krieger, W. (1936): Zur Ökologie der Pflanzenwelt, insbesondere der Algen, des Vulkans Pangerango in West-Java. Ber. Deutsch Bot. Ges. **54.**

Kolkwitz. R. and Marsson, H. (1909): Ökologie der pflanzlichen Saprobien. Ber. D. Bot. Ges. 26a. Vgl. Kolkwitz, Pflanzenphysiologie, 1935.

Kolkwitz, R. and Zahn, C. (1919): Untersuchungen uber Bekampfung der Abwasserpilze auf Rieselfeldern. Mitt. a. d. Landesanst. f. Wasserhyg. H. 25.

Kossinskaja, C. (1940): Die Algen des Neva-Beckens. Act. Inst. Bot. Acad. Sci. U.R.S.S. Ser.2. **4** (1938).

Kraatz, W.C. (1923): A Study of the Food of the Minnow *Campystoma anomalum*. Ohio Jour. Sci. **23.**

Kraus, G. (1869): Einige Beobachtungen über den Einfluss des Lichtes und der Wärme auf die Stärkeerzeugung im Chloroplasten. Pringsheim's Jahrb. f. wiss. Bot. **7.**

—(1872): Zur Kenntnis der Chlorophyllfarbstoffe. Stuttgart.

Krieger, W. (1930): Algenassoziationen von den Azoren und aus Kamerun. Hedwigia. **70.**

Kufferath, H. (1930): La florule algologique de Rouge-Cloître. Bull. Soc. R. Bot. Belg. **42.**

Kursanoff, L. (1912): Über Befruchtung, Reifung und Keimung bei *Zygnema*. Flora N.F. **4.**

Kurz, A. (1912): Die Lochseen und ihre Umgebung. Arch. f. Hydrobiol. **8.**

—(1922): Grundriss einer Algenflora des appenzellischen Mittel-und Vorlandes. Jahrb. St. Gallisch. Naturwiss. Ges. **58.**

Küster, E. (1907): Über die Beziehungen der Lage des Zellkernes zu Zellwachstum und Membranbildung. Flora. **98.**

—(1927): Zur Physiologie und Pathologie des Chloroplasten. Protoplasma. **2.**

—(1932): Protoplasmabewegungen in zentrifugierten Zellen. Ber. oberhess. Ges. f. Natur-u. Heilk. Giessen. **15.**

—(1933): Anisotrope Plastiden. Ber. Deutsch Bot. Ges. **51.**

—(1934): Anisotrope Plastiden und Zellkerne. *Ibid.* **52.**

—(1935): Die Pflanzenzelle. Jena.

—(1936a): *Plagiospermum* in Hessen. Ber. Oberhess. Ges. f. Natur. und Heilk. zu Giessen N.F. Nat. Abt. **17.**

—(1936b): *Mesogerron* in Hessen. *Ibid.*

—(1936c): Über kernlose Zellen. Cytologia. **7.**

—(1937a): Zur Teratologie der Plastiden. Cytologia.

—(1937b): Pathologie der Pflanzenzelle II. Pathologie der Plastiden. Protoplasmamonogr. **13.**

—(1937c): Über die Plasmaamöben der Konjugatenzelle. Sitz-Ber. Akad. Wiss. Budapest. **56.**

—(1938): Die Entwicklung der Lehre von der Pflanzenzelle. Protoplasmamonogr. **17.**

Kusunoki, S. (1937): Üntersuchungen über die Geshlechtszellen von *Sirogonium sticticum* Kütz. Cytologia.

Kützing, F.T. (1843): Phycologia generalis. Leipzig.

—(1845): Phycologia germanica. Nordhausen.

—(1849): Species Algarum. Leipzig.

—(1855): Tabulae phycologicae. 5. Nordhausen.

—(1878): Die Algenflora von Nordhausen und Umgebung. Osterprogr. der Nordhäuser Realschule

Lagerheim, G. (1883): Bidrag till Sveriges Algflora. Oefvers. K. Vet.-Akad. Förhandl. **40.**

—(1884): Zur Algenflora der Wasserfälle vom Lulea Elf.

—(1886): Algologiska Bidrag. I. Contributions algologiques à la flore de la Suède. Bot. Notiser.

—(1888): Sopra alcune alghe d'aqua dolce nuove o rimarchevoli. Nuov. Notarisia. **3.**

—(1889a): Algologiska och mykologiska anteckningar fran en botanisk resa i Lulea Lappmark. K. Vet. Akad, Förhandl.

—(1889b): Note sur la *Chaelomorpha Blancheana* Mont. Nuov. Notarisia. **4.**

—(1890): Contributiones a la Flora algológica del Ecuador. Añnal. Univ. Quito. **4.**

—(1893): Chlorophyceen aus Abessinien und Kordofan. Nuov. Notarisia. **4.**

—(1895): Über das Phycoporphyrin, einen Conjugatenfarbstoff. Vid. Stelskap. Srk. I. Math-naturw. Kl. No. 5. Kristiania.

—(1902): Untersuchungen über fossile Algen I. Geol. Fören. Förhandl. **24.**

Langer, G. (1913): *Spirogyra proavita* n. sp. Bot. Közl. **12.**

—(1930): Uber das Kriechen der *Spirogyra nitida*-Faden. Fol. Crypt. **1.**

—(1934): Monographische Bearbeitung der Spirogyren mit besonderer Berücksichtigung der vorkriegs-ungarischen Verhältnisse. *Ibid.*

—(1934): Algologische Notizen aus dem Burgenland. *Ibid.*

—(1932): *Spirogyra hungarica* n. sp. Fol. Krypt. **1.**

Lapicque, L. (1921): Influence des acides et des bases sur une algue d'eau douce. C.R. Soc. Biol. **84.**

—(1922): Mécanisme des changes entre la cellule et le milieu ambiant. Ibid. **174.**

—(1924): Phénomenes mecaniques intracellulaires chez les Spirogyres. Bull. Acad. Soc. Medec.

Lapicque, L. and Kergomard, T. (1923): Acidification par l'asphyxie chez les Spirogyres, reaction morphologiques consécutives. C.R. Soc. Biol. **88.**

Lapicque, L. and Liacre de St.-Firmin (1923): Sur l'irritabilite des chromato phores des Spirogyres. *Ibid.*

Larsen, E. (1904): The Freshwater Algae of East Greenland. Meddel. om Grönland. **30.**

—(1907): Ferskvandsalger fra Vest-Grönland. *Ibid.* **33.**

Leblond, E. (1924) : Algues du littoral septentrional du Golfe d'Ajaccio (Corse). Rev. Algol. **1.**

—(1925) : Contributions a la flore algologique du Boulonnais. Trav. Stat. Zool. Wimereux. **9.**

Lederer, B. (1935) : Färbungs., Fixierungs-und mikrochirurgische Studien an Spiragyra-Tonoplasten. Protoplasma. **22.**

Lemmermann, E. (1891) : Algologische Beiträge I. Abh. Naturw. Ver. z. Bremen.

—(1893) : Versuch einer Algenflora der Umgebung von Bremen (excl. Diatomaceen). Abh. naturw. Ver. Bremen. **12.**

—(1895) : Verzeichnis der in der Umgebung von Plön gesammelten Algen. Forsch. Ber. Biol. Stat. Plön. **3.**

—(1896a) : Zweiter Beitrag zur Algenflora des Plöner Seengebietes. Ibid. **4.**

—(1896a) : Zur Algenflora des Riesengebirges. Ibid.

—(1897a) : Beitrage zur Algenflora von Schlesien. Abh. naturw. Ver. Bremen. **14.**

—(1897b) : Resultate einer biologischen Untersuchung von Forellenteichen. Ber. Biol. Stat. Plön. **5.**

—(1898a) : Beitrag zur Algenflora von Schlesien. Abh. naturw. Ver. Bremen. **14.**

—(1898b) : Beitrage zur Kenntnis der Planktonalgen II. Beschreibung neuer Formen. Bot. Centralbl. **76.**

—(1903a) : Brandenburgische Algen II. Das Phytoplankton des Müggelsees und ciniger benachbarter Gewässer. Zeitschr. f. Fisch. **11.**

—(1903b) : Beiträge zur Kenntnis der Planktonalgen XV. Das Phytoplankton einiger Ploner Seen. Forsch-Ber. Biol. Stat. zu Plön. **10.**

—(1904a) : Beiträge zur Kenntnis der Planktonalgen XIX. Das Phytoplankton der Ausgrabenseen bei Plön. Ibid. **11.**

—(1904b) : Das Plankton schwedischer Gewässer. Ark. f. Bot. **2.**

—(1905a) : Die Algenflora der Sandwichinseln. Engl. Bot. Jahrb. **34.**

— (1905b) : Beiträge zur Kenntnis der Planktonalgen XXI. Das Phytoplankton sächsischer Teiche II. Ploner Forsch-Ber. **12.**

—(1907) : Das Plankton des Jang-tse-Kiang (China). Arch. f. Hydrobiol. **2.**

—(1908) : Algologische Notizen VI. Algen aus der Biviera vow Lentini (Sizilien). Ibid. **4.**

—(1910) : Beitrage zur Kenntnis der Planktonalgen XXVI. Das Phytoplankton des Paraguay. Ibid. **5.**

Lepeschkin, W. (1910) : Zur Kenntnis der Plasmamembran. Ber. Deutsch Bot. Ges. **28.**

—(1923) : The Constancy of the Living Substance. Stud. Plant Phys. Laborat. Charles Univ. Prague. **1.**

—(1927) : Über den Zusammenhang zwischen mechanischen und chemischen Schädigungen des —Protoplasma und die Wirkungsart einiger Schutzsotoffe. Protoplasma. **2.**

—(1928) : The effect of Ethyl Alcohol on the Turgor Pressure of Spirogyra. Amer. Jour. Bot. **15.**

—(1939) : Über den Einfluss des Wasserverlustes des Protoplasmas auf seine Permeabilität für gelöste Stoffe. Protoplasma. **32.**

Levander, K.H. (1900) : Zur Kenntnis des Lebens in den stehenden Kleingewässern der Skäreninseln. Act. Soc. Fauna. et Flora. Fenn. **18.**

Lewin, M. (1888) : Uber spanischen Süsswasseralgen. Bih. K. Sv. Vet.-Akad. Handl. **14.** Abt. 3.

Lewis, F.J. (1898) : The Action of Light on Mesocarpus. Ann. Bot. **12.**

Lewis, J.F. (1925) : A New Conjugate from Woods Hole. Amer. Jour. Bot. **12.**

Li, L.C. (1933) : New Species and Varieties of Freshwater Algae from China. Ohio Journ. Sci. **30.**

—(1934) : Annotated List of the Freshwater Algae of Wuch'ang. Hupeh. Sc. Rep. National Tsing Hua Univ. B. **2.**

—(1935) : Contributions to our Knowledge of the Freshwater Algae of Eastern Szechuan. Bull. Fan Memor. Inst. Biol. (Bot.) **6.**

—(1936) : The Freshwater Algae of Tsingtao, Shantung. Ibid. **7.**

—(1937a) : Freshwater Algae from Anhwei, Kiangsi and Hupeh. Ibid. **8.**

—(1937b) : Zygnemopsis wuchangensis and Aulosira sinensis, two New Species of Freshwater Algae. Bull. Chinese Bot. Soc. **3.**

—(1938) : A Contribution the Freshwater Algae of Kiangsi. Bull. Fan Memor. Inst. Biol. (Bot.) **8.**

Leljeblad, S. (1816) : Utkast till en svensk flora eller afhandling om svenska vaxternas väsendliga kännetecken och nytta. 3. upl med norska växter tillökt (utg. af J. Wallmann). Upsala.

Lillick, L.C. (1936) : Freshwater Algae from Texas. Pap. Mich. Acad. Sc. **22.**

Limanowska, H. (1911/12) : Die Algenflora der Limmat. Arch. f. Hydrobiol. **7.**

Link, H.F. (1809) : Nova plantarum genera e classe Lichenum, Algarum, Fungorum, Schraders N. Jour. f. Bot. **3.**

—(1820) : Epistola de algis aquaticis in genera disponendis. Bonn.

—(1829-33) : Handbuch zur Erkennung der nutzbarsten und am häufigsten vorkommenden Gewächse. Berlin.

Linkola, K. (1911) : Kaevullisuudesta eräissä Lonnais-Suomen pikkujävissä ja sen raunoilla. Luonnon ystävä.

Lloyd, F.E. (1924a) : The Fluorescent Colors of Plants. Science. **59.**

—(1924b) : Some Effects of Narcotics on *Spirogyra*. Anesthisia and Analgesia.

—(1924c) : Conjugation in *Spirogyra*. Trans. R. Canad. Inst. **15.**

—(1926a) : Studies in *Spirogyra* I. Maturation and Conjugation in *Spirogyra longata*. *Ibia.*

—(1926b) : Studies in *Spirogyra* II. Additional Studies on Conjugation. Adhesions and Geniculations. Trans. R. Soc. Canada 2. Ser. **20.**

—(1927a) : Some Behaviors of *Vampyrella lateritia* and the Response of *Spirogyra* to its Attack. Pap Mich. Acad. Sc. **7.**

—(1927b) : Cell Disjunction in *Spirogyra*. *Ibid.* **6.**

—(1928a) : Further Observations on the Behavior of Gametes during Maturation and Conjugation in *Spirogyra*. Protoplasma. **4.**

—(1928b) : The contractile vacuole. Biol. Rev. **3.**

—(1929) : The Problem of Excretion with Special Reference to the Contractile Vacuole. Proc. Intern. Congr. Plant. Sci. Ithaca. 1926.

Lloyd, F.E. u. Barnes, T.C. (1932) : Changes in the Cells of *Spirogyra* associated with the Presence of Water Polymers. Proc. Nat. Ac. Sc. Washington. **18.**

Loew, O. (1883a) : Ein weiterer Beweiss, das Eiweiss des lebenden Protoplasmas eine andere chemische Konstitutions besitzt als das des abgestorbenen. Pflügers Arch. **30.**

—(1883b) : Sind Arsenverbindungen Gift für das Protoplasma. *Ibid.* **32.**

—(1883c) : Zur Kenntnis des aktiven Albumins. *Ibid.*

—(1885) : Giftwirkungen bei verschiedenen Organismen. Bot. Centralbl. **6, 1.**

—(1892) : Über die physiologischen Funktionen der Calcium und Magnesiumsalze im Pflanzenorganismus. Flora. **75.**

—(1903) : Unter welchen Bedingungen wirken Magnesiumsalze schädlich auf Pflanzen. Flora. **92.**

—(1905) : Über die Giftwirkung von Fluornatrium auf Pflanzen. *Ibid.* **94.**

—(1906) : Über die Veränderung des Zellkerns durch kalkfällende Mittel. Bul. Coll. Agricult. Tokyo. **7.**

—(1925) : Über das Kalkbedürfinis von Algen und Pilzen. Bot. Centralbl. **45.**

Loew, O. and Aso, K. (1907) : On physiologically balanced Solutions. *Ibid.*

Loew, O. and Bokorny, Th. (1881) : Über das Absterben pflanzlichen Plasmas unter verschiedenen Bedingungen. Pflügers Arch. **26.**

—(1887a) : Die chemische Kraftquelle im lebenden Protoplasma. Jahrb. wiss. Bot. **18.**

—(1887b) : Über das Vorkommen von aktivem Albumin im Zellsaft und dessen Ausscheidung in Körnchen durch Basen. Bot. Zeitg. **45.**

—(1887c) : Chemisch-physiologische Studien über Algen. Jour. f. prakt. Chemie. N.F. **36.**

Loitelsberger, K. (1888) : Beitrag zur Algenflora Oberösterreichs. Verh. k.k. zool. Ges. Wien. **38.**

Lommen, C.P. (1897) : Ein Fall von Kopulation zweier Zygoten einer Spirogyra. Sp. Arch. f. mikr. Anat. u. Entwicklungsgesch. **49.**

Lotsy, J.P. (1907) : Vorträge zur botanischen Stammesgeschichte **1.** Jena.

Lowe, Ch. W. (1923) : The Freshwater Algae of the Canadian Arctic Expedition Rep. Canad. Arct. Exp. 1913-18. **4.** Botany.

—(1924) : The Freshwater Algae of Central Canada. Trans. R. Soc. Canada.

Lubimenko, V.I. (1935) : Remarks on the Role of Filamentous Algae in the Autopurification of Water Reservoirs under the Conditions of their Mass Development. Microbiologie. **4.**

Lucks, R. (1905) : Übersicht der im Linaugebiet aufgefundenen mikroskopischen Wasserbewohner. Jahr. West. preuss. Lehrerver. f. Naturk. **1.**

—(1907) : Planktonstudien in westpreussischen Seen. Ber. Westpreuss. bot.-zool. Ver. Danzig.

Lyngbye, H.C. (1819) : Tentamen Hydrophytologiae Danicae. Hafniac.

Macfarlane (1881) : The Structure and Division of the Vegetable Cell. Cells of *Spirogyra nitida*. Trans. a. Proc. Bot. Soc. Edinburgh. **14.**

MacKay, H.H. (1924) : A Quantitative Study of the Plankton of the Shallow Bays of Lake Nipigon. Univ. Toronto Stud. Biol. Ser. **25.**

Magdeburg, P. (1925a) : Vergleichende Untersuchung der Hochmooralgenflora zweier deutscher Mittelgebirge. Hedwigia. **66.**

—(1925b) : Neue Beiträge zur Kenntnis der Ökologie und Geographie der Algen der Schwarzwaldhochmoore. Ber. Naturf. Ges. Freiburg. **24.**

—(1926) : Über vegetative Konjugation bei *Mougetia*. Arch. Protistenk. **23.**

Mainx, F. (1923) : Über eine Zygnemacee mit rotem Zellsaftfarbstoff. Lotos. **71.**

Mangenot, G. (1929) : Sue les constituants morphologiques du cytoplasma des *Spirogyra*. C.R. Soc. Biol. **104.**

Manguin, M. (1935) : Catalogue des algues d'eau douce du Canton Fresnaysur-Sarthe II. Bull. Soc. Agricult., Sci. et Arts de la Sarthe. **54.**

—(1937) : Les Algues de rochers suintants de Saint Léonhard-des-Bois (Sarthe), *Ibid.*

Mannoni, S.A. (1936) : A Survey of the Green Algae of Crawford County, Kansas. Trans. Kansas Acad. Sc.

Marchesoni, V. (1939) : Le alghe epilitiche del alta montagna nel gruppo del Cevedale. Nuov. Giorn. Bot. Ital. **46.**

Marissal, F.V. (1850) : Catalogue des especes omises dans la flora du Hainaut et observées dans les environs de Tournai. Mém. Soc. Hist. et Litt. Tournai. **1.**

Marklund, G.G. (1936) : Vergleichende Permeabilitätsstudien an pflanzlichen Protoplasten. Act. Bot. Fenn. **18.**

Martel, E. (1885) : Contribuzione alla conoscenza dell'Algologia Romana. Ann. Ist. Bot. Roma. **1.**

Martens, G.v. (1866) : Die Tange in : Die preussische Expedition nach Ostasien. Berlin.

—(1870) : Conspectus algarum Brasiliae hactenus detectarum. Vid. Medd. Nat. For. i. Kopenhagen.

Mattausch, F. (1936) : Ein Beitrag zur Kenntnis der Verlandungserscheinungen am Hirschberger Grossteiche. Beih. Bot. Centralbl. **54 B.**

McAllister, F. (1932) : The Formation of the Achromatic Figure in *Spirogyra setiformis*. Amer. Jour. Bot. **18.**

McInteer, B.B. (1930) : Preliminary Report of the Algae of Kentucky. Ohio Jour. Sci. **30.**

—(1939) : A Check List of the Algae of Kentucky. Castanea, Journ. S. Appalach. Bot. Club. **4.**

Mehra, K.R. (1957) : Studies on the algae of Bombay and its environs. Pt. I. A taxonomic survey of the Zygnemataceae of Bombay and its environs. (M.Sc. thesis. Bombay University).

Menke, W. (1934) : Chloroplastenstudien. Protoplasma. **21.**

Menon, M.A.S. (1945) : Observations on the seasonal distribution of the plankton of the Trivandrum Coast. Proc. Indian Acad. Sci. **B. 23.**

Meneghini, G. (1838) : Cenni sulla organografia e fisiologia delle Alghe. Negli Atti della R. Acad. di Sci. lett. et art. Padova.

Merriman, M.L. (1906) : Nuclear Division in *Zygnema*. Bot. Gaz. **51.**

—(1913) : Nuclear Division of *Spirogyra* I. *Ibid.* **56.**

—(1916) : Nuclear Division of *Spirogyra* II. *Ibid.* **61.**

—(1920) : Studies in the Conjugation of *Spirogyra ternata*. Bull. Torrey Bot. Club. **47.**

—(1922) : A New Species of *Spirogyra* with Unusual Arrangement of the Chromatophores. Amer. Jour. Bot. **9.**

Messikommer, E. (1927) : Biologische Studien am Torfmoor von Robenhausen unter besonderer Berücksichtigung der Algenvegetation. Diss. Zürich.

—(1935a) : Algen aus dem Obertoggenburg. Jahrb. St. Gall. Naturw. Ges. **67.**

—(1935b) : Die Algenwelt der inneren Plessuralpen. Vierteljahrsschr. Naturf. Ges. Zürich. **80.**

Meuche, A. (1939) : Die Fauna im Algenbewuchs. Arch. f. Hydrobiol. **34.**

Meunier, M.A. (1887) : Le nucléole des *Spirogyra*. La Cellule. **3.**

Meyen (1827) : Über das Genus *Spirogyra* Link und über die Bewegung und Metamorphose der *Spirogyra princeps* insbesondere. Linnaea. **2.**

—(1835) : Beitrage zur Physiologie und Systematik der Algen. Nov. Act. Phys. Med. Acad. Caes. Leop. Carol. Nat. cur. **14.**

Meyer, A. (1904) : Orientierende Untersuchungen über Verbreitung, Morphologie und Chemie des Volutins. Bot. Zeitg. **62.**

# BIBLIOGRAPHY 457

Meyer, A. (1920, 1926) : Analyse der Zelle der Pflanzen und Tiere. Jena.

Meyer, I. (1827) : Kritische Beitrage zum Stussium der Süsswasseralgen Flora.

Meyer, K. and Reinhardt, L. (1924/25) : Zur Algenflora des Baikalsees und Transbaikaliens. Bull Soc. Natur. Moscou.

Mez, C. (1924) : Bemerkungen zur Phylogenie der Algen und Pilze. Bot. Arch. **5.**

Michel-Durand, E. (1925) : Sous quelle forme existent les tannins chez les Spirogyres. C.R. Acad. Sc. **180.** Paris.

Migula, W. (1888) : Über den-Einfluss stark verdünnter Säurelösungen auf Algenzellen. Breslau.

—(1907) : Kryptogamenflora von Deutschland. Deutsch-Österreich und der Schweiz. **2,** 1. Gera.

Miranda, F. (1931) : Sobre las algas y Cianoficeas del Cantabrico especialmente de Gijon. Trab. Mus. Nac. Cienc. Nat. Ser. Bot. Nr. 25.

Misra, J.N. (1937) : *Zygnemaceae* of Kashmir I. Proc. Indian Acad. Sci. **5.**

Mitzkewitsch, L. (1898) : Über die Kernteilung bei *Spirogyra*. Flora. **85.**

M'Keever, F.L. (1910-11) : A Contribution to the Alga-Flora of Mid-Lothan. Trans. Edinburgh Field Nat. Micr. Soc.

Möbius, M. (1888) : Über einige in Portorico gesammelte Süsswasser-und Luftalgen. Hedwigia. **27.**

—(1889) : Bearbeitung der von H. Schenck in Brasilien gesammelten Algen. Hedwigia. **27.**

—(1890) : Algae brasilienses a cl. Dr. Glaziou collectae. Nuov. Notarisia. **5.**

—(1892a) : Australische Süsswasseralgen. Flora. **75.**

—(1892b) : Über einige brasilianische Algen. Ber. Deutch Bot. Ges. **10.**

—(1893) : Beitrag zur Kenntnis der Algenflora Javas. *Ibid.* **11.**

—(1894) : Australische Süsswasseralgen II. Abh. Senchkenb. Naturf. Ges. **18.**

—(1895) : Über einige brasilianische Algen. Hedwigia. **34.**

—(1897) : Beiträge zur Lehre von der Fortpflanzung der Gewachse. Jena.

Moecs, G. (1904) : Brassö vidékének lavegön és folyóvizben étö moszaljai. Különyomat a brassói áll föreálésteola 19-ite értesitöjéböl. Brassó.

Mohl, H. von (1835) : Über die Vermehrung von Pflanzenzellen durch Teilung. Tübingen.

Molisch, H. (1895-96) : Die Ernährung der Algen. Sitz. -Ber. Akad Wiss. Wien. Math.-nat. Kl. **104, 105.**

—(1926) : Pflanzenbiologie in Japan. Jena.

Moll, J.W. (1893) : Observations on Karyokinesis in *Spirogyra*. Verh. d. kon. Ak. v. Wetensch. te Amsterdam, Abt. Nat. **2.**

Montagne, C. (1845) : Sur l'existence des tetraspores dans une Algue de la tribus des Zygnémacées. C.R. Akad. Sc. Paris. **21.**

—(1846) : Über *Thwaitesia*, eine neue Gattung der Algen. Flora. **29.**

—(1856) : Sylloge generum specierumque plantarum cryptogamarum. Paris.

Montemartini, L. (1901) : Appunti di Ficobiologia. Nuov Notarisia. **12.**

—(1925) : Di uno speciale adattamento delle Chloroficee all'asciuta delle acqua. Atti dell'Istit. Bot. Univ. Pavia 3. ser. **2.**

Moore, (1888) : Studies in Vegetable Biology. II. The Influence of Light upon Protoplasmatic Movement. Jour. Linn. Soc. Bot. **24.**

Moore, G.T. (1902) : The Contamination of Public Water Supplies by Algae. Yearbook Depart. Agricult.

Moore, G.T. and Carter, N. (1923) : Algae from Lakes in the Northeastern Part of North Dakota. Ann. Missouri Bot. Gard. **10.**

Moore, G.T. and Kellermann, K.T. (1904) : A Method of destroying or preventing the Growth of Algae and certain Pathogenic Bacteria in Water Supplies. U.S. Dep. Agric. Bur. Plant Ind. Bull. 64.

Moreau. F. (1913) : Les corpuscules métachromatiques chez les Algues. Bull. Soc. Bot. France. **60.**

Morteo, E. (1904) : Contributo alla conoscenza delle alghe di acqua dolce in Liguria (1902-03). Malpijhia. **18.**

Mottier, F.A. (1899) : The Effect of Centrifugal Force on the Cell. Ann. Bot. **13.**

Mueller, O.F. (1782) : Flora danica. T.88 Kopenhagen.

—(1785) : De confervis palustribus oculo nudo invisibilibus. Nov. Act. Acad. Petrop. **3.**

Nägeli, C. (1847) : Die neueren Algensysteme und Versuch zur Begründung eines eigenen Systems der Algen und Flechten. Neue Denkschr. d. allg. Schweizer. Ges. f. d. ges. Naturw. **9.**

—(1893) : Über oligodynamische Erscheinungen in lebenden Zellen. Denkschr. d. schweiz. naturf. Ges. **33.**

Nägeli, G. and Cramer (1855) : Pflanzenphysiologische Untersuchungen I. Zürich.

Namyslowskie, B. (1925) : Recherches sur l'Hydrobiologie de la Pologne. Ann. Biol. Lacustre **14.**

Nathansohn, A. (1900) : Physiologische Untersuchungen über amitotische Kernteilung. Jahrb. wiss. Bot. **35.**

Neuenstein, H.v. (1915) : Über den Bau des Zellkerns bei den Algen und seine Bedeutung för ihre Systematik. Arch. f. Zellforschung. **13.**

Newcomb, M.A. (1938) : A Polygamus *Spirogyra.* Trans. Kansas Akad. Sci. **40.**

Nieuwland, J.A. (1909a) : Resting Spores of *Cosmarium bioculatum* Breb. The Midland Natural. **1.**

—(1909b) : The "Knee-joints" of Species of *Mougeotia, Ibid.*

Nitardy, E. (1897) : Die Algen des Kreises Elbing. Sitzber. Naturf. Ges. Danzig. N.F. **9.**

Nordstedt, O. (1873) : Beskrifning öfver en ny art af slägtet *Spirogyra* . Lunds Univ. Arsskr. **9.** (1872)

—(1878) : De algis aquae dulcis et Characeis ex insulis Sandvicensibus. Minnesskr. utg. k. fysiogr. säälsk. i Lund mad anledning af dess Hundraärsfest d. 3. Okt. 1878.

—(1882) : Algologiska smäsaker. III. Über einige Algen aus Argentinien und Patagonien. Bot. Notiser.

—(1888a) : *Conjugatae*, in Forschungsreise S.M.S. Cazelle IV. Botanik.

—(1888b) : Freshwater Algae collected by Dr. S. Berggren in New Zealand and Australia. Bih. Sv. Vet.-Akad. Handl. **22.**

—(1897) : Sötvattensalger frän Kamerun. Bot. Notiser.

Northen, H.T. (1936) : Is Protoplasm Elastic? Bot. Gaz. **98.**

—(1938a) : Studies in Protoplasmic Structure in *Spirogyra* I. Elasticity. Protoplasma. **31.**

—(1938b). Studies in Protoplasmic Structure in *Spirogyra*. III Effects of Anesthetics on Protoplasmic Elasticity. Bot. Gz.

—(1938c) : Effect of Drought on Protoplasmic Elasticity. Plant. Physiol. **13.**

—(1939a) : Studies of Protoplasmic Structure in *Spirogyra*. IV. Effect of Temperature on Protoplasmic Elasticity. *Ibid*

Northen, H.T. u. R.C. (1938) : Studies in Protoplasmic Structure in *Spirogyra*. II. Alteration of Protoplasmic Elasticity Protoplasma. **31.**

Nygaard, G. (1932) : Contributions to our Knowledge of the Freshwater Algae and Phytoplankton from the Transvaal. Trans. R. Soc. S. Africa. **20.**

Oberdorfer, E. (1928) : Lichtverhältnisse und Algenbesiedlung im Bodensee. Zeitschr. f. Bot. **20.**

Olney, S.T. (1871) : Algae Rhodiaceae. Providence R.1.

Oltmanns. F. (1922-23) : Morphologie und Biologie der Algen. Jena. 2. Aufl.

Ondratschek, K. (1935) : Über die Brauchbarkeit einiger Glassorten für Algenreinkulturen. Arch. f. Mikrobiol. **6.**

Opic, M. (1816) : Deutschlands cryptogamische Gewächse. Prag.

—(1823) : Boheims phanerogamische und cryptogamische Gewächse. Prag.

Ostenfeld, C.H. (1907) : Beiträge zur Kenntnis der Algenflora des Kossogol-Beckens in der nordwestlichen Mongolei. Hedwigia. **46.**

—(1908) : The Phytoplankton of the Aral Sea and its Affluents with an Enumeration of the Algae observed. Wiss. Ergeb. d. Aralsee-Exp. Bd. 8. Petersburg.

Osvald, H. (1923) : Die Vegetation des Hochmoores Komosse. Svensk. Växtsoc. Sällskap. Handl. **1.**

Overton. C.E. (1888) : Über den Conjugationsvorgang bei *Spirogyra.* Ber. Deutsch Bot. Ges. **6.**

—(1896) : Über zwei für die Schweiz neue Algenarten. Jahreshber. d. Zürich. Bot. Ges. 1894-96.

—(1897) : Notizen über die Grünalgen des Oberengadins. Ber. Schweiz. Bot. Ges. **7.**

Oye, P. van (1922a) : Contribution â la connaissance de la flore et de la faune microscopiques des Indes Nèerlandaises. Ann. Biol. Lacustre. **11.**

—(1922b) : Zur Biologie des Potamoplanktons auf. Java Intern. Rev. Hydro-biol. u. Hydrogr. **1.**

—(1923) : Biologische zelfreiningung van het water. Natuurwet. Tijdsc. **5.**

—(1924a) : Korte bijtrage tot de systematiek en de biologie der wieren van Balgisch Kongo. Bot. Jaarb. **19.**

—(1924b) : Zur Biologie des Potamoplanktons auf Java II. Intern. Rev. ges. Hydrob. u. Hydrogr. **12.**

—(1924c) : Biologie et Ecologie du Phytoplancton d'un lac tropical. Bull. Soc. R. Bot. Belg. **56.**

—(1926a) : Le Potamoplancton du Ruki an Congo-Belge et d‹s pays chauds en général. Intern. Rev. d. ges. Hydrob. u. Hydrog. **16.**

Oye, P. van (1926): Tropisch-Algologische Aanteekeningen, K. Vlaam. Acad. voor Taal en Letter kunde. Versl. en Medd.
—(1927): Over de Wierflora van Belgisch Kongo. Bot. Jaarb. **20.**

Pal, N.L. (1934): Studies on the Respiration of conjugating *Spirogyra* with Special Reference to Fat Metabolism. New Phytol. **33.**

Palla, E. (1894a): Über eine pyrenoidlose Art und Gattung der Conjugaten. Ber. Deutsch. Bot. Ges. **12.**
—(1894b): Über ein neuses Organ der Konjugatenzelle. *Ibid.*

Pampanini, R. (1931): Prodromus della Flora cirenaica. Forli.

Papenfuss, G.F. (1946): Proposed names for the phyla of algae. Bull. Torrey Bot. Club **73.**

Pardo, L. (1925): Datos para el estudio del Plancton de Reinosa (Santander). Asoc. Esp. para el Progr. d. 1. sc. Congr. d. Coimbra **6.**

Pascher, A. (1906): Neuer Beitrag zur Algenflora des südlichen Böhmerwaldes. Lotos.
—(1907): Über auffallende Rhizoid-und Zweigbildungen bei einer *Mougeotia* Art. Flora. **97.**
—(1913): *Zygnemales*, Allgemeiner Teil in: Süsswasserflora **9.**
—(1914): Über Flagellaten und Algen. Ber. Deutsch Bot. Ges. **32.**
—(1931): Systematische Übersicht über die mit Flagellaten in Zusammenhang stehenden Algenreihen und Versuch einer Einreihung dieser Algenstämme in die Stämme des Pflanzenreiches. Beih. Bot. Centralbl. **48.**

Paul, H. and Ruoff, S. (1927—1932): Pollenstatische und stratigraphische Mooruntersuchungen im süd südlichen Bayern. Ber. d. Bayr. Bot. Ges. **19 and 20.**

Pavillard, J. (1910): Etat actuel de la Protistologie végétable. Progr, rei bot. **3.**

Payne, Ch. L. (1889): List of Algae from Granville, Ohio. Bull. Sc. Labor. Denison Univ. **4.**

Pée-Laby, E. (1896): Flore analytique et descriptive des Cryptogames cellularies des environs de Toulouse. Toulouse.

Pennington, M.E. (1897): A Chemical Physiological Study of *Sp. nitida*. Publ. Univ. Pennsylvania. N.S. Nr. 2.

Pero, P. (1894): I Laghi alpini valtellinesi. VIII II lago d'Augloga. Nuov. Notarisia.

Peterschilka, F. (1922): Kernteilung und Pyrenoidvermehrung bie *Mougeotia*. Arch. Protistenk. **45.**
—(1923): Beitrag zur Kernteilung und Parthenosporenbildung von *Spirogyra mirabilis* Kütz. Ibid. **46.**

Petersen, H.E. (1910): An Account of Danish Freshwater Phycomycetes. Ann. Mycol. **8.**

Petersen, J. B. (1915): Studier over Danske aerofile alger. Mém. Acad. R. Sc. et Lettr. Danemark. 7 sér. sect sc. 12H.7.
—(1928): The Aerial Algae of Iceland. The Bot. Iceland. **2.**
—(1932): The Algal Vegetation of Hammer Bakker. Bot. Tidsskr. **42.**
—(1935): Studies on the Biology and Taxonomy of Soil Algae. Dansk Bot. Ark. **8.**

Petit, P. (1884): Observations critiques sur les genres *Spirogyra* et *Rhynchonema*. Bull. Soc. Bot. France. **21.**
—(1879): *Spirogyra lutetiana*. Brébissonia. **1.**
—(1880): Les Spirogyres des environs de Paris, Paris.

Petkoff, St. (1904): Troisieme contribution á la connaissance des algues de Bulgarie, Period. Spis.
—(1910a): La flore aquatique et algologique de la Macédonie du SO. Acad. bulg. d. Sc.
—(1910b): Les algues de la Bulgarie du SO. et leur disprersion. L'Ann. Univ. Sofia.
—(1911): Contribution supplémentaire á l' tude des Algues du sommet Kom et seenvirons. *Ibid.*
—(1922): La végétation des eaux de Vitocha. *Ibid.* **18.**
—(1925): La flore algologique du monst Pirin-planina. Rec. Acad. bulg. Sc. **20.**
—(1929): Un habitat algologique important et son changement partiel défavorable. Trav. Soc. Bulg. Sc. Nat. **14.**
—(1932a): Notes sur la Flore algologique du village Géravana et ses environs. *Ibid.* **15,** 16.
—(1932b): Sur la flore algologique des côtes Bulgares de la mer noire. Bull. Soc. Bot. Bulg. **5.**
—(1933): La végétation des sources d'eau douce potable dans la ville de Lovetsch et ses environs. Bull. Soc. Bulg. Geogr. **1.**
—(1934/35): Les *Zygnemales* de la Bulgarie et leur dispersion. Ann. Univ. Sofia. Fac. Sc. Hist. Nat. **31.**

Petrova, I. (1936): Über den Einfluss der Strahlen auf die Permeabilität der Zelle. Beih. Bot. Centralbl **54A.**

——(1940): Über den Einfluß der ss-Strahlen auf die Permeabilität der Zelle. *Ibid.* **60.** Abt. A.

Petter, H.F.M. (1933): La réaction nucléaire de Feulgen chez quelques végétaux inférieurs. C.R Acad. Sci. **157.**

Pevalek I. (1916a): O biologiji i o geografiskom rasprostranjenju alga u Sjevernoj Hrvatskoj. Prirod, istrfiiv. Hrv. I. Slav. Sv. 8.

——(1916b): Zur Kenntnis der Biologe und der geographischen Verbreitung der Algen in Nordkroatien. Acad. Sc. Arts. des Slaves du Sud. de Zagreb. Bull rav. Cl. Sc. Math. et. Nat. **5.**

——(1924): Geobotanische und algologische Erforschung der Moore in Kroatien und Slovenien. Rad. 230.

——(1925): Ein Beitrag zur Kenntnis der Algen des Moorgebietes Jezero und Poljana bei Dedno polje in den julischen Alpen. Nuova Notarisia. **36.**

——(1929): Contribution to the Flora of Freshwater Algae of the Croatian Island Krk. Act. Bot. Inst. Bot. Univ. Zagreb. **4.**

Pfeffer. W. (1886): Über die Aufnahme der Anilinfarben in die lebende Zelle. Unt.a.d. Bot. Inst. Tübingen. **2.**

Pfeiffer, H. (1921/22): Einführjng in die mikroskopische lebewelt städtischer Strassenrinnen und Pfützen. Mikrokosmos. **15.**

Pignatti, S. (1958): Secondo contributs alla floro algologica del Pavese. Atti. **15** (5).

——(1922/23): Die Methoden zur Erzielung von Fortpflanzungszuständen bie Algen. *Ibid.* **16.**

Pfeiffer, R. v. Wellhiem (1894): Zur Präparation der Süsswasseralgen. Jahrb. wiss. Bot. **26.**

Pickett, F.L. (1912): A case of changed Polarity in *Spirogyra elongata.* Bull. Torrey Bot. Club. **39.**

Pitard, C.J. (1913): Botanique de l'exploration scientifique due Maroc organisée par la Société de Géographie de Paris.

Playfair, G.F. (1913): Contributions to a Knolwege of the Biology of the Richmond River. Proc. Linn. Soc. N.S. Wales. **39.**

——(1915): Freshwater Algae of the Lismore District. *Ibid.* **40.**

——(1918): New and Rare Freshwater Algae. *Ibid.* **43.**

Pochmann. A. (1940): Mikrofloristischer Streifzug im Riesengebirge. Mikrokosmos. **33.**

Poljansky, V.T. (1940): Zur. Algaenflora der Stadt Sluzk. Act. Inst. Bot. Acad. Sci. U.R.S.S. Ser. 2. **4** (1938).

Ponomarew, A.P. (1914): Zur Kenntnis des Chloroplastenbaues. Ber. Deutsch Bot. Ges. **32.**

Pop, E. (1940): Bätrânetea si moartea plantelor. Cluj.

Poretzky, W.S. (1927): Beiträge zur Erforschung von Bewüchsen in den Gewässern Kareliens. Ber. Akad. Borodin Boil. Sübwasser-Stat. **5.**

Prain, D. (1905): The Vegetation of the Districts of Hughli Howrah and the 24, Pergannahs. Rec. Bot. Survey India. **4.**

Pràt, S. (1929): Studii o biolithogenesi. Ceskà akad. véd a cemóni. Prag.

Pràt, S. and Hamàckovà, J. (1931): *Conjugatae* in kalziumkarbonat. Presila.

Prescott, G.W. (1931): Jowa Algae Univ. Iowa Stud. in Nat. Hist. **13.**

Prescott, G.W. (1947): New Zygnemataceae from Ecuador. Ohio Jour. Sci. **47.**

Price, S.R. (1911): A New Species of *Debarya.* New Phytol. **10.**

——(1914): Some Studies on the Structure of the Plant Cell by the Method of Dark-ground Illumination. Ann. Bot. **28.**

Pringsheim, N. (1852): Algologische Mitteilungen I. Über Keimung der ruhenden Sporen und über eine —Form beweglicher Sporen bei *Spirogyra.* Flora.

——(1855): Über die Befruchtung der Algen. Monatsber.K. Akad. Wiss. Math-phys. Kl. Berlin.

——(1857): Zur Kritik und Geschichte der Untersuchungen über das Algen geschlecht. Berlin.

——(1879-81): Über Lichtwirkung und Chlorophyllfunktion in der Pflanze. Jahrb. wiss. Bot.

——(1888): Über die Entstehung der Kalkinkrustationen an Süsswasser pflanzen. Jahrb. wiss. Bot. **19.**

Pringsheim, H. and Müller, O. (1922): Zur Physiologie der Polyamylose. Zeitschr. f. phys. Chemie. **118.**

Printz. H. (1915): Beiträge zur Kenntnis der Chlorophyceen und ihrer Verbreitung in Norwegen. K. Norsk. Vid. Selsk. Skr. No. 2.

——(1916): Contributiones ad floram asiae interioris pertinentes. I. Die Chlorophyceen des südlichen Sibiriens und des Uriankailandes. *Ibid.*

Printz. H. (1927): Chlorophyceae in: Engler and Prantl, Die natürlichen Pflanzenfamilien. **3**,2. Aufl.

Proshkina-Lavrenko, A. (1924): Contribution à l'étude de la microflore des bassins subsalés du district Kupjansk du gouv. de Charkow. Journ. Soc. Bot. Russie. **9**.

Puymaly, A. de (1922): Adaption á la vie aérienne d'une Conjugaée filamenteuse (*Zygnema peliosporim* Wittr.). C.R. Acad. Sci. Paris. **175**.

—(1924a): Sur le vacuome des Algues vertes adaptiées á la flora aérienne. *Ibid.* **178**.

—(1924b): Recherches sur les Algues vertes aériennes. Thése Fac. Sc. Paris.

—(1927): Sur un *Spirogyra* fixé, pérennant, se multiplicant par marcottage. C.R. Acad. Sci. Paris. **184**.

—(1929): Sur un *Spirogyra* (*fluviatilis* Hilsé) fixe, pérennant, se multiplicant par marcottage et par propagules. Le Bot. **21**.

Quelle, F. (1908): Algenflora von Nordhausen. Mitt. Thür. Bot. Ver. **23**.

Rabanus, A. (1915): Beiträge zur Kenntnis der Periodizität und der geographischen Verbreitung der Algen Badens. Ber. Naturf. Ges. Freiburg. **21**.

Rabenhorst, L. (1847): Die Algen Deutschlands mit Berücksichtigung der Schweiz und der südlich angrenzenden Länder. Leipzig.

—(1843): Zu *Spirogyra Flechsigii* Rabenh. Hedwigia.

—(1863): Kryptogamenflora von Sachsen, der Oberlausitz. Thüringen und Nordböhmen, mit Berücksichtigung der benachbarten Lander. I Abt. Leipzig.

—(1868): Flora europaea algarum aquae dulcis et submarinae III. Leipzig.

Raciborski, M. (1888): Materyjaly do flory glonów polski. Sprwozd. MKomiskyi fizyogr. Akad. Umiget.

Randhawa, M.S. (1934): *Ghosella indica* gen. et sp. nov., A New Member of the *Conjugatae*. Jour. Indian Bot. Soc. **13**.

—(1936a): Marked Periodicity in Reproduction of the Punjab Freshwater Algae. Proc. Indian. Acad. Sci. B. **3**.

—(1936b): Occurence and Distribution of the Freshwater Algae of North India. *Ibid.* **4**.

—(1936c): Three New Species of *Zygnema* from Northern India. *Ibid.* **4** (3).

—(1936d): A Note on some attached Forms of *Spirogyra* from the Punjab. *Ibld.* **4** (3).

—(1937): Genus *Zygnemopsis* in Northern India. *Ibid.* **5**.

—(1938): Observations on some *Zygnemales* from Northern India, I, II. *Ibid.* **8**.

—(1940): *Zygogonium kumaoensis*, a new species of *Zygogonium* from Kumaon. Jour. Indian Bot. Soc. **19**.

—(1941): *Zygnema terrestris* from the Kumaon Himalayas. Current Sci. **9**.

—(1941a): Some peculiarities in conjugation in a new Himalayan species of *Zygnema*. Proc. Indian Acad. Sci. **11**.

—(1941b): *Sirocladium*, a new terrestrial member of the Zygnemales. Bot. Gaz. **103**.

—(1943): A critical review of some recently created new species of Indian Zygnemales. Proc. Indian Acad. Sci. B. **18**.

—(1943): On Akinete formation in *Zygnema terrestris* Randhawa. Current Sci. **12**.

—1958a): Further observations on the genus *Sirocladium*. Bot. Gaz. **119** (3).

—(1958b): Notes on some new and interesting algae from India. Bot. Gaz. **120** (1).

—(1958c): A note on two new species of *Spirogyra* and *Sirogonium*. Jour. Indian Bot. Soc. **37**.

—(1959): Reproduction in *Zygogonium ericetorum* Kütz. Current Sci. **28**.

Rao, C. (1937): The *Zygnemoideae* of the United Provinces, India I. Jour. Indian Bot. Soc. **16**.

—(1938): The *Zygnemoideae* of the Central Provinces, India I. *Ibid.* **17**.

Raphélis, A. (1922): Variation due *Spirogyra orbicularis* Kütz. Ann. Soc. Linn. Lyon. **69**.

—(1924): Additiona la flore des Algues de Cannes. Rev. Algol. **1**.

Reed, F.D. (1928): Holdfast Cells in *Spirogyra*. Proc. Indiana Acad. Sci. **37**.

Reese, M.J. (1937): The Microflora of the non-calcareous streams Rheidol and Melindwr with special reference to water pollution from lead mines in Cardiganshire. Jour. Ecol. **25**.

Rehbronn, E. (1937): Beiträge zur Fischereibiologie märkischer Seen. II. Dass natiürliche Nahrungsangebot, insbesondere der Aufwichs, und die Ernbrung der Fishnahritiere im Litoral eines eutrophen Sees. Zeitschr. f. Fisch. **35**.

Reinbold, D. Th. (1889): Die Chlorophyceen der Kieler Förde. Naturwiss. Ver. f. Schleswig-Holstein. **8**.

Reinhard, F.G. (1931) :   The Plancton Ecology of the Upper Mississippi, Minneapolis to Winona.   Ecol. Monogr. **1.**

Reinhard, L. (1904) :   Zur Kenntnis des Phytoplanktons von Donjec.   Arb. Ges. Erf. Nat. Univ. Charkow. **39.**

Reinhardt, M.O. (1899) :   Plasmolytische Studien zur Kenntnis des Wachstums der Zellmembranen. Bot. Untersuch. (Schwendener).

Reinsch, P. (1867a) :   De specibus generibusque nonnulis novis ex Algarum et Fungorum  classe.   Act. Soc. Senckenb. **6.**

—(1867b) :   Die Algenflora des mittleren Telis von Franken.   Abh. d. Naturh. Ges. a. Würzburg. **3.**

—(1878) :   Contributiones ad floram algarum aquae dulcis Promontorii Bonae Spei. Jour. Linn. Soc. Bot. **16.**

—(1879a) :   Beobachtungen über entophytische und entozoischme Pflanzenparasiten.   Bot. Zeitg.

—(1879b) :   Algae aquae  dulcis insulae Kerguelensis.   Phil. Trans. R. Soc. London. **168.**

Reiter, K. (1919) :   Die Bedeutung der Seefelder bei Reinerz für Pflanzenforschung und Naturdenkmalpflege. Beitr. z. Naturd enkmalpfl.

Resende, F. (1938) :   Nucleoli and Sat-Chromosomes.   Bol. d. Soc. Broteriana. **13.**

Riabinine, D.B. (1888) :   Les Chlorophycées des environs de Kharkow.   Bull. Soc. Imp. Nat. Moscou.

Rich, F. (1925) :   The Algae of Leicestershire.   Jour. Bot.

—(1932) :   Contributions to our Knowledge of the Freshwater Algae of Africa. 10. Phytoplankton. from South African Pans and Vleis. Trans. R. Soc. S. Africa.  **20.**

—(1935) :   Contributions to our Knowledge of the Freshwater Algae of Africa. 11, Algae from a Pan in  Southern  Rhodesia.  *Ibid.*  **23.**

Richter, A. (1892) :   Über Anpassung der Süsswasserälgen an Kochsalzlösungen.   Flora.  **75.**

Richter, O. (1911) :   Die Ernährung  der Algen. Monogr. u. Abh. z. Intern. Rev. d. ges. Hydrogr. u. Hydrobiol.  **2.**

Richter, P. (1897) :   Süsswasserälgen aus  dem Umanakdistrikt.   Bibl. Bot. H. 42.

Ripart, J. (1868) :   Observations sur le *Mougeotia genuflexa* Ag. et sur la formation de ses spores.   Ann. Sci. Nat. Bot.  **9.**

—(1876) :   Notices sur quelques espéces rares ou nouvelles de la flore cryptogamique de la France. Bull. Soc. Bot. France.  **23.**

Rivet (1870) :   Sur une Algue nouvelle, observée aux environs de Paris.  *Ibid.* France.  **17.**

Robertson, R.A. (1899a) :   Unusual Mode of Conjugation of *Spirogyra.*   Bot. Mag. Tokyo.  **13.**

—(1899b) :   On abnormal conjugation in *Spirogyra.*   Transact, and Proc. Bot. Soc. Edinburgh.  **21.**

Röhrs. F. (1933) :   Die Algen des Wollingster Sees.   Schr, Ver. Naturk. a.d. Unterweser. N.F.  **6.**

Roll, I. (1926) :   Untersuchungen am Phytoplankton der Binnengewässer in Ukraijna.   Arch. Russes de Protistol.  **5.**

Rosa, K. (1924) :   Prehled ceskych ras sroubatkovitych.   Narodni Mus.

—(1931) :   Beitrag zur Kenntnis der Bedeutung der Algen in der Nahrung  des Zooplantkotons. Narodn. Mjs.

Rose, J.N. (1885) :   Notes on the Conjugation of *Spirogyra.*   Bot. Gaz.  **10.**

Rosenvinge, L.K. (1983) :   *Spirogyra groenlandica* nov. spec. og. dens Parthenopsoredannelse. Oefv. K. Vet. Akad. Foerh. Stockholm.  **40.**

Roth, A.G. (1797-1806) :   Catalecta botanica I-III.   Leipzig.

Royers, H. (1903) :   Beitrag zur Algenflora des bergischen Landes und benachbarter Gebiete.

Ruhland, W. (1914/15) :   Weitere Beiträge zur Kolloidchemie und physikalischen Chemie der Zelle. Jahrb. wiss Bot.  **54.**

Rumm, C. (1895) :   Zur Kenntnis der Giftwrkung der Bordeauxbriuhe und  ihrer Bestandteie auf *Spirogyra lomgata* und die Uredosporen von *Puccinica coronata.*   Ber. Deutsch Bot. Ges.  **13.**

Sachs (1896) :   Phylogenetische Aphorismen und uber innere Gestaltungsursahen oder Automorphosen. Physiologische Notizen 10.  Flora.  **82.**

Sagatz, K. (1931) :   Vergleichende Untersuchungen der Assimilationsleistungen bei  Süsswasserälgen und *Vaucheria* aus einer Solquelle in Abgestuften Salzolsungen. Biol. d. Pflanz.  **19.**

Sakamura. T. (1922) :   Uber die Selbstvergiftung der  *Spirogyra* in dstilliertem  Wasser.  Bot. Mag. Tokyo.  **36.**

—(1933) :   Beitrage  zur  Protoplamaforschung an *Spirogyra*-Zellen.   Jour. Fac. Sci. Hokkadido Imp. Univ. Sapporo. Ser. 5.  **2.**

Sakamura, T. and Loo, T. (1925) : Uber die Beeinflussung des Pflanzenplasmas durch die H-Ionen in verschhiedenen Konzentrationnen. Bot. Mag. Tokyo **39.**

Samano, A. (1925) : Algunas *Zygnemataceae* de Chapultepec. Anal. Inst. Biol. Mexiko. **6.**

Saunders, D.A. (1901) : The *Algae* in : Papers from the Harriman Alaska Expedition XXB. Proc. Washington Acad. Sci. **3.**

Saunders, H. (1931) : Conjugation in *Spirogyra*. Ann. Bot. **44.**

Scarth, G.W. (1923a) : Adhesion of Protoplasma to Cell Wall and the Agents which cause it. Trans. R. Soc. Canada. Sect. V. **17.**

—(1923b) : Colliodal associated with Protoplasmic Contraction. Quart. Jour. Exper. Physiol. **14.**

—(1924a) : The Toxic Action of distilled Water and its Antagonism by Cations. Trans. R. Soc. Canada. Sect. V. **18.**

—(1924b) : The toxic Action of Cations on the Contraction and Viscosity of Protoplasm in *Spirogyra*. Quart. Jour. Exper. Physiol. **14.**

—(1925) : The Penetration of Cations into living Protoplasm. Amer. Jour. Bot. **12.**

—(1926) : The influence of External Osmotic Pressure and of Disturbance of the Cell Surface on the Premeability of *Spirogyra* for Acid Dyes. Protoplasma. **I.**

—1929) : The Influence of H-ion Concentration on the Turgor and Movement of Plant Cell with Special Reference to Stomatal Behaviour. Proc. Intern. congr. plant. sci. Ithaca 1926.

Scarth, G.W. and Lloud, F.E. (1927) : The Role of Kinosplasm in the Genesis of Vacuoles. Science. **65**

Schaarschmidt. J. (1881) : Specimen Phycologicae Aequatoriensis. Magyar Novenyteni lap. **5.**

—(1884) : Notes on Afghanistan Algae. Jour. Linn. Soc. Bot. **21.**

Schaedel, A. (1916) : Produzenten und Konsumenten im Teichplankotn, ihre Wechselwirkung und ihre Beziehungen zu den physikalischen und chemischen Milieueinflussen. Arch. f. Hydrobiol. **11.**

Schenk, A. (1875) : Algologische Mittel/ungen.1. *Chytridium* A. Br. Verh. Phys. Mediz. Ges. **8.**

Scherffel, A. (1925) : Zur Frage Warrum finden sich auf Conjugaten sozusagen Keine Bacillariaceen ? Folia Crypt. **I.**

—(1927) : Nochmalas die Frage : Warum finden sich auf den Faden der Zygnemaceen sozusagen keine epiphytischehen Bacillariaceen ? Bot. Kozlem. **24.**

—(1928) : Einiges zur Kenntnis der Kopulation einiger Konjugaten. Arch. Protistenk. **62.**

—(1930) : Einige intersantere niedere Organismen aus dem Balaton und dessen Umgebung. Arb. 1. Unger. Biol. Forschungsinst.

Schiller, J. (1935) : Kulturversuche mit niederen und höheren Pflanzen im radioaktiven Gasteiner Thermalwasser. I. Biol. General. **11.**

Schindler, H. (1938a) : Tötungsart und Absterbebild. I Der. Alkalitod der Pflanzenzelle. Protoplasma. **30**

—(1938b) : Tötungasart und Absterbebild. II Der. Säuretod der Pflanzenzelle. *Ibid.*

Schirschov, P. (1933) : Vergleichende Ubersicht der Coenose der Rheophilalgen im Flusse Tuloma und verschiedenen anderen Wasserbecken. Act. Inst. Bot. Acad. Sci. U.R.S.S. Sec. II. Pl. Crypt. **1**

Schleiden, M. (1844) : Beitrage zur Botanik. I. Uber das Zerfallen der Conferven in ihre einzelenen Glieder. Leipzig.

Schlenker, G. (1915) : Das Schwenninger Zwischenmoor und zwie Schwarzwaldmoore in Bezug auf ihre Entstehung, Pflanzen-usd Tierwelt. Jahresber. Ver. vaterl. Natruk. Wurttemb. **64.**

Schmidle, W. (1893a) : Beitrage zur Algenflora des Schwarzwaldes und der Rheinebene. Ber. Naturf. Ges. Freiburg. **7.**

—(1893b) : Algen aus dem Gebiete des Oberrheins. Ber. Deutsch Bot. Ges. **11.**

—(1895a) : Weitere Beitrage zur Algenflora der Rheinebene und des Schwarzwaldes. Hedwigia. **34.**

—(1895b) : Einige Algen aus Sumatra. *Ibid.* **34.**

—(1896) : Süsswasseralgen aus Australien. Flora. **82.**

—(1897a) : Beitrag zur Algenflora des Schwarzwaldes und des Oberrheines VI. Hedwigia. **36.**

—(1897b) : Zur Entwicklung von *Zygnema* und *Calothrix*. Flora. **84.**

—(1897c) : Algologische Notizen IV. Einige neue und seltene Algen aus Polynesien. Allg. Bot. Zeitschr. **3.**

—(1899a) : Über Planktonalgen und Flagellaten aus dem Nyassasee. Engl. Bot. Jahrb. **27.**

—(1899b) : Einige Algen aus preüssischen Hochmooren. Hedwigia. **38.**

—(1900a) : Über einige vom Prof. Hansgirg in Ostindien gesammelte Algen. *Ibid.* **39.**

Schmidle, W. (1900b) : Einige von Dr. Holderer in Centralisien gesammelte Algen. Ibid. **39.**

—(1900c) : Algologische Notizen XIV. Über einige vom Prof. Hansgrig in Vorderindien gesammelte Sússwasseralgen. Allgem. Bot. Zietschr. **6.**

(1901a) : Die von W. Gotze am Rukwa-und Njassasee gesammelten Pflanzen. Engler's. Bot. Jarhb. **30.**

—(1901b) : Algen aus Brasilien. Hedwigia. **40.**

—(1901c) : Algen aus Istrien und Dalmatien, Montenegro, Hercegowina und Bosnien. Allgem Bot. Zeitschr. **7.**

—(1901d) : In A. Engler, Beiträge zur Flora von Afrika XXII. Engler's Bot. Jahrb. **30.**

—(1902a) : in : A. Engler, Berichte uber die botanischen Ergebnisse der Nyassasee-und Kinga-Ge- birgsexpedition. *Ibid.*

—(1902b) : Algen aus dem Nyassassee und seiner Umgebung, gesammelt von Dr. Fulleborn. *Ibid.* **32.**

—(1902c) : Das Chloro-und Cyanophyceenplankton des Nyassa und iniger anderer innerefrikanischer Seen. *Ibid.* **33.**

—(1904) : Algen von der inaihalbinsel. Allgcm. Bot. Zietchr.

Schmidt. E.W. (1914) : Das Verhalten von *Spirogyra*-Zellen nach Einwirkung hoher Zentifugalkrafte. Ber. Deutsch. Bot. Ges. **32.**

Schmidt. M. (1903) : Grundlagen einer Algenflora der Luneburger Heide. Diss. Gottingen. Hildesheim.

Schmitz (1879) : Uber die Zellkerne der Thallophyten. Sitzber. D. niederrh. Ges. f. Natur-und Heilk.

—(1882) : Die Chromatophoren der Algen. Verh. Naturhist. Vet. Preuss. Rheinlande und Westfalen. **40.**

Schmucker, Th. (1924) : Rechts-und Linkstendenx bie Pflanzen. Beih. Bot. Centralbl. **42.** Abt. 1.

Schmula (1899) : Über abweichende Kopulation bei *Spirogyra bitida*. Hedwigia. **38.**

(1900) : Über Algen in Obserschlesien. Jahresber. Schles. Ges. vat. Cultur. **78.**

Schoddyun, R. (1925) : Contributions a l'etude biologique du canal de Roubaix (Nord de la France) d'apres les materaiaux recoltes ar M.P. et j. Surbayrole. Ann. Biol. Lacustre. **14.**

(1926) : Materiaux pour servir a l'etude biologique des cours d'eau de la Flandre francise. Wateringues, Fossees, Watergangs. Grachts. *Ibid.*

(1926-27) : Materiaux pur le'tude de la Faune et de la Flore des eaux douces de Funchal (-adere). *Ibid.* **15.**

Schoenau, K. v. (1918) : Neuere Beobachtungen uber die Zellkryptogamenflora Bayerns. Kryptg. Forsch. H. 3.

Schonleber, K. (1925) : Reizplasmoschise bie *Spirogyra*. Planta. **24.**

Schramm, I.R. (1914) : Some Pure Culture Methods in the *Algae*. Ann. Missouri Bot. Garden. **1.**

Schroder, B. (1895) : Die Algenflora der Hochgebirgsregion des Riesengebirges. Jahresber. d. Schles. Ges. vaterl. kultur. zool-bot. Sekt.

—(1897) : Die Algen der Versuchsteiche des Schlessischen Fishereivereins zu Trachenberg. Forsch. Ber. Ploner Biol. Stat. **5.**

—(1898) : Neue Beriträge zur Kenntnis der Algen des Riesengebirges. *Ibid.* **6.**

—(1902) : Untersuchungen über Gallertbildungen der Algen. Verh. Narturw. Ver. Heidelberg. N.F. **7B.**

—(1918) : Phytoplankton aus dem Schlawasee. Ber. Deutsch Bot. Ges. **35.**

—(1919) : Beitrag zur Kenntnis der Algenvegetation des Moores von Gorss Iser. *Ibid.* **37.**

Schroter, J. (1883) : Neue Beiträge zur Algenkunde Schlesiens. Jahreshber. Schles. Ges. vat. Kultur.

Schurhöff, P.N. (1922/23) : Die Kernteilung der Diatomeen und Konjugaten. Mikrokosmos. **16.**

—(1924) : Plastiden in : Handubuch der Pflanzenanatomie.

Schüssnig, B. (1915) : Beitrag zur Kenntnis der Süsswasseralgen ds österreichischen Küstenlandes. Österr. Bot. Zeitschr. **65.**

—(1919) : Über den Zellkern der Protophyten. Ber. Deutsch Bot. Ges. **37.**

—(1924) : Die Bedeutung der Cytologie fur die Systematick der Protophyten. Verh. zool. bot. Ges. Wien. **73.**

—(1925a) : Die systematische Stellung der Konjugaten. Nuov Notorisia.

—(1925b) : Betrachtungen über das System der niederen Pflanzen. Verh. zool. bot. Ges. Wien. **74,** 75.

Schüssnig, B. (1927) :   Die pflanzliche Zelle im Licht der Phylogenie.   Wien u. Leipzig.

—(1938) :   Vergleichende Morphologie der niederen Pflanzen.   Berlin.

Schulz, P. (1923) :   Kurze Mitteilungen uber Algenparasiten.   Schr. f. Susswasserund Meeresk.

Schwarz. F. (1887) :   Die Morphologie und chemische Zusammensetzung des Protoplasmas.   Beitr. z. Biol. d. Pfl.   **5.**

Scücs, J. (1913) :   Über einige charakteristiscehe Wirkungen des Aluminium-Ions auf das Protoplasma. Jahrb. wiss. Bot.   **52.**

Seckt, H. (1929) :   Estudios Hidrobiologicos en la Argentina IV.   *Conjugatae*.   Bol. Acad. Nac. Sienc. **31.**

Senn, G. (1908) :   Die Gestalts-und Lageveränderung der Pflanzenchromatophoren.   Leipzig.

Sernander, R. (1915/16) :   Svenska Kalktuffer.   Geolog. Förening. Stöckholm Forhandl.   **37.**

Sernander, R. (1939) :   Lina Myr. Geol. Fören. Stockholm Förhandl.

Setchell, W. and Gardner, N.L. (1903) : Algae of Northwestern Ameria.   Univ. Calif. Publ. in Botany. **1.**

Shadbolt, G. (1851) :   On the Sporangia of the Filmentous Freshwater Algae.   Trans. Micr. Soc. London.   **3.**

Shinke N. and Shigenaga, N. (1933) :   A Histochemical Study of Plant Nuclei in Rest and Mitosis, Cytologia.   **4.**

Silfvenius, A. J. (1902) :   Zur Kenntnis der Verbreitung finnischer Chlorophyceen und Cynophyceen. Meddel. Soc. Fauna et Flora Fenn.   **29.**

Singh, K.P. (1958a) :   Some observations on conjugation in *Sirocladium kumaoensis* Randh. Current Sci.   **28,**

—(1958b) :   Some peculiarities in conjugation in *Zygnema terrestris* Randh.   Sci. & Culture.   **24.**

—(1958c) :   The distribution and periodicity of *Sirocladium kumaoense* in Nainital. Sci. & Culture.   **24.**

Singh, R.N. (1938) :   The *Zygnemiodeae* of the United Provinces, India II.   Jour, Indian Bot. Soc.   **17.**

—(1945) :   On Randhawa's " A critical review of some recently created new species of Indian Zygnemales."   Proc. Indian Acad. Sci. B.   **22.**

Skuja, A. (1926) :   Zwei neue Zygnemaceen nit blauem Mesospor.   Act. Hort. Bot. Univ. Latv.   **1.**

—(1928) :   Vorabetien zu einer Algenflora von Lettland IV.   *Ibid.*

—1929) :   Süsswasseralegen von den westestinischen Inseln Saaremaa und Hiiumaa.   *Ibid.*   **4.**

—(1931) :   Die Algenflora der Insel Moritzehom im Usaitensee.   Arb. Naturforsch. Ver. Riga. N.F. **19.**

—(1932) :   Le genre *Pleurodiscus* doit-il être maintenu ?   Rev. Algol.   **6.**

—(1934) :   Beitrag zur Algenflora Lettlands I.   Act. Hort. Bot. Univ. Latv. 7 (1932).

—(1937a) :   *Algae* in : Symbolae Sinicae herausgeg. v. H.Handel-Mazzetti, Wien.

—(1937b) :   Süsswasseralgen aus Griechenland und Kleinasien, gesammelt von C. Regel. Hedwigia.   **77.**

Skvortzow, B.W. (1925) :   Zur Kenntnis der *Phycomycetes* aus der Nordmandschurei, China. Arch. Protistenk.   **51.**

—(1926) :   Über einige Süsswasseralgen aus der Nordmandschurei im Jahre 1916 gasemmelt. Arch. f. Hydroibiol.   **16.**

—(1927a) :   Studies on the Occurrence and Reproduction of *Zygnemaceae* in the Environs of Harbin. Proc. Sungaree Riv. Biol. Stat.   **1.**

—(1927b) :   Sur la végétation lacustre de la vallée Sungari en Manshourie.   Bull. Jard. Bot. Princ. de l'U.S.S.R.   **26.**

—(1927c) :   Freshwater Algae and Phytoplankton of the Lakes and Rivers of the Zaisan District. Altai Moutains, Sibiria.   Jour. Bot.   **65.**

—(1928) :   Über das Phytoplankton des Zaisansees, Südsibirien.   Arch. f. Hydrobiol.   **19.**

—(1937) :   Notes on the Algal Flora of Manchoukuo I-IV Bot. Mag. Tokyo.   **51.**

Silva, H. (1949) :   Additions to the algae of the southeastern United States.   Jour. Elisha Mitch, Sci. Soc. **65.**

Smith, E. Ph. (1922) :   A note on Conjugation in *Zygnema*.   Ann. Bot.   **36.**

Smith, G.M. (1920) :   Phytoplankton of the Inlaad Lakes of Wisconsin I. Bull Wisc. Geol. and Nat. Hist. Surv.   **57.**   Madison.

—(1933) :   The Freshwater Algae of the United States.   New York.

—(1947) :   The historical significance of names applied to reproductive structures of algae. Farlowia.   **3.**

—(1956) :   The role of study of algae in the development of botany.   Amer. Jour. Bot.   **43.**

Smith. W. (1853): On the Stellate Bodies occuring in the Cells of Freshwater Algae. Quart. Jour. Microsc. Soc. **1.**

Sparrow, F.K. (1932): Observation on Aquatic Fungi of Cold Spring Harbour. Mycologia. **24.**

Sparrow, F.K. (1938): Some Chytridiaeeous Fungi from North Africa and Borneo. Brit. Mycol. Soc. **21.**

Spencer, W.J. (1882): On the Freshwater Algae of New Zealand. Trans. and Proc. N. Zeal. Inst. **14**

Stadler, E. (1905): Ein kleiner Beitrag zur Kenntnis der Süsswasseralgen von Dalmatien. Lotos. N.F. **25.**

Stalberg. N. (1939): Lake Vattern, Acta Phytogeogr. Suec. **11.**

Stahl, E. (1880): Über den Einfluss von Richtung und Stärke, der Beleuchtung auf einige Bewegungserecheinungen im Pflanzenreich. Bot. Zertg. **38.**

Steinecke, F. (1916): Die Algen des Zehlaubruches in systematischer und biologischer Hinsicht. Schr. Phys. ok. Ges. Konigsberg. i. Pr. **56.**

—(1922): Die Algen des Pakledimmer Hochmoors. Bot. Arch. **1.**

—(1923a): Über Beziehungen zwischen Färbung und Assimiliation bie einigen Süsswasseralgen. *Ibid.* **4.**

—(1923b): Limonitbildende Algen der Neide-Flachmoore. *Ibid.* **4.**

—(1924a): Die Zygospoeir der Zygophyceen als terrestrische Anpassung. *Ibid.* **8.**

—(1924b): Mikrooraganismen der Hochmoore am Kranichbruch. Beitr. a.d. Tierk. Widmungsschr. f. Geheimarat Prof. Dr. Braun.

—(1924c): Die Algen des *Betula nana*-Moores bei Neu-Linum. Bot. Arch. **5.**

—(1926a): Die Zweischaligkeit im Membranbau von Zygnemalen und ihre Bedeutung für die Phylogenie der Conjugaten. *Ibid.* **13.**

—(1926): Der Schachtelbau der Zygnemalen-Membran. *Ibid.* **16.**

—(1928a): Sexualdimorphismus bei *Zygnema stellinum*. *Ibid.* **24.**

—(1929b): *Harpochytrium vermiforme* sp. n. Bot. Arch. **24.**

—(1931): Die Phylogenie der Algophyten. Schr. Königsberg. Gelehrten-Ges. Naturw. Kl. **8.**

—(1937): Zur Geschichte der Galtgarben-Moore. Schr. Phys.-ök. Ges. Königsberg. (Pr). **59.**

Steinecke, F. and Lindemann, E. (1923): Die Mikroflora des Zwergirkenmoores bie Neulinum. Schr. f. Süsswasser- u. Meeresk. **3.**

Stokmayer, S. (1894): Nachträge zur systematischen Aufzahlung der im Erzherzogtum Österreich ob der Enns bisher beobachteten samenlosen Pflanzen (Kryptogamen) I. Wien.

Stolley, I. (1930): Über die Centrosom-ähnlichen Gebilde und die Kernteilungserscheinungen bei *Spirogyra nitida*. Zeitschr. Bot. **23.**

Strasburger, E. (1880): Zellbldung und Zellteilung. 3 Aufl.

—(1882a): Über den Teilungsvorgang der Zellkerne und das Verhältnis der Kernteilung zur Zellteilung. Arch. f. mikr. Anat. **21.**

—(1882b): Über den Bau und das Wachstum der Zellhäute. Jena.

—(1884): Die Controversen der indirekten Kernteilung. Arch. f. mikr. Anat. **23.**

—(1888): Histologische Beiträge I. Jena.

Ström, K.M. (1920a): Freshwater Algae from Caucasus and Turkestan. Nyt. Mag. Naturvid. **57.**

—(1920b): Freshwater Algae from Tuddal in Telemark. *Ibid.*

—(1921): Some Algae from Hot Springs in Spitzbergen. Bot. Notiser. **.**

—(1926): Norwegian Mountain Algae. Skr. Norsk, Vod. Ak. i. Oslo. I. Math. Nat. Kl. No. 6.

Suchlandt, O. and Schmassmann, W. (1935): Limnologische Beobachtungen an acht Hochgebirgseen der Landschaft Davos. Zeitschr, f. Hydrolog. **7.**

Suematsu, S. (1936): Karyological Study of *Spirogyra* by Means of Nucleal Reaction. Sci. Rep. Tokyo Burnrika Daigaku. Sect. B. **3.**

Suessenguth, K. (1920): Beitrag zur Kenntnis der Algenflora Südbayerns. Kryptg. Forsch. H. 5.

Suringer, W.F.R. (1857): Observations phycologicae in floram Batavam. Leovardiae.

—(1868): Notice sur l'histoire des faisceaux chlorophylliques de la *Spirogyra lineata*. Arch. Néerland: d. sc. exact. **3.**

—(1870): Algae japonicae musei botanici Lugdunobatavi. Harlem.

Saxena, M.R. (1953): Critical notes on some of the freshwater algae collected from Hyderabad State. (Abst). Proc. Indian Sci. Congress. (40) **3.**

Swirenko, D.O. (1927): Algologische Untersuchungen eines interessanten Tümpel-Sumpfes bei Dnjepropetrowsk. Acad. Sc. Ukraine Mém. C. Sc. Phys. Math. **3.**

Swirenko, P. (1928): Uberblick über die Algen des Flusses Ingul. Arch. Russ. Protistol. **7.**

Szeinmann, A. (1933): Observation vitales sur la formation des pyrénoides chez *Spirogyra*. Act. Soc. Bot. Pol. **10.**

Taft. C.E. (1939): Additions to the Algae of Michigan. Bull. Torrey Bot. Club. **66.**

—(1947a): *Spirogyra hollandia*, a new species from New Guinea. Ohio Jour. Sci. **47.**

—(1947b): Some Algae, including new species from New Mexico. *Ibid.* **47.**

Tangl, F. (1882): Über die Teilung der Kerne in *Spirogyra*-Zellen. Sitz. Ber. Akad. Wiss. Wien. Math-nat. Kl. **85.**

Tansley, A.G. (1939): The British Islands and their Vegetation. Cambridge.

Tarnavschi, I.T. (1930): Contributii la cunoasterea algelor din Bucovina I. Bull. Fac. Stiinite din Cernauti. **4.**

—(1931): Contributii la conaosterea algelor din Bucovina II. *Ibid.* **5.**

Taylor. W.R. (1921): Additions to the Flora of Mount Desert, Maine. Rhodora. **23.**

—(1922): Notes on some Algae from British Columbia. *Ibid.* **24.**

—(1924): Further Notes on British Columbia Algae. *Ibid.* **26.**

—(1928): The Alpine Algal Vegetation of the Mountains of British Columbia. Proc. Acad. Nat. Sci. Philadephia. **80.**

—(1934): The Freshwater Algae of Newfoundland I. Pap. Mich. Acad. Sc. Arts and Lett. **19** (1933).

(1935): Alpine Algae from the Santa Marta Mountains, Colombia. Amer. Jour. Bot.

Taylor, W.R. (1954): Algae: non-planktonic. Bot. Rev. **20.**

Taylor, W.R. and Colton, H.S. (1928): The Phytoplankton of some Arizona Pools and Lakes. *Ibid.* **15.**

Teodoresco, E.C. (1907): Matériaux pour la flore algologique de la Roumanie. Beih. Bot. Centralbl. Abt. II. **21.**

Théobald, G. (1853/54): Algues des environs de Genève. C.R. Soc. Hallérienne de Geneve.

Thunmark, S. (1926): Bidrag till kännedomenom recenta Kalktuffer. Geol. För. i. Stockholm Förhandl.

Thurston, H.W. (1919): Sex in the *Conjugatae* and the Relative Frequency of the Different Types of Conjugation. Bull. Torrey Bot. Club. **46.**

Tiffany, L.H. (1921): Algal Food of the Young Gizzard Shad. Ohio Jour. Sci. **21.**

—(1924a): A Physiological Study of Growth and Reproduction among certain Green Algae. *Ibid.* **24.**

—(1924b): Some New Forms of *Spirogyra* and *Oedogonium. Ibid.* **24.**

—(1926): The Filamentous Algae of Northwestern Iowa. Trans. Amer. Microsc. Soc. **45.**

—(1927): New Species and Varieties of *Chlorophyceae*. Bot. Gaz. **83.**

—(1936): Wille's Collection of Puerto Rican Freshwater Algae. Brittonia. **2.**

—(1937): The Filmentous Algae of the West End of Lake Erie. Amer. Midland Nat. **18.**

Tilden, J.F. (1894): List of Freshwater Algae collected in Minnesota during 1893. Minnesota Bot. Studies. **1.**

—(1898): List of Freshwater Algae collected in Minnesota during 1896-1897. Ibid. **2.**

Tischler, G. (1921/22): Allgemeine Pflanzenkaryologie. Handbuch. der. Pflanzenanatomic.

Torka, V. (1906): Algen der Ordnung *Conjugatae* aus der Umgebung von Schwiebus. Helios. Berlin. **23.**

Trahms, O.K. (1939): Beiträge zur Ökologie küstennaher Brackwässer. I. Das Plankton des groBssen Jasmunder Boddens. Arch. f. Hydrobiol. **35.**

Transeau, E.N. (1913): The Periodicity of Algae in Illinois. Trans. Amer. Micr. Soc. **32.**

—(1914): New Species of Green Algae. Amer. Jour. Bot. **1.**

—(1915)- Notes on the *Zygnemales*. Ohio Jour. Sci. **16.**

—(1916): The Perodicity of Freshwater Algae. Amer. Jour. Bot. **3.**

—(1917): The Algae of Michigan. Ohio Jour. Sci. **17.**

—(1918): A New Species and a New Variety of Algae from Oneida Lake. Techn. Publ. No. 9. N.Y. State Coll. Forestry.

—(1919): Hybrids among *Spirogyra*. Amer. Naturalist. **53.**

—(1925): The Genus *Debarya*. Ohio Jour. Sci. **25.**

—(1926): The Genus *Mougeotia. Ibid.* **26.**

—(1932): The Genus *Temnogametum. Ibid.* **32.**

Transcau, E.N. (1933) : The Genus *Zygogonium*. *Ibid.* **33.**

—(1934a) : Notes on *Zygnemataceae*. *Ibid.* **34.**

—(1934b) : The Genera of the *Zygnemataceae*. Trans. Amer. Micr. Soc. **53.**

—(1938) : Notes on *Zygnemataceae*. Amer Jour. Bot. **25.**

—(1951) : The Zygnemataceae. Ohio State Univ. Press. Columbus. 327 pp.

Transeau, E.N., Tiffany, L.H., Taft. C.E., and Li. L.C. (1934) : New Species of *Zygnemataceae*. Trans. Amer. Micr. Soc. **53.**

Trealease, W. (1885) : Biology of the *Conjugatae*. Bot. Gaz. **10.**

Tripolitowa. T.K. (1928) : Beiträge zur Flora der Sporenpflanzen des Altai und des Gouvernements Tomsk II. Algen. Ber. Tomsk. Staatsuniv. **79.**

Troendle, A. (1907) : Über die Kopulation und Keimung von *Spirogyra*. Bot. Zeitg. **65.**

—(1911) : Über die Reduktionsteilung in den Zygoten von *Spirogyra* und die Bedeutung der Synapsis. Zeitschr f. Bot. **3.**

—(1912) : Der Nucleolus von *Spirogyra* und die Chromosomen höherer Pflanzen. *Ibid.* **4.**

Tschernow, W.K. (1940) : Matériaux de la flora des Algues de la region de Leningrad. Les Algues des petits bassins dans le massif de collines de Valdia. Act. Inst. Bot. Acad. Sci. U.R.S.S. Ser. 2. **4**

—(1938).

Tschugunoff, N.L. (1921) : Über das Plankton des nördlichen Kaspi-Sees. Arb. Biol. Wolgastat. **6.**

Turner, C. (1910) : *Spirogyra*. Ann. Report a. Trans. Manchester Micr. Soc.

Turner, W.B. (1892) : Algae aquae dulcis Indiae orientalis, K. Sv. Vet. Akad. Handl. **25.**

Turrill, W.B. (1952) : Some taxonomic aims, methods, and principles ; their possible applications to the algae. Nature. **169.**

Ueda, K. (1956) : Structure of plant cell with special reference to lower plants I. Mitosis in *Spirogyra setiformis*. Cytologia, **21** (4).

Ulehla, V. (1923) : Über ($Co_2$)-und ph-Regulation des Wassers durch einige Süsswasseralgen. Ber. Deutsch Bot. Ges. **41.**

Unrath, K. (1935) : Über den Erregungsvorgang bei *Spirogyra* und *Vaucheria* und über Potentialmessungen an Pflanzenzellen. Protoplasma. **22.**

Uspenski, E.E. (1924) : Contributions to the Study of the Action of Different Quantities of Iron. Trans. Inst. Fertelisers. Nr. **23.** Moskau.

—(1927) : Eisen als Faktor fur die Verbreitung niederer Wasserpflanzen. Pflanzenforsch. H. 9.

—(1935) : Die Umwandlung einiger erbicher Formen iin andere und die Entstehung neuer For-Genus *Spirogyra*. Probl. theoret. Biol. Arb. Timirjaseff-Inst. f. Biol. Moskau.

Ussatschev, P.I. (1928) : Kurze Beschresbung der Algenflora des Weletminskij-Teiches (Gouv. Nishnij Novgorod, MittelruBland). Arb. a d. biol. Okastat. **5.**

Vailionis, L. (1930) : Medziagos zinpsuys Lietuvos dumbliu augmenijai paxiuli. Kosmos. K. wno.

Vaucher, I.P. (1803) : Histoire des Conferves d'eau douce. Geneve.

Venkataraman, G.S. (1953) : A study of the algal succession in some of the ponds and puddles of the University campus. (M.Sc. Thesis). Banaras Hindu University.

—(1957) : The algal flora of the ponds and puddles inside the Banaras Hindu University grounds, India. Jour. Bombay Nat. Hist. Soc. **54.**

—(1959) : Notes on three interesting species of Zygnemaceae from South India. Proc. Nat. Inst. Sci., India (In press).

Vetter, H. (1937) : Limnologische Untersuchungen über das Phytoplankton und seine Beziehungen zur Ernährung des Zooplanktons im Schleinsee bei Langenargen am Bodensee. Internat. Rev. d. ges. Hydrogr. u. Hydrobiol. **39.**

Voss, M. (1927) : Die Algenflora des Kieshofer Moores (bei Greifswald). Beitr z. Naturdenkmalpfl. **12.**

Vouk. V. (1937) : Vergleichende biologische Studien über Thermen. Bull. jugoslw. Akad. **31.**

Virieux, M.J. (1908) : Note sur les Spirogyres des environs de Besancon. Bull. de la Soc. Hist. Nat. du Doubs **1910.**

—(1913) : Plancton du lac Victoria Nyanza. Boy. Ch. Alluand et R. Jeannel en Afr. orient. 1911-12, Result. sc. Paris.

Voigt, M. (1903) : Beiträge zur Kenntnis des Planktons pommerscher Seen. Ploner Forsch.-Ber. **9.**

Vries, H. de (1885) : Plasmolytische Studien uber die Wand der Vakuolen. Jahrb. wiss. Bot. **16.**

Vries, H. de (1888) : Über den isotonischen Koeffizienten des Glyzerins. Bot. Zeitg. **46.**

—(1889) : Über die Contraktion der Chlorophyllbänder bei *Spirogyra.* Ber. Deutsch Bot. Ges.

Vuathier, Ch. (1926) : Notes sur la flore thermale des eaux sulfureuses de Merens (Ariege). Bull. Soc. Bot. France. **73.**

Wailes, G.H. (1930) : Munday Lake and its Ecology. Mus. a. Art Notes Vancouver. **5.**

Wailes, G.H. and Tiffany, L.H. (1929) : Some Algae from British Columbia. *Ibid.* **4.**

Wallner, J. (1938) : Einführung in die Biogeodynamik. Zeitschr. f. d. ges. Naturw.

Walton, L.B. (1908) : Zygospores of *Spirogyra* in Relation to Theories of Variability. Torreya. **8.**

Walz, J. (1870) : Beiträge zur Kenntnis der Saprolegnieen. Bot. Zeitg. **28.**

Wang, C.C. (1933) : Species of *Spirogyra* from Nanking. Contr. Biol. Lab. Sc. Soc. China. Bot. Ser. **8.**

—(1934a) : Notes on the Algae of Anhwei I. *Ibid.* **9.**

—(1934b) : Notes on the Algae from Chungehing, Szechuan. *Ibid.*

Wang, C. C. (1939) : On some Freshwater Algae from West Tung Ting Shan, Kiangsu. *Ibid.* **10.**

Wawrzyniak, K.F. (1924) : La flore des lacs de la grande Pologne. Soc. amis sc. Poznan. Trayv. comm. Sc. math. et nat. **2** Sér. B Biol. Sc.

Weber, F. (1921) : Zentrifugierungsversuche mit ätherisierten Spirogyren. Biochem. Zeitschr.

—(1924a) : Krampfplasmolyse bei *Spirogyra.* Pflügers Arch. **206.**

—(1924b) : Protoplasmaviskositat kopulierender Spirogyren. Ber. Deutsch Bot. Ges. **42.**

—(1925a) : Plasmolyseform von *Spirogyra* vor der Kopulation. Zeitschr. f. wiss. Mikrosk. **42.**

—(1925b) : Schraubenplasmolyse. Ber. Deutsch Bot. Ges. **43.**

—(1925c) : Über die Beurteilung der Plasmaviskosität nach der Plasmolyseform. Zeitschr. f. wiss. Mikrosk. **42.**

—(1929a) : Fadenziehen des Endoplasmas bei *Spirogyra.* Protoplasma. **6.**

—(1929b) : Plasmolyseort. Ibid. **7.**

—(1931a) : Harnstoffpermeabilität ungleich alter *Spirogyra*-Zellen. *Ibid.* **12.**

—(1931b) : Plasmolyseresistenz und-permeabilität bei Narkose. *Ibid.* **14.**

—(1933) : Myelinfiguren und Sphärolithe aus *Spirogyra*-Chloroplasten. Protoplasma. **19.**

—(1934) : Alkoholresistenz ungleich alter *Spirogyra*-Zellen. *Ibid.* **20.**

Weber, F. and Hohenegger, H. (1923) : Reversible Viskositätserhühung des Protoplasmas bei Kälte. Ber. Deutsch. Bot. Ges. **41.**

Weevers, Th. (1911) : Untersuchungen über die Lokalisation und Funktion des Kaliums in der Pflanze. Rec. Trav. bot. Néerl. **8.**

Wehrle, E. (1927) : Studien über Wasserstoffionenkonzentrationsverhältnisse in der Umgebung von Freiburg im Breisgau. Zeitschr. f. Bot. **19.**

Weimann, R. (1937) : Uber Fadenalgen und ihre Bekampfung. Zeitschr. f. Fischerei. **35.**

Wehrle, E. (1939) : Zur Kenntnis der Algen im Naturschutzget iet Weingartener Moor bei Karlsruhe. Beitr. z. naturkundl. Forsch. in Südwestdeutschl. **4.**

Welwitsch, F. (1857) : Systematische Aufzählung der Süsswasseralgen des Erzherzogthums Österreich unter der Enns. Abh. Zool. bot. Ver. Wien.

West, G.S. (1899) : The Algae Flora of Cambridgeshire. Jour. Bot. **37.**

—(1904) : A Treatise of the British Freshwater Algae. Cambridge.

—(1907) : Report on the Freshwater Algae, including Phytoplankton of the Third Tanganyika Expedition. Jour. Linn. Soc. Bot. **38.**

—(1909a) : The Algae of the Yan Yean Reservoir, Victoria. *Ibid.* **39.**

—(1909b) : The Algae of the Birket Quarun, Egypt. Jour. Bot. **47.**

—(1912a) : Freshwater Algae of the Percy Sladen Memorial Expedition to S.W. Africa. Ann. S. Afr. Mus. **9.**

—(1912b) : Algological Notes VI. Some African Algae. Jour. Bot. **50.**

— (1914) : A Contribution to our Knowledge of the Freshwater Algae of Columbia. Mém. Soc. Neuchatel. Sc. Nat. **5.**

—(1916) : *Algae.* Cambridge Bot. Handbooks.

West. W. (1889) : The Freshwater Algae of North Yorkshire. Jour. Bot. **26.**

—(1890) : Contribution to the Freshwater Algae of North Wales. Jour. R. micr. Soc.

West, W. (1891) : Sulla conjugazione delle Zygnemee. Nuov. Notarisia. **6.**

—(1892a) : Nonnullae algae aquae dulcis Lusitanicae. *Ibid.* **7.**

—(1892b) : Algae of the English Lake District. Jour. R. micr. Soc. **6.**

West, W. (1802c) : A Contribution to the Freshwater Algae of West Ireland. Jour. Linn. Soc. Bot. **29.**
—(1803) : Notes on Scotish Freshwater Algae. Jour. Bot. **31.**
—(1902) : A New *Mougeotia. Ibid.* **40.**
—(1903) : *Mougeotia immersa. Ibid.* **41.**
West, W. and G.S. (1894) : On some Freshwater Algae from the West Indies. Jour. Linn. Soc. Bot. **30.**
—(1895) : A Contribution to our Knowledge of the Freshwater Algae of Madagascar. Trans. Linn. Soc. London. Ser. 2. **5.**
—(1896) : Algae from Central Africa. Jour. Bot. **34.**
—(1897a) : Welwitschs African Freshwater Algae. *Ibid.* **35.**
—(1897b) : A Contribution to the Freshwater Algae of the South of Eng. land. Jour. R. micr. Soc. London.
—(1898) : Observations on the *Conjugatae.* Ann. Bot. **12.**
—(1899) : A Further Contribution to the Freshwater Algae of the West Indies. Jour. Linn. Soc. Bot. **34.**
—(1901a) : The Alga-Flora of Yorkshire. Trans. Yorksh. Natural. Union. **22, 23, 25, 27.**
—(1901b) : Freshwater Chlorophyceae in : Flora of Koh Chang. Bot. Tidsskr. **24.**
—(1902a) : A Conribution to the Freshwater Algae of Ceylon. Trans. Linn. Soc. Bot. Ser. 2 **6.**
—(1902b) : A Contribution to the Freshwater Algae of the North of Ireland. Trans. R. Irish. Acad. **32** Sec. B.
—(1903) : Notes on Freshwater Algae. Jour. Bot. **41.**
—(1905) : Freshwater Algae from the Orkneys and Shetlands. Trans. and Proc. Bot. Soc. Edinburgh. **23.**
—(1907) : Freshwater Algae from Burma, including a few from Bengal and Madras. Ann. R. Bot. Gard. Calcutta. **6.**
—(1909) : The British Freshwater Phytoplankton. Proc. Roy. Soc. London. **31.**
West, G.S. and Fritsch, F.E. (1927) : A Treatise of the British Freshwater Algae. Cambridge.
West, G.S. and Starkey, Cl. B. (1915) : A Contribution to the Cytology and Life-History of *Zygnema ericetorum* (Kütz.) Hansg. with some Remarks on the "Genus" *Zygogonium.* New Phytol. **14.**
Wettstein, F. V. (1921) : Zur Bedeutung und Technik der Reinkultur für Systematik und Floristik der Algen. Österr. bot. Zeitschr. **70.**
Wettstein, R. (1896) : Die Systematik der Thallо₁ hyten mit besonderer Berücksichtigung der Abhandlung von J. Sachs "Phylogenetische Aphorismen". Lotos.
Wildeman, E. de (1887, 1890a, 1893a) : Contributions à Pétude des Algues de Belgique. Bull. Soc. R. Bot. Belg.
—(1890b) : Sur les crampons der Conjuguées. La Notarisia. **6.**
—(1890c) : Observations algologiques. Bull. Soc. Bot. Belg. **29.**
—(1893b) : Quelques Algues récoltées aux environs de Malmédy. Bull. Soc. Belg. Micr. **20.**
—(1895a) : Tableau comparatif des Algues de Belgique. Bull. Soc. R. Bot. Belg. **34.**
—(1895b) : Catalogue de la flore algologique de la Suisse. Mem. Soc. R. Sc. de Liége. 2. sér. **19.**
—(1895c) : Matériaux pour la flore algologique du département de la Meuse (France). La Notarisia.
—(1896) : Census Chytridinearum. Bull. Soc. Bot. Belg. **35.**
—(1897) : Algues rapportées par J. Massart d'un voyage aux Indes Néerlandaises. Ann. Jard. Bot. Buitenzorg. I. Suppl. Leiden.
—(1900a) : Les Algues de la flore de Buitenzorg. Leiden.
—(1900b) : Une nouvelle Chytridiacée. Mém. Herb. Boissier. Nr. **3.**
—(1930a) : Morphologie du *Zygnema ericetorum* (Kutz.) Hansg. Bul. Cl. Sc. Acad. R. Belg. 5 sér. **16.**
—(1930b) : Sur les spheres attractives dans quelques cellules végétales. *Ibid.* 3. sér. **21.**
—(1930c) : Sphére attractive et centrosome chez des *Spirogyra.* Ibid. 5. sér. **16.**
— (1935) : Observations sur les Algues in : Expéd. antarct. Belge. Résult. voy. d. 1. Belgica en 1897-99. Botanique. Anvers.
Wille, N. (1879) : Ferskvandsalger fra Novaja Semlja samlede af Dr. F. Kjellman paa Nordenskiolds Expedition 1875. K. Vet.-Akad. Förhandl. **36.**
—(1880) : Bidrag til Kundskaben om Norges Ferskvandsalger I. Christiania Vid. selsk. Förhandl.
—(1884) : Bidrag till Sydamerikas Algflora. Bihang t. K. Sv. Ver. Akad. Handl. **18.**

Wille, N. (1887): Algologische Mitteilungen 9. Über Akineten und Aplanosporen. Jahrb. wiss. Bot. **18.**

—(1890): *Zygnemaceae, Mesocarpaceae* in: Engler-Prantl, Die natürlichen Pflanzenfamilien.

—(1896): Eine für Norwegen neue Alge, *Spirogyra ricularis* Rabenh. Biol. Centralbl. **16.**

—(1897): Om Faeröernes Ferskvandsalger og om Ferskvandsalgernes Spredningmaader. Bot. Notiser.

—(1900): Algologische Notizen VI. *Spirogyra fallax* (Hansg.). Nyt Mag. f. Naturvid. **38.**

—(1901): Algologische Notizen VII. Zur Verbreitung der Süsswasseralgen im südlichen Norwegen. *Ibid.* **39.**

—(1909/10): *Conjugate* in: Engler and Prantl, Die natürlichen Pflanzenfamilien. Teil 1, Abt. 2.

—(1922): Algen aus Zentralasien, gesammelt von Dr. Sv. Hedin. Southern Tibet. **6** III.

—(1924): Süsswasseralgen von der Deutschen Südpolarexpedition auf dem Schiff "Gauss". Deutsche Südpolarexp. Bot. **8.**

Williams, E., Kneer, L., Wickwire, G.C., Verda, D.J., and Burge, W.E., (1931): Increase of Sugar Utilization in *Spirogyra* by means of Commercial Fertilizers. Bot. Gaz. **92.**

Winchster, D.E. (1923): Oil Shale of the Rocky Mountain Region. U.S. Geol. Surv. Bull. 729.

Winkler, E. (1902): Krümmungsbewegungen von *Spirogyra*. Diss. Leipzig.

Wisselingh, C. van (1898): Über den Nucleolus von *Spirogyra*. Bot. Zeitg. **56.**

—(1900a): Über Kernteilung bei *Spirogyra*. Flora. **87.**

—(1900b): Über mehrkernige *Spirogyra*-Zellen. *Ibid.*

—(1902): Untersuchungen über *Spirogyra*. Bot. Zeitg. **60.**

—(1903a): Untersuchungen über den Einfluss von Chloralhydrat auf die Kernteilung bei *Spirogyra*. *Ibid.* **61.**

—(1903b): Über abnormale Kernteilung. *Ibid.* **61.**

—(1908): Zur Physiologie der *Spirogyra*-Zelle. Beih. Bot. Centralbl. **24.**

—(1914): On the Nucleolus and Karyokinesis in *Zygnema*. Rec. Trav. Bot. Néeıl. **11.**

—(1920): Uber Variabilität und Erblichkeit. Zeitschr. f. indukt. Abstamm· u. Vererbungslehre. **22.**

—(1921): Zehnter Beitrag zur Kenntnis der Caryokinese. Beih. Bot. Centralbl. Abt. I. **38.**

—(1924): Die Zellmembran. In: Handbuch der Pflanzenanatomie. **3.**

Wittrock, V.B. (1867): Algologiska studier I-II. Upsala.

—(1869): Bidrag till kännedomen om Sveriges Zygnemacéer och Mesocarpéer. Bot. Notiser. 1868

—(1871): Beitrag zur Kenntnis der Zygnemaceen und Mesocarpacen. Hedwigia. **10.**

—(1872): Om Gotlands och Oelands sötvattensalger. Bih. Sv. Vet.-Akad. Handl. **1.**

—(1878): On the Spore-formation of the Mesocarpeae especially of the New Genus *Gonatonema*. Bih. till K. Svenska Vet.-Akad. Handl. **5.**

—(1880): Points-Forteekning ofver Skandinaviens växter 4. Teil. Lund.

Wittrock, V. B. and Nordstedt, O. (1889, 1901): Algae aquae dulcis exsiccatae. Index. Lund.

Woicicki, Z. (1907): Über pathologische Wachstumserscheinungen bei *Spirogyra*-und *Mougeotia*-Arten in Laboratoriumskulturen. Ber. Deutsch Bot. Ges. **25.**

Wolle, F. (1877): Freshwater Algae III. Bull. Torrey Bot. Club. **6.**

—(1879): Freshwater Algae. Synopsis of Discoveries and Researches in 1878. *Ibid.*

—(1880): Freshwater Algae IV. *Ibid.* **7.**

—(1881): Freshwater Algae V. *Ibid.* **8.**

—(1883): Freshwater Algae VII. *Ibid.* **10.**

—(1885): Freshwater Algae X. *Ibid.*

—(1887): Freshwater Algae of the United States. Bethlehem Pa.

Wollny, R. (1877): *Spirogyra margaritata* sp. n. und *Sp. degans* sp. n. Hedwigia. **16.**

Woloszynska, J. (1910): Das Algenleben im oberen Prut. Sprawozd. Komis. fizyogr. Akad. Umijet. Krakow. **45.**

—(1914): Studien über das Phytoplankton des Viktoriasees. Hedwigia. **55.**

Wonisch, F. (1910): Zur Algenflora des Andritzer Quellgebiets. Mitt. Naturwiss. Ver. Steiermark. **47.**

Wood, H.C. (1869): Prodromus of a Study of the Freshwater Algae of Eastern North America. Proc. Amer. Phil. Soc. **11.**

—(1872): A Contribution to the History of the Freshwater Algae of North America. Smithson. Publ. to Knowledge. Nr. **241.**

Woronichin, N.N. (1923): Algae nonullae novae e Caucaso. Notul. system. ex Inst. Crypt. Hort. Bot. Petropolitani. **2.**

—(1926a): Materialien zur Flora der Süsswasseralgen des Kaukasus. Trav. Stat. Biol. Caucase du Nord. **5.**

—(1926b): Grundrise der Algenvegetation des Kaukasus. Arch. f. Hydrobiol. **17.**

—(1929): Versuch einer vergleichenden Untersuchung des Sees Don-ty (Komi-Gebiet) und seine Ablagerungen. Bull. Saprop. Komité. **5.**

—(1930): Algen des Polar-und Nordurals. Trudy Leningradskogo obstschestva estestv. **60.**

—(1940a): Matériaux pour servir à une flore des Algues d'eau douce de la région de Leningrad. I. Les Algues du Bassin de la Neva. Act. Inst. Bot. Acad. Sci. U.R.S.S. Ser. 2. **4** (1938).

—(1940b): The Algae of the Kurgan Forest Steppe Lakes. Ibid.

Werdack, M.E. (1923): Chemical Composition of the Walls of Certain Algae. Ohio Jour. Sci. **23.**

Wyplel, M. (1893): Über den Einfluso einiger Chloride, Fluoride und Bromide auf Algen. 24. Jahresber. d. niederösterr. Landesreal-Gymn. in Waidhofen a. d. Thaya.

Yamaha, G. (1935): Über die Nuklealreaktion des pflanzlichen Karyoplasmas. Bot. u. Zool. **3.**

York, H.H. (1913): Geschlechtsunterschiede bei *Spirogyra*. Naturw. Wochenschr. **28.**

Yuasa, A. (1935): Review of the Nucleus of *Spirogyra*. Kagaku. **5.**

Zacharias, E., (1885): Über die chemische Beschaffenheit des Nucleolus. Bot. Zeitg. **43.**

—(1909): Die chemische Beschaffenheit von Protoplasma und Zellkern. Progr. rei bot.

Zanardini, G. (1847): Prospetto generale della flora Veneta. Venedig.

—(1872): Phycearum indicarum pugillus a cl. E., Baccaris ad Borneum Singapore et Ceylanum annis 1865-67 collectarum. Mem. Reale Ist. Veneta. **17.**

Zaneveld, J.S. (1950): Three centuries of algae research in Indonesia (1950-1950). (In Dutch). Chron. Nau. **106.**

Zeller, G. (1873): Algae collected by Mr. J. Kurz in Arracan and British Burma. Jour. Asiat. Soc. Bengal. **42.**

—(1876): Algae brasilienses circa Rio de Janeiro a Dr. A. Glaziou horti publici directore collectae. Vid. Meddel. Nat. Foren. i. Kopenhagen.

Zimmermann, A. (1896): Morphologie und Physiologie des pflanzlichen Zellkerns. Jena.

Zimmermann, W. (1927): Über Algenbestände aus der Tiefenzone des Bodensees. Zeitschr. f. Bot. **20.**

Zopf, W. (1878): Über einen neuen parasitischen Phycomyceten aus der Abteilung der Oosporeen. Verh. Bot. Ver. Prov. Brandenburg.

—(1884): Zur Kenntnis der Phycomyeten. I. Zur Morphologie und Biologie der Ancyliteen und Chytridiaceen. Nov. Act. Leopold. **47.**

—(1885): Zur Morphologie und Biologie der niederen Pilzthiere. Leipzig.

Zukal, H. (1879): Parthenogenesis bei einer *Spirogyra*. Osterr. Bot. Zeitschr. **29.**

# INDEX TO GENERA AND SPECIES